LOCAL AREA NETWORKS

LOCAL AREA NETWORKS

SURESH K BASANDRA
B.Sc.Engg., M.Tech.
Consultant
Digital Equipment (India) Ltd
(Formerly Associate Professor, Computers
Management Development Institute, Gurgaon)

&

S. JAISWAL, Ph.D.

1997

Galgotia Publications Pvt Ltd
5, Ansari Road, Daryaganj, New Delhi-110 002
Tel : 3263334

Basandra, Suresh K. & S. Jaiswal

LOCAL AREA NETWORKS

1994 Copyright Galgotia Publications Pvt Ltd

First Edition 1993
Second Revised Edition 1994
Third Revised Edition 1996
Fourth Revised Edition 1997

ISBN 81-86011-17-X

Published by:
Suneel Galgotia for
Galgotia Publications Pvt. Ltd.
5, Ansari Road, New Delhi-110002

Laser Typeset at: DATA VISION D-2, MCD Flats, R-Block, Greater Kailash-I

Printed by: Cambridge Printing Works B-85 Naraina Industrial Area Phase-II New Delhi

Dedicated to
my mother
SMT SUBHADHRA DEVI BASANDRA

ABOUT THE AUTHOR

Mr. Suresh K Basandra graduated in Electrical and Electronics Engineering from Delhi University in 1978 and obtained his M.Tech. in Computer Technology from I.I.T. Delhi in 1983. He is a Life Member of Computer Society of India (CSI), Institute of Electronics and Telecommunication Engineers of India (IETE), Indian Institute of Materials Management (IIMM), and Indian Science Congress Association.

He has more than fourteen years research, development and teaching experience in hardware and software. He has worked as Research Engineer at I.I.T. Kanpur, as Senior Software Engineer at C-DOT, New Delhi, as Executive Officer (EDP) in Indian Ports Association, New Delhi, as Associate Professor and Incharge, Computer Centre in Management Development Institute, Gurgaon, as Project Manager, Computer Division, Howe (India) Pvt Ltd, New Delhi. Currently he is working as a Consultant with Digital Equipment (India) Ltd, New Delhi, an affiliate company of Digital Equipment Corporation (DEC), USA.

His research interests are in the area of networks, software engineering, data bases, information systems, application software and computer applications in management decision-making.

He has over fifty research papers and articles in the area of hardware and software to his credit. These have appeared in various reputed journals and magazines like Information Processing Letters (Netherlands), CSI Communications, DataQuest, Information Technology, Instruments and Electronics Developments, Indian Ports, and Electronics For You. He is contributing editor to Information Technology since June 1991.

Besides this book, he also has five more books to his credit: 'Computer Science Question Bank', 'Understanding Computers Through Common Sense', 'Computers Today', 'Software Engineering' and 'Computers for Managers', first four published by Galgotia Publications Pvt Ltd, New Delhi and the last published by Global Business Press, New Delhi.

His biographical details has been included in 'Reference Asia: Asia's Who's Who of Men and Women of Acievement', Vol V, published by Rifacimento International, Delhi and 'Biography International', Vol 3, published by Biography International, Delhi. He has been guest faculty to SBI Staff Training College, IIMM and IGNOU. He has guided B.Tech. students at I.I.T. Kanpur and M.B.A. students of IGNOU for their projects. He has been involved in the development of Computers Courses conducted by IGNOU and AIMA.

PREFACE

Evolution of Local Area Networks

In the early 1970s, a trend began in computing away from large centralized mainframes towards smaller departmental minicomputers. The first microcomputer was introduced around 1971 and since then cheaper and more powerful machines have appeared in the market. This trend gathered momentum and has developed into a definite movement towards single-user workstations.

One of the disadvantages of this is that facilities that were available on larger, centralized systems were lacking in the new workstation approach. These included the ability to share resources such as information, peripheral devices like printers, disks and so on, and send messages from one user to another.

While computing devices were getting smaller, cheaper and more powerful, simultaneously advances were also being made in communications technology. In particular a new generation of networks emerged which operated in a limited geographical area, but much more reliably and at higher data transmission rates than previous networks.

The introduction of these high speed local area networks (LANs) opened up the possibility of attaining the advantages of workstations without losing those of centralized mainframe systems. Information could flow between individual workstations at speeds which, to a large extent, hid the fact that they were not working on the same system. LANs are attractive for such features as high availability and the ability to support multiple vendor equipment.

Now that millions of homes and offices have personal computers (PCs), we are finding that it is important to be able to connect PCs together. In an office setting, one way to connect PCs is with a LAN. The benefits are many:

- Costly peripherals such as laser printers, hard disks, high capacity tape drives, and modems can be shared by all users of a LAN.
- Information too can be shared; for example, all members of an office can use their own PCs to access and update an important database.
- Another plus is electronic mail -- using PCs to send and receive inter-office memos or messages. Some LANs allow PCs to link up with minicomputers, mainframes, and even computer networks in other locations.
- For management, LANs represent a way to increase productivity with a modest outlay. Usually, PCs have already been purchased for the office; a LAN makes their use more efficient.
- In addition, an office with a LAN requires fewer hard disks and printers.
- For those using PCs, a LAN can make work less frustating -- fewer floppies to keep track of, easier access to files, and ready use of all the hardware on the system.

Work also becomes less solitary -- electronic mail makes it easier to work together with the people in your office.

The rate of development of LANs has been truly remarkable over the past few years, but the rapid appearance of new products, and equally rapid disappearance of some old products, has left many potential users and buyers confused and apprehensive about how to proceed. And, although the technology is rapidly evolving, the principal architectural forms and design approaches have emerged.

Objectives

It introduces the concepts behind the major LANs, bridging the gap between "full-blooded" textbooks of a highly technical and mathematical nature, and laymen's guides usually supplied by equipment manufacturers. Since LAN product offerings are rapidly changing, a delibrate attempt has been made to emphasize more on underlying fundamental technology, architecture, standards, operating characteristics, and management, rather than specific LAN products.

This book treats the subject of networks at the levels of potential purchaser, installer, manager, and end-user. It is also designed to give those who wish to buy LAN familiarity with the concepts involved. Here again, the aim is not to survey the current product offerings, but rather to assist the buyer in making an intelligent evaluation and selection.

In terms of the style, the book is primarily:

*   Descriptive: Terms are defined and the key concepts and technologies are discussed in some detail.
*   Comparative: Wherever possible, alternative or competing approaches are compared and their relative merits, based on suitable criteria, are discussed.

Intended Audience

This book is intended for a broad range of readers interested in LANs.

This book is intended for students, computer professionals, telecommunication managers, business managers, and others who want to become more familiar with the LANs. It is suitable for use as a higher level under-graduate and post-graduate textbook.

The book is intended to be self-contained. No prior knowledge of networks is assumed, but a basic understanding of the field of computer systems will be helpful. For the reader with little or no background in data communications, a brief primer is included. In fact, this book is for anyone who wants to have an edge on a technical field that promises to expand for atleast the next decade.

Plan of the Text

This book answers the questions most often asked about LANs. The remainder of this preface explains the layout of the book in little more detail.

Chapter 1 begins by defining what exactly we mean by the term network, and how a LAN is distinguished from other types. It gives a brief historical development of LANs, looks at some of the applications, advantages as well as disadvantages and why a business should install one.

Chapter 2 introduces most of the underlying communication concepts.

Chapter 3 covers the ways in which the machines are connected (topology) and the choices available in terms of communication media.

In Chapter 4, the concept of layered protocols is introduced.

In Chapter 5, we examine some of the standards that have been developed in this area. Important standards introduced by IEEE and IBM are explained in understandable terms.

In Chapter 6, the costs and benefits of a LAN are explored, to help you decide whether to purchase one.

Chapter 7 outlines the factors that should influence your evaluation and selection, should you decide that a PC network is appropriate for you.

Chapter 8 discusses the issues involved in evaluating and selecting the applications software for LAN.

Chapter 9 examines in detail the planning and installation of a network, and includes a discussion of how much hardware and software to buy. It covers proven techniques for successful LAN installation.

Chapter 10 tells you how to use a network to run both existing applications and new ones that take advantage of the special features a network offers.

Chapter 11 is an overview of mainframe connections. It reviews the IBM data communications, describes present products, and assesses the prospects for the future.

Chapter 12 discusses the broad aspects of network security.

Chapter 13 discusses the client/server concepts, architecture and different types of servers and services.

Chapter 14 examines the issues involved with LAN databases, uses of LAN databases, and different types of servers.

Chapter 15 provides an overview of a Novell Network.

Chapter 16 discusses the evolution of Ethernet, its features, formats, components and method of operation.

Chapter 17 discusses the historical development of Digital Network Architecture and its various phases.

Chapter 18 discusses the evolution of Systems Network Architecture, its components, layers and comparision with Digital Network Architecture.

Chapter 19 discusses the TCP/IP protocol, its structure, working, applications and how it is implemented.

Chapter 20 is concerned with extending LANs beyond their basic design limitations, and with the linking of LANs to other LANs and to wide area networks (WANs). The connection of LANs to existing networks is one of the main constraints to LAN market growth and is receiving considerable attention.

The next chapter, chapter 21, is concerned with the often neglected subject of LAN management, from the nuts and bolts of installation to management systems which allow operations staff to control the network and investigate problems in an efficient manner.

Chapter 22 provides an overview of office automation. It discusses office activities, office system elements, office system functions, how an automated office is built, its benefits and communication infrastructure to support office automation activities.

Chapter 23 examines in detail what is E-Mail, its uses, advantages, drawbacks, how E-Mail is used and different types of mails.

Chapter 24 introduces the concepts involved with electronic data interchange, its advantages over a paper-based document system, how it works, different EDI standards and cost benefit analysis of EDI.

Chapter 25 provides an overview of CCITT X.25.

Chapter 26 discusses the evolution of ISDN, its standards and protocols, ISDN implementation, and ISDN chips.

Chapter 27 provides an overview of wide area networks, different types of networks, private and public networks, circuit switched and packet switched networks, WAN applications and design considerations.

Chapter 28, examines those developments in both hardware and software which will have a large impact in the next few years.

Chapter 29 discusses an overview of Wireless LANs, need of wireless LANs, components of wireless LANs, wireless receiving devices and Future evolution of Wireless LANs.

Chapter 30 focusses on the wireless LAN media components: Radio Wave LANs, Infrared LANs and Microwave LANs.

The final chapter, chapter 31 discusses the One-to-One Operations, One-to-Many Operations, and Many-to-Many Operations. It also focussed on planning, setup and installation of wireless LANs. The Long Distance Wireless LAN Technologies, such as Cellular Connection, Low Earth Orbiting Satellites (LEOS), Medium Earth Orbit Satellites, and USAT Satellites are also explained in detail.

In addition, the book includes Questions and Answers on LANs, Selecting Personal Computers, Computer Viruses, Encoding Schemes, Standards Organisations, ISO OSI

Standards Documents, a list of frequently used Abbreviations and Acronyms, an extensive Glossary, list of Computer Journals and References.

Acknowledgements

Many people have directly or indirectly contributed to the development of this book. I wish to thank them all. I am grateful to the publisher Mr Suneel Galgotia and his staff who took all the pains to see that no compromise is made in the quality of the book and it comes out well in time.

My thanks to all those of you who have purchased this book. I hope you will find it enlightening, entertaining and useful in your networking endeavours.

Finally my deepest thanks are to my wife, Karuna Basandra, for keying- in the complete manuscript and also because she had to endure the loss of my attention for far too long while I was producing the manuscript.

Good Networking

SURESH K BASANDRA

CONTENTS

PARTICULARS		PAGE NO.
PREFACE		*ix*
ILLUSTRATIONS		*xxxiii*
CHAPTER 1.	Local Area Networks	1
CHAPTER 2.	Data Communications	38
CHAPTER 3.	Topologies and Transmission Media	77
CHAPTER 4.	Protocols	119
CHAPTER 5.	Network Architecture and Standards	134
CHAPTER 6.	Cost Benefit Analysis of a LAN	162
CHAPTER 7.	Evaluating and Selecting a LAN	183
CHAPTER 8.	Evaluation and Selection of Software Packages	218
CHAPTER 9.	Planning and Installing a LAN	236
CHAPTER 10.	Utilising a LAN	265
CHAPTER 11.	Mainframe Connection	287
CHAPTER 12.	Network Security	311
CHAPTER 13.	Client/Server Computing	389
CHAPTER 14.	LAN Databases	344
CHAPTER 15.	An Overview of Novell Network	355
CHAPTER 16.	Ethernet	362
CHAPTER 17.	Digital Network Architecture	382
CHAPTER 18.	Systems Network Architecture	392
CHAPTER 19.	Transmission Control Protocol/Internet Protocol	402
CHAPTER 20.	Internetworking and Connectivity	417
CHAPTER 21.	Network Management	444
CHAPTER 22.	Office Automation	467
CHAPTER 23.	Electronic Mail	490
CHAPTER 24.	Electronic Data Interchange	501

CHAPTER 25.   X.25 Overview   517

CHAPTER 26.   Integrated Services Digital Network   542

CHAPTER 27.   Wide Area Networks   556

CHAPTER 28.   Future Trends in Local Area Networks   574

CHAPTER 29.   Wireless LANs   587-1

CHAPTER 30.   Wireless LAN Media Components : AIR   587-19

CHAPTER 31.   Wireless LAN Operations & Connections   587-28

APPENDIX A   Questions and Answers on LANs   580

APPENDIX B   Selecting Personal Computers   616

APPENDIX C   Computer Viruses   638

APPENDIX D   Encoding Schemes   650

APPENDIX E   Standards Organisations   652

APPENDIX F   ISO OSI Standards Documents   654

APPENDIX G   Abbreviations and Acronyms   656

APPENDIX H   Glossary   667

APPENDIX I   List of Computer Journals   686

APPENDIX J   References   689

                 Readers Comments Form   691

DETAILED CONTENTS

Particulars	Page No.
ILLUSTRATIONS	
PREFACE	

CHAPTER 1.   **Local Area Networks** — 1

Introduction	1
Defining the Issues	2
The Importance of Networking	3
Types of Networks	6
Private Networks	6
Value Added Networks	6
Local Area Networks	7
Switched Networks	7
What is a Local Area Network?	8
Features of Local Area Networks	11
Resource Sharing	12
Productivity	13
Communications	13
Management	14
Network Topologies	16
Bus Networks	17
Star Networks	17
Ring Networks	18
Hybrid Networks	18
Communication Techniques within Networks	19
LAN Components	20
Workstation	21
File Server	23
Gateway	24
Network Interface Unit	25
Active Hub	29
Passive Hub	29
LAN Cable	29
Networking Operating System	29
Sharing Data	30
File and Record Locking	31
Disk Space Allocation	32
Sharing the Printer	34
Applications Software	35
Comparison of Minicomputer with LAN	36

CHAPTER 2.   **Data Communications**   **38**

Introduction   38
Data Communications   39
Data Communication System   39
Data Communication Software   40
Data Communication Concepts   41
    Common Ground: The ASCII Standard   41
    Units of Measure   44
    Communication Rate   45
    Digital and Analog Communication   46
    Parallel and Serial Communication   48
    Synchronous and Asynchronous
       Communication   49
    Protocols and Buffers   51
    Detecting Errors   53
    Simplex, Half-Duplex, and Full-Duplex
    Communication   53
    Multiplexing   55
Communication Hardware   56
    Communication Adapter   56
    Accoustic Couplers and Modems   57
Communication Procedures   60
    Communication Between Two Microcomputers   60
    Communication Between a Microcomputer
      and a Larger Computer   61
    Front-End Processors   61
    Going On-Line   62
    File Transfer   63
    Choosing Parameters   63
    Logging Off   65
Communication Processing   65
    Packets   65
Communication Channels   67
    Wired Transmission   67
        Telephone Lines   69
           Leased Lines   69
           Switched Lines   70
        Coaxial Cables   70
    Optical Fibre Transmission   71
    Microwave Transmission   71
    Infrared Transmission   72
    Laser Transmission   72
    Radio Transmission   72
    Satellite Transmission   73
Applications of Data Communication   75

	Using External Databases	75
	Sharing Data Files	75
	Electronic Mail	76
	Bulletin Board Systems	76
CHAPTER 3.	**Topologies and Transmission Media**	**77**
	Introduction	77
	LAN Topologies	79
	Topology Evaluation Factors	79
	Star or Radial Topology	80
	Advantages of the Star	82
	Disadvantages of the Star	83
	Star Evaluation Factors	83
	Bus Topology	84
	Advantages of the Bus	85
	Disadvantages of the Bus	85
	Bus Evaluation Factors	86
	Ring Topology	86
	Advantages of the Ring	87
	Disadvantages of the Ring	88
	Ring Evaluation Factors	88
	Hybrid Topologies	89
	Tree Topology	89
	Advantages of the Tree	91
	Disadvantages of the Tree	91
	Star-Ring Topology	91
	Advantages of the Star-Ring	91
	Disadvantages of the Star-Ring	93
	Choosing a Topology	93
	Transmission Media	93
	Media Evaluation Factors	94
	Twisted Pair Wire	97
	Components of a Twisted Pair Network	97
	Twisted Pair Evaluation Factors	98
	Baseband Coaxial Cable	99
	Components of a Baseband Coaxial Network	99
	Baseband Coaxial Evaluation Factors	100
	Broadband Coaxial Cable	100
	Components of a Broadband Coaxial Network	101
	Broadband Coaxial Evaluation Factors	103
	Fibre Optic Cable	104
	Components of a Fibre Optic Network	106
	Fibre Optic Evaluation Factors	107

	Relationship Between Medium and Topology	108
	Communication Swithing Techniques	110
	Circuit Switching	110
	Message Switching	112
	Packet Switching	114
CHAPTER 4.	**Protocols**	**119**
	Introduction	119
	LAN Protocols	123
	Protocol Evaluation Factors	123
	Contention	124
	Contention Evaluation Factors	125
	Carrier Sense Multiple Access	126
	Carrier Sense Multiple Access with Collision Detection	127
	Carrier Sense Multiple Access with Collision Avoidance	128
	Polling	128
	Polling Evaluation Factors	130
	Token Passing	130
	Token Passing Evaluation Factors	133
CHAPTER 5.	**Network Architecture and Standards**	**134**
	Introduction	134
	What is Network Architecture?	134
	Standards	135
	The Open Systems Interconnection Model	139
	OSI Layers	139
	Layer 1: Physical	142
	Layer 2: Data Link	142
	Layer 3: Network	142
	Layer 4: Transport	143
	Layer 5: Session	143
	Layer 6: Presentation	143
	Layer 7: Application	144
	Operation of the OSI Model in a Network	145
	IEEE 802 Project	146
	802.1 - Higher Layer Interface Standard	148
	802.2 - Logical Link Control Standard	148
	802.3 - CSMA/CD Bus	148
	802.4 - Token Passing Bus	149
	802.5 - Token Passing Ring	149
	New Committees	149
	802 Reference Model	149
	Ethernet	151
	Ethernet Specification	152

	Arcnet	154
	IBM PC Network	157
	IBM Token Ring	159
	Summary	161
CHAPTER 6.	**Cost Benefit Analysis of a LAN**	**162**
	Introduction	162
	Uses of a Network	163
	Cost Benefit Analysis	165
	The Costs	165
	Hardware and Software	166
	Personnel Costs	167
	Benefits of a Network	168
	Figuring Value	169
	Alternate Systems	171
	Sharing Hardware	172
	Sharing Information	173
	Network Application Software	175
	Connections to Other Networks	176
	Centralized Control and Distributed	
	Computing	176
	Should You Wait to Buy a LAN?	177
	Size of Investment	177
	Standards	177
	Prices	178
	Software	179
	LANs and Multiuser Systems	179
	Conclusions	181
CHAPTER 7.	**Evaluating and Selecting a LAN**	**183**
	Introduction	183
	General	183
	Applications	184
	Existing Software	185
	New Software	185
	LAN Evaluation	185
	The Physical Site	187
	Network Functions	188
	Workstations	188
	Evaluating NICs	189
	Evaluating Servers	190
	Evaluating Operating Systems	194
	Connections	195
	Estimating Hardware Performance	201
	Standards	203

	Software	203
	Hardware	204
	Mainframe Connections	205
	Gateways	205
	Direct Connection	206
	Message and File Transfer	206
	Terminal Emulation	207
	Data Extraction	207
	Remote Job Entry	207
	Program-to-Program Communication	207
	Security	208
	Hardware Compatibilty	208
	What do you want from a **LAN**?	208
	Specifying a LAN	210
	Matching LANs to Users	211
	Purchasing a LAN	215
	LAN Acquisition Strategies	216
CHAPTER 8.	**Evaluation and Selection of Software Packages**	**218**
	Introduction	218
	Trends in Software Evolution	218
	Systems Software	219
	High Level Languages	219
	Application Software	220
	The Need for Softare	220
	Software Packages	220
	Software Packages and In-House Software	222
	Software Package	223
	In-House Developed Software	223
	Software Development Costs	223
	Software Package Costs	223
	Software Quality	226
	Assessing a Package	226
	When to Select a Package	227
	Areas of Concern for Management	230
	Advantages and Disadvantages of Acquiring a Software Package	23
	Advantages	23
	Disadvantages	23
	Software Vendor Checklist	23
	Conclusion	23
CHAPTER 9.	**Planning and Installing a LAN**	23
	Introduction	23
	Planning the Installation	23

Software Planning 239
    Applications Software 242
    Systems Software 247
Hardware Planning 251
    Workstation Planning 251
    Server Planning 253
    Connection Planning 256
Doing the Installation 257
    Hardware and Software Installation 258
    Diagnosing Problems 258
    Training Network Users 259
    Managing the Networks 259
Common Problems in Physical Installation 260
    Cabling 260
    Operating Software 262
    Expandability 262
    Standardization 263

CHAPTER 10.   **Utilising a LAN** **265**
Introduction 265
Motivation 265
Advantages of LANs 266
Properties of Centralized Systems 268
Problems with LANs 268
Sharing 269
Spectrum of LAN Usage 269
Software Issues 271
    Copy Protection 272
    Disk Access 273
    Printing 274
    Shared Servers 278
Using Applications 278
    Word Processing 279
    Spreadsheets 279
    Database Management System 279
    Accounting Systems 280
    Graphics Software 280
    Electronic Mail 281
    Electronic Calender 282
    Multiuser Shared Databases 283
Backup Strategies 284
Software Licensing 285
    Single User Licenses 285
    Multiuser Licenses 285

	Site Licenses	285
	Examples of LAN Usage	286

CHAPTER 11.	**Mainframe Connection**	**287**
	Introduction	287
	What is a Mainframe?	288
	Why Talk to Mainframe?	289
	Brief History of IBM Data Communications	290
	Office Software Protocols	292
	Terminal Emulation	292
	How to Evaluate an Emulator?	294
	The Emulator on the Network	295
	Mainframe Gateways: Alternatives to Terminal Emulation	295
	PCs as Mainframe Workstations	297
	Back-up On the PC	298
	Reliability of Mainframe Connection	299
	Connecting Mainframe to LANs	299
	Mainframe Products for the Token Ring	300
	System/370 Hardware for the Token Ring	300
	System/370 Software for the Token Ring	302
	System/36 Hardware for the Token Ring	303
	System/36 Software for the Token Ring	304
	Series/1 Hardware for the Token Ring	205
	Mainframe Products for the PC Network	305
	System/370 Hardware for the PC Network	305
	System/370 Software for the PC Network	306
	Series/1 Hardware for the PC Network	306
	Series/1 Software for the PC Network	306
	Future of Mainframe and LAN Communications	307
	Potential Roadblocks to Peer-to-Peer Communications	308

CHAPTER 12.	**Network Security**	**311**
	Introduction	311
	What Network Security Means?	312
	Risk Analysis	313
	Types of Threats	314
	Passive Threats	316
	Active Threats	317
	Determining What Secure Means to You and Your LAN	317
	Securing Workstations and Servers	318
	Securing Network Passwords	319
	Securing Files and Programs	319

Levels of Security   320
   Physical Security   321
   Access Controls   321
   Personnel Identification   324
   Passwords   324
   Securityin log-in   325
   Encryption   325
   Encryption Keys   326
   Conventional Encryption   327
   The data Encryption standard   328
   Commercial Communications security
      Endoresement programme   329
   Key Distribution   329
   Public Key Encryption   331
   On Line Coders   333
   The Diskless PC   334
   Protection Against Cable Radiation   334
   Call Back Security   335
Management Level Concerns   336
Securityin TCP/IP Networks   338
Firewall-Friendly FTP   338-1
   Recommendation   338-2
Security Considerations   338-2
Circuit Gateways   338-3
Conclusions   338-3

CHAPTER 13.   **Client/Server Computing**   **339**
Introduction   339
File Servers   340
    Central-File-Server Systems   341
    Peer-To-Peer LANs   341
Print Servers   341
Database Servers   342
Facsimile Servers   342
Batch-Processing Servers   342
Communications Servers   342
Which Services Go Where?   343

CHAPTER 14.   **LAN Databases**   **344**
What To Look For In A LAN Database?   344
What is a Database Management System?   345
What are You Using the DBMS For?   346
Database Service and Server-based Applications   348
SQL DBMS Servers   352

	Novell Netware SQL	352
	Gupta SQLBase	352
	Fox Software FoxServer	353
	Ashton-Tate/Microsoft SQL Server	353
	Oracle	354
CHAPTER 15.	**An Overview of Novell Network**	**355**
	Components	355
	Software	356
	Working Copies	356
	Software Options	356
	File Servers	357
	Computer Type	358
	Hard Drives	358
	File Server RAM	358
	UPS	359
	Workstations	359
	Computer Types	359
	Hard Drives	359
	Workstation RAM	359
	Network Interface Cards	360
	Type of Cabling	360
	Speed of Transmission	360
	Method of Collision Control	360
	Network Distance	361
	Buffer Size	361
	Data Base Size	361
	Overall Speed	361
CHAPTER 16.	**Ethernet**	**362**
	Introduction	362
	Evolution	363
	Features of Ethernet	365
	Medium Access Control Frame Formats	365
	Components of Ethernet	368
	Method of Operation	371
	Ethernet IC Chips	373
	Applications of Ethernet	373
	System Limitations	373
	Segment Configurations	373
	10Base5 Extensions	374
	Modification of Ethernet	376
	Improving Ethernet for Manufacturing	378
	Automation	378

	Ethernet for Data and Voice	378
	Thin Wire CSMA/CD	379
	Broadband CSMA/CD	380
	Twisted Pair CSMA/CD	381
	Conclusion	381
CHAPTER 17.	**Digital Network Architecture**	**382**
	Introduction	382
	Historical Development	382
	Phase I	384
	Phase II	384
	Phase III	385
	Phase IV	386
	Phase V	386
	How Does DECnet Work?	387
	DECnet Vs. SNA	391
CHAPTER 18.	**Systems Network Architecture**	**392**
	Introduction	392
	Evolution	392
	SNA Vs. DECnet	393
	Network Space	394
	SNA Layers	397
	Physical Control Layer	397
	Data Link Control Layer	398
	Path Control Layer	398
	Transmission Control Layer	398
	Data Flow Control Layer	399
	Presentation Services Layer	399
	Transaction Services Layer	399
	Network Topologies	399
	SNA Directions	400
	Summary	401
CHAPTER 19. Transmission Control Protocol/Internet Protocol		**402**
	Introduction	402
	Origin of TCP/IP	403
	TCP/IP Communications Architecture	404
	TCP/IP The complete suite	408
	Upper Layer Protocols	409
	Lower Layer Protocols	409
	TCP/IP Protocol Set Structure	409
	Internet Protocol	411
	User Datagram Protocol	412

Transmission Control Protocol   413
Ethernet Technology   414
ProNET Token Ring Technology   416-4
Internet Architecture   416-7
TCP/IP Network Planning   416-10
   Size and Growth Rate   416-10
   Existing Standards   416-11
   Traffic Flows and Capacity   416-12
Partition the Network   416-12
Using Bridges   416-13
   Bridges Filtering Rate   416-14
   Limited Horizon   416-14
   Broadcasts, Broadcast Storms and Multi-Cast Frames 416-14
   Bridging to a Backbone   416-16
   Hub Bridges   416-17
Identifying a Network connection   416-17
Planning the IP Address scheme   416-18
   Internet Protocol   416-18
   IP Addressing   416-18
   MAC Addresses   416-19
Characteristics of the IP Address   416-19
Network Numbers and Host Numbers   416-21
   Distinguishing the class address   416-22
IAB and Network Number Registration   416-23
Configuring the IP Address   416-23
Reserved IP Addresses   416-24
   IP Addresses with routers and dialog devices 416-24
How TCP/IP works   416-25
What TCP was Built To Do   416-26
   From One Socket to Another   416-26
   TCP Sequencing   416-27
   TCP Needs Not an IP   416-28
What in an IP   416-28
   Gateways and IP   416-29
TCP/IP Applications   415-30
Telnet Protocol   416-30
   Telnet Commands   416-31
   Telnet Negotiation   416-32
Telnet Security   416-35
Rlogin Protocol   416-36
File Transfer Protocol   416-37
   Data Representation   416-38
   FTP Service Commands   416-40
FTP Replies   416-42

Connection-Management	416-42
Trivial File Transfer Protocol	416-45
Bootstrap Protocol : BOOTP	416-47
Simple Mail Transfer Protocol : SMTP	416-49
SMTP Commands	416-51
SMTP Replies	416-52
SMTP Size Limitations	416-54
Relay Agents	416-55
E-Mail Pieces: Envelopes, Headers and Body	416-55
NetBIOS	416-56
Name Formate	416-57
General Format of Name Service Packets	416-59
Header	416-59
Question Section	416-62
Resource Reocrd (RR)	416-63
Finger Protocol	416-65
Whois Protocol	416-66
Gopher	416-67
Veronica	416-67
Archie	416-67
WAIS: Wide Area Information Servers	416-67
Ping	416-68
WWW: World Wide Web	416-68
X Window System	416-68
The X terminal	416-70
The X Window System	416-71
The Network File System	416-71
NFS Architecture	416-72
Remote Procedure Call (RPC)	416-74
eXternal Data Representation(XDR)	416-78
Port Mapper	416-79
Mount Protocol	416-79
The Future of TCP/IP	416-80
FutureGrowth and Technology	416-81
Future of Internet Architecture	416-81
New Applications	416-82
Uses of the Technology	416-83
Challenges for the Future	416-83
Summary	416-84
CHAPTER 20. **Internetworking and Connectivity**	**417**
LAN-to-LAN Connections	417
Repeaters	417
Bridges	421
Transparent Bridges	423

Source Routing Bridges   423
Routers   424
    NetWare Routers   426
Bridge/Router Hybrids (Brouters)   427
Remote Bridges and Routers   427
    Synchronous and Asynchronous
        Communication   427
    Remote Communication Links   428
    Remote Bridge and Router Performance   428
    NetWare Asynchronous Remote Router   429
    Microtest LANMODEM and Shiva Netmodem/E   429
    NetWare Link/Newport LAN2LAN Routers   429
    Novell's Packet Burst Technology   430
Asynchronous Communication Servers   431
    Dial-Out Services (Modem Pooling)   431
    Remote Login and Remote Access Services   434
LAN-to-Host Gateways and Communications
    Services   436
    SNA and 3270   438
TCP/IP   443
Other Connectivity Options   443

CHAPTER 21.   **Network Management**   **444**
Introduction   444
Network Management Functions   445
Elements of Network Management   447
Test, Monitor and Control Equipment for
    Aiding Network Management   448
Standards in Network Management   449
Network Owners and Users   450
Distribution of Management   450
Control Mechanisms   454
Management Modules   454
Centralised Vs. Decentralised Management   454
Symmetrical Session Management   458
Permanent Sessions   460
Session Failure   462
The Network Operators   462
Network Operator Commands   463
Maintenance   465
Security   466
Other Administrative Functions   466
SNMP: Simple Network Management Protocol   466
    The Internet Naming Hierarchy   466-1
Management Information Base   466-2

       system Group 466-2
       interface Group 466-3
       address translation (at) Group 466-5
       ip Group 466-5
       icmp Group 466-8
       tcp Group 466-9
       udp Group 466-11
    Structure of Management Information(SMI) 466-11
    Simple Network Management Protocol (SNMP) ... 466-12
    SNMPv1 and SNMPv2 466-14
    Summary 466-15

CHAPTER 22.   **Office Automation** **467**
    Introduction 467
    Office Activities 468
    Old and New Systems Perspective 470
    Office System Elements 471
    Common Office System Functions 474
    Building an Automated Office 479
       Equipment Needed 479
       Strategies for Designing an Automated Office ... 481
    Benefits 483
    Communication Infrastructure to Support OA ... 484
      Actvities 485
    Local Area Networking 486
    A PABX Controlled Network 489
    Optimum Approach for Next Five or Ten Years ... 490
    Conclusion

CHAPTER 23.   **Electronic Mail** **490**
    Introduction 490
    What is Electronic Mail? 491
    Uses for E-mail 494
    Advantages 495
    Drawbacks 496
    Charges 497
    Using Electronic Mail 497
    Sending Messages 499
    Private E-mail 499
    International E-mail 499
    Summary 500

CHAPTER 24.   **Electronic Data Interchange** **501**
    Introduction 501
    What is EDI? 502
    Why Use EDI? 504

Advantages of EDI over a Paper-Based
    Document Transfer System 504
How EDI Works? 505
EDI Standards 508
    Variable-Length EDI Standards 509
Motivation 510
Cost Benefit Analysis of EDI 511
EDI Strategy for Competitive Advantage 511
Digital's Approach to EDI Implementation 5,13
Beyond EDI: Electronic Trading Networks 514

CHAPTER 25.   **X.25 OVERVIEW** **517**
Introduction 517
Permanent Virtual Circuits 520
Access to the Network 520
The PAD Interface 520
Layers of Communication 523
    Layer 1: Physical Control 524
    Layer 2: Link Control 524
    Layer 3: Network Control 524
Packet Format 525
Local Channel Numbers 526
Initiating a Virtual Call 527
Priority 528
The Flow of Packets 530
Disconnecting a Virtual Call 530
Data Transfer 531
Sequence Numbers 533
Interrupt Packets 534
Reset 535
Restart 536
State Diagrams 537
Optional Facilities 540

CHAPTER 26.   **Integrated Services Digital Network** **542**
Introduction 542
Today's Telecommunications Networks 543
The Way to ISDN 543
Evolution of ISDN 545
Some Facts about ISDN 546
Other Considerations Relating to ISDN 547
    Network Transitions 547
    Multifunctional Terminals 549

Division of Functions Between Terminal
and Network 549
ISDN for Wideband Communication 549
Telemetry and Remote Control 550
The ISDN Standards and Protocols 550
The ISDN Implementation 553
ISDN Chips 553
Standardization is Deciding 555

CHAPTER 27.   **Wide Area Networks** **556**
Introduction 556
Private Networks 556
Public Networks 557
Circuit-Switching and Packet-Switching 558
Packet-Switching Networks 558
Fast-Connect Circuit-Switching Networks 561
DTE's and DCE's 562
Connections Between Networks 563
Eight Types of Tariffs 564
Need of Packet Switching and X.25 564-1
Packet Switchstream (PSS) Service 564-1
    Customer's Equipment 564-2
    Permission to Connect 564-2
    Access Facilities 564-2
    Packets and Calls 564-2
    Addressing 564-2
Interconnection of Public and Private Data Network. 564-4
Features of Public Packet Switched Network 564-6
Role of PSS 564-6
Benefits of PSS 564-7
Value Added Networks 565
Standards and Capability 566
Common Principles 568
WAN Applications 568
Design Considerations 570

CHAPTER 28.   **Future Trends in Local Area Networks** ... **574**
Introduction 574
Compatibility 574
Standards and the High-Cost, Low-Cost Split 575
Future Open Systems Standards 576
    Functional Standards 577
    Manufacturing Automation Protocol 577
    Technical and Office Protocol 579
Future Hardware 581

	FDDI - a Future Fibre LAN	582
	Integrated Services Digital Networks	584
	Falling Costs and Chip Sets	585
	Network-to-Network Connections	586
	General	586
CHAPTER 29	**Wireless LANs**	**587-1**
	Introduction	587-1
	Need of Wireless LANs	587-2
	Components of Wireless LANs	587-3
	Equipments Levels	587-4
	Mobile Equipments	587-5
	Wireless Receiving Devices	587-6
	Laptop or Notebook computers	587-6
	Personal digital Assistants (PDAs)	587-7
	Wireless resource Interfacing	587-8
	Transceivers	587-8
	Coupling Wireless LANs	587-8
	Wireless LANs vs Wired LANs	587-9
	Advantages of Wireless LANs	587-11
	Disadvantages of Wireless LANs	587-13
	Distance and Speed limitations	587-14
	Costs and Benefits of Wireless LANs	587-15
	Uses of Wireless LAN Applications	587-15
	Health Care	587-15
	Educational System	587-16
	Temporary Setup	587-17
	General Services	587-18
	Future Evolution of Wireless LANs	587-18
CHAPTER 30	**Wireless LAN Media Components : AIR**	**587-19**
	Introduction	587-19
	Radio Wave LANs	587-21
	Frequency Hopping	587-23
	Direct Sequence Coding	587-23
	Directional and Omnidirectional Antennes	587-23
	Infrared LANs	587-24
	Microwave LANs	587-26
CHAPTER 31	**Wireless LAN Operations an Connections**	587-28
	One-to-one Operations	587-28
	One-to-many Operations	587-28
	Many-to-many Operations	587-29
	Planning of Wireless LAN	587-29
	Setup of Wireless LAN	587-31

Installation of Wireless LAN 587-31
Wireless-to-wire Connections 587-33
   Remote Access 587-34
   Resource Manager 587-34
   Bridging and Routing 587-35
   Central Servers 587-35
   Locations 587-36
   Loads 587-36
   Control 587-36
LANE To LAN Operations 587-37
   Recognition 587-38
   Acceptance 587-38
   Speed matching 587-38
   Packet Conversion 587-39
   Flows 587-39
   Errors 587-39
   Losses and reconstitution 587-39
LANE-To-LAN Couplings 587-39
Cross Couplings 587-40
   Wireless-to-wireless to wired LANs 587-40
   Multiple couplings 587-40
   Protocol conversions 587-41
   Security 587-41
Global Interconnecting 587-41
LAN-LAN Hopping 587-41
   Interlining 587-42
   Integration 587-42
   Local to global 587-43
   Mixing of technologies 587-43
Long-distance wireless LAN Technologies 587-43
   Cellular connections 587-43
   Personal communication services 587-44
   Low Earth Orbiting Satellites (LEOS) 587-46
   Medium Earth Orbit Satellite (MEOS) 587-48
   VSAT satellites 587-48

APPENDIX A Questions and Answers on LANs **588**

APPENDIX B Selecting Personal Computers **616**

APPENDIX C Computer Viruses **638**

APPENDIX D Encoding Schemes **650**

APPENDIX E Standards Organisations **652**

APPENDIX F ISO OSI Standards Documents **654**

APPENDIX G Abbreviations and Acronyms   **656**

APPENDIX H Glossary   **667**

APPENDIX I List of Computer Journals   **686**

APPENDIX J References   **689**

Readers Comments Form   **691**

1

LOCAL AREA NETWORKS

INTRODUCTION

If we look back by a decade, we find that the market was inundated by large computers. A large number of mainframe computers and minicomputers were installed and operated as stand alone systems. The concept then was to centralise the control of all EDP (Electronics Data Processing) operations and user departments would only give their requirements and interact with the systems analysts or programmers. As the demands of the user departments grew both in terms of volume and complexity, an increasing need of computing power was felt necessary.

The falling prices and the increasingly powerful microcomputers made this possible and offered a cost-effective solution. The easy availability of the microcomputers with standardised hardware and software made them an extremely viable solution. These microcomputers also provided a user-friendly menu-driven environment where the end-users could interact directly with the computer and feel comfortable. The availability of a large number of applications software for every requirement or area of specialisation offered the end-users with the tools they were looking for. This reduced their dependence on systems personnel and increased the personnel productivity by about 10-15%. Then microcomputers became extremely popular with researchers, scientists, technocrats, students, decision-makers and managers.

With the increasing use of microcomputers, it was felt that although users were provided computation power at their desk, these could not suffice all their needs because applications often demanded exchange of data between several such users. The need for communication between these microcomputers was clear and local area network (LAN) offered itself as a viable and attractive solution.

In the face of ever-growing requirements of computer users, these clusters of microcomputers in a LAN had their own limitations. In fact, most applications of these end-users required a shared database which could not be distributed among several workstations in the LAN. Also these users required peripherals like fast printers, back-up devices, etc. This kind of a totally decentralised and distributed environment often forced replication of data.

There was a backward shift and the need for a powerful central facility offering high capacity hard disk storage, sharable printers, magnetic tapes, etc. was felt in the existing distributed environment. This compromise offered them the most cost-effective solution as:

1.   It provided total computing facility at each user end.

2.   It provided communication facilities amongst several such users.

3.   It offered access to mass storage systems, high speed printers and other service computers.

4.   It was very economical because these resources were shared by all the users in the LAN.

As an outcome of these powerful features, the overhead on the LAN was enormous and various techniques started evolving. A separate piece of software was required for the LAN management. Consequent to this certain supplementary features also became necessary, like monitoring the network activities, security features, mail, etc.

DEFINING THE ISSUES

Although organisations are increasingly aware of the necessity of managing information, (as evidenced by the multiplication of computers, microcomputers, information services and endless articles about information centres), we have not yet learned to deal efficiently with the sheer volume of data and with the rapidly decreasing time between when information is presented and when we must act on it. Few organisations can guarantee that information is available when needed. As a result, too many vital business decisions are based on incomplete, incorrect or outdated information.

When we add computers into the situation, the problem becomes more complex:

-    How do you manage the information stored in the microcomputer? How do you get the right data to the right people at the right time and in the right form? How do you keep track of the programmes in use and insure that the data is current and that everyone is actually using the "same" data?

-    How do you manage access? Frequently, microcomputer use is seen as desirable, even if unnecessary. Many machines become status symbols, not productive tools. Concurrently, workers with real microcomputer needs may not have access to one. How do you ensure that users have access to the resources they really need, not simply the ones that they think they need? Perhaps most difficult of all, how do you identify and restrict the people who should not have access to the system?

-    How do you accommodate the effects? Microcomputers do change the way people work, as well as the way jobs are defined. Rarely are these changes fully considered beforehand. The effect of a microcomputer on the individual and on the whole organisation tends to be ignored.

- How do you control costs? Microcomputer hardware costs are relatively easily defined and therefore budgeted. But software and training, which can more than double the cost of the system, are often not counted in the costs.

- How do you control acquisition? In an environment with multiple, scattered resources, automation anarchy can, and usually does, flourish. Proliferation of equipment begets further proliferation. Users find ways to disguise the purchase of computers and to develop systems on their own, neatly sidestepping control by the central data processing department.

- Who manages the microcomputers as they rapidly proliferate? Very often, managers assigned to deal with microcomputer issues have had little or no formal computer experience. Yet these managers are expected to oversee the spread of microcomputers throughout their department. To say the least, systems so developed tend to be inefficient.

You should not be surprised by the problems. When you employ a new, rapidly changing technology to manage a scarcely understood resource — information — without instituting corresponding controls, the result is bound to be catastrophic.

One proposed solution to the problem of information and microcomputer chaos is the local area network (LAN), a communication system which permits the interconnection of computers.

THE IMPORTANCE OF NETWORKING

A computer network is a collection of computers and peripheral devices (the network components) connected by communication links that allow the network components to work together. The network components may be located at many remote locations or within the same office. In any case, data communication is the glue that holds the network together (see Figure 1.1)

Table 1.1 lists some of the major benefits of a local network. Whether these are realized or not, of course, depends on the skill and wisdom of those involved in selecting and managing the local network.

TABLE 1.1 : Benefits and Pitfalls of Local Networks

Potential Benefits

System evolution : incremental changes with contained impact

Reliability/availability/survivability : multiple interconnected systems disperse functions and provide backup capability

Resource sharing : expensive peripherals, host, data

Multivendor support : customer not locked in to a single vendor

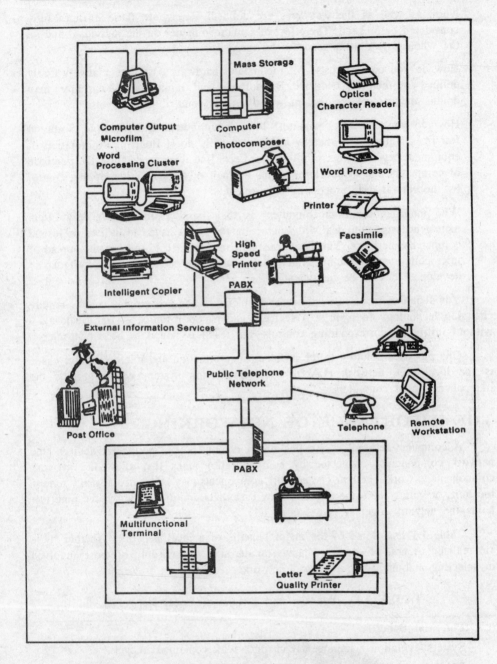

Fig. 1.1 : Local Area Network-
An integrated electronic office where internal and external communications are possible

Improved response/performance

User needs single terminal to access multiple systems

Flexibility of equipment location

Integration of data processing and office automation

Potential Pitfalls

Interoperability is not guaranteed: software, data

A distributed data base raises problems of integrity, security/privacy

Creeping escalation : more equipment will be procured than is actually needed

Loss of control : more difficult to amanage and enforce standards

Networking serves five important purposes:

1. It allows departments to share hardware. Companies often want peripheral devices that are affordable only if they are shared by several computers. For example, a high-speed laser printer may be an unaffordable luxury if it is used only by a single department. If the costs are shared by several departments, however, the laser printer can provide faster printing at a price each department can justify. Networking allows each department's computer to use the laser printer.

2. It allows information to be shared. Some files may be used constantly throughout a company. For example, in an insurance company, all offices throughout the country use files containing information about premium rates. The files are kept in the central computer in the main office and are constantly updated to reflect the latest financial and actuarial data. The central computer also contains programmes that are used to prepare insurance proposals. A network gives each office access to the files and programmes in the central computer.

3. It allows for the electronic transfer of text. Organisations often transfer textual data from one place to another. Through a network, an electronic mail system may be used to distribute copies of memos or reports. Each user of the electronic mail system has a "mailbox" located in the memory of his or her own computer. The electronic mail system distributes messages by storing them in the appropriate mailboxes. The user can check the mailbox for messages. If there is a message, it is displayed on the screen. The user can then use the electronic mail system to send a response.

4. It allows for decentralisation of various data processing functions. As microcomputer use spreads throughout an organisation, some data processing and analysis functions that had been performed by the data processing department become decentralised and are taken care of locally within other departments. To perform these functions, it is crucial that the local computers have access to data from the mainframe computer. A network can provide such access.

5. It allows for communication between organisations. Various organisations cooperating in performing certain tasks can link their computers in a network in order to share information. This allows for sharing of data and software and for rapid communication among the various network members.

Even small organizations have a number of computers and peripheral devices. Networking is one way of getting all the devices to talk to one another and to use the same data files.

Table 1.2 lists organizational effects of local networks, both positive as well as negative effects. The range of applications for local networks is wide. Table 1.3 lists some of the potential applications. Not all local networks are capable of supporting all of them.

TABLE 1.2 : Organizational Effects of Local Networks

Affected Area	Positive Effects	Negative Effects
Work quality	Wider data accessibility : fewer "lost" items. Wider participation in creating and reviewing work	Indeterminate or mediocre data quality; reduced independence and initiative
Productivity	Increased work load handled by more powerful office-systems equipment	Greater resources used to perform inconsequential work
Employee changes	Improved skill levels in current staff More challenging work Reduced status distinctions	Fewer jobs for marginal performers Less personal interaction Insufficient status distinctions
Decision-making effectiveness	Quicker availability of relevant facts Greater analytic capability More people involved in hypothesis building and testing	Factual component of decision making becomes too high "Forest and trees" problem could encourage "group think"
Organizational structure	More effective decentralization	Decentralization can get out of control
Costs	Overall cost reduction	Overall cost increase; soft benefits used as justification
Total impact	Permits the planning of new	Creates increased complexity and poorly functioning dependence relationships

TYPES OF NETWORK

Private Networks. Some networks are designed specifically for and used completely by individual organisations. They are called private networks. The communication equipment that forms the network is purchased or leased in the name of the organisation.

Value Added Networks. Another type of network is the value-added network. This is an established data communication network that owns or leases communication facilities and computers to manage communication. The facilities may include microwave antennas and communication satellites. The owners design and maintain the value-added network. They then rent the network simultaneously to many subscribers, who link their own equipment to the facilities. Using a value-added network saves organisations the time and cost of designing and maintaining their own networks.

Communication networks allow data transmission, voice transmission or both. Common carriers provide transmission facilities and sometimes products and services. The telephone companies are the largest carriers, but there are others who own transmission networks or purchase bulk service for resale in smaller segments to the ultimate users. The primary service of these other carriers is data transmission, with voice a distant second.

If "intelligence" is added to a communication network, usually in the form of a computer for transmission switching or processing to provide compatibility between devices, the network becomes a value-added network (VAN).

Local Area Networks. While some networks may connect computers separated by hundreds or thousands of miles, many networks connect computers within a limited distance of one another, perhaps within the same building or within the same office. This type of network is called a local area network.

Though LAN technology is still young, it is widely used. A number of companies are marketing LANs which can be used to link personal computers. These companies supply and install the various components of a LAN, the cables connecting the computers and the electronic components to be installed into the computers so that they may talk to each other over the cables.

Some of the LANs connect more than just computers. For example, IBM has developed an "industrial LAN" that can be used to link devices in a factory, including robotic systems, machine tools, data collection computers and industrial computers.

Many buildings are now being prewired for LANs. The LAN cabling is installed inside the walls as the buildings are constructed. Tenants can plug their components into modular wall jacks similar to telephone outlets. With the growing use of computers in business, it may not be very long before access to a LAN is considered as indispensable to a business as access to telephone and electricity lines.

Switched Networks. To transmit between two points in a network of numerous transmission links requires selection of a combination of links to handle the job. Switched networks are those in which a specific route is temporarily established for the duration of each individual transmission. Such circuits provide direct connection and are interactive, permitting two-way communication.

In message-switching networks, the transmission is intercepted at a switching point and stored in a computer. In some systems, the message is retransmitted to the next switching point as soon as a link is available; in others the message remains stored until the intended recipient establishes connection with the computer.

Packet-switching networks (see Figure 1.2), like statistical multiplexers, use all available transmission time by filling in the gaps between spurts of data or spoken words with parts of other transmissions. The computer at the switching centre breaks up the data it receives into groups of characters or packets. To each packet 10 added a network address, a transmission identification and an incremental sequence number. Each computerised switching centre is connected to at least two similar centres. Once a packet is assembled, the computer system searches for the shortest available network path to the destination and inserts the packets in the first gap on that path. Likewise, each successive packet takes any path that offers the first available gap, rather than following the same routing. At the final computer switchpoint, the system groups incoming packets according to identification, code arranges them according to packet sequence number, and strips away all characters added by the packet-switching process. The data then move on to the ultimate recipient, usually a user's computer or terminal. The process is carried out with transparent speed. With digitised telephone service, it is possible to apply packet-switching to voice communications.

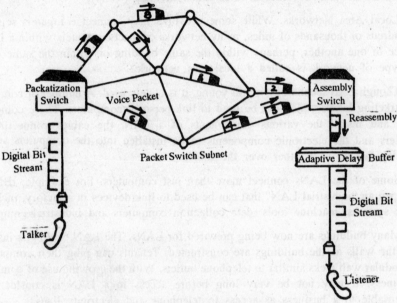

Fig. 1.2 : Packet-switching network

WHAT IS A LOCAL AREA NETWORK?

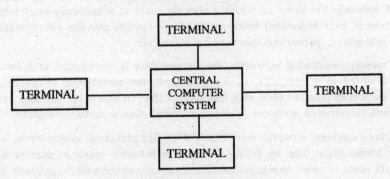

Fig. 1.3 : A multiuser system

A personal computer works in stand-alone state with its own CPU (Central Processing Unit). Many times the need is felt to share the data stored on one or more personal computers. Therefore organisations need multiuser environment which allows sharing of data as well as expensive resources like printers and storage space (see Figure 1.3). A local area network provides modularity, connectivity, superior performance, security and reliability in its operation.

Suppose you have several microcomputers that need to be interconnected. First let us assume that the machines are not too far apart, say within the same building or in several close buildings. Certainly we are talking about fewer than several kilometers. These are the distances spanned by LANs.

At the two extremes of communication speeds, we have the low data rates of wide area networks (WAN) and the high data rates of communication between components inside a machine. Wide area networks are established with existing telephone networks, something similar to using modems (modulator-demodulator) to reach remote databases or public bulletin boards. These networks often span continents, and communication is slow.

At the other extreme is the proximity of individual component boards within a computer and communicating over an internal bus. The components are right next to each other, so the data transmission rate between them is very high. LANs fall between these two extremes.

A local area network is a system of interlinked personal computers, sharing common resources like disks, printers,etc. Processing on a local area network is performed at the individual PC workstation. Novell NetWare is an example of a file server based network. This LAN incorporates star-wired topology and ARCNET (Attached Resource Computer Network) interface.

A LAN works on the principle of 'Load Sharing' because the programme to be executed is downloaded into the personal computer's memory. Therefore it is a multiuser system based on multiple or distributed processing power.

Local area network links a number of computers (workstations) together to allow many people to use the same computer programmes and share information. Each user accesses the network from an individual personal computer workstation.

In LANs we want fast communication between components. We want to approximate the speed of communication within a computer, at what is called bus speed, which is a data transmission rate above 10 megabits per second (Mbps).

Figure 1.4 shows various communication components plugged into the motherboard of a personal computer. The typical communication rates for telephone modems are 300 or 1200 bps (bits per second). 2400 bps modems are also becoming popular. One may communicate between personal computers over a serial connection (or null modem) at even faster rates.

On the other hand, when bits are moved between components within the computer, they typically travel at 10 Mbps. How fast is this? Suppose we have a 10,000

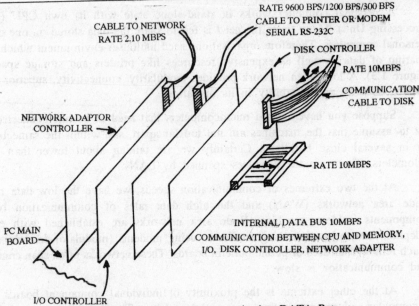

Fig. 1.4 : Comparison of communication DATA Rates

word document with an average of six letters per word including spaces between words. This means it contains 60,000 letters or characters. The computer uses 8 bits (one byte) to represent a character or letter. We then have 480,000 bits.

If we send this document over a modem, we will normally have to add two extra bits for every byte (for protocol). So we have 20,000 extra characters, making a total of 500,000 bits. At 300 bps, this would take 1,667 seconds or 27 minutes. At 1200 bps it would take one eighth of that time or 3 1/2 minutes.

How fast would this transfer take within the computer at 10 Mbps? Considering that within the computer we do not need the extra 2 bits per character, then 480,000 bits at 10 Mbps would take 0.48 seconds or 48 milliseconds.

LANs are characterised by communication rates between 1 and 10 Mbps. While it is true that moving data bits over LANs is not as simple as either of the cases presented above because we have to contend with extra protocol bits, for the most part LANs do approach data transfer speeds equal to those within the computer.

Another useful characteristic of LANs is the presence of a network operating system (NOS), which ties all the components together and makes operations transparent to the user. This turns a group of isolated personal computers into a functional system with transparent resource sharing. A special network operating system runs on each file server and a special workstation shell runs on each workstation.

Most LANs are wholly owned by an organisation such as a department of company. This is similar to ownership of individual personal computers. It is in market contrast to the company mainframe computer that is amortised by charging the user departments. It is also different from wide area networks where the network service are leased from a vendor.

Restricted geographical area, fast intercomputer communication, the presence of a LAN operating system and complete departmental ownership are the hall marks of a LAN of personal computers.

FEATURES OF LOCAL AREA NETWORKS

A LAN is characterised by the following:

- A common communication medium over which all user devices can share information, programmes, and equipment without regard to the physical location of the user or the resource.

- A high transmission rate intended to accommodate the needs of both people and equipment. The system normally is able to support transmission between workstations at the maximum speed at which the these can communicate.

- A limited geographic range: generally defined as less than 10 miles or 16 kilometers. LANs stand between two traditional computer networks: the very limited distance computer bus and the global distance of the long-haul telephone network (see Figure 1.5).

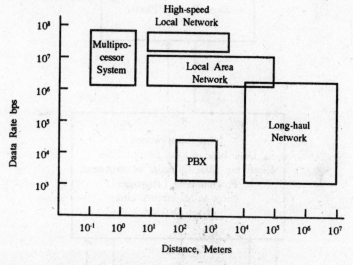

Fig. 1.5 : Comparision of Multiprocessor Systems, Local Networks, and Long-Haul Networks

- A low error rate. An unreliable system, that is, one which distorts or corrupts the data it conveys, is worthless. A built-in method of detecting and compensating for system errors is implied.

- User-administrated private ownership, not subject to regulation by the State Telecommunications Departments or Commissions. Connections over common carrier (telephone) facilities, public cable television and public local networks generally are not considered LANs.

RESOURCE SHARING

LAN eliminates the possibility of overspending by allowing workstations to share peripherals like printers, plotters, digitisers, tape drives and hard disks. This lowers the overall cost of data processing. As LAN is easy to learn and use, it again eliminates the cost of training. LAN's Electronic Mail System reduces the cost of documentation across departments and provides for efficient and flexible communication.

By providing a facility through which a wide variety of computer equipment can be shared by many people, the local area network presents a cost-effective solution. Rarely will each person in an organisation require full-time use of a hard disk or letter-quality printer. Yet everyone will need occasional access to such equipment. With a LAN, one letter-quality printer might serve five or six users. As Figure 1.6 shows, the shared resources need not be just hardware. Software and information also may be shared.

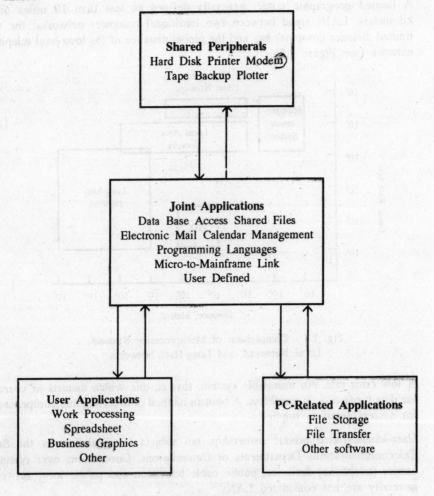

Fig. 1.6 : Shared Network Resources

As a resource sharing tool, a LAN can:

- Permit sharing of expensive hardware.

- Facilitate sharing of complex programmes and the information that they generate and manage.

- Aid in the integration of all aspects of information processing, particularly by transforming a group of individual, not very powerful microcomputers into a powerful distributed processing system.

PRODUCTIVITY

An organisation has four major resources: manpower, equipment, financeand information. Productivity depends on insuring that the people have timely access to the equipment and information required to perform their job. Workers are not demanding more access to computers and intelligent machines just on a whim. They know how much more productive they can be (and how much easier their job is) when they have the right tools. And increased productivity of workers translates directly into profits.

LAN increases productivity because key individuals in the organisation will be able to get access to and share databases, documents and expensive peripherals without bothering about where they are physically located.

As a productivity tool, a LAN can:

- Enable wider distribution of information and the technologies needed to deal with it.

- Improve information retrieval, processing,storage and dissemination through a distributed database. The sooner the user has the needed information, the faster the job can be done.

- Minimise or even possibly eliminate redundant and repetitive tasks.

- Improve efficiency by facilitating the unification of systems and procedures.

- Provide graphic capabilities and other specialised applications that are not cost-effective on stand-alone micros.

COMMUNICATION

Communication, with or without a computer network, is of major importance to an organisation. Workers constantly need information to write orders, type letters and memos, discuss projects, listen to the latest developments, or give sales talks. The services provided by a local area network are designed to expedite this communication among workers.

LAN facilitates communication through its powerful Electronic Mail System (EMS) among authorised network users across time bounderies and distance. Network provides fast responses and transmits urgent notes, messages and circulars.

As a communications resource, a LAN can:

-   Facilitate communication within the organisation by supplying an additional channel for coordinating the work of various groups, exchanging data, sending messages and sharing information. In the long run, the benefits gained through the enhancement of person-to-person communication may outweigh all the technical and economic benefits of networking.

-   Provide in-house, computer-to-computer communication at high speed without the complex masses of cable required in a system of directly connected machines.

-   Supply a method of accessing remote resources, thereby facilitating communication with the world outside the immediate organisation.

MANAGEMENT

The classic management problem is how to accommodate the changing needs of the organisation and its people. To do so, management requires appropriate tools. A well-designed network can evolve gradually as the work load grows, rather than requiring major replacements or upgrades. Equipment can be added, relocated, or removed as needed. The investment in equipment can become a variable cost.

As a management tool, the LAN can:

-   Increase system performance through the distribution of tasks and equipments.

-   Improve the availability of computer resources. Tasks can be assigned to several machines; if one is occupied with a different task, the second can perform the work.

-   Increase system reliability. Crucial processes can be duplicated and/or divided so that, on the failure of one machine, other machines can quickly take up the load.

-   Minimise the adverse effects of loss of any one system.

-   Help regain administrative control of equipment, especially the large number of microcomputers that have appeared on desks, but whose purchase never was officially known or approved.

LAN improves the efficiency with more information accessible at workstation which can be used for taking better and timely decisions. LAN can have dramatic impact on efficiency where the data is dynamic; it must be current to be accurate and also shared by many individuals at different locations.

The LAN server concept allows efficient centralisation of information by allowing control over who uses the network and for what purpose. A LAN has extensive security system which can be implemented in accordance with management policy to protect the confidential files. The security features allow data to be shared the way it should be, and there is sort of authority with responsibility.

A LAN is a scalable, modular network with configuration flexibility. PCs and other resources can be added as and when needed. A LAN can talk to your minicomputer or mainframe computer to maintain compatibility of operations from your earlier investment.

The advantages of local area networks can be enumerated:

1. Local Area Networks are the best means to provide a cost-effective multiuser computer environment.

2. A LAN can fit any site requirements.

3. It can be tailored to suit any type of application.

4. Any number of users can be accomodated.

5. It is obsolescence-proof.

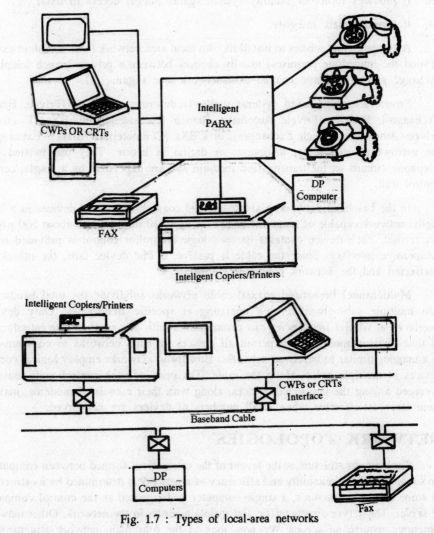

Fig. 1.7 : Types of local-area networks

6.   It is flexible and growth-oriented.

7.   It offers existing single users a familiar Disk Operating System (DOS) environment.

8.   Itcanuse existing software if the original language supports multiuser environment.

9.   It offers electronic mail as an in-built facility.

10. It allows sharing of mass central storage and printers.

11. Data transfer rates are above 10 Mbps.

12. It allows file/record locking.

13. It provides foolproof security system against illegal access to data.

14. It provides data integrity.

A company that wishes to install its own local area network (which seldom extend beyond the immediate premises) usually chooses between a private branch telephone exchange and a baseband coaxial cablenetwork (see Figure 1.7).

Private telephone-based systems variously described as PBXs (Private Branch Exchanges), PABXs (Private Automatic Branch Exchanges), EPABXs (Electronic Private Automatic Branch Exchanges), or CBXs (Computerised Branch Exchanges) are narrowband and either analogous or digital in nature. They use twisted pair telephone circuits as the transmission medium and are dependent on a single, central control unit.

In the baseband network, a single-channel coaxial cable links devices in a local digital network capable of transmission speeds up to 10 megabits (or about 500 pages) per second. Each device contains its own logic control,or control is provided in an inexpensive interface. Since the cable is passive, if one device fails, the others are unaffected and the network continues to operate.

Multichannel broadband coaxial cable networks subdivide the total bandwidth into multiple sub-networks, each operating at specific frequencies. Only devices interfaced at similar frequencies can communicate with one another. The introduction of time-division modems will permit all devices on such networks to communicate in a manner similar to baseband networks. Broadband networks employ logical control devices at multiple points along the cable. The price of such control units must be averaged among the connected devices, along with their associated modems, making them less cost-effective when small numbers of devices are networked.

NETWORK TOPOLOGIES

Topology or structure is the layout of the connections formed between computers. To some extent, the reliability and efficiency of a network is determined by its structure. In some network structures, a single computer is designated as the control computer, or server. The server directs traffic and maintains order in the network. Other network structures require no server. We now look at the four main network structures.

1.   Bus Networks. If the computers are all attached to one single cable, we call
     that a broadcast bus. Broadcasting of messages, where one computer transmits
     and all other computers can listen simultaneously, is the characteristic feature
     of this topology. Figure 1.8a shows a schematic diagram or flowchart of this
     topology.

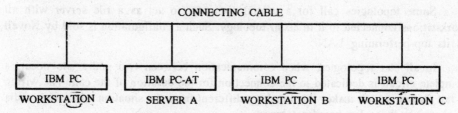

Fig. 1.8a : Bus network topology

     In a bus network, the computers are connected by a cable called a bus. Messages
are sent along the bus. The connected computers can hear the message and determine
whether it is for them. A bus network is commonly used in LANs. In a bus network,
the failure of a single computer does not affect the performance of the rest of the
network. Computers may be easily added or removed from the network.

2.   Star Networks. On the other hand, when all communication must go through
     a central point, we call that topology a star. A good example is the telephone
     switching computer in the office. To call someone you pick up your telephone
     receiver and dial. Your phone, attached to the central switch, communicates to
     that switch which you are trying to reach. The connection is attempted and,
     if the other party is not busy , the switch completes the connection. The
     conversation is between you and the other party, but the connection must go
     through the central switch.

     Such switches are often used to connect computers as well as telephones. State-
of-the-art switching computers are called PBXs. They can handle medium-speed
communication between computers at 64 kilobits per second and more. Contrast this
with typical telephone switches, which usually handle 1200 bps computer links. Figure
1.8b shows a typical star topology. In this arrangement it is not as easy to broadcast
messages to all stations.

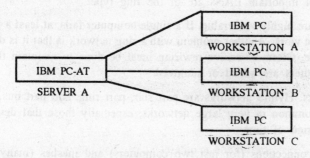

Fig. 1.8b : Star network topology

A star network has a server at its centre. All messages must go through the server. When a message is going from one computer to another, it is first sent to the server, which then retransmits the message to its destination. A star network is vulnerable only if the server fails; if this happens, the entire network does not work. It is reasonably easy to add or remove computers from a star network.

Some topologies call for a central computer to act as a file server with all workstations connected to it in a star topology. Such a configuration is sold by Novell as its top-performing LAN.

In all star topologies, when communication between two nodes isto occur, a complete circuit is dedicated to the connection for the duration of the call. The wiring is not shared, which makes this topology different from the situation where the media is shared such as for broadcast buses.

3.   Ring Networks. In a ring network, the computers and peripheral devices are arranged so that the communication links connect the components in a ring (see Figure 1.8c). In this structure, any computer can communicate with any other by sending a signal around the ring. Each message is tagged with its destination. As the message proceeds around the ring, each computer determines whether it is the recipient of the message. If not, the message is sent to the next computer.

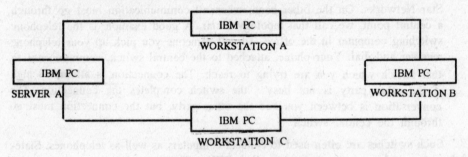

Fig. 1.8c : Ring network topology

Ring topologies are more interesting. They are similar to broadcast buses but the media interconnecting the machines makes a complete loop. A message goes from station to station, making a ring. Each station takes an active role in transferring the messages. Several important LANs are of the ring type.

Ring networks are highly vulnerable. If a single computer fails, at least a portion of the network will not work. Another problem with a ring network is that it is difficult to change its structure. Often, extensive rewiring must be done to maintain the ring structure when computers are added or removed.

4.   Hybrid Networks. Hybrid networks are part star, part ring, and part bus. These structures are common in very large networks, especially those that developed over a long period of time.

Point to point connections (for just two computers) and meshes (many point-to-point connections) are two other topologies. The first is of little interest since few

LANs are of this type. The second is not supported with current LAN software on personal computers.

Networks can be configured in several ways. Hub or Star networks, the simplext to develop, pass all communication through a single switch or node. Multidrop networks (see Figure 1.8d) connect all devices to a single meandering set of links. These are inexpensive, full-time networks, but loss of service at any point will immediately deny access to those further along the network. Loop or ring networks form an endless loop, they also are relatively inexpensive, and can provide an alternate route in case of loss of service at a given point. Mesh networks (see Figure 1.8e) permit any two devices within the network to communicate directly. This type of configuration is very dependable, since it provides multiple routes into and out of each location.

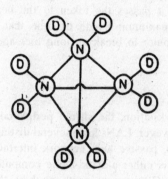

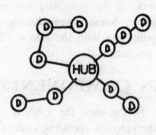

Fig. 1.8d : Multi-Drop   Fig. 1.8e : Mesh

(N) : Node (Computer or Controller)   (D) : Automation Device

Typical network configurations

COMMUNICATION TECHNIQUES WITHIN NETWORKS

Each network structure has rules that define how and when a computer may send a message and how the message is received by the destination computer.

A star network generally uses some form of addressing scheme. Each message has an address on it. The server examines the address and sends the message to its destination. If there are many messages for a single destination, the server forms a waiting line, or queue, of messages. In some systems, messages have various levels of priority, and high-priority messages can move to the front queue, ahead of other, low-priority messages.

Bus and ring networks have no server to direct traffic, so some other scheme must be used to keep order in the network. Two common schemes are carrier-sensed multiple access (CSMA) and token passing.

In a CSMA network, a computer that wants to send a message listens to the line. If it hears no traffic, it begins sending. There are two problems with the CSMA scheme. First, long messages may monopolise the network for long periods of time.

Second, two computers may start transmitting at the same time, causing a collision between the two signals. The first problem is generally solved by breaking long messages into smaller messages called packets. Each packet has address information and tells the receiver where it fits within the longer message. Once a packet has been transmitted, the other computers have a chance to grab the network. In this way, long messages cannot monopolise the network. The problem of collisions is handled by having each computer wait a random length of time and try to retransmit the message. The collision is then resolved in favour of the computer that gets back to the network first.

Token passing is an alternative to CSMA. In this scheme, a collection of bits, called a token, is passed in a certain order, among the computers in the network. The computer currently holding the token has the right to send a message over the network. If the computer has no message to send, it passes the token to the next computer. Some token passing schemes dictate a maximum length of time that a computer can hold the token. This requires the computer to break up long messages into packets.

LAN COMPONENTS

To the user, the LAN is composed of the workstation, the shared peripherals, and the network operating system (see Figure 1.9). However, LANs have several distinct components like file server, work-station, active hub, passive hub, network interface card, LAN cable, etc. Every computer on the LAN is either a stand-alone computer (such as a workstation), a file server, or a gateway. Other components, such as the media or LAN operating system, perform some communication functions.

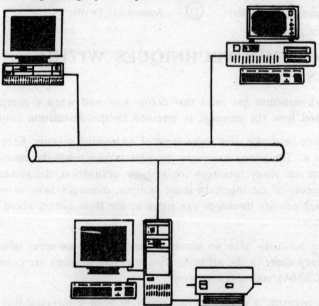

Fig. 1.9 : The main components of a local area network are network stations and a cabling system that links them together

We associate here all the hardware components, the media and the LAN interface units, used to interconnect the network. Media is the term that refers to the LAN components that carry the communication signals between computers. Typically this is either a coaxial or twisted-pair cable. In both cases the communication is transmitted by means of electric signals.

WORKSTATION

The most common component of a LAN is the workstation. A workstation is an individual, single-user microcomputer with communications capabilities added. The term includes the microcomputer itself as well as all its attached bits and pieces — memory cards, CRT, floppy disk drives, hard disks and printers. A workstation is distinguished from a personal computer by the network operating system software that controls what the workstations can and cannot do and by a network interface unit that supplies the communications capabilities.

A workstation is any personal computer capable of supporting the hardware and software necessary to connect to a LAN. For our purposes, we narrow this definition further: a workstation must be able to run dBASE IV or Lotus 1-2-3 under either the PC Network Programme or the Novell NetWare operating system. It must also allow a LAN interface board to be plugged into its motherboard. Any IBM-Compatible PC/AT/80X86 can be designated as the workstation. Every workstation has the network interface card or unit (NIC or NIU) which is the hardware interface between network and a workstation.

Every workstation will run a memory resident software, called Workstation Shell, which is the software interface between file server and workstation. This will filter local and network requests/commands.

A workstation can send or receive messages to or from other workstations or file server.

For some LANs, the connection to a workstation can be made with a serial port. In that case, the LAN interface unit is not a plug-in board internal to the computer but an external component. The LAN interface unit (or LAN adapter) communicates with the LAN at high speed. A plug-in board is preferred over an external interface unit because the serial connection is slow, which defeats the purpose of having a 1 to 10 Mbps LAN.

Workstations may have from one to several floppy-disk drives and hard-disk drives. Figures 1.10a and 1.10b shows a workstation attached to the LAN. One or more printers may be attached to this computer as well.

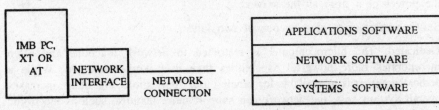

Fig. 1.10 a : Block of workstation hardware   Fig. 1.10 b :   Block diagram of
                                                                  workstation software

Workstations may be divided into two classes: users and servers. User workstations are microcomputers on the network which have a primary responsibility to an individual user. Server workstations perform a service to other workstations on the network. All workstations on the network communicate and cooperate with one another. The primary difference between server and user workstations is in the directly attached resources and programmes which they run.

User workstations normally do not, and cannot fulfill requests from other workstations. Resources attached to a user workstation, such as floppy disk drives, can only be accessed by the user of that workstation.

In contrast, resources attached to a server are shared by all users of the network. Broadly, any workstation that can supply services to other workstations can perform server functions. More than one server may be attached to a network, with each server providing a different function, or one server fulfilling several roles. See Figure 1.11 for a typical network with servers.

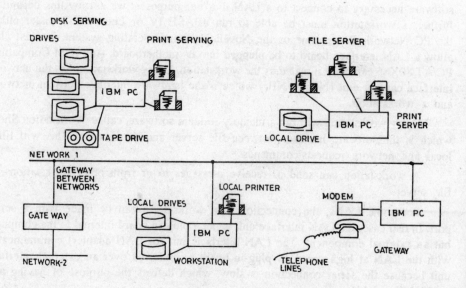

Fig. 1.11 : Logical Network Components

Normally the server is the most powerful workstation on the network, associated with the disk drive and printer. Some LANs use a small minicomputer or a supermicro with the power of a mini as the server.

Server workstations may be one of two kinds:

Dedicated: The microcomputer is restricted to network functions and often incorporates more powerful capabilities than user workstations do. While a dedicated server is unavailable for running user applications, and hence increases overall system cost, the network can support more features, such as electronic mail service or multiple hard disks, and provides faster system response. Larger networks usually require dedicated servers.

- Non-dedicated: The microcomputer can act as an individual workstation even while it controls the network. Network operation usually requires at least 1 MB of memory. (Many networks require more). Additional memory is required for all but the simplest tasks. Under light load, performance of a non-dedicated server may be slightly less than that of a workstation; under heavy processing demand, the individual user of the server may find work impossible.

Some network servers are capable of operating in both dedicated and non-dedicated mode, depending on the user's selection.

FILE SERVER

One purpose of a LAN is to facilitate simultaneous sharing of data among users on separate workstations. This is accomplished by providing one workstation with some hard disks that are shared by all the users. The LAN software allows calls to be made by any workstation to access these files.

The file server is a powerful computer which runs special software to act as a file server. As the name suggests, it serves the files to networked computers which share and use these files. The files can be programmes, text or data. The file server is a completely enclosed logical structure which is secure against accidental or malicious abuse as it can be accessed only through Network Operating System (NOS).

The activity of each file server can be monitored from the file server's screen. The system supervisor monitors and controls operation of each individual network through the file server and uses it to control the print spooling, send/broadcast messages and perform many other system functions. The file server has a comparatively large volume of memory which is used for caching directories and files, and directory hashing.

Novell NetWare, for example, requires users on a workstation to log on to a file server to enter the LAN. Under Novell NetWare, specifically designated machines are converted to file servers. Under the PC Network Programme, any workstation can perform the function of file serving on any files that have been designated as public. Under Novell Advanced NetWare, up to 100 file servers in any one LAN can operate simultaneously. This becomes extremely useful when the LAN has many files; the LAN administrator can redistribute the load between file servers to speed up the LAN.

Imagine the amount of work that a file server does. It may be queried by every workstation at the same time. For this reason, the machines acting as file servers are normally more powerful than a run-of-the-mill workstation. An IBM PC/AT/80X86 compatible, or any other computer running at a fast clock rate of 33 MHz is preferable to an ordinary workstation with added hard disks.

Under all versions of Novell, the file server may also double as a workstation operating in what is called nondedicated mode. However, in most cases, it is preferable not to have the file server perform both file serving and workstation functions. A file server is a resource that should be available to all workstations at all times. If the file server is forced to operate as a workstation at the same time, it then must divide its processing time and memory between two tasks, with the performance of both suffering. In small LANs with just a few nodes, this dual mode of operation might be acceptable. With many nodes, however, it is advantageous to dedicate a computer to the file serving task full time. As the number of nodes increases, it may also be necessary to add another file server to maintain adequate performance.

Fast tape drives for the backup of files on the LAN are an expensive resource. Nevertheless, it is convenient and economical to place a tape backup unit at the file server to back up its files. One may even go as far as to back up local workstation files over the LAN to a stand-alone workstation with a tape acting as a tape back-up server. When the LAN is lightly loaded (light workstation traffic), this is a convenient back-up method.

One characteristic of LANs is the sharing of print resources. A workstation might be dedicated as the print server on the LAN, as shown in Figure 1.11. Queuing of print jobs is a major function of print servers. Under Novell, the queuing function is performed transparently, and the printers appear to users on workstations as if they were local.

One of the key tests to determine whether a software package has been designed for a LAN is to check its print function. Does the software enable you to print as easily with the LAN version as with the single user version? Or, do you have to direct the output to a print file, exit the software, and then issue the print command from the operating system? Effective LAN software should offer printing from within the software as a transparent task.

A file server may also function as a print server. However, for larger installations, these functions are better performed by a separate machine. On the average, if you have six or fewer workstations, one file server is sufficient and can also function as a print server. If you have more than six workstations on a LAN, you might consider separating the print serving and file serving functions. You could do this by either having your in-house programmer write print serving software or by adding an additional file server to act as the print server.

GATEWAY

LANs may have a component called gateway. Suppose the sales department of the corporation HIPL installed a LAN several years ago. Today HIPL's accounting department wants to install a LAN but wants to use the latest technology. The hardware will be different, but now the two departments want their LANs to communicate with each other. What can they do? Under Novell, for example, they can connect the two different LANs with a special component called a gateway (bridge in Novell terminology).

The gateway assists in transferring bits from one LAN to the other. If the sales department is already running Novell software, then the new LAN, which features state-of-the-art hardware, should also run Novell. A workstation is dedicated to act as the gateway. Network adapter cards for both types of LANs are inserted in the machine, and a special set of Novell programmes transfers the bits from one LAN to the other. Figure 1.12a shows how this works. Similarly a LAN can also be connected to another mainframe computer by a gateway as depicted in Figure 1.12b. A server can also act as the bridge by installing a card from both the old and new LANs. This eliminates the need to tie up a workstation.

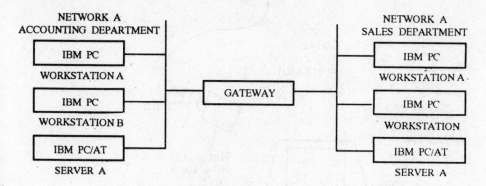

Fig. 1.12 a : Gateway connecting a LAN to another LAN

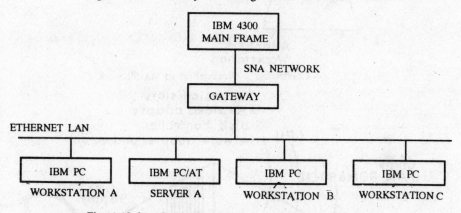

Fig. 1.12 b : Gateway connecting a LAN to a mainframe

NETWORK INTERFACE UNIT

The network interface unit is a microprocessor-based device containing hardware and software which supply the intelligence to control access to and communication across the network and to perform all communication processing. It is the means by which the workstations are connected functionally and physically to the network.

On most microcomputer networks, the network interface is a printed circuit board installed in the microcomputer. Depending on the vendor, it may be called a network card, network adapter, or network interface unit.

On some networks, the network interface may be implemented as a stand-alone box, termed a wiring centre, or hub, attached between the main network cable and

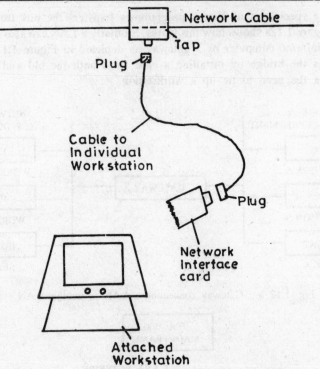

Network Cable

Tap

Plug

Cable to
Individual
Workstation

Plug

Network
Interface
card

Attached
Workstation

Fig. 1.13 a : Connecting a Workstation to the Network

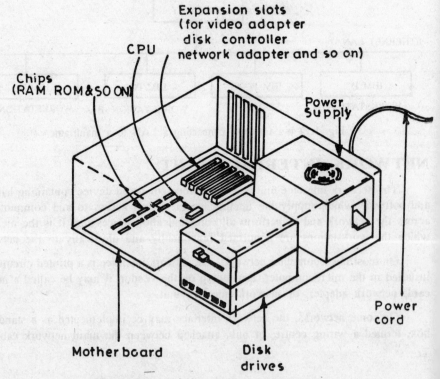

Expansion slots
(for video adapter
disk controller
network adapter and so on)

CPU

Chips
(RAM ROM&SO ON)

Power
Supply

Motherboard

Disk
drives

Power
cord

Fig. 1.13 b : Inside your PC's system unit

the workstation. Figure 1.13 shows how the microcomputer is connected to the network through the interface card.

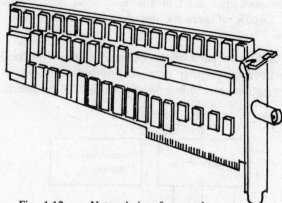

Fig. 1.13 c : Network interface card

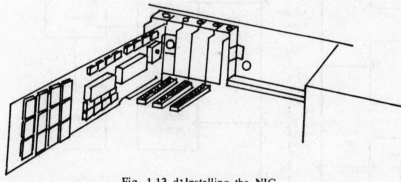

Fig. 1.13 d: Installing the NIC

An assumption is made that networking ability is not already present in the microcomputer, but has to be added. Microcomputers with built-in communication and networking facilities will not need added hardware; the functions of the network interface already will be present in the machine. The crucial factor is not where or how the interface is located, but what functions it serves.

Network interface functions are realised through chips on the interface unit: network bus drivers, communication controller chips, specialised microprocessors, RAM buffers and ROM code that is executed by the workstation itself. For most LANs, the network interface unit for all user workstations is identical. Server interface units may include additional ROM code to implement additional functions. Physical connection to the network is provided through a standard communication or input/output interface.

Through the network interface, data on the medium is available to all attached workstations and peripherals. System users never need to know what it takes to get from one point to another; they simply indicate the desired destination. The network interface unit provides transmission and data control, formats the data into manageable units, translates the data rate and protocols of the attached workstation to that of the network communication medium and vice versa, and supplies address recognition capabilities. Details of network operation are hidden from users of the attached workstations.

Technically, two parts of the network interface can be identified: the communication interface, containing network oriented functions, and the host interface, containing computer specific functions. Both parts of the interface are shown in Figure 1.14.

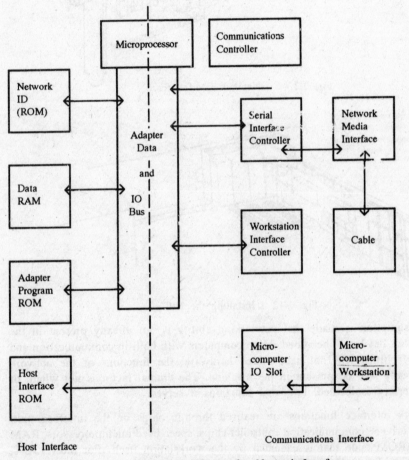

Fig. 1.14 : Parts of a Network Interface

The communication interface is the unit which logically interfaces to the network. It performs all transmission related functions. It accepts data from the attached workstation, buffers the data until the communication channel is available, and then transmits the data. The communications interface also monitors the channel for messages addressed to its workstation, stores the data and transfers the data to the device.

The actual physical connection between the workstation and the network is achieved by running a secondary cable between the communications interface and the main network cable. The two cables are joined by a tap.

The host interface supplies the connection between a specific workstation's internal circuitry and the communication interface unit. It fits into the input/output structure of a particular computer, and governs all data exchange between the workstation and the communication-oriented portion of the network interface. Because of the many methods of implementing network and workstation functions, the host interface is workstation- and vendor-specific.

ACTIVE HUB

An active hub is a powered distribution point with active devices which drive distant nodes upto 1 kilometer away. Active hubs can be cascaded to connect 8 connections to which passive hubs, file servers or another active hubs can be connected. Maximum distance covered by an active hub is about 2000 ft.

PASSIVE HUB

As the name suggests it is a passive distribution point which does not use power or active devices in a network to connect upto 4 nodes within a very short distance. Maximum distance covered by a passive hub is about 300 ft.

LAN CABLE

LAN uses coaxial cable RG-62. This is a relatively superior cable that allows for baseband transmission. The cable is capable of transfering upto 10 Mbps. Special end connectors are used to interface with network interface card or hubs.

The advantages of the coaxial cable are:

1. Wider band width.

2. Interference resistance.

3. High conductivity without distortion.

4. Longer distances covered.

New technologies are making inroads in the traditional interconnection techniques. One commercially important new technology is fiber optics. Signaling in this medium is done by flashes of very pure light.

NETWORK OPERATING SYSTEM

Unifying all the LAN components is the LAN operating system. The LAN operating system is the software that facilitates file and print serving, as well as ordinary communication between workstations, such as electronic mail. There are two popular operating systems, Novell Advanced NetWare and PC Network Program. Each provides its services transparently to users. This means that the user spends no extra effort to retrieve data from a file or to print a file over the LAN.

If used to a multiuser environment, you would like to see the LAN operating system provide all the functionality available on such systems. The application software should operate transparently over the LAN and do it as well as it does on a multiuser system. From the single user's point of view, the application software should work as well as it does on a stand-alone microcomputer while adding the benefits of the LAN.

The following are typical features of network operating system software:

1. 26 logical drives which can be mapped.
2. Elevator seeking disk access algorithm.
3. Directory hashing.
4. Disk file caching.
5. File / record locking.
6. System fault tolerance.
7. Transaction tracking system.
8. LAN security system.
9. Printer spooling.
10. On-line HELP.
11. Menu utilities.
12. Simple DOS-like operating system commands.

The major task of a server is running the network operating system. Network performance is directly dependent on the quality of the network operating system that manages the shared resources of the network. The network operating system is the directly visible aspect of the many layers of internal network software. In broad terms, it is the network's counterpart to MS-DOS or CP/M, the directions that tell how tasks are done on a network. Like a computer operating system, the network operating system works in the background, constantly governing and monitoring network activities.

In most LANs, the network operating system exists in conjunction with the computer's operating system. System requests are processed first by the computer operating system. When a local request is made, that is, one that requires only the immediate resources/capabilities of your workstation, it is fulfilled by the local machine. When a request is made that requires network resources or network activities, it is passed to the network software for processing.

Among other tasks, the network operating system is responsible for controlling access to data, allocating disk space and controlling the sharing of networked printers.

SHARING DATA

When the user of a stand-alone microcomputer requests access to a file, a single-user oriented computer operating system reads its internal directory to find the stored file and retrieve it. The table is updated as files are written to disk. By reading the information on unused sectors, the system knows where it can safely write additional data.

In a networking environment, with many users attempting to read the same data and to write to a single shared disk, the network needs some mechanism to synchronise users with each other, to arbitrate between requests and to govern data writingto the disk, thus allowing several users to access the programmes data at the same time.

FILE AND RECORD LOCKING

Several alternative techniques exist to handle the difficulties caused by using single-user operating systems and single-user application programmes never meant to deal with more than one user at a time. Generally, the techniques may be classified

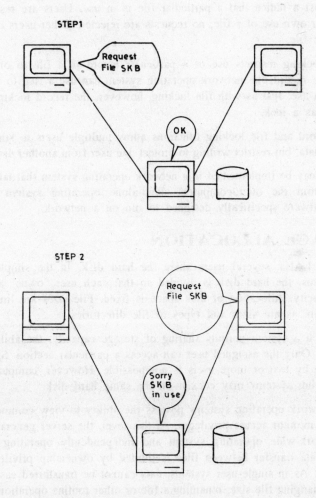

Fig. 1.15 : File Looking

as file locking/unlocking and record locking/unlocking. Figure 1.15 illustrates the file locking concept.

File locking restricts use of a whole file to one user at a time. When a file is accessed, the programme sets a "flag" or marker. Flags consist of bytes of data that are stored along with file names in a table on disk or in memory. Depending on the value of the byte, the file is marked as locked or unlocked. The operating system rejects subsequent requests during the time when the flag indicates that the file in use. When the original user finished with the file, the flag is removed or reset.

For file locking to work, the individual application programmes in use must recognise the flags and respond appropriately to them. Effective use of flags is entirely dependent upon the cooperation of all programmes involved. Alternatively, the system may simply post a notice that a particular file is in use. Users are responsible for controlling their own use of a file; no requests are rejected. Other users can still read or write to the file.

Record locking restricts use of a particular record in a file to one user at a time. To lock a record, the network operating system can use a flag to indicate that the record is in use. Just as with file locking, however, the record locking flag must be recognised as a lock.

Some record and file locking functions allow multiple users to simultaneously read the same data, but restrict writing to protect one user from another user's updates.

Locking may be implemented in a network operating system that takes over file management from the microcomputers stand-alone operating system or through applications software specifically designed to run on a network.

DISK SPACE ALLOCATION

On most LANs, several users share the hard disk. In the simplest network operating systems, the hard disk is divided so that each user "owns" a portion of its storage capacity. Allocation of disk space is fixed. File sizes are limited by the operating system, as are sizes and types of file directories.

While such a system permits sharing of storage capacity, the ability to share data is lacking. Only the assigned user can access a particular section. Simultaneous access to a file by two or more users is not possible. However, computers running different operating systems may coexist on the same hard disk.

Many network operating systems possess the ability to view common data and can assign and monitor access privileges. At this level, the server generally supports a single, network-wide operating system and independently operating application programmes. Data transfer between files is limited by ownership privileges and by the type of file. As in single-user systems, data cannot be transferred easily between applications. Changing file size, renaming a file or other routine operations can upset access by other users.

In many of the newer LANs, hard disks are divided into volumes. The portion of total network disk space that is to be devoted to a particular task or set of users is controlled. Volumes may be named or numbered, depending on the operating system.

- A public volume contains data that may be read by all network users. It stores basic utilities and shared programmes. The files are write protected; they cannot be changed or erased except by the volume's creator. Several network users may access the data simultaneously.

- Shared volumes contain files that are available to a defined group of users. Members of the group may both read and write to the volume. To preserve data integrity, when multiple users attempt to change the same record or file simultaneously, some method of data locking is needed.

- Private volumes contain personal or confidential data. Access is restricted to the creator ("owner") of the volume, who may read and write data to it.

- Each volume usually contains a number of subdirectories. Access privileges to the volume and to individual subdirectories within the volume are defined so that a user can be granted access to precisely the data he needs without access to data he does not have the right to view. Typical user access rights are shown in Figure 1.16.

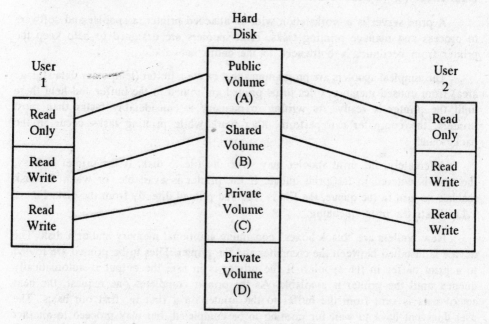

Fig. 1.16 : User Access Rights

Volume and file sizes are limited by the operating system, the size of the shared disk and the number of users sharing the disk. The directory structure and size are limited by the specific operating system. For shared volumes, actions by one user can upset others.

Some network operating systems provide for file "caching". Server memory, designated as a "cache block", is reserved for holding current data, much like a mailbox. When a request for information is processed by the file server, the data is read into the available cache block. Subsequent requests to read the data found in a cache block will be retrieved from memory, rather than from the disk. A request to write is first written to the cache block and then completed as a background task to the normal disk or network operating system. Caching improves response time and decreases the number of times the disk is read from and/or written to.

In systems offering file caching, directory caching also may be available. The entire disk directory is stored in memory for immediate access. The location of needed files can then be determined by reading the memory, rather than reading the disk. The process is considerably quicker - up to 100 times faster than directly reading the disk and saves on physical wear

Network operating system software may also include routines for prioritising file retrieval requests, for alphabetising the directory, for password protection and for error-checking and recovery.

SHARING THE PRINTER

A print server is a workstation with an attached printer, a spooler and software to process and manage printing tasks. Print spoolers are designed to help keep the printer from becoming a bottleneck to the entire network.

The simplest spoolers are programmes that create a buffer (temporary data storage area) from unused memory. Files to be printed are routed to the buffer and held there until the printer is ready. As writing to memory is considerably faster than most printers, the computer can perform other work while printing tasks occur in the background.

Alternately, the print spooler may write the file to disk. If the printer is busy, the task is entered in the print queue. If the printer is available, or when the task reaches its turn in the queue, the file is read and printed directly from the disk. Figure 1.17 illustrates print queueing.

Newspoolers are "black boxes" containing additional memory and/or a disk. The device is installed between the computer and the printer. Files to be printed are routed to a print buffer in the spooler. If the printer is in use, the output is automatically queued until the printer is available. As the printer completes one request, the next set of data is sent from the buffer to the printer on a first in, first out basis. The user does not have to wait for printing to be completed, but may proceed to another task.

Sophisticated print servers allow the user to specify the number of copies, the printer to be used, special fonts and priority. Users may be able to query the state of the print queue, to know when their printing is ready and to change the order of the queue.

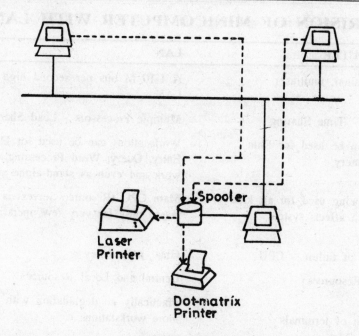

Fig. 1.17 : Print Server

APPLICATIONS SOFTWARE

dBASE IV is an example of application software that will function over the LAN as well as it does on a stand-alone machine. Some word processing packages like WordStar also work over the LAN. It takes extra effort for the software manufacturer to integrate an applications package with the LAN operating system. So, you should determine that file locking and record locking are integrated transparently in the LAN version of the software.

Under LAN operating system practically any software that is available under MS-DOS, such as popular spreadsheets, word processors, data management software, language compilers and other utilities,can be used directly. In addition to the above, multiuser versions of ANSI-74 COBOL, BASIC and DBMS with synchronisation functions like record locking and file locking are also available to LAN users. For the commercial data processing environment, a powerful Sort/Merge utility capable of sorting very large files at an amazing speed is also available. Gateways to other minicomputers and networks have also been developed to enable communication with various kinds of hardware under different operating systems.

Furthermore, when shopping for software that works over a LAN, it should be determined how much manipulation of the file and the environment has to be done at the LAN operating system level to accomplish tasks. If too many LAN commands need to be issued to use the programme or its associated files, then the software vendor has not done a good integration job.

COMPARISION OF MINICOMPUTER WITH LAN

MINICOMPUTER	LAN
A multi terminal, multiuser computer	A 1-10 M bits per second high speed LAN
Single CPU - Time Sharing	Multiple Processors - Load Sharing
Terminals can be used for Data Entry and Query	Workstations can be used for Data Entry, Query, Word Processing, MIS work and even as stand-alone systems
Main CPU being used for all kind of jobs which affects system throughput	Main CPU (Resource Server) is addressed only for very few operations
Single point of failure - CPU	Great redundancy
Centralised Resources	Central and Local Resources
Degradation with addition of terminals	Practically no degradation with more workstations .
In case of many terminals, the same CPU has to be used. Degraded response time	In case of many nodes, multiple File Servers are possible
Single function terminal - Usually Dumb	Multifunction Workstations - Basically Computers
Upgradation in quantum jump	Upgradation in single units
Fear of obsolescense	Workstations procured as and when required with latest technology
Cabling distance upto 2.4 km	Cabling distance upto 64 km
Technology upgrade implies replacement	Implies changing or adding workstations
Proprietory OS, Limited Software	Standard OS, Popular user-friendly software. LAN provides better reliability with cost effective hardware redundancy. LAN provides minicomputer functions with superior performance and better reliability in a user-friendly way
No special productivity packages like Supercalc IV, dBASE IV, etc. are possible	Such packages are available on all nodes and LAN servers

Suitable for an on-line data processing requirement.	Ideal for an environment with mixed applications like MIS, Word processing,
Terminals can be used.	data processing, data entry, query.
One-time block investment	Staggered investment, system grows with your needs

DEPARTMENTAL COMPUTING

*   In line with organisational structure
*   Powerful PC compatible microcomputers
*   Distribution of processing power within department
*   Application sites unified by LAN

ADVENT OF MICROCOMPUTERS

*   Shift of computing power from EDP to user
*   Menu-driven user-friendly popular application software
*   Emergence of high-end PC compatibles

OVERALL DDP (DISTRIBUTED DATA PROCESSING) SCHEME IN LAN

*   Departmental LANs with departmental resources
*   Unification of departmental LANs
*   Functional information distributed
*   Control information integrated
*   Fault tolerance, improved response

2

DATA COMMUNICATIONS

INTRODUCTION

Computers are used to generate information. Generated information is not useful in itself. The information must be delivered to the individuals who use it, and it must be delivered in a timely fashion. Often, the information must be transmitted from one location to another. This process is called data communication. Here, we will be concerned with the hardware, software and procedures used in data communication.

Communication, the transfer of information, is the basis of office automation. Advances in communication technology, combined with rapidly evolving computer technology, have made possible much of the progress in the field. Electronic communication consists of telecommunication and data communication. Telecommunication is the use of telephone, teletypewriting, telegraph, radio, or television facilities to transmit information, either directly or via the computer. Data communication is the transfer of data or information between computer-devices. Office automation integrates the two.

Data communication is so common that each of us has probably seen it in action without thinking much about it. Some examples of everyday data communication are:

1. Airlines Reservations: When you reserve seats on an airplane flight, the agent enters the reservation on a terminal connected to the airline's computer. Since the computer is usually located far from the agent (sometimes several thousand miles away), data communication must be used to relay data from the terminal to the computer and back.

2. Automated Banking: Most banks now provide a wide range of banking services through automatic teller machines (ATMs). Users can make deposits and withdrawals, check balances, and even pay utility bills through the machines. An automatic teller machine is connected to the bank's main computer, which

may be located at the other end of the city or even in another state. The transaction request is sent to the computer using a data communication system.

3.   Point-of-Sale Terminals: Many retail stores use point-of-sale terminals instead of cash registers. These terminals send records of sales to a central computer, which maintains accounting and inventory records.

Communication offers so many opportunities, it is tough to know where to begin. You can turn your personal computer into a terminal and take advantage of massive mainframe processing power. If you are feeling sociable, you can send an electronic letter to a friend or even meet new people through an on-line service. Best of all, you can access huge reserves of information on virtually any subject. Once you are on-line, you may find linking up with the outside world a fascinating addiction.

Along with these attractions, mysteries abound. In fact, communication is one of the most difficult computer applications to comprehend. In the self-contained quarters of word processing, spreadsheets and data base management, all you need worry about is your PC and its software. As Figure 2.1 illustrates, linking up with the outside world adds a whole new set of considerations. Your system, a modem (modulator-demodulator), a communications network, and the remote computer's hardware and software must work in tandem for a successful exchange of data to take place.

DATA COMMUNICATION

Data communication is the active process of transporting data from one point to another. Networks are communication systems designed to convey information from a point of origin to a point of destination. Note that they are communication systems, not computer systems. The operative word is communication, the transfer of information from one person or device to another.

Networks come in two flavours: local as in local area networks, which cover a small area and have a finite, relatively small, number of users; and global or long-haul, which cover great distances and have an unlimited number of users. Telephone networks are long-haul networks.

Two basic principles govern the operation of a communication system: first, the system exists to transfer information from one point to another. All services supported by the network are designed to facilitate this exchange of information. Second, the receiver must understand the message. Without understanding, no communication takes place.

To be useful, the data communication network (or any communication system) must be able to accept input data; structure the data so that it can be sent quickly and accurately; transmit the data to a specific destination; and once the data has arrived, reconvert it to a form understandable by the destination.

DATA COMMUNICATION SYSTEM

A data communication system consists of five basic components, as shown in

Figure 2.1, but there are many possible variations. Figure 2.2 shows a typical telecommunication configuration. The five basic components are:

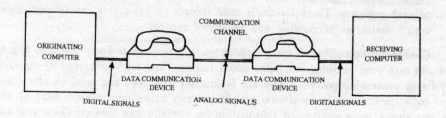

Fig. 2.1   : The components of a Data communication system

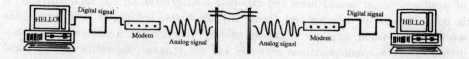

Fig. 2.2 : The basic elements that make up a communications link between two computer systems

1.   The sending or originating computer. The originating computer or terminal has data to transmit. The data may consist of a file on a disk or may be entered on a keyboard, transmitted as it is typed.

2.   A data communication device attached to the sending computer. The data communication device converts the data into a form that can be transmitted.

3.   A communication channel. The communication channel (also called a communication link) carries the data from place to place. There are many possible communication channels, including telephone lines and microwave relay systems.

4.   A data communication device attached to the receiving computer. This data communication device converts the transmitted data into a form that the receiving computer can understand.

5.   The receiving computer. The receiving computer or terminal receives the data, displays them on a screen, prints them or stores them in a file.

DATA COMMUNICATION SOFTWARE

Most computer applications, including data communication, require both appropriate hardware and software. Specialised data communication software is required to set up a communication link between two computers and to transmit data.

Data communication software performs a number of jobs. One is to send data at the proper speed; if the receiving and sending computers do not agree on the communication rate, the receivingcomputer will not be able to understand the communication. Another job is to monitor signals from the receiving computer that indicate any transmission errors.

The communication programme you choose plays a key role in data exchange between computers. If you are on the receiving end, communication software lets you decide whether you want to save data to disk, send it to a printer or simply let it scroll off the screen. When you transmit data, most programmes let you choose between sending it from a disk file or typing it directly from the keyboard.

Software for communication also stores telephone numbers, modem commands and other critical settings. Usually, these parameters reside in a dialling directory, so you do not have to re-enter them each time you want to hook up with a remote system. A well-designed communication programme makes it easy to select a remote system from the directory and begin connection procedures.

Many communication programmes direct modems to dial, hang up and answer incoming calls automatically. While it is the modem that actually performs these tasks, the software provides the appropriate instructions. For example, when the programme sends the modem a dial command and a phone number, the modem automatically goes off-hook (the same as lifting a telephone handset), waits for a dial tone, and proceeds to generate click pulses or tones that dial the number.

Most modems provide an audible indication that dialling is in progress, followed by a signal that a connection has been made. You will hear the modem beeping out tones like fast fingers on a touch-tone phone. Then, if all goes well, you should hear the remote system's line ring and the remote modem "pick up" the call. The remote modem then generates a high-pitched answer tone, to which your modem responds with a burst of tones of its own. This opening interchange is called handshaking. Once two modems are locked on to each other, most communication programmes display a 'Connect' message on screen.

In the foregoing paras, we listed the rudimentary features of a communication programme but a typical onehas many additional features. Some programmes allow users to redial a number repeatedly (if the line is busy, for example) until a connection is made, and others allow users to take remote control of the computer at the other end. That is, the programme user can control the other computer from his own keyboard. This allows communication with no one in attendance at the other end. Some programmes allow users to dial a sequence of numbers one after the other. These are sometimes used to generate recorded advertising calls.

DATA COMMUNICATION CONCEPTS

1.   Common Ground: The ASCII Standard

The first step toward understanding communication is to look at computer data at its most basic level. Computers manage, store and exchange data using electronic pulses that come in only two varieties: high and low. A device using digital signals can differentiate only between the presence ("on") and absence ("off") of electronic impulses; "on" equals the numeral one and "off" equals zero. Numerically, these types of pulses are represented in binary form as either a 1 (one) or a 0 (zero). The use of these two digits in various combinations to express any numeric quantity is known as binary arithmetic and the two numerals are called binary digits. A bit, a contraction of binary digit, is the smallest element of data or information dealt with by digital equipment. For convenience, bits are sometimes combined into larger units (usually groups of eight) called bytes.

Every character (letter, numeral, symbol or punctuation mark) is composed of a group of eight bits called byte. The way the bits are arranged within each byte, that is, the order in which the 1s and 0s appear, determines which character a byte represents. The meaning of the bits and bytes is determined by the coding data of within the computer for the computer's own use and if transmission. To avoid enormous incompatibility between systems, the computer industry has created a number of standards that establish hard-and-fast relationships between bit combinations and their corresponding characters. The diversity of codes in use is one source of incompatibility, a principal handicap in office automation.

Coding, the language of digital equipment, represents alphanumeric characters, special characters (such as #, @, *), and equipment-control characters (such as carriage returns) in terms of bits. The common expressions, "five-bit code","five-unit code" or "five-level code", all indicate the number of bits required to represent each of the alphanumeric or other characters.

Many different codes have been developed for use in data processing. The American Standard Code for Information Interchange (ASCII) character set is the most widely used coding convention for all computers, used both for internal computer data manipulation and for communication with other devices.

ASCII is a seven-bit code; that is, it uses seven bits to define each character. As the number of bits per character determines the maximum number of characters in the code, the basic ASCII code can represent 128 characters, covering upper- and lower-case letters, numbers, punctuation marks and special characters known as control characters. Table 2.1 lists the complete ASCII character set.

TABLE 2.1 : ASCII Character Set

ASCII Value	Character	Translation	ASCII Value	Character	ASCII Value	Character
000	NUL	(null)	046	.	092	\
001	SOH	(start of header)	047	/	093	]
002	STX	(start of text)	048	0	094	^
003	ETX	(end of text)	049	1	095	_
004	EOT	(end of transmission)	050	2	096	`
005	ENQ	(enquiry)	051	3	097	a
006	ACK	(acknowledge)	052	4	098	b
007	BEL	(bell)	053	5	099	c
008	BS	(backspace)	054	6	100	d

009	HT	(horizontal tab)	055	7	101	e
010	LF	(line feed)	056	8	102	f
011	VT	(vertical line)	057	9	103	g
012	FF	(form feed)	058	:	104	h
013	CR	(carriage return)	059	;	105	i
014	SO	(shift out)	060	<	106	j
015	SI	(Shift in)	061	=	107	k
016	DLE	(data link escape)	062	>	108	l
017	DC1	(data control 1)	063	?	109	m
018	DC2	(data control 2)	064	@	110	n
019	DC3	(data control 3)	065	A	111	o
020	DC4	(data control 4)	066	B	112	p
021	NAK	(negative acknowledgement)	067	C	113	q
022	SYN	(synchronization)	068	D	114	r
023	ETB	(end of transmission block)	069	E	115	s
024	CAN	(cancel)	070	F	116	t
025	EM	(end of medium)	071	G	117	u
026	SUB	(substitute)	072	H	118	v
027	ESC	(escape)	073	I	119	w
028	FS	(file separator)	074	J	120	x
029	GS	(group separator)	075	K	121	y
030	RS	(record separator)	076	L	122	z
031	US	(unit separator)	077	M	123	{
032	SP	(blank space)	078	N	124	_
033	!		079	O	125	}
034	"		080	P	126	=
035	#		081	Q	127	DEL
036	$		082	R		
037	%		083	S		
038	&		084	T		
039	`		085	U		
040	(		086	V		
041	)		087	W		
042	*		088	X		
043	+		089	Y		
044	'		090	Z		
045	-		091	[		

Control characters are used to give instructions. The control characters may precede, accompany or follow a block of information. Most control characters are nonprinting: they trigger an action rather than producing a readable letter or number. Control characters may affect the following activities:

- Processes occurring within a document, such as a tab or sounding a bell.

- Processes to be performed by another device, for example, a form feed on a printer.

- Communications, which indicate the start and stop of a message or acknowledge receipt of data.

This code assigns a different number to each letter of the alphabet (with separate numbers for upper-case and lower-case), as well as to each numeric digit, each common punctuation mark and several special symbols. Table 2.2 shows some examples of keyboard characters and their ASCII code values in both decimal and binary form. The letter A, for example, corresponds to the decimal number 65, which is equivalent to the binary number 01000001.

TABLE 2.2: Keyboard characters and their decimal and binary equivalents

| | ASCII code | |
Character	Decimal	Binary
A	65	01000001
a	97	01100001
3	51	00110011
!	33	00100001
<Ctrl>C	3	00000011

During a communication session, a computer transmits a byte representing the letter A starting with the on the bit extreme right: first a 1, then five 0s, a 1 and a final 0. At the receiving end, that series of bits is compared with a built-in electronic ASCII table, which translates 01000001 into the letter A.

Obviously, a misplaced 1 or 0 in a stream of bits means the receiving computer will come up with the wrong ASCII character. The slightest crackle on the telephone lines can cause this kind of error. Fortunately, most communication programmes use bits added to each character to detect and correct mistransmission.

The standard ASCII table contains characters numbered from 0 through 127. The PC and many other computers assign ASCII values to an additional set of 128 characters, up to number 255. Characters in this second group are called high-bit characters, because the eighth bit of each byte is always a 1 or high.

However, no universal standard exists for high-bit ASCII characters. On the PC and compatibles, this character set consists of foreign language symbols and graphics characters. But on other computers, high-bit characters are entirely different or even nonexistent. Therefore, to send or receive ASCII high-bit graphics and foreign language characters, a PC or a compatible is neededon both ends of a communication link

2.   Units of Measure

Hertz and bandwidth define the volume of signals that can be transmitted through communication channels. Hertz measures the speed of electromagnetic waves, which oscillate up and down. From the top centre of one curve to the same point on the next curve represents one cycle, as depicted in Figure 2.3. One wave passing by in one second or one cycle per second, equals one Hertz (Hz). Kilohertz (KHz, thousands of hertz), megahertz (MHz, millions of hertz) and gigahertz (GHz, billions of hertz) are the units most frequently encountered in office automation or data communication

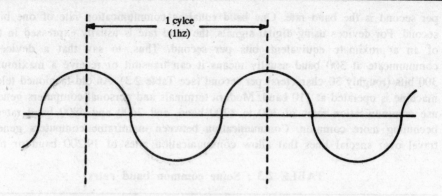

Fig. 2.3 : Direction of "wave" motion --> Electromagnetic waves

Bandwidth, expressed in Hertz, defines the minimum and maximum volume of cycles that can be sent through a transmission channel in one second, and thus, the amount of information can be transmitted in one second (see Figure 2.4). In the transmission of electronic signals, bandwidth is critical. A typical voice-grade telephone circuit has a bandwidth of 300 to 3,400 hertz, which is a narrowband channel. A VHF (Very High Frequency, 30-300 MHz) broadcast television signal requires a transmission capability of up to 300 megahertz (300 million cycles per second), which is considered a broadband channel. It is not possible to transmit television signal through a standard telephone circuit, because the electronic path is too narrow.

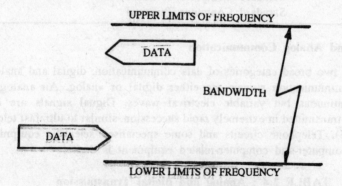

Fig. 2.4 : Bandwidth

Baseband is a signalling technique in which the signal is transmitted in its original form and not changed by modulation. Broadband makes use of multiple channels over the same medium by frequency division of the bandwidth.

3. Communication Rate

The speed at which data travel over a communication channel is called the communication rate (also known as the transmission speed). This rate is sometimes measured in bits per second or baud. The number of signalling elements transmitted per second is the baud rate. One baud equals a communication rate of one bit per second. For devices using digital signals, the baud rate is usually expressed in terms of an approximate equivalent, bits per second. Thus, to say that a device can communicate at 300 baud usually means it can transmit or receive a maximum of 300 bits (roughly 30 characters) per second (see Table 2.3). An old-fashioned teletype machine is operated at 110 baud. Modern terminals and personal computers generally use communication rates of 300 to 1200 baud, and 2400 and 4800 baud rates are becoming more common. Communication between mainframe computers generally travel over special lines that allow communication rates of 19,200 baud or more.

TABLE 2.3 : Some common baud rates

Baud rate	Typical usage
45.45	U.S. Government and Bell System 60 wpm
75	IBM MOdel 1050 (Optional)
110	Teletype Corporation Models 33, 35 Teletypes
134.5	IBM Models 2740, 2741, 1050 standard speed
150	Standard Computer Terminal
300	Standard Computer Terminal
600	Standard Computer Terminal
600	IBM System 1030
1200	Standard Computer Terminal
2400	Standard Computer Terminal
4800	Standard Computer Terminal
9600	Standard Computer Terminal

4. Digital and Analog Communication

There are two broad categories of data communication: digital and analog (see Table 2.4). Communication signals are either digital or analog. An analog signal consists of continuous but variable electrical waves. Digital signals are discrete electronic units transmitted in extremely rapid succession, similar to ultrafast telegraphy (see Figure 2.5). Telephone circuits and some specialised scientific equipment are analog; most computer-and computer-related equipment is digital.

TABLE 2.4 : Analog and digital Transmission

(a)   Treatment of Signals

	Analog Transmission	Digital Transmission
Analog Signal	Is propagated through amplifiers; same treatment for both analog and digital data	Assumes digital data; at propogation points, data in analog signal is generated
Digital Signal	Not used	Repeaters retransmit new signal; same treatment for both analog and digital data

(b)   Possible Combinations

	Analog Transmission	Digital Transmission
Analog Signal	Analog signal	Digital signal
Digital Signal	Analog signal	Digital signal Analog signal

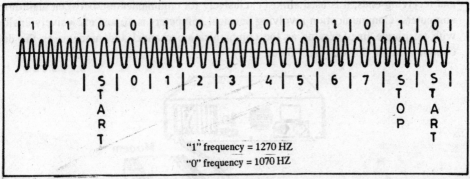

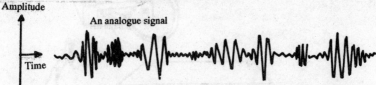

Fig. 2.5 a : Analog signal for "B" as transmitted by phone line

An analog signal can take on values from A continuous range of possible values over A length of time.

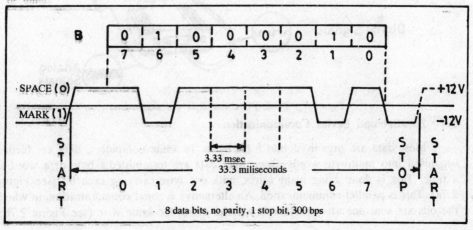

Fig. 2.5 b : Digital signal for an ASCII "B"

A digital signal can take on only a limited set of possible values (one of only two values for a binary signal) and transitions between these values occur raptly.

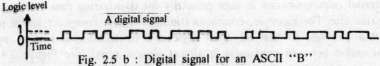

Digital communication uses special equipment that transmits data directly in binary form, that is, as sequences of 0s and 1s. Analog communication uses general purpos~ communication channels, such as telephone lines. In order for computer data in binary form to be transmitted over these channels, the 0s and 1s must be translated into electrical signals compatible with the channel. This is usually done using a device called a modem (modulator-demodulator).

Since digital communication requires expensive equipment at both the sending and receiving ends, it is used almost exclusively for communication between mainframe computers. Communication involving personal computers is almost exclusively analog, with telephone lines serving as the communication channel and modems as the data communication devices (see Figure 2.6).

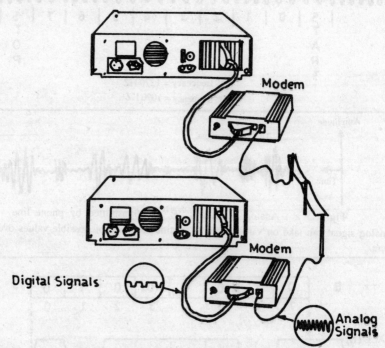

Fig. 2.6 : PC-to-PC connection via phone line

5.   Parallel and Serial Communication

Most data are organised into 8-bit bytes. In some computers, data are further organised into multibyte words. Sometimes data are transmitted,a byte or a word at a time. This is done using many wires, with one wire carrying each bit (see Figure 2.7a). This is parallel communication. An alternative is serial communication, in which the bits are sent one after another in a series along the same wire (see Figure 2.7b).

Parallel communication is used primarily for transferring data between devices at the same site. For example, communication between a computer and a printer is most often parallel, so that an entire byte can be transferred in one operation. Communication between computers is almost always serial (see Figure 2.8).

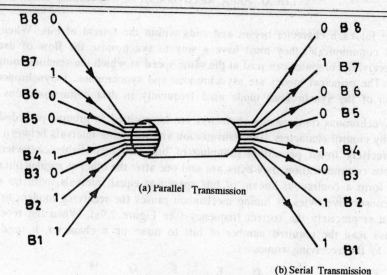

(a) Parallel Transmission

(b) Serial Transmission

Fig. 2.7 a : Parallel and Serial Communication

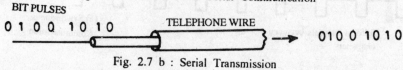

BIT PULSES

0 1 0 0 1 0 1 0   TELEPHONE WIRE   010 0 1010

Fig. 2.7 b : Serial Transmission

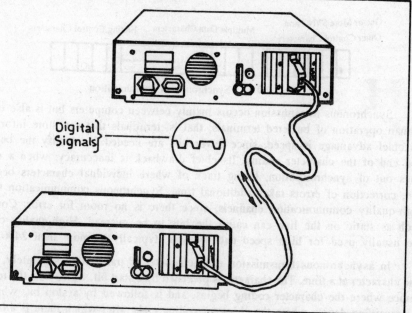

Fig. 2.8 : Direct serial connection between two computers

Synchronous and Asynchronous Communication

The mode of transmission is the way in which the coded characters are assembled the process of transmission and permits the receiving devices to identify where the coding for each character begins and ends within the torrent of bits. When two computers communicate, they must have a way to synchronise the flow of data so that the receiving computer can read at the same speed at which the sending computer transmits. The principal modes are asynchronous and synchronous. Bisynchronous is a variation of the synchronous mode used frequently in data communications.

In synchronous transmission characters are transmitted as groups, preceded and followed by control characters. The transmission and receiving intervals between each bit are precisely timed permitting grouping of bits into identifiable characters. In synchronous communication, data bytes are sent one after the other at regular intervals. The data form a continuous stream of bits spaced at equal intervals, with no space between consecutive bytes. A timing mechanism causes the receiving modem to read the stream at precisely the correct frequency (see Figure 2.9a). When the receiving modem has read the required number of bits to make up a character, it sends the character to the receiving computer.

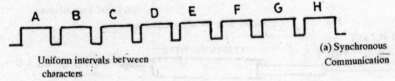

(a) Synchronous Communication

Uniform intervals between characters

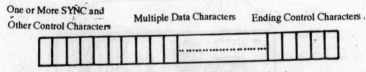

Fig. 2.9 a : Synchronous Communication

Synchronous transmission occurs mainly between computers but is also used for human operation of buffered terminals, that is, terminals that can store information. Its chief advantage is speed, since fewer bits are needed to identify the beginning and end of the character coding. Its chief drawback is inaccuracy: when a receiver goes out of synchronisation, losing track of where individual characters begin and end, correction of errors takes additional time. Synchronous communication requires high-quality communication channels, since there is no room for error. Conditions such as static on the line can cause the bits to be misread. High-quality channels are usually used for high speed data transfer, typically at more than 2400 baud.

In asynchronous transmission each character is transmitted separately, that is, one character at a time. The character is preceded by a start bit, which tells the receiving device where the character coding begins, and is followed by a stop bit, which tells the receiving device where the character coding ends, after which there is an interval of idle time on the channel (see Figure 2.9b). Then the next character is sent, start bits first, character bits next, stop bits last. The start and stop bits (and the interval of time between consecutive characters) allow the receiving and sending computers to synchronise the transmission. This is the most common mode worldwide, especially

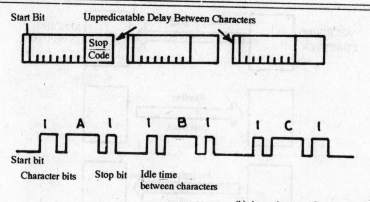

(b) A synchronous Communication

Fig. 2.9 b : Asynchronous Communication

for operation of interactive computer terminals and teletypewriters. Its principal advantage is accuracy. Its main drawback is slow transmission time, caused by the great number of start and stop bits.

Asynchronous communication is slower than synchronous communication; it is typically used at communication rates lower than 2400 baud. Asynchronous communication, however, does not require the complex and costly hardware required for synchronous communication and is, therefore, the method used almost exclusively with microcomputers.

One exotic mode, called isochronous, involves synchronous transmission of asynchronous format.

7.   Protocols and Buffers

Protocols are technical customs or guidelines that govern the exchange of signal transmission and reception between equipments (see Figures 2.10a and 2.10b). Each protocol specifies the exact order in which signals will be transferred, what signal will indicate that the opposite device has completed its transfer, and so forth. Both hardware and software are designed to handle specific protocols, and protocols are often named for the device with which they are associated. Teletypewriters (TTYs), for example, use TTY protocol. Only devices using the same protocols can communicate directly with one another. Devices using dissimilar protocols must transmit and receive through an intermediate interpretation device or programme.

Data communication between computers takes place independently of the CPU through the use of buffers at both the receiving and sending ends. A buffer is a section of RAM that holds data being transmitted or received. When the sending computer's buffer is almost empty, the CPU is interrupted and asked to refill the buffer. At the receiving end, the receiving buffer interrupts the CPU when it is full, and the data are moved to their ultimate destination (screen, printer or disk).

If the buffer size is large or the communication rate slow, the buffer may be manipulated without interrupting the transmission of data. If the buffer size is small or the communication rate high, the sending and receiving modems use a protocol,

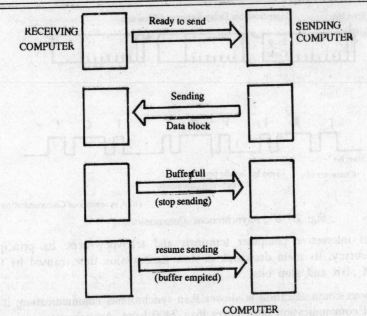

RECEIVING COMPUTER — Ready to send → SENDING COMPUTER

← Sending / Data block

Buffer full (stop sending) →

resume sending (buffer empited) →

COMPUTER

Fig. 2.10 a : The use of protocols

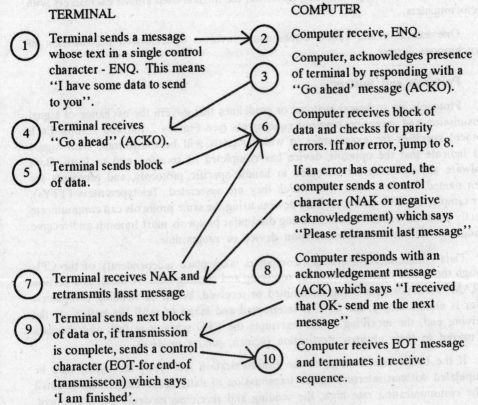

TERMINAL

1 Terminal sends a message whose text in a single control character - ENQ. This means "I have some data to send to you".

4 Terminal receives "Go ahead" (ACKO).

5 Terminal sends block of data.

7 Terminal receives NAK and retransmits lasst message

9 Terminal sends next block of data or, if transmission is complete, sends a control character (EOT-for end-of transmisseon) which says 'I am finished'.

COMPUTER

2 Computer receive, ENQ.

3 Computer, acknowledges presence of terminal by responding with a "Go ahead' message (ACKO).

6 Computer receives block of data and checkss for parity errors. Iff nor error, jump to 8.

If an error has occured, the computer sends a control character (NAK or negative acknowledgement) which says "Please retransmit last message"

8 Computer responds with an acknowledgement message (ACK) which says "I received that OK- send me the next message"

10 Computer reeives EOT message and terminates it receive sequence.

Fig. 2.10 b : Data transmission using Bisynch

or prearranged sequence of signals, to interrupt the transmission while the buffer is filled or emptied. When the receiving computer's buffer is full, the receiving modem sends one signal to tell the sending computer to stop. When the buffer has been emptied, the receiving modem sends another signal to tell the sending computer to resume sending (see Figure 2.10a).

8.   Detecting Errors

A number of methods are used to detect errors in transmitted data. The most common method is inserting a parity bit alongside data bits for a character. If the receiving modem detects an incorrect parity bit, it can ask the sending modem to retransmit the character (see Figures 2.11a and 2.11b).

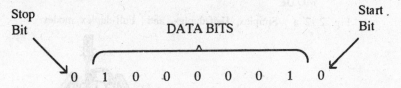

Fig. 2.11 a : String of data with start and stop bits

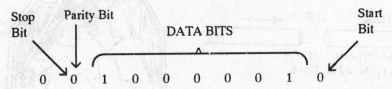

Fig. 2.11 b : String of data with parity bit added.

9.   Simplex, Half-Duplex and Full-Duplex Communication

There are three distinct modes in which a communication channel may be used: simplex, half-duplex and full-duplex.

In simplex mode, the communication channel is used in one direction only (see Figure 2.12a). The receiver can listen to the sender but cannot talk back. Since the use of protocols and the detection of errors require two-way communication, the simplex mode is rarely used for data communication.

In half-duplex mode, the communication channel is used in both directions, but only in one direction at a time (see Figure 2.12b). The use of a half-duplex communication channel is similar to the use of a citizens' band (CB) radio. Only one party can speak at a time. When the speaker is done, he says, 'Over', and the other party begins to speak. Some time is lost in changing the direction of speaking on a CB. The same is true on a half-duplex communication channel. It takes from 1/20 to 1/4 second to change the direction of transmission. If many changes take place, the communication rate is slowed appreciably.

In full-duplex mode, the communication channel is used in both directions at once (see Figure 2.12c). The use of a full-duplex communication channel is similar

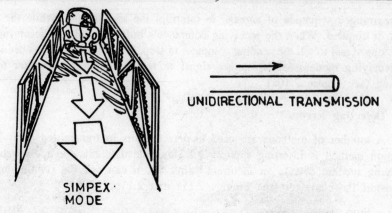

UNIDIRECTIONAL TRANSMISSION

SIMPEX
MODE

Fig. 2.12 a : Simplex, Half-duplex, and Full-duplex modes

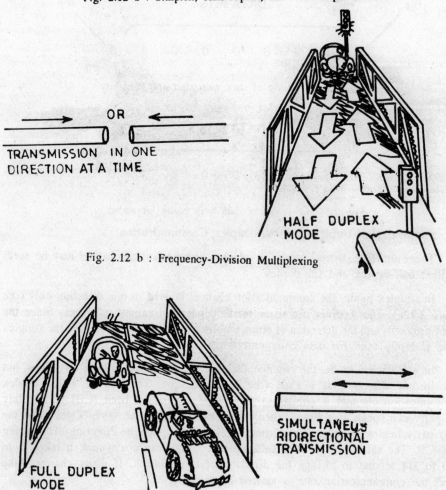

OR

TRANSMISSION IN ONE
DIRECTION AT A TIME

HALF DUPLEX
MODE

Fig. 2.12 b : Frequency-Division Multiplexing

FULL DUPLEX
MODE

SIMULTANEUS
RIDIRECTIONAL
TRANSMISSION

Fig. 2.12 c : Time-Division Multiplexing

to the use of a telephone, in that both parties are allowed to speak at the same time. The difference is that both computers connected by a full-duplex channel can hear and understand what the other says. The full-duplex mode is used for high-speed data communication between mainframe computers where the use of the half-duplex mode would seriously lower the communication rate.

10. Multiplexing

Multiplexing is a form of data transmission in which one communication channel carries several transmissions at the same time. The telephone lines that carry our daily conversations can carry thousands or even more of conversations at a time using multiplexing. The exact number of simultaneous transmissions depends on the type of communication channel and the communication rates.

User seldom needs to tax the full capacity of a transmission system, resulting in inefficient utilisation. On the other hand, a user sometimes needs limited amounts of both narrowband transmission and lower-range broadband for high-speed data transmission. Several devices subdivide wideband circuits into multiple narrowbands and link other circuits electronically to resemble wideband circuits.

Multiplexers, nicknamed "muxes", permit a single transmission link to perform as if it were several separate links. A frequency-division multiplexer (FDM) divides the actual bandwidth into smaller units of frequency and assigns each to a specific device (see Figure 2.13a). Each device sharing the circuit communicates on its individually assigned frequency as if it had its own dedicated circuit. Frequency-division multiplexing works best with low-speed devices. A time-division multiplexer (TDM) apportions very small segments of time in the bandwidth to each device, then polls each in sequence and permits it to communicate (see Figure 2.13b). The polling occurs so quickly that each device seems to have a separate circuit.

Concentrators operate synchronously and offer the functions of a multiplexer but can also store groups of characters, convert formats, check for errors and perform other functions.

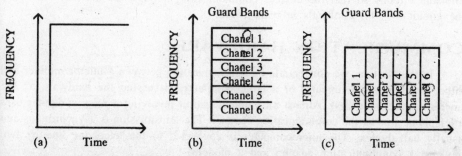

Fig 2.13 a : A telecommunication channel can be represented by its bandwidth available over a length of time. The telecommunication channel of (a) can be fully utilized in one of two ways : (1) By subdividing it into narrower frequency bands, or channels to (b).
(2) By allocating its full bandwidth to a set of channel in term IC (c).

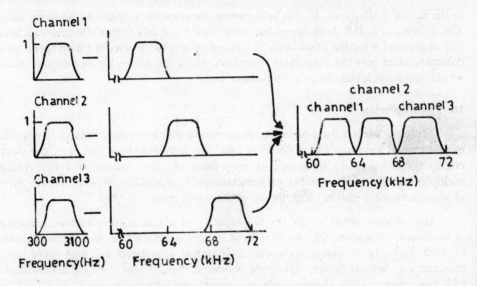

Fig. 2.13 b : Frequency-division multiplexing. (a) The original bandwidths. (b) The bandwidths raised in frequency. (c) The multiplexed channel

A statistical multiplexer is a hybrid of an FDM, TDM and concentrator. Although a terminal or computer is intermittently inactive during interactive transmission, a TDM continues to offer it time regardless of need. An FDM likewise apportions a small portion of the bandwidth to each terminal regardless of need. But statistical multiplexer will bypass a momentarily inactive terminal and give the bandwidth to an active one. If the volume of traffic from all the devices exceeds the capacity of the circuit, the statistical multiplexer will store the traffic until circuit time is available.

Some devices can combine two or more channels into a wider one by fragmenting data transmissions into segments of equal size and sending alternate segments down alternate physical links, then,at the receiving end,collate the signals before transferring them to the ultimate receiving device A biplexer, for example, can link two 9.6 kilobaud circuits so that the devices communicating through the biplexer will view the circuit as 19.2 kilobauds in band width.

COMMUNICATION HARDWARE

In this section, we concentrate on communication between a microcomputer and either another microcomputer or a large computer, discussing the hardware on the microcomputer side first. Almost all communication involving a microcomputer uses a telephone line as the communication channel. The transmission is asynchronous and usually half-duplex. The microcomputer is connected to the telephone line by two devices: a communication adapter and a modem.

Communication Adapter

Bits flow between computers in one of two ways. The most common method sends bits in a continuous stream like a string of boxcars riding a rail-road track. This type of data transmission is termed serial because bits flow in a series. The other prevalent variety of data transmission is referred to as parallel. In this method, each of the eight bits that make up a character travels down a separate wire simultaneously. While parallel data flow is impractical for communication over telephone lines, it is the predominant way of linking computers to printers.

To communicate with the outside world, your PC must have an external serial connector, usually located on the end of a plug-in board. The three most common names for this connector are serial port, RS-232C connector/interface and asynchronous communication port/adapter.

These terms are less slippery than they first appear. Port, for example, merely refers to any connector on your computer that acts as a point of data entry or departure. RS-232C is the label assigned to a technical standard that specifies how each pin of a serial connector is wired and which pin fulfills what function. The term asynchronous means, in its broadest sense, that data is transferred in byte-size pieces, rather than in a continuous, synchronised stream of bits. Synchronous communication is common in the mainframe world, but most PC-to-PC communication falls into the asynchronous category.

A communication adapter is a circuit board that handles the transfer of data between the computer and the telephone line. It reads and writes data to and from a buffer in RAM. It signals to the CPU when the buffer needs to be refilled or emptied. During transmission, it formats the data, adds start bits, stop bits and parity bits, and controls the communication rate. When it receives data, it strips away the start bits, stop bits and parity bits and signals the sending computer to transmit the next character.

The communication adapter may be built into the computer, or it may be an optional circuit board. The communication adapter connects to the outside world via a 25-pin connector. The signals carried by each of the pins is defined by an internationally agreed-upon standard. For example, one pin carries a signal that, if present, indicates that the computer at the other end is ready to accept data; another pin carries the actual data; and so on for each of the other 23 pins. A cable plugs into the 25-pin connector and carries the signals to the modem.

If you use a special cable to connect one computer directly to another via their serial ports, the signals going through the cable are the same digital pulses that flow within the computers themselves. This "null modem connection" is the purest possible method of communicating data from one computer to another. There is little chance of error creeping in, provided the cable is not too long.

Acoustic Couplers and Modems

Digital transmission via an analog circuit requires the use of acoustic couplers or modems to resolve incompatibility. Communicating with a computer over the telephone lines is a different story from establishing a simple cable connection. Because telephone lines handle only audible signals, you cannot transmit digital pulses (see Figures 2.14a and 2.14b).

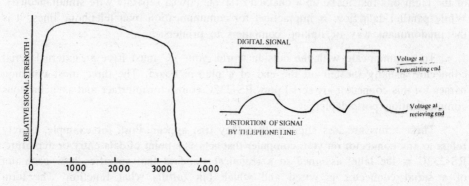

Fig. 2.14 a : Characteristic curve due to   Fig. 2.14 b : Digital signal and its
                 conditioning   distortion

To send data you must modulate these pulses or convert them into sounds that represent high and low bits. At the receiving end, the audible signals need to be demodulated back into digital pulse form. This MOdulation and DEModulation is performed by the aptly named modem. Modem is used to convert data from digital form into a form that can be transmitted or read over a telephone line. The modem is connected to the communication adapter at one end and to a telephone line at the other. Modem directly convert signals from a computer or other digital device into analog form for transmission over analog links, and vice versa. They can operate at up to 9,600 baud (300/600/1200/2400/4800/9600 BPS) over voice-grade telephone lines, but slower speeds are more common. Three types of modems are available; one is acoustic, while the other two are direct-connect modems.

The designs and capabilities of modems are quite varied. Modems can be either external or internal. An external modem is a box that is separate from the computer and connected to the communication adapter by a cable. An internal modem is contained on a printed circuit card inside the computer and combines the communication adapter with the modem. It is connected either to a modular telephone wall jack or to the jack on a telephone instrument. An internal modem is very neat and convenient, but the type chosen depends on the model of the computer. On the other hand, an external modem can plug into the communication adapter of any computer.

A second difference in design is that the modem can be connected to the telephone line in one of two ways. The first way is through a direct connection, in which the modem, called a direct-connect modem, is connected directly to a telephone line though a modular jack (see Figure 2.15a). The second way is through an acoustical connection, in which the modem, called an acoustical modem, uses a telephone receiver to transmit signals. The modem is connected to an acoustical coupler that converts the data into

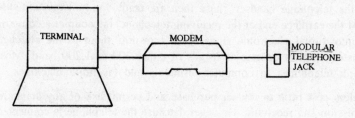

(A) A Direct-connect modem.

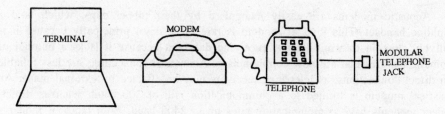

(B) Operation of/on acoustical coupler

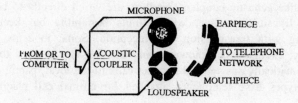

Fig. 2.15 : Modems - The use of
(a) a direct - connect modem; and
(b) an acoustical modem

audible signals. The telephone receiver rests in the cradle of the acoustical coupler, receives the audible signal and transmits the signal to the telephone line (see Figure 2.15b).

More likely, you will be using a direct-connect modem. Direct-connect modems for the PC come in two styles. One is a stand-alone modem, so called because it sits apart from the PC, connected by cable to the PC's serial port. The other type, referred to as an internal modem, is usually a plug-in expansion board but may be built' in at the factory, a common practice with laptop computers.

Both stand-alone/external and internal modems usually have two modular telephone jacks on their rear panels. One connects the modem to the telephone wall jack. You can plug your telephone in to the other and perform both voice and data communications over the same line.

An acoustic coupler is a small device with two openings that accommodate the earpiece and microphone ends of a telephone handset. The coupler converts outgoing electronic signals from the digital device into analog sounds and transmits them to the microphone of the telephone handset; these then are ready for transmission into the telephone line. At the earpiece end of the receiving telephone, the coupler reconverts the analog sounds into digital electronic signals and transmits them to the attached digital device. Acoustic couplers operate at speeds of either 300 or 1,200 baud. Most acoustic couplers link telephones to computer terminals and fascimile machines.

Acoustic couplers cost little to rent or purchase and permit use of any standard telephone for transmission and receiving. However, because the telephone is connected acoustically instead of being wired to the computer or fascimile device, loud background noises can sometimes penetrate the acoustical seal and cause transmission errors.

Acoustic modems are easily recognised by their rubber cups, which hold a telephone handset. This kind of modem is rare these days, principally because it is relatively slow in transmitting and receiving data and because it lacks a number of automatic features that are now commonplace. Acoustical connections are less reliable than direct connections, as telephone receivers may be affected by external noise. An acoustical modem is limited to a communication rate of 300 baud, whereas direct-connect modems have communication rates up to 2400 baud. Both types of modems are in common use.

Unlike acoustic couplers, modems are wired directly to both the digital devices and the transmission line, which limits portability but keeps room noises from interfering with transmission and reception. Some modems have only a dial-out capability; another type, known as auto-answer, can be used for dialling out and can also automatically answer and connect calls to the local, parent device. Some modems of both types have telephones attached for normal call placing and receiving.

COMMUNICATION PROCEDURES

All communications between computers are managed by data communication software. The precise procedures used depend on the particular software, but the following account outlines the general procedures.

Communication Between Two Microcomputers

A small business that uses microcomputers has accumulated information that it wants to send to a customer who also uses microcomputers. The procedure used to send the information is as follows:

1. Both the business and the customer start the communication programme, which gives them a menu of options.

2. Both the business and the customer choose the same options, including the number of start and stop bits, the type of parity checking, the communication rate, full-duplex or half-duplex transmission, and so on.

3. The communication link is established. The users decide who will originate the telephone call, and the originator enters the telephone number. The communi-

cation programme then instructs the modem to dial the number and reports to the users if a connection has been made.

4.   After the connection has been made, the users can have an on-line conversation. They can type messages back and forth to each other and can record their conversation.

5.   When the business is ready to transfer the information, it sets its computer to send; the customer sets its computer to receive. The business starts the transfer. The communication programme takes over by reading the information from the disk and sending it through the communication link. The receiving computer stores the incoming information on a disk. The transfer proceeds without any further human attention.

6.   When the transfer has been completed, the business and the customer say "goodbye" and terminate the connection.

Communication Between a Microcomputer and a Larger Computer

The procedure for communication between a microcomputer and a minicomputer or mainframe is similar. One difference is that the larger computers have safeguards that limit access to files and facilities to authorised users. The most common safeguards are the user identification number and the user password.

After the communication link has been established, the receiving computer asks for the user's identification number. This number is assigned to the microcomputer user by the operators of the larger computer. When requested to do so, the microcomputer user types in the user identification number. The receiving computer checks that the identification number is valid. It then asks for the user's password. A password is a confidential sequence of characters that allows access to the system. An example of a password is:

S17K64B#

The password is required for the user to obtain access to the larger computer. It also determines exactly which files and facilities the microcomputer user is allowed to read. If the typed password is valid, the microcomputer user is allowed access to the large system.

Front-End Processors

Keeping track of communication activities is a complex data processing task. In the case of high speed data communication between two mainframes, such "housekeeping" can occupy 20 to 25 percent of the processing time of the CPU. To alleviate this problem, some data communication tasks are often given to a mini or microcomputer. Such a computer is called a front-end processor and sits between the main computer and the modem (see Figure 2.16). The front-end processor typically performs the data formatting and checking activities that would be handled by the communication adapter of a microcomputer.

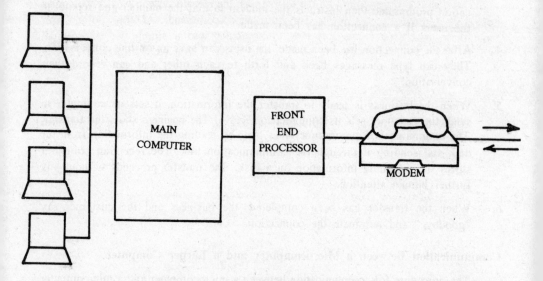

Fig. 2.16 : Front-end processors. Front-end processors are computers that handle communication processsing to lift the burden from the main computer

Going On-Line

Before you establish a communication link, you must adjust various settings to match those of the computer you want to connect with. Called communication parameters, these settings vary with different types of computers and programmes. Fortunately, most communication programmes let you store and retrieve the parameters that apply to various remote systems.

When you connect to a remote system such as an on-line information service, you will probably be asked to reply to one or more on-screen questions. Generally, you will need to provide some kind of identification, such as your name, an account number and a password. This brief dialoge between you and the remote system is often called a logon procedure.

Some remote systems compare your identification with a list of paid subscribers. Obviously, if you are not on the list, you would not be able to access the service. Other systems use the logon procedure as a security measure, protecting valuable records from tampering. In either case, the remote system maintains a record or log of every caller.

Many communication programmes support automated logon procedures. When you log on for the first time, the programme "records" your entries for later use. Subsequently, when you access the remote system, these entries are automatically supplied in response to prompts from the remote system. Many communication software packages let you dial, connect and log on to a remote system at the touch of a single function key.

Once you have gone through the formalities, the remote system usually welcomes you with a greeting and waits for your next command. At this point, your communication software has turned your computer into a simple video terminal, allowing you to use the remote system's software as if you were connected directly to the system.

File Transfer

Transferring files to and from your disk drive is one of the most common communication applications. These files may be bulletins, electronic mail messages, airline information or even computer programmes.

In addition to matching communication parameters, file transfer requires that both systems in a communication link agree on a common protocol. A protocol consists of the technical details that regulate data transmission between computers. Fortunately, you need only a rough idea of how a protocol works in order to use one.

The simplest to understand is the text or ASCII protocol. This method sends a file as one uninterrupted stream of ASCII characters. While this protocol offers transmission of maximum characters in the shortest possible time, it is also the one most likely to produce errors, especially over noisy telephone lines.

To combat flaws in file transfer, most protocols offer error correction. Specific methods vary from protocol to protocol, but the basic error correction scheme is the same: breaking up a file into small blocks and then comparing the received blocks to those that were sent to make sure they are identical. Each block includes an extra character mathematically derived from the ASCII values of the characters it contains. If the receiving computer comes up with a different value for that character after it receives a block, it assumes an error has occurred and requests that block again. While this procedure reduces throughput, error checking and correction virtually assure error-free file transfer. Common error-correction programmes now include more advanced session level protocols that check for errors throughout an entire communication session, not just during file transfer.

Choosing Parameters

Before logging on, you must make sure that you and the remote system are using the same communication parameters — the various settings that regulate the means of communication. To clarify this point, baud rate, parity, stop bits and echo are further discussed.

Baud rate refers to the rate or "speed" of data transfer. In common parlance, this means the number of bits per second (bps) sent or received. Technically, baud rate refers to the rate of the phase-shifting method a modem uses to transmit information - which is not necessarily the same as the bps rate. However, most modem manufacturers use baud rate to describe bps, and this corruption of the technical term is now commonplace. Since transmitting one character usually takes 10 bits, dividing the baud rate by 10 will give you a rough approximation of how many characters per second are being transferred.

Which baud rate you use depends on the capabilities of your modem, as well as the equipment used by the remote system. Most modems for personal computers transfer data at 300, 1200 or 2400 baud. Whatever baud rate your modem supports, it has to be seen that the rate for your modem and the remote system must be identical.

Sometimes a remote system will have different phone access numbers for different baud rates. In general, you should communicate at the highest baud rate possible, since this reduces the amount of connect time you are charged for. However, some commercial information systems charge premium rates for communication at higher baud rates. Even so, the time saved makes using higher baud rates more economical when transferring large files.

Parity refers to a scheme using a single bit along with each character to test for accurate data transfer. The most popular configuration for PC communications uses seven bits for data and the eighth bit for even parity. Using even parity during data transfer means that the eight bit always makes the 1 and 0 bits within a character add up to an even number. If the receiving computer detects an odd number, it either requests retransmission or ignores the character completely. Sometimes, however, eight bits are used for data and an additional bit is used for parity, resulting in another common setting: eight bits and no parity. Other parity schemes, such as odd number, space, and mark are also used, but they are rather uncommon in PC communications.

Here are four examples of even parity:

Memory byte	Parity (even)
00000000	0
00000001	1
00000011	0
01000001	0

Stop bits refer to the variable number of bits used to mark the end of each character transferred. Often, you may see parity, the number of data bits and the number of stop bits in one reference.

"E-7-1," for example, means even parity, seven data bits and one stop bit. One stop bit is used almost universally in personal computer communication, and many communication programmes automatically use this setting unless you specify otherwise.

Echo refers to a remote system's practice of sending back the characters you transmit, giving you on-screen verification that the characters have been received. Mainframe computers and commercial information services often use this procedure, while most PC link-ups omit echo.

When you are on-line, it is easy to determine whether to turn the echo function on or off. If you see no characters on the screen as you type, turn echo on; if the characters you type appear in duplicate, turn echo off. Most communication programmes let you adjust the echo setting while you are engaged in a communication session.

Logging Off

When you have finished a session with a remote system, you need to formally log off. Usually, the system displays a message on screen confirming that log off procedures have been properly completed. Standard log off commands include log out, Bye, Quit, Off and Exit. If you disconnect without formally logging off the system, the remote system may be fooled into believing you are still connected. When you are using a commercial service that charges by the minute for connect time, this can be quite an expensive mistake. Therefore, it is a good idea to watch for the remote system's log off confirmation on screen.

COMMUNICATION PROCESSING

Communication processing is the collective term for all the activities that help ensure the successful entry, transmission and delivery of information. Just as data processing involves taking raw data and adding value by changing the inherent information content, communication processing adds value to the raw message by insuring that the message arrives at its destination in a timely manner, in the proper form, at the proper speed, in the proper language and without errors.

The basic responsibilities of communication processing can be divided into three major areas: editorial, conversion and arbitration. Editorial functions include formatting of the message, editing the data and controlling errors. Conversion functions include translating transmission speed and code. Arbitration functions involve network control and message routing.

Communication processing can be performed in any intelligent device, using the storage and processing capabilities of that device. In the microcomputer based LAN, most communication processing occurs within the microcomputer itself.

Within a network, communication processing is implemented as protocols, the rules that govern the transmission of information.

The following are sample communication processing services:

- Accommodating differing video display characteristics such as screen size, line strength and paging.

- Translating data into the standard network format and subsequently retranslating the data to meet the requirements of the receiving station.

- Controlling the sequence in which messages are sent.

- Assembling and transmitting messages on the basis of time interval, order received, receipt of particular character or other characteristics.

- Alerting users to error conditions and possible problems.

Packets

It is neither practical nor advantageous to transmit long messages as a single entity. Therefore, for the purpose of data transmission, particularly in local area networks,messages are broken down into segments, called packets. As shown in Figure 2.17, each packet normally contains five parts:

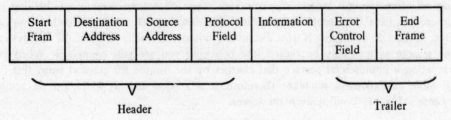

Start Fram	Destination Address	Source Address	Protocol Field	Information	Error Control Field	End Frame

Header   Trailer

Fig. 2.17 : Packet

- A start frame, identifying the beginning of the packet.

- A header, containing information for maintaining control of the packet and the network.

- An information field, containing a segment of the total text information or data to be communicated.

- An error control field, permitting the system to verify packet integrity.

- An end frame, signifying the end of the packet.

The control information contained in the header includes the source address, which identifies where the packet originated; the destination address, to which the segment is to be delivered; the packet sequence number, which helps insure that the packets can be reassembled in proper order; and a control block, which helps prevent duplication, loss or looping (in which a packet is routed back and forth in an endless circle) of the packet. Additional information to insure proper operation of the network under various overload or impaired operating conditions also may be included. Figure 2.18 further dissects the address fields.

```
                        What's  in  an  Address  ?
Destination  Address  :
    Name        -       What  workstation/resource  is  being  sought  ?
    Address     -       Where  is  it  ?
    Route       -       How  to  get  there.
Source  Address  :
    Name        -       Who  sent  the  message  ?
    Address     -       Where  is  it  ?
    Route       -       Has  to  send  a  reply
```

Fig. 2.18 : What's in an Address

Overhead is the additional information that must be transmitted through the network in order to facilitate the proper transmission and delivery of messages. It is created by the system's need to maintain control of all transactions. A percentage of overall network capacity is dedicated to this control information.

Overhead information exists on the network in two basic forms: data appended to each user packet, such as the control, and error-checking fields named above. The amount of data appended to a basic message varies from one system to another, and inself-contained acknowledgement and control packets, which are transmitted from one device to another. These packets keep the system advised of the status of the components.

COMMUNICATION CHANNELS

Besides telephone lines being used as communication channels, there are a number of other types of communication channels, representing both the wide range of possible uses of data communication and the various new technologies in the communication industry.

1.   Wired Transmission

Transmission media are the electronic roadways along which signals are transferred. They range from telephone circuitry to laser beams and fibre optics (see Table 2.5).

TABLE 2.5 : Transmission media tools, capabilities, appliction, cost and security

Medium	Application	Narrowband	Broadband	Range	Cost	Security	Other factors
Hard-wiring	Telephone and narrowband local networks	X		Local	Low	Low	Simplicity
Coaxial cable	Long-distance telephone calls		X	Unlimited with	Local: low Long distance : high	Moderate	Compactness and versatility
Microwave	Local area and		X	25 miles (more relay stations)	Moderate	Moderate	Line-of-sight;
Infrared	Local networks	X		Several hundred feet	Low to moderate	Moderate	Line-of-sight; affected by weather
Laser	Local and are networks		X	3-15 miles	Low to moderate	Moderate	Line-of-sight
Satellite	Video Telephones High-speed fax Teletypewriter		X	7000-8000 terrestrial miles	High to very high	High with encoder	Line-of-sight; "echo" affected by weather
Radio :							
Class A	Area voice communication (commercial)	X		10 miles	Low	Low	License; no data trans.; assigned channels
Class D	Area voice communication (citizens band)	X		10 miles	Low	None	License; no data trans.; 40 unassigned channels

One of the most common transmission methods is termed hardwired, which means that two or more devices are connected directly by wiring. A twisted pair means that the connection uses two wires, sometimes in the same cord (see Figure 2.19). A twisted pair handles narrowband transmissions. Coaxial cable also uses two wires, but one is a tube woven from very fine strands of metal; the second wire passes through the centre along the length of the first (see Figure 2.20). It is used for long-distance service by telephone companies and for both baseband and broadband transmission in local area networks.

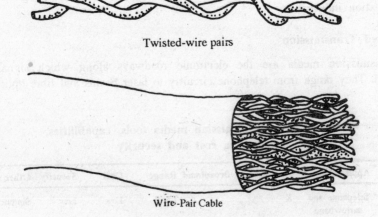

Twisted-wire pairs

Wire-Pair Cable

Fig 2.19 : Twisted-wire pairs

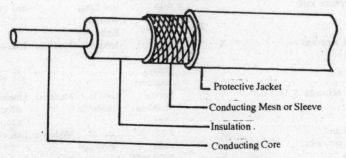

Protective Jacket

Conducting Mesn or Sleeve

Insulation .

Conducting Core

Fig. 2.20 : Coaxial cable

Twisted-Pair Wiring Characteristics:

1.   Inexpensive

2.   Easy to install

3.   Easy to tap

4.   Low noise immunity

5.   Speed of up to 4 Mbps

6.   Can accomodate up to 1,000 devices

7.   Adequate for network span up to 1/2 mile.

Coaxial Cable Characteristics:

1.   Widely available

2.   Good noise immunity, high usable bandwidth

3.   Speed up to 10 Mbps

4.   More difficult to tap than twisted-pair wiring

5.   More expansive than twisted-pair wiring.

Direct distance dialling (DDD) is the standard, voice-grade telephone service that provides direct dialling to other telephones without operator intervention. Such circuits accommodate narrowband analog transmission between 300 and 3,400 hertz or a maximum of 10,000 bits per second. A user can obtain similar circuits with the same bandwidth on a dedicated basis but only for access between the devices to which the circuit is connected, such as between a terminal in one city and a computer in another. Telephone companies also provide broadband analog and digital circuits to accommodate special needs. Digital circuits for data transmission eliminate the need for acoustic couplers or modems.

Telephone Lines

Using modems, telephone lines may be used to transmit computer data. The lines themselves may be either leased or switched.

Leased Lines

A leased line is a telephone line that is leased for the express purpose of maintaining a communication channel between two computers. The line is not shared with any other users and is available at all times for data communication between the computers. A leased line is similar to a telephone connection that is always open. Both computers are always listening for a signal to start the communication (see Figure 2.21). Leased lines are used in computer networks where computers or terminals in the network must be in constant contact with one another. For example, leased lines are used in a network employing point-of-sale terminals, as the terminals must be in constant contact with the main computer.

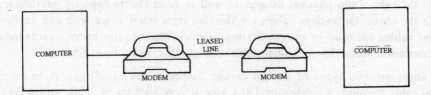

Fig. 2.21 : A Leased Line

Leased lines are often conditioned to limit the level of noise on the line. Conditioned leased lines are usually necessary to carry on high speed data communication. Security requirements often require that leased lines be shielded from outside interference and unauthorised snooping.

Switched Lines

A switched line can be used for either voice or data communication and is switched from user to user, as requirements dictate (see Figure 2.22). When switched lines are used, one computer must establish contact with the other by dialling a telephone number. After the transmission has been completed, the connection between the computers is broken, just as if a telephone receiver were hung up.

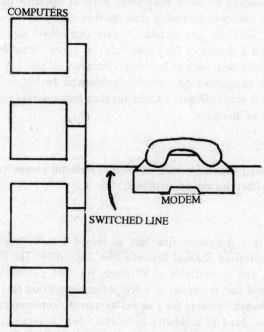

Fig. 2.22 : A Switched Line

Coaxial Cables

A coaxial cable consists of many small cables in a protective cover. The cover shields the cable from physical dangers as well as from electromagnetic interference. Within the cover, the various cables are shielded from interference with one another. Coaxial cables are used in communication networks that require many simultaneous communication links. Each coaxial cable can provide more than 5000 links.

There are two types of coaxial cables: baseband and broadband. A baseband coaxial cable transmits a single signal at a time at very high speed, while a broadband coaxial cable can transmit many simultaneous signals using different frequencies. A baseband cable transmits a single stream of digital data at a very high communication rate (millions of bits per second) but must be amplified every 1000 feet or so. It is mainly used for local area networks. A broadband coaxial cable can carry only an analog signal, so it must be used in conjunction with a modem. It is more complex to use in a network.

2. Optical Fibre Transmission

Optical fibre systems consist of a transmitter, the glass fibre filaments along which data travel as high-speed pulses of light, and a receiver. Lighter, thinner and stronger than copper wire, optical fibres carry a great deal more data (see Figure 2.23). Further, they are impervious to electromagnetic interference and are highly secure: being optical. in nature, they do not radiate electronic signals.

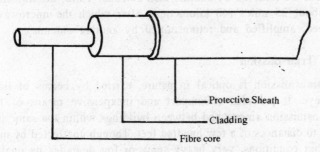

Protective Sheath

Cladding

Fibre core

Fig. 2.23 : Optical fiber construction

A fibre-optic cable consists of strands of glass-like thread, each about the diameter of a human hair. Through the use of a laser, data are transmitted from one end of a cable to the other. Fibre optic cables will increase the capacity of like-sized coaxial cables by at least a factor of 10. This makes them valuable for use in a variety of applications, especially in communication networks. It is likely that they will eventually completely replace copper wire cables for communication applications.

3. Microwave Transmission

Microwave signals are similar to radio and television signals and are used to transmit data without the use of cables. Microwave signals are transmitted by antennas placed on local peaks, such as the tops of buildings or mountains. Microwave signals provide very high speed data transmission. However, their range of transmission is limited to about 30 miles as they use the upper atmosphere as a reflective surface. To transmit over longer distances, it is necessary to bounce the microwave signals through a chain of towers or to combine the microwave signals with some other communication channel (see Figure 2.24).

Fig. 2.24 : Microwave Transmission

Microwave transmission has become widely used for broadband communication and telephone service. Private microwave service is especially useful for organisations that need to link a number of locations within a limited area. Banks, for instance, often use it to connect suburban branch offices with city headquarters. Although private microwave service can provide dedicated communication at moderate cost, there are limitations to its use. First, microwave channels are generally assigned by the Federal Governments, and in some cities few or no channels remain open. Second, unlike telephone wires and commercial radio signals, microwave transmission is line-of-sight: the signals, which pass through the atmosphere, must originate from a dish antenna, travel in a straight line free of material obstacles such as topographical features or tall buildings, and be received by another dish antenna. Third, the transmission range is limited to about 25 miles (40 kilometres), after which the microwaves must be relayed (received, amplified and retransmitted by another antenna).

4.   Infrared Transmission

Infrared transmission is optical in nature, carried by beams of light invisible to the naked eye. It provides a compact and inexpensive means of line-of-sight, narrowband transmission among and between buildings within the same general area, for it is limited to distances of a few hundred feet. Though unaffected by most artificial light and weather conditions, very heavy snow or fog degrades its quality. Infrared is not subject to governmental licensing since it operates outside the boardcast portion of the radio spectrum. It is moderately secure.

5.   Laser Transmission

Communication laser are generally very low powered and narrowly focused beams of light, invisible to the naked eye, that rely on sensitive receiving equipment. The equipment is marketed in both narrowband and broadband versions. The usual line-of-sight transmission range of 15 miles can be greater or less depending on the percentage of operating time acceptable to the user. Repeater (relay) stations can increase the total transmission distance. Laser communication provides a high degree of inherent security.

6.   Radio Transmission

Within the United States, the Federal Communications Commission has allocated certain radio frequencies for use by private businesses for direct voice communication. Word codes may be employed, but data transmission (or telemetry in radio parlance) is prohibited. Private citizens and business users may be licensed to operate either a Class A or D radio station, with a mobile or fixed location. The range of both classes is about 10 miles.

Users of Class A stations, such as taxicabs and delivery vehicles, operate only on a single, assigned frequency. Users of Class D stations, generally known as Citizens Band (CB) radio, operate on any of the 40 designated frequencies (channels) on a shared basis.

A mobile CB radio can be equipped with a special keypad and an unattended, fixed (stationery) CB with a matching device to make it possible for the user to dial into a telephone connected to the stationary radio. Once the circuit is completed, the person using the mobile CB radio can converse with the person answering the telephone call as if both were using a telephone. Owing to the special signalling requirements, the typical range between the mobile and base radio equipment is about three miles.

Security of such communication links is almost nonexistent. Even so, the equipment has many advantages and is widely used by taxi, repair, courier and delivery services.

7.   Satellite Transmission

Both microwave signals and telephone signals can be relayed to an earth station for transmission to a communication satellite (see Figure 2.25). The earth station consists of a satellite dish that functions as an antenna and communication equipment to transmit and receive data from satellites passing overhead.

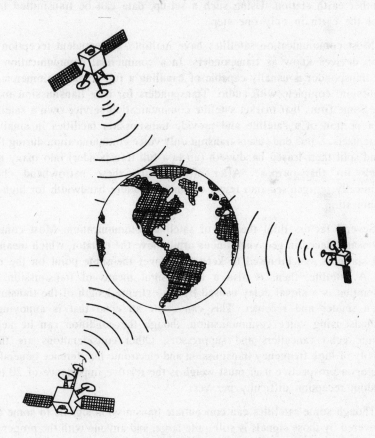

Fig. 2.25 a : Communication satellite in orbit 22,300 miles above the earth

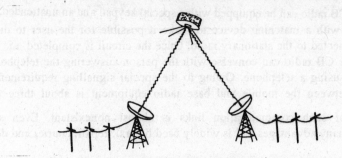

Fig. 2.25 b : Using a Communication sattelite to relay communications
Earth station : satellite antenna   Earth station satellite antenna

A number of communication satellites, owned by both governments and private organisations, have been placed in stationery orbits about 22,300 miles above the earth's surface. These satellites act as relay stations for communication signals. The satellites accept data/signals transmitted from an earth station, amplify themand retransmit them to another earth station. Using such a set-up, data can be transmitted to the other side of the earth in only one step.

Most communication satellites have multiple, independent reception and transmission devices know as transponders. In a commercial communication satellite, a single transponder is usually capable of handling a full-colour, commercial television transmission, complete with audio. Transponders for data transmission may be even larger. Some firms that market satellite communication service own a satellite. Others lease a portion of a satellite and provide transmission facilities in smaller units to ultimate users. Some end- users transmit only voice communication during the working day and split their leased bandwidth (up to a full transponder) into many narrowband channels for that purpose. After office hours, these narrowband channels are electronically reorganised into fewer channels of wider bandwidth for high-speed data communication.

Several factors limit the use of satellite communication. Most communication satellites are placed in geosynchronous orbit above the equator, which means that their orbital speed is synchronised to keep them over the same point on the earth at all times. A satellite, then, is also a line-of-sight means of transmission. A second consideration is a signal delay caused by the extreme length of the transmission path between sender and receiver. This can cause an echo that is annoying to some individuals using voice communication, though the condition can be negated with electronic echo cancellers and suppressors. Other considerations are the weather sensitivity of high frequency transmission and electronic interference generally. Among the factors a prospective user must weigh is the relative importance of 20 to 40 hours of random reception difficulty per year.

Though some satellites can concentrate transmission signals to some degree, the area covered by those signals is still quite large, and anyone with the proper equipment can listen in. Security is usually provided by the user through coding and decoding equipment.

APPLICATIONS OF DATA COMMUNICATION

Many applications of data communication for computing fall into one of four categories: using external databases, sharing data, electronic mail and Bulletin Board Systems.

1. Using External Databases

One of the most important applications of data communication is the ability to access external databases. There are literally thousands of databases containing information on almost every conceivable subject. Users can subscribe to many of these databases at a cost of the initial fee and a charge for the amount of time spent accessing the database. Users can locate information in an index or can just browse through the database as they would browse through books at a public library.

The types of information available through services vary greatly, as can be seen in the following examples. The Dow Jones News Services provides current news, current stock and commodity prices, and securities research data. The stock prices are very nearly the same up-to-the-minute prices that are simultaneously crossing the tape at the major stock exchanges. This allows users to use the service for the data on which they base trading decisions.

A number of multiple-listing real estate services offer on-line options. This allows a broker to find all homes meeting particular criteria (price range, neighbourhood, size, and so on) to match client demands. Also in the real estate field, services supply on-line listings of currently available mortgage money, interest rates and restrictive terms. These services allow a prospective home buyer to shop the entire country to obtain the best mortgage terms.

A number of subscription services supply on-line transactions. For example, a number of banks now allow subscribers to bank through a communication link to a personal computer. Some services even allow users to pay bills in this way. Personal computers may also be used to execute stock trades through several on-line brokerage systems. Transaction-oriented services are in their infancy. In the years to come, they will certainly grow in number and sophistication.

2. Sharing Data Files

Probably no single data communication application is as important to a large business as is the link between its microcomputers and its mainframe computers. In the last few years, businesses have purchased millions of personal computers to increase their employees' productivity. The initial applications of personal computers were stand-alone activities, such as word processing and the use of spreadsheets. To increase productivity further, businesses are taking the additional step of making data stored in mainframe computers available to microcomputer users. The savings including financial ones can be huge.

With data communication and networking, the tasks of data collection, analysis, decision making, report writing and data distribution can be integrated into a single, efficient system. In effect, the entire office (or even the entire company) becomes one large communication network.

3.   Electronic Mail

The smooth operation of a business depends on the efficient exchange of information between different parts of the business and between the business and the outside world. Much of this exchange has been traditionally carried out through paper documents, delivered by secretary, mail or messenger service. With the growing use of personal computers, a more efficient alternative has emerged: electronic mail.

Electronic mail is usually used to exchange messages and data files. Each user is assigned an electronic mailbox. Using the appropriate command, the user can scan a list of messages in the mailbox, display the contents of a particular message, send a message to another user, and so forth. To send a message, it is not necessary for the recipient to be present at the computer. The message resides in the mailbox until it is read.

The sender may restrict delivery of the message to authorised readers by using a password. That is, the recipient must "sign" for the message by typing his or her identifying password.

Many other features of standard mail delivery are implemented in electronic mail systems. For example, mail can be forwarded, stored for delayed delivery and sent to anyone at a particular phone number. In addition, electronic mail systems implement many new features. An electronic mail system can deliver copies of a message to all individuals listed in a certain file. It also allows merging of standard data (from a data file) with a particular message.

Recently, several companies have started subscription to electronic mail services. These services are accessed through a modem and allow users to communicate with other subscribers to the service. The service may also accept a message and transmit it to its destination city. There the message is printed out and delivered with the next day's mail. This technique can be used to communicate with people who are not subscribers to the network.

4.   Bulletin Board Systems

Closely related to electronic mail are bulletin board systems. A bulletin board is a communication system that allows users to call in and either leave or retrieve messages. It is similar to an electronic mail system, but there are no private mailboxes, only a single large mailbox. The messages may be directed to all users of the bulletin board or only to particular users. But all messages can be read by all users.

Some computer equipment manufacturers maintain bulletin boards that users may call to determine the status of company products, corrections to programmes, and the like. Users may report problems, ask for literature or place orders. Some computer user groups maintain bulletin boards for notifying members of meetings and other group activities. Other bulletin boards are maintained by individuals as meeting places for like-minded people.

3

TOPOLOGIES AND TRANSMISSION MEDIA

INTRODUCTION

The pattern of interconnection of modes in a network is called the topology. Formally, topology can be defined as the geometric arrangement of workstations and the links among them. Topologies are designed to create order out of the potential chaos of randomly arranged workstations. The issue where do you locate a workstation in relation to the network? At the end of a branch attached to the cable? At a junction point common to two or more cables? At the end of the cable? All of the above?

There are three connection possibilities:

1. Point-to-point joins two, and only two, adjacent workstations without passing through an intermediary workstation.

2. Multipoint is a single cable shared by more than two work-stations.

3. Logical implies that workstations are able to communicate, whether or not a direct physical connection actually exists between them.

The workstations in a local area network communicate based on some combination of physical (point-to-point or multipoint) and logical connection.

Given the location of workstations and peripherals, the goal of topology is to find the most economical and efficient way to connect all users to the network resources while providing adequate capacity to handle user demands, maintain system reliability and minimise delay. The number of parameters and variables that bear on the solution is huge. Rapid change in user demands complicates the problem further.

Control of the network also affects topology. Control and topology are so intertwined that topology often is defined as the means of implementing the control protocol. The two facets of control are <u>access</u> — which workstations send messages and when,and <u>allocation</u> — how long the workstation has accessand, where broadband media are in use, how much of the channel may be used.

Control may be <u>centralised</u>, in which access to the network and allocation of channel is determined by one node. Intelligence also may be concentrated in the central node with the attached workstations serving primarily as terminals. Or it may be <u>distributed</u>, in which caseworkstations can access the network channels independently, according to a shared set of protocols. The intelligence of the network is distributed throughout the connected workstations.

The selection of a topology for a network cannot be done in isolation as it affects the choice of media and the access method used. Because it determines the strategy used in wiring a building for a LAN, it may represent the greatest single cost to be faced, and accordingly deserves some study. There are a number of factors to consider in making this choice, the most important of which are set out below (see Table 3.1).

TABLE 3.1 : Topology Comparison

Feature	BUS	Ring	Dual Ring	Star
Reliability	* High	Low	Mod	Log
Complexity	Mod	Low	Mod	* Low
Flexibility	* High	Mod	Mod	Low
Expandibility	* High	Mod	Mod	Low
Cost	* Low	Mod	High	M-High

1.   Cost - Whatever transmission medium is chosen for a LAN, it has to be physically installed in the building. This may be a lengthy process involving the installation of cable ducts and raceways. Ideally, it is carried out before the building is occupied and should be able to accommodate foreseen growth requirements. For a network to be cost-effective, one would strive to minimise installation cost. This may be achieved by using well-understood media and also, to a lesser extent, by minimising the distances involved.

2.   Flexibility - One of the main benefits of a LAN is the ability to have the data processing and peripheral nodes distributed around a given area. This means that computing power and equipment can be located close to the ultimate user. Because the arrangement of furniture, internal walls, etc. in offices is often subject to change, the topology should allow for easy reconfiguration of the network. This involves moving existing nodes and adding new ones.

3.   Reliability - Failure in a LAN can take two forms. Firstly, an individual node can malfunction. This is not nearly as serious as the second type of fault where the network itself fails to operate. In the second case, although the individual nodes can function, any software making use of the facilities of the LAN will be rendered useless. The topology chosen for the network can helping by detecting the location of the fault and providingsome means of isolating it.

LAN TOPOLOGIES

Many topologies have been developed to cope with communication over a limited geographical area, but three major ones have influenced LAN design and implementation. Three topologies are commonly used for microcomputer local area networks. Table 3.2 gives the classification of LAN by topology. These are:

TABLE 3.2 : A LAN Classification matrix

	topology	Feature access protocol	data rate
Standard LAN			
Ethernet	bus (tree)	CSMA/CD	10 Mbits/sec
token bus	bus	token passing	1, 5 or 10 Mbits/sec
token ring	ring	token passing	1 or 4 Mbits/sec
Cambridge Ring	ring	empty slot	10 Mbits/sec
Non-standarrd LAN			
PABX	star	(not applicable)	(variouis)
micronet	bus or ring	(various)	typically < 1 Mbits/sec

1. the star or radial topology (example: PABX);

2. the bus (example: CSMA/CD, Token Bus);

3. the ring or loop (example: Token Ring, Slotted Ring).

There are also a number of hybrid network topologies which combine features of the above. Mesh topology, common in long-haul and complex mainframe networks, currently is not used by microcomputer LANs.

Bus networks are multipoint: workstations are connected to the single central communication link by individual secondary lines. Ring and Star networks use a point-to-point topology: each physical segment of cable connects two, and only two, workstations without passing through an intermediate workstation. All three are considered structured topologies.

Combinations of topologies not only are possible, but also they are becoming increasingly popular, particularly star-wired rings. The three basic LAN topologies and the major variations or hybrids will be discussed below.

TOPOLOGY EVALUATION FACTORS

Topology is of most interest as it affects LAN use in your installation. To help you select the "best" topology for your situation, a checklist of evaluation factors follows the technical definitions of each topology. Points covered include the following:

1. Application: in what size installation is the topology most appropriate?

2. Complexity: how technically complex is the topology? This factor affects installation and maintainence of the cabling.

3. Pe.formance: how much of a traffic load can the system support?

4. System overhead: what is the comparative price forexcess capability?

5. Vulnerability: how susceptible is the topology to failure? to damage?

6. Expandability: when you are ready to extend the LAN, how easily can the topology accommodate additional workstations and cover larger distances?

Importance of the various factors is relative, not absolute, when selecting a specific LAN being maximum affected by your requirements.

STAR OR RADIAL TOPOLOGY

In a star configuration (see Figure 3.1a), each workstation is connected to a central server through a dedicated point-to-point channel. Messages are passed from a workstation to the server.

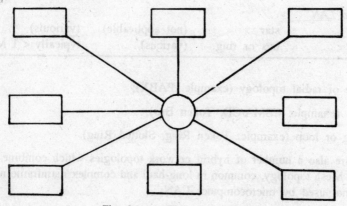

Fig. 3.1 a : The star topology

Control of the network may be allowed in one of three ways:

1. Control resides in the central server which performs all routing of messages. Data received by the central workstation may either be processed internally or forwarded for processing. In this case, the server normally provides the main computing power.

2. Control may be exercised by an outlying workstation rather than the central device. The server operates as a switch, establishing connections between workstations.

3. Control may be distributed equally to all workstations. The server is used to route messages to their destinations and to resolve conflicting requests for connections between workstations.

In all three cases the central server is the critical node: if it fails, the whole network stops.

The server provides a logical location for directly attaching the major shared resources. Generally, individual workstations do not have to make routing decisions, as all communication must pass through the central workstation before going to their destinations. **Compound star networks** (see Figure 3.2) are those in which a workstation on one network may act as server and/or controller for a secondary network. The term **snowflake** is used sometimes to refer to a compound star.

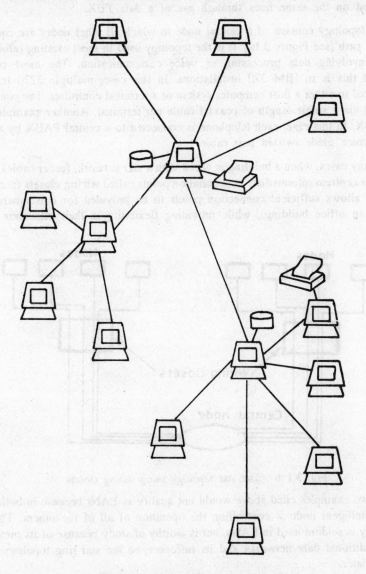

Fig. 3.2 : Compound Star or Snowflake

The size and capacity of the network is a direct function of the power of the central workstation, with the burden of compatibility placed on the central server.

Workstations do not compete for local capacity: heavy demand by one workstation does not necessarily cause a delay in network response time.

The star topology eliminates the need for each workstation on the network to make routing decisions. All message routing is localised in the central server.

Conceptually, a star is compatible with basic telephone services and is often implemented on the same lines through use of a data PBX.

This topology consists of a central node to which all other nodes are connected by a single path (see Figure 3.1a). It is the topology used in most existing information networks involving data processing or voice communication. The most common example of this is in IBM 370 installations. In this case, multiple 3270 terminals are connected to either a host computer system or a terminal controller. The connection is achieved via a single length of coaxial cable per terminal. Another example is the office PABX. In this case, each telephone is connected to a central PABX by a single dedicated voice grade twisted pair cable.

In many cases, when a building is wired with a star network, feeder cables radiate out from the centreto intermediate concentration points called **wiring closets** (see Figure 3.1b). This allows sufficient connection points to be provided for one subarea (e.g. a floor of an office building), while providing flexibility in their allocation within that area.

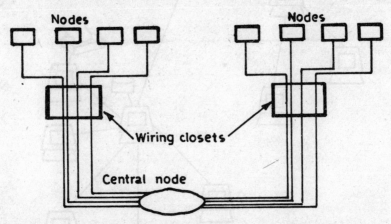

Fig. 3.1 b : The star topology using wiring closets

The two examples cited above would not qualify as LANs because in both cases, a central intelligent node is controlling the operation of all of the others. The pure star topology is seldom used in LANs, but is worthy of study because of its prevalence in more traditional data networks and its influence on the star-ring topology which is covered later.

Advantages of the Star

1.   Ease of service: The star topology has a number of concentration points, i.e.

at the central node or at intermediate wiring closets. These provide easy access for service or reconfiguration of the network.

2.   One device per connection: Connection points in any network are inherently prone to failure. In the star topology, failure of a single connection typically involves disconnecting one node from an otherwise fully functional network.

3.   Centralised control/problem diagnosis: The fact that the central node is connected directly to every other node in the network means that faults are easily detected and isolated. It is asimple matter to disconnect failing nodes from the system.

4.   Simple access protocols: Any given connection in a star network involves only the central node and one peripheral node. In this situation, contention for who has control of the medium for transmission purposes is easily solved. Thus in a star network, access protocols are very simple.

Disadvantages of the Star

1.   **Long cable length:** Because each node is directly connected to the centre, the star topology necessitates a large quantity of cable. While the cost of the cable is often small, congestion in cable ducts and maintenance and installation problems can increase costs considerably.

2.   **Difficult to expand:** The addition of a new node to a star network involves a connection all the way to the central node. Expansion is usually catered for by providing large numbers of redundant cables during the initial wiring. However, problems can arise if a longer cable length is needed or an unanticipated concentration of nodes is required.

3.   **Central node dependency:** If the central node in a star network fails, the entire network is rendered inoperable. This introduces heavy reliability and redundancy constraints on this node.

The star topology has found extensive application in areas where intelligence in the network is concentrated at the central node. The tendency in recent computer systems is away from host-based computing power, and the advent of microprocessor-based systems where all nodes possess a high level of processing power has led to a fall off in the use of this topology. Nevertheless, the technology is well understood and, because it is currently the dominant configuration in traditional data communication, it is likely to be with us for many years to come.

Star Evaluation Factors

-   **Application:** Presently, a star network is the best way to integrate voice and data services. A star-based data network using the newer digital PBXs often can be justified by the savings and features for voice-based telephone services alone.

-   **Complexity:** The star can be quite complex: workstations attached to the central workstation may in turn act as the central server for other workstations or may be connected to communication links.

- **Performance:** Good for moderate load. However, the size and capacity of the network and hence the performance, is a direct function of the power of the central node.

- **System overhead :** Network overhead is high: the server usually cannot be used for any other purpose while acting as network server. The number of separate lines is also high.

- **Vulnerability:** System reliability is dependent on central server. If the server fails, all activity on the network ceases. Failure of an individual workstation does not affect thesystem. In either case, identification of problems and repair is simplified by centralised control.

- **Expandability:** Expandability may be severely restricted; most servers can support a limited number of network interfaces. Bandwidth and data rate limitations are often imposed on each user. The limits are necessary to protect the central processing functions from overload due to the aggregate rate of all the service ports and to keep the cost of each port on the central server low.

BUS TOPOLOGY

Another popular topology for data networks is the bus. This consists of a single length of the transmission medium (see Figure 3.3). This topology is used in traditional data communication networks where the host at one end of the bus communicates with several terminals attached along its length. This configuration is known as a multidrop line. It is also the topology used in the Ethernet LAN.

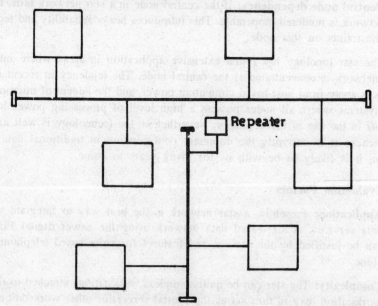

Fig. 3.3 : The bus topology

In a bus configuration, all workstations are connected to a single shared communication link through interface units and cable taps, as shown in Figure 3.3. Messages are broadcast along the whole bus. In order to receive a transmission, the workstations must be able to recognise their own address. Devices attached to a bus therefore must possess a high degree of intelligence or have the required intelligence provided by the bus interface unit.

The transmitters and receivers used by the network must tolerate a wide range of signal levels because workstations closest to the sending workstation receive a stronger signal than workstations at the far end of the bus. Signal-strength problems commonly are handled by limiting the length of the cable segments and the number of attached workstations. On some networks, amplifiers or repeaters may be used to maintain strength and clarity of the signal. Bus taps must be designed so as not to greatly reduce the signals reaching the other taps.

Advantages of the Bus

1. **Short cable length and simple wiring layout:** Because there is a single common data path connecting all nodes, the bus topology allows a very short cable length to be used. This decreases the installation cost, and also leads to a simple, easy to maintain, wiring layout.

2. **Resilient architecture:** The bus architecture has an inherent simplicity that makes it very reliable from a hardware point of view. There is a single cable through which all data passes and to which all nodes are connected.

3. **Easy to extend:** Additional nodes can be connected to an existing bus network at any point along its length. More extensive additions can be achieved by adding extra segments connected by a type of signal amplifier known as a repeater.

Disadvantages of the Bus

1. **Fault diagnosis is difficult:** Although the simplicity of the bus topology means that there is very little that can go wrong, fault detection is not a simple matter. In most LANs based on a bus, control of the network is not centralised in any particular node. This means that detection of a fault may have to be performed from many points in the network.

2. **Fault isolation is difficult:** In the star topology, a defective node can easily be isolated from the network by removing its connection at the centre. If a node is faulty on a bus, it must be rectified at the point where the node is connected to the network. Once the fault has been located, the node can simply be removed. In the case where the fault is in the network medium itself, an entire segment of the bus must be disconnected.

3. **Repeater configuration:** When a bus-type network has its backbone extended using repeaters, reconfiguration may be necessary. This may involve tailoring cable lengths, adjusting terminators, etc.

4. **Nodes must be intelligent:** Each node on the network is directly connected to

the central bus. This means that some way of deciding who can use the network at any given time must be performed in each node. It tends to increase the cost of the nodes irrespective of whether this is performed in hardware or software.

Bus Evaluation Factors

- **Application:** Bus networks are a good choice for small networks and networks with low traffic.

- **Complexity:** Bus networks tend to be relatively uncomplex.

- **Performance:** Excellent under light load, may degrade rapidly as load increases.

- **System overhead:** Comparatively low, particularly because much of the hardware is fully developed and readily available. Some redundancy of communication channel is advisable to reduce the vulnerability to channel outrage.

- **Vulnerability:** Failure of one workstation on a bus network does not usually affect the network. Bus networks are vulner- able to failure from damage to the main link and other problems affecting the bus. Problems on the bus are hard to locate. Once located, however, problems are easy to repair.

- **Expandability:** Expansion and reconfiguration of a bus network are easy. A new or relocated device may be connected to the nearest convenient network access point with little disruption of the network. Interconnecting microcomputers and equipment from different manufacturers is difficult because all connected devices must be able to accept the same forms of address and data.

RING TOPOLOGY

In the case of ring or loop topology, each node is connected to two and only two neighbouring nodes. Data is accepted from one of the neighbouring nodes and is transmitted onwards to another (see Figure 3.4). Thus data travels in one direction only, from node to node around the ring. After passing through each node, it returns to the sending node, which removes it.

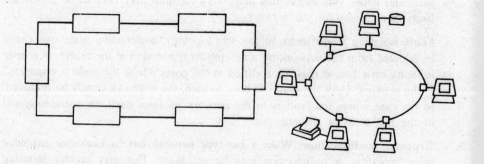

Fig. 3.4 : The ring topology

It is important to note that data 'passes through' rather than 'travels past' each node. This means that the signal may be amplified before being 'repeated' on the outward channel. It is a simple matter for the recipient to mark a message as read before resending it. This means that when the message arrives back at the sender, this mark can serve as an acknowledgement that the message was correctly received.

Ring networks consist of an unbroken circle of point-to-point connections of adjacent workstations. Messages travel from workstation to workstation in a round robin fashion. Workstations are connected to the cable through an access unit which is connected to a repeater which, in turn, retransmits messages addressed to other workstations.

In order to receive messages, each workstation must be capable of recognising its own address. However, no routing capability is required as messages automatically travel to the next workstation on the network. Originally, information flow on the ring was strictly in one direction. Now, two channel rings transmit information in different directions on each of the two channels.

When a ring topology is used to distribute control in local networks, the protocol used with it must avoid conflicting demands for shared channel.

A **loop** (see Figure 3.5) is a ring network using centralised control. One workstation will be designated as server, responsible for access to and control over the channel.

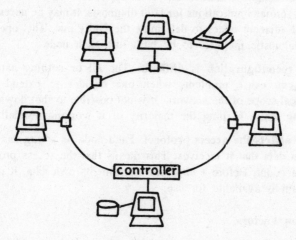

Fig. 3.5 : Loop

In practice, ring networks have been designed as single loops. Theoretically, a ring network could consist of several interconnected rings and form two or more hierarchical levels.

Advantages of the Ring

1. **Short cable length:** The amount of cabling involved in a ring topology is comparable to that of a bus and is small relative to that of a star. This means

that less connections will be needed, which will in turn increase network reliability.

2.   **No wiring closet space required:** Since there is only one cable connecting each node to its immediate neighbours, it is not necessary to allocate space in the building for wiring closets.

3.   **Suitable for optical fibres:** Optical fibres offer the possibility of very high speed transmission. Because traffic on a ring travels in one direction, it is easy to use optical fibres as a medium of transmission. Also, since a ring is made up of nodes connected by short segments of transmission medium, there is a possibility of mixing the types used for different parts of the network. Thus, a manufacturing company's network could use copper cables in the office area and optical fibres in the factory areas, where electrical interference may be a problem.

Disadvantages of the Ring

1.   **Node failure causes network failure:** The transmission of data on a ring goes through every connected node on the ring before returning to the sender. If one node fails to pass data through itself, the entire network has failed and no traffic can flow until the defective node has been removed from the ring.

2.   **Difficult to diagnose faults:** The fact that failure of one node will affect all others has serious implications for fault diagnosis. It may be necessary to examine a series of adjacent nodes to determine the faulty one. This operation may also require diagnostic facilities to be built into each node.

3.   **Network reconfiguration is difficult:** The all or nothing nature of the ring topology can cause problems when one decides to extend or modify the geographical scope of the network. It is not possible to shut down a small section of the ring while keeping the majority of it working normally.

4.   **Topology affects the access protocol:** Each node on a ring has a responsibility to pass on data that it receives. This means that the access protocol must take this into account. Before a node can transmit its own data, it must ensure that the medium is available for use.

Ring Evaluation Factors

-   **Application:** A ring is good in situations where capacity must be allocated equally or where a small number of workstations operating at high speeds over short distances are to be connected.

-   **Complexity:** A ring requires relatively complex hardware to implement. Message routing, on the other hand is simple: since only one message path is possible, the sending workstation need only know an address for the destination workstation. Routing information is not necessary.

-   **Performance:** Performance under heavy traffic remains stable with less delay and degradation of service than other networks. Average transmission delays are long, however, even under light traffic. Actual performance is dependent on the control protocols implemented.

- **System overhead:** Duplication of resources or a method of bypassing failure points is needed if the ring is to keep functioning when equipment fails.

- **Vulnerability:** Failure in a single workstation or in the channel can cause system failure because of the interdependence of workstations. Locating a failed repeater is particularly difficult; in a system with wide geographical distribution it may not be possible to immediately repair or circumvent the problem.

- **Expandability:** It is moderately easy to add or delete workstations on a ring network without making numerous connections for each change. Therefore, system modification costs are relatively low. Expansion does disrupt the whole system, even though it may be only briefly.

HYBRID TOPOLOGIES

By modifying or combining some of the characteristics of the 'pure' network topologies, a more useful result may be obtained. These combinations are called hybrid topologies.

TREE TOPOLOGY

The tree topology is a variant of the bus. The shape of the network is that of an inverted tree with the central root branching and sub branching to the extremities of the network (see Figure 3.6). It is normally implemented using coaxial cable as the transmission medium and broadband transmission techniques. One of the best known example is IBM's Personal Computer Network.

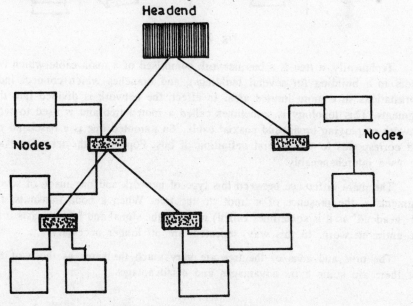

Fig. 3.6 a : The tree topology

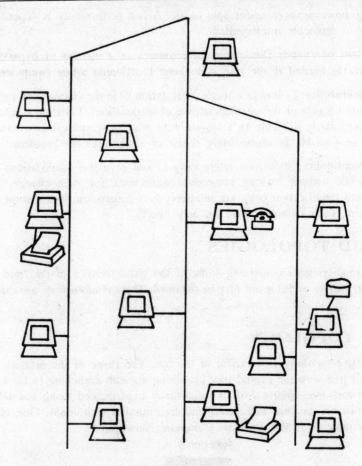

Fig. 3.6 b : Tree

Technically, a tree is a bus network comprised of a main cable which connects floors in a building (or several buildings), and branches which connect individual workstations in a more limited area. In effect, the network is divided into different segments. This topology is sometimes called a rooted tree and is used to refer to a network employing broadband coaxial cable. An unrooted tree is a baseband network and corresponds to the general definition of bus. Popularly, the terms tree and bus are used interchangeably.

The main difference between this type of network and one made of several bus segments is the presence of a 'root' to the tree. When a node transmits, the root (or 'headend' as it is sometimes called) receives the signal and rebroadcasts it through the entire network. In this way, repeaters are no longer necessary.

The pros and cons of the tree are very much the same as those of the bus, but there are some extra advantages and disadvantages.

Advantages of the Tree

1. **Easy to extend:** Because the tree is, of its very nature, divided into subunits, it is easier to add new nodes or branches to it.

2. **Fault isolation:** It is possible to disconnect whole branches of the network from the main structure. This makes it easier to isolate a defective node.

Disadvantages of the Tree

1. **Dependent on the root:** If the 'headend' device fails to operate, the entire network is rendered inoperable. In this respect, the tree suffers from the same reliability problems as the star.

STAR-RING TOPOLOGY

It has beenseen that all of the 'pure' network topologies have associated advantages and disadvantages. In the star-ring, two topologies have been combined with the aim of achieving the best of both.

The configuration consists of a number of concentration points connected together in a ring. These concentration points would, in practice, consist of wiring closets located on each floor of a building. From each closet, nodes are connected in a star configuration, using some or all of the connection points.

Electrically, the star-ring operates exactly in the same way as a normal ring. The difference is that the physical wiring is arranged as a series of interconnected stars. Because of this, this topology is sometimes more descriptively called the star-shaped ring.

Star-shaped rings (see Figure 3.7), in which the cable between workstations passes through a central wire centre, have been gaining favour because of the need to keep the ring operating when a device or the cable fails. Automatic bypass relays which can be used to reconfigure network operations are located at the wire centre. If a failure occurs, the "dead" section of the ring may be effectively eliminated. Remaining workstations can keep operating. The star-shaped ring also facilitates maintenance by providing a centralised monitoring and reconfiguration point.

Advantages of the Star-ring

1. **Fault diagnosis and isolation:** The presence of concentration points in the network greatly eases fault diagnosis. If a fault is detected on the network, the initial problem is to find out which concentration point in the ring is to blame. The fact that this ring is quite small in relation to the total size of the network makes this problem more manageable. The offending concentration point can be isolated easily, leaving the network in a fully functional state while further fault diagnosis is carried out.

2. **Ease of expansion:** The modular construction of a star-ring network means that new sections may be easily added. When designing the network originally, each

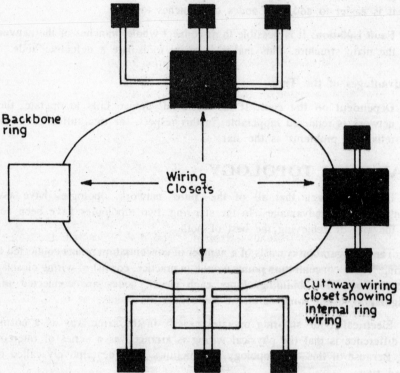

Fig. 3.7 a : The star-ring or star-shaped ring topology

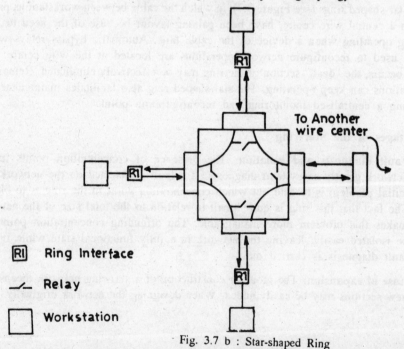

Fig. 3.7 b : Star-shaped Ring

concentration can have extra, unused lobes which can be called upon later, if needed. The next growth step involves adding a new concentration point and wiring it into the ring.

3. **Cabling:** The concentration points in a star-ring are connected via a single cable. This simplifies wiring between areas in an installation and cuts down on the congestion of cable ducts. Also, the wiring practices involved are very similar to that of telephone system installation. These techniques are well understood by building engineers and lend themselves well to the prewiring of buildings.

Disadvantages of the Star-ring

1. **Intelligent concentration points required:** Depending on the implementation used, the concentration points may need to have built- in intelligence/processing ability. This will be necessary if it is to assist in network fault diagnosis, node isolation or conversion from one form of transmission medium to another.

2. **Cabling:** The intercloset cabling in a star-ring is critical to its operation. This may mean that redundant cabling in the form of one or more back up rings may be necessary to meet reliability requirements. The largest section of the network (i.e., between the concentration points and the nodes) is laid out in a star. This means that a considerable amount of cable may be required.

CHOOSING A TOPOLOGY

In choosing a topology for a local area network, many factors must be considered. It must be easy to install both in existing buildings and those that are being prewired. Once installed, it must be able to cope with growth requirements. These may be sporadic and not well distributed geographically. It should be possible to carry out extensive changes to the network without completely depriving current users of service.

As with any other equipment, breakdowns in a LAN are to be expected. It is desirable to have a system where faults can be detected quickly and subsequently isolated, leaving the main section of the network operating normally.

The choice of topology can affect the range of possible media and the access method used to share it. Both of these can in turn affect the complexity and speed of operation of the individual nodes.

The star topology is of most interest from a historical point of view and also because it is the topology against which the others are measured. It is more appropriate for terminal-host configurations than for LANs. The remaining two 'pure' topologies both have good and bad points, some of which can be improved by combining them with other topologies.

TRANSMISSION MEDIA

Transmission lines, the backbone of the network, come in two basic varieties: baseband and broadband. Baseband communication links are twisted pair wire and baseband coaxial cable. Broadband media are broadband coaxial and fibre optic cable. Description of the cables, along with the additional devices required to turn a piece of cable into a network, will occupy the rest of this section.

MEDIA EVALUATION FACTORS

Each media is better suited to certain types of installation than to others. Factors influencing media choice follow the descriptions of the media and network components. Topics covered include the following:

- **Application:** In what size installation is the media most appropriate? How great a distance can it cover easily?

- **Application restrictions:** Under what conditions should the media be avoided?

- **Topology:** Which topologies use the cable?

- **Attraction:** In what situation is the cable to be preferred?

- **Network Reliability:** How dependable is the necessary equipment (other than the microcomputer workstations and the network interface cards)?

- **Vulnerability:** What are the major causes of equipment failure?

- **Susceptibility to noise:** How prone to interference is the network?

- **Implementation costs:** Installation of cabling and associated equipment is the great hidden cost of networking.

    For all media, the cost of installation easily exceeds that of the cost of the wire itself.

- **Security:** How open to tapping is the media?

    Tables 3.3 and 3.4 gives various factors or attributes forcomparing the major media.

TABLE 3.3 : Comparing the Major Media

	Twisted pair wire	Baseband coaxial cable	Broad band coaxial cable	Fiberoptic cable
Topologies supported	Ring, star, bus, tree	Bus, tree, ring	Bus, tree	Ring star, tree
Maximum number of nodes per network	Generally, up to 1024	Generally, up to 1024	Generally, up to 1024	Generally, up to 1024
Maximum geographical	3 kilometers	10 kilometers	50 kilometers	10 kilometers and up
Type of signal	Single-channel, uni-directional, analog or digital, depending ontype of modulation used, half- or full-duplex	Single channel, bidirectional, digital, half-duplex	Multi-channel unidirectional RF analog, half-duplex (full-duplex can be achieved by using	One single-channel, unidrectional, half-duplex, signal-encoded lightbeam per fiber; multiple fibers per cable; full-

			two channels or two cables	duplex can be achieved by using two fibers
Maximum bandwidth	Generally, up to 4 Mbps	Generally, up to 10 Mbps	Up to 499 MHz (aggregate total)	Up to 50 Mbps in 10 kilometer range, up to 1 Gbps in experimental tests
Major advantages	Low cost May be existing plant; no rewiring needed; very easy to install	Low maintenance cost Simple to install and tap	Supports voice, data, and video applications simultaneously Better immunity to noise and interference than baseband More flexible topology (branching tree) Rugged, durable equipment, needs no conduit Tolerates 100% bandwidth loading Uses off-the-shelf industly-standard CATV components	Supports voice, data, and video applications simultaneously Immunity to noise, crosstalk, and electrical interference Very high bandwidth Highly secure Low signal loss Low weight diameter; can be installed in small spaces Durable under adverse temperature, chemical, and radiation conditions
Major disadvantages	High error rates at higher speeds Limited bandwidth Low immunity to noise and crosstalk Difficult to maintain, troubleshoot Lacks physical ruggedness. requires conduits, trenches, or ducts	Lower noise immunity than broadband (can be improved by the use of filters, special cable and other means) Bandwidth can carry only about 40% load to remain stable Limited distance and topology Conduit required for hostile environments	High maintenance costs More difficult to install and tap than baseband RF modems required at each user staion; modems are expensive and limit the user device's transmission rate; complex initial engineering	Very high cost, but delining Require skilled installation and maintenance personnel Experimental technology; limited commercial availability Currently limited to point-to-point connections
Bandwidth (partial)	Low	Moderate	High	Very High
Data Transfer Reliability	Low	High	High	Very High
Noise Susceptibility	High	Moderate	Low	None
Transmission Security	Low	Low	Low	High
Length	Low	Moderate	High	Very High
Installation	Easiest	Hard	Hardest	Moderate

TABLE 3.4 : Transmission Media Alternatives

	Twisted Pair	Coax	Optical Fiber
Proven technology	Yes	Yes	Yes
Two-way	Yes	Yes	Yes
Availability	Yes	Yes	Limited
Maintainability	Yes	Yes	Limited
Reliability	High	High	High
Expandability	Limited	High	Very high
Immunity to :			
radio frequency interference	No	No	Yes
power line interference	No	No	Yes
electromagnetic statis	No	No	Yes
cross-talk	No	No	Yes
Bit error rate (BER)	High	Medium	Very low
Bandwidth			
Up to 24 64 KBPS channels	Yes	Yes	Yes
Up to 50 video channels	No	Yes	Yes
Beyond 150 video channels	No	No	Yes
Ability to use system for power	Limited	Yes	No
Technical support required	Low	Medium	High
Electronics costs	Low	Medium	High
Overall system price	Low	Medium	High
Estimated construction costs per mile:			
Aerial	$13,000	$15,000	$20,000
Underground	$23,000	$25,000	$40,000
Installation cycle in days	90	120	120
Third-party disruption	Yes	Yes	No
Workman safety	Low	Low	Very high
Impact by weather	Medium	Medium	Low
Geographic penetration	High	Medium	Limited

TWISTED PAIR WIRE

Twisted pair wire (see Figure 3.8) is familiar as the cable used for telephone systems. Since the start of the computer age, it has been used to connect terminals and other low-speed data equipment to the mainframe. Use of twisted pair wire is so widespread that it is frequently pre-installed in buildings.

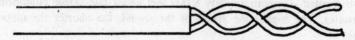

Fig. 3.8 : Twisted Pair Wire

As the name implies, pairs of wires are spiralled about each other. Gauge (size) of the base wire varies, as does the number of twists per foot. The twisting standardises the electrical properties throughout the length of the cable and minimises the interference created by adjacent wires in multipair cable. Normally, copper is used for the wire. Twisted pair tends to be unshielded or only minimally shielded. As a result, the cable is light and relatively easy to install.

Components of a Twisted Pair Network

A twisted pair wire network (see Figure 3.9) consists of the main cable, plus the following:

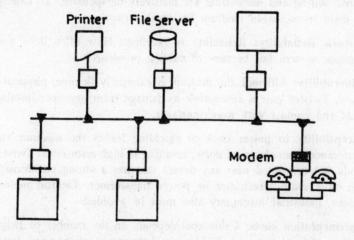

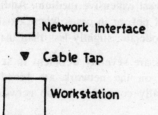

Fig. 3.9 : Twisted Pair Network

- **Transceivers:** Network interface units which provide the intelligence for reading message addresses and for other network-oriented communication functions.

- **Cable taps:** Connect the transceiver to the main cable.

- **Repeaters:** Boost the strength of the signal as the messages pass from one cable section to another. The distance unamplified digital signals can travel on twisted pair is limited — approximately 8,000 feet under favourable conditions, without a repeater. The higher the speed of the signal, the shorter the distance it can travel.

Twisted Pair Evaluation Factors

- **Application:** Twisted pair cable is most suitable for point- to-point applications where low speed, low demand devices are interconnected. Average data rates are severely restricted, dropping rapidly as the distance between devices increases.

- **Application restrictions:** Most implementations restrict the number of workstations on the lines and limit distances to the area within a single building.

- **Topology:** Twisted pair is used in star, bus and ring topologies.

- **Attraction:** One major attraction of twisted pair is its wide use for other communication purposes, particularly telephone networks. A second attraction is cost: wiring and installation are relatively inexpensive. To date, it has been the main transmission medium for local network.

- **Network Reliability:** Reliability is excellent. How often does your in-house telephone system fail because of cabling problems?

- **Vulnerability:** Although the medium is extremely flexible, physical ruggedness is low. Twisted pair is susceptible to damage from improper installation, sharp bends and contact with rough surfaces.

- **Susceptibility to noise:** Lack of shielding leaves the medium vulnerable to interference from electrical noise, resulting in high error rates. Twisted pair wire should not be routed near any device that has a strong electromagnetic field, such as a radio transmitter or power transformer. Electric motors, gasoline engines, industrial machinery also must be avoided.

- **Implementation costs:** Cable cost depends on the number of twists per foot; the type of insulation and shielding; and the guage of the wire. Based on cable costs alone, twisted pair is the least expensive medium. Additionally, it already is installed in many buildings. If not, or in cases where existing wiring cannot be used, installation costs are moderate, slightly less than that of coaxial cable.

- **Security:** Twisted pair networks are severely deficient in security due to lack of shielding. Electrical signals on the network are broadcast and may be intercepted by stations not actually connected to the network.

BASEBAND COAXIAL CABLE

Coaxial cable has been used for many years in the telephone network in applications with requirements similar to those of a LAN. It also is used for CATV (Community Antenna Television) systems. Both baseband and broadband coaxial cable are available. Although they are similar in construction, their installation and applications differ. Therefore, they will be discussed in separate sections.

In baseband coaxial cable (see Figure 3.10), a central carrier wire is surrounded by a fine woven mesh of copper which forms an outer shell. The space between the wire and the outer shell is insulated to separate the two conductors and to maintain the electrical properties. The entire cable is covered by protective insulation to minimise electrical emissions. The cable is usually approximately 3/8 inch diameter.

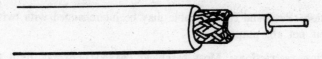

Fig. 3.10 : Baseband Coaxial Cable

The cable carries a single digital signal at a very high data rate — up to 10 to 12 megabits per second. Transmission frequency is relatively low. Bits are put directly on the cable without modulation.

Components of a Baseband Coaxial Network

In most respects, baseband coaxial is similar to twisted wire pairs. To transform a simple cable into a network (see Figure 3.11), the following parts are needed:

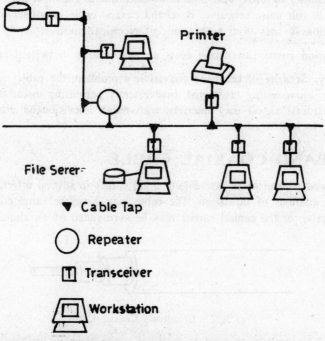

Printer

File Serer

▼ **Cable Tap**

◯ **Repeater**

[T] **Transceiver**

[▢] **Workstation**

Fig. 3.11 : Baseband Coaxial Network

- **Transceivers:** Network interface units, which provide the intelligence for reading message addresses and for other network-oriented communication functions.

- **Cable taps:** Connect the transceiver cable to the main cable.

- **Repeaters:** Amplify the signal as the messages pass from one cable section to another.

The main network cable is installed in a wire trough, which may be located beneath a raised floor, inside walls or above a dropped ceiling. Local outlets may be provided in each office to facilitate connecting an individual workstation to the network.

Baseband Coaxial Evaluation Factors

- **Application:** Baseband coaxial cable may be interchanged with twisted pair for many, but not all, purposes.

- **Application restrictions:** Most baseband coaxial networks limit the distance covered and the number of workstations.

- **Topology:** Baseband coaxial cable is frequently used for bus networks.

- **Attraction:** Baseband coaxial offers greater resistance to noise and better performance than twisted pair for an only slightly higher cable cost.

- **Network Reliability:** Reliability is good to excellent.

- **Vulnerability:** The cable itself is physically rugged.

- **Susceptibility to noise:** Although less susceptible to electrical noise than twisted pair, it is still noise sensitive. Baseband coaxial cable is not recommended for installation in sites with high levels of electrical noise.

- **Installation costs:** Installation costs are comparable to twisted pair.

- **Security:** Security of baseband coaxial is a problem; the cable may act as an antenna, broadcasting the signal, inadvertently permitting unauthorised taping. The broadcast signal may interfere with radio, televisionand other broadcast systems located nearby.

BROADBAND COAXIAL CABLE

Broadband coaxial cable (see Figure 3.12) comes in several different diameters with varying amounts of insulation. The cable may have the same construction as baseband coaxial, or the central carrier may be surrounded by an aluminium sleeve.

Fig. 3.12 : Broadband Coaxial Cable

The space between the core and the shell is filled with insulation, and the whole is enclosed in a protective coat of insulation. Broadband coaxial cable can carry 50 to 100 television channels or thousands of voice and low speed data channels at rates of 9.2 to 50 kilobits per second.

Components of a Broadband Coaxial Network

Broadband coaxial networks (see Figure 3.13) usually are implemented with off-the-shelf CATV hardware. The radio frequency signal carrier propagates in one direction only. Table 3.5 gives a comparative analysis of baseband versus broadband.

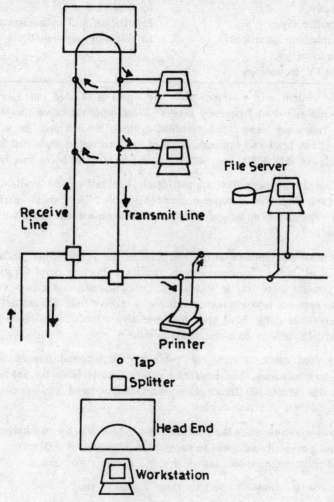

Fig. 3.13 : Broadband Coaxial Network

TABLE 3.5 : Baseband versus Broadband

Advantages	Disadvantages
Baseband	
Cheaper-no modem	Single channel
Simpler technology	Limited capacity
Easy to install	Limited distance
	Grounding concerns
Broadband	
High capacity	Modem cost
Multiple traffic types	Installation and maintenance complexity
More flexible configurations	Doubled propagation delay
Large area coverage	
Mature CATV technology	

If the system uses a single cable, the signal is divided into inbound (transmit) and outbound (receive) frequency ranges. Workstations receive messages within the outbound frequency range and transmit within the inbound frequency range. A translator at the head end converts inbound frequencies to outbound frequencies. On a 300 MHz or 400 MHz line, 40 to 50 channels of 6 MHz can be provided.

For local area networks, approximately one-half of the available channels are used for each direction, a scheme called Mid split. The "split" in the name refers to the placement of unassigned frequencies, required as guardband to minimise interference.

The head end, located at the midpoint of the single cable, serves as the point of origin of all radio frequency signals and the collection point for all signals being generated on the network. It acts as the inbound-outbound cross-over point which divides the network into a transmit half and a receive half. Shared devices frequently are located at the cable head end. As noise also returns to the head end, the return signals may be subject to noise degradation.

In a dual cable system, one cable carries inbound transmissions, the other outbound transmissions. The head end passes signals from the inbound line to the outbound line across all frequencies. Workstations send and receive on the same frequency, but on different cables.

In both systems, when the network cable is installed, the two halves are positioned parallel and physically adjacent to each other. Operational differences between LANs using mid-split single cable and dual cable systems are minor.

The coaxial network contains three levels of line:

- **Trunk:** The main network cable, which transports radio- frequency signals between amplifiers. Each floor in a multi-floor installation will have a trunk cable. It also is used for long runs between buildings. Trunk cable is normally thicker and more rigid than other cables in the network.

- **Branch:** Carries the network to the general area of the user. Branch distribution cables may extend from other branches, subject only to signal quality considerations.

- **Drop:** Connects the user outlet to the branch. The cable used is thin and more flexible than other broadband coaxial cables. Several drop cables may be attached to each connector.

The cable is installed above a dropped ceiling or below a false floor where it can be "pulled" into position. Risers bring the main cable from one floor to another. Usually a building will have only two riser cables. Each floor will have a pair of trunk cables split at various points into branches. The cable may be buried for runs between buildings or hung on poles (as is done for CATV).

To the lines are connected:

- **Radio-Frequency Modems:** Used as network interface. Broadband systems require modems to translate the data onto and off the carrier signal. The modem must be able to transmit and/or receive on a variety of frequencies and is therefore sometimes called frequency-agile.

- **Amplifiers:** Used to "boost" the signal. Amplifiers (also called Repeaters) are necessary over long distances, such as an installation encompassing multiple floors of a building or multiple buildings.

- **Power supply:** The system as a whole runs on electrical power. Distributing power over the coaxial cable eliminates the need for a separate power supply at each amplifier location, resulting in greater flexibility in the placement of amplifiers. For reliability, electrical grounding is necessary.

- **Directional couplers:** Insure that signals transmitted by any network device will be transmitted only toward the head end.

- **Splitters and combiners:** Permit branching of cable.

- **Terminators:** End a line. Terminators limit noise reflection in the system and minimise undesirable signals.

To run the system, a power supply is necessary. Power may be provided at the head end or with a power outlet at each amplifier.

In installations where user outlets have been liberally supplied, adding workstations or moving existing workstations from one location to any other location served by the network is achieved easily. In many cases, connection and/or disconnection of a workstation will not affect the operation of the network as a whole. Reconfiguration of the network into a hierarchy with subnetworks is possible.

Broadband Coaxial Evaluation Factors

- **Application:** Coaxial cable is preferred for high-frequency, wide bandwidth, high-speed applications. It is currently the most practical choice for networks covering moderate distances; requiring digital, voiceand video transmission; and/or having a large number of workstations.

- **Application restrictions:** The cost of the system makes broadband coaxial impractical for small networks.

- **Topology:** Basic broadband coaxial topology is extremely flexible. Star or tree are suggested by the transmission technology.

- **Attraction:** All transmission devices are readily available

CATV components with proven high reliability.

- **Network Reliability:** The basic technology is highly dependable. Network reliability depends on the reliability of individual parts. Cable amplifiers tend to be the major point of failure, particularly when new. If amplifiers survive the first several months, they usually do not fail until near end of guaranteed life.

- **Vulnerability:** The cable is susceptible to damage from careless installation, improperly installed devices and failure in cable components. It cannot make sharp bends around corners. In addition, the cable is sensitive to temperature changes.

- **Susceptibility to noise:** Transmission is susceptible to interference from low-frequency electromagnetic noise. The actual noise immunity is dependent on the physical location and method of implementation. Coaxial cable can be used in many environments where twisted pair wire or other unshield-ed cable could not be used.

- **Implementation costs:** While the cable itself is not expen- sive, system costs are high because of initial equipment and upkeep costs. Installation and maintenance of CATV equipment is routine.

- **Security:** Unlike baseband coaxial, broadband coaxial cable does not broadcast the electrical signals that it carries. Security, however, still may be a problem: coaxial cable can be easily tapped by anyone who can gain physical access to the cable.

FIBRE OPTIC CABLE

Fibre optic cable (see Figure 3.14) is a relatively new medium for local area networks. Light signals are transmitted through a cable/waveguide composed of a bundle glass or plastic fibres. Each individual strand has a centre core of plastic or glass with a high refractive index, surrounded by a cladding layer (overcoat) with a slightly lower index. The cladding layer isolates the fibres and prevents interference

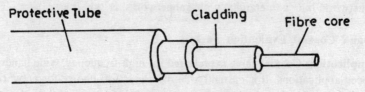

Fig. 3.14 : Fibre Optic Cable

between adjacent strands, as well as providing some physical protection for the core. The whole usually is enclosed by additional protective outer layers which play no role in the actual transmission.

Three basic types of cable are available:

- Single mode fibres have an extremely thin core diameter. While the thinness provides high performance, it makes connection to light transmitters and other cable segments extremely difficult.

- Stepped index fibres contain a core of high resolution within a shell of lower resolution. The boundary between core and cladding is abrupt. Connections are easier than with other types of fibre.

- Graded index fibres vary in density from the core outward. The gradation moderates the dispersion of signals. Graded index fibre is currently the most commonly available, because it is preferred for telecommunications. It has the highest transmission rate of the three types of cable.

Table 3.6 gives a comparative analysis of three types of optical fibres. Figure 3.15 depicts the three optical fibre transmission modes.

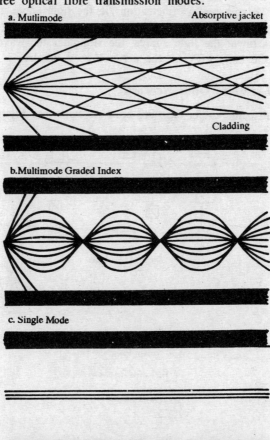

Fig. 3.15 : Optical Fiber Transmission Modes

TABLE 3.6 : Comparison of Three Types of Optical Fibers

	Step-index Multimode	Graded-Index Multimode	Single-mode
Light Source	Led or laser	Led or laser	laser
Bandwidh	wide (up to 200 MHz/km)	very wide (200 Mhz to 3 GHz/km)	extremely wide (3 GHz to 50 GHz/km)
Splicing	difficult	difficult	difficult
Typical Application	computer data links	moderate-lengh telephone lines	telecommunication long line
Cost	least expensive	more expensive	most expensive
Core Diamter (μm)	50 to 125	50 to 125	2 to 8
Cladding Diameter (μm)	125 to 440	125 to 440	15 to 60

Cable segments must be aligned precisely for the signal to continue from one segment to the next, because light tends to travel in a wave-like motion rather than a straight line. The greater the fluctuations in the light wave, the more rapidly the performance degrades and the greater the dispersion of the signal. The thinner the optic and the narrower the light source, the straighter the wave is forced to travel and, therefore, the more efficient the network as a whole.

Components of a Fibre Optic Network

In addition to the cable, the fibre optic network (see Figure 3.16) requires the following:

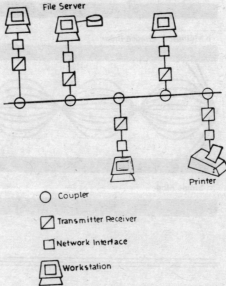

Fig. 3.16 : Fiber Optic Network

- **A Transmitter:** Consisting of a light source and a power supply. Light is supplied by either a LED (Light Emitting Diode) or a laser diode.

- **Receivers:** Also called detectors, which sense the light signals and convert them back to electrical signals.

- **Repeaters:** Necessary for very long networks. Fibre optic sysiems use far fewer repeaters than any other media.

- **Couplers and connectors:** Used to join two lengths of cable.

Any mating of fibre optic cable requires a great deal of care, because minor mismatches can cause a large loss of efficiency.

In operation, a workstation sends data in standard electrical form to a transmitter, where it is converted into light pulses. The light signals are collected by the waveguide and carried to a receiver. At the receiver, the light pulses are retranslated to electrical pulses and delivered to the destination workstation.

Unlike coaxial cable, fiber optic systems generally do not require repeaters over the distances typically found in LANs. Repeaterless runs of up to 4 kilometers or more can be accommodated, as compared to only 1 1/2 kilometers for coaxial cable.

The light signals may be digital or analog. Digital light signals are created by on/off pulses; analog signals use varying light intensity. Each cable can transmit in one direction only. Two-way communications require two optic cables.

Performance of the system is a function of transmission speed, bandwidth and the amount of signal dispersion or degradation, over the length of the cable. The wider the range of light wavelengths at the source, the sooner the signal disperses.

Fibre Optic Evaluation Factors

- **Application:** Fibre optic is particularly suited to systems with very-high speed data and video transmission requirements; for transmission over distances greater than other media can support; for installations which anticipate rapidly increasing demand for communication capabilities; and where space and signal interference cause problems.

- **Application restrictions:** Fibre optic is not suitable for small installations or where cost is a major factor.

- **Topology:** Currently, fibre optic systems are most suitable for point-to-point transmission, suggesting star or ring topologies. Bus topology is possible, but currently is infrequently implemented.

- **Attraction:** Fibre optic networks support an extremely high data rate — over 1 gigabit per second (10 to the 9th power bits per second) — on a potentially unlimited bandwidth, with extremely high reliability and high quality output. Fibre optic cable is thin, light weight, very flexible and extremely resistant to ordinary transmission hazards.

- **Network Reliability:** Fibre optic cable is rugged, has a long life and has displayed high reliability under adverse physical conditions.

- **Vulnerability:** Fibre optic networks are susceptible to signal loss from improper splicing or interfacing, bending and pressure. The light source may be heat sensitive.

- **Susceptibility to noise:** Due to its resistance to electrical, electromagnetic and radio frequency noise, fibre optic may be the only functional choice for a heavily industrial installation. The fibre optic cable is electrically isolated and therefore cannot broadcast its signal outside the network. It has the added advantage of not emitting sparks and thus does not present a potential fire hazard.

- **Implementation costs:** Currently fibre optic networks are very expensive. Installation and equipment costs, particularly of coupling and interfacing devices, are high. The installation is complex, especially as connections must be precise. However, costs of all parts of the network are dropping rapidly and will continue to do so.

- **Security:** Fibre optic is the best choice where light security is mandatory. It is virtually invulnerable to tapping.

RELATIONSHIP BETWEEN MEDIUM AND TOPOLOGY

The choice of transmission medium and topology are not independent. Table 3.7 shows the preferred combinations. The ring topology requires point-to-point links between repeaters. Twisted-pair wire, baseband coaxial cable and optical fibre can all be used to provide the links. However, broadband coaxial cable would not work well in this topology. Each repeater would have to be capable of receiving and transmitting data simultaneously on multiple channels. It is doubtful that the expense of such devices could be justified. Table 3.8 summarises representative parameters of transmission media for commercially available ring LANs.

TABLE 3.7 : Relationship Between Medium and Topology

Medium	Topology			
	Bus	Tree	Ring	Star
Twisted par	x		x	x
Baseband coaxial cable	x		x	
Broadband coaxial cable	x	x		
Optical fiber			x	

TABLE 3.8 : Characteristic for
Transmission Media for Local Networks : Ring

Transmission Medium	Data Rate (Mbps)	Spacing	Number of Repeaters
Unshielded Twisted Pair	4	0.1	72
Shielded Twisted Pair	16	0.3	250
Baseband Coaxial Cable	16	1.0	250
Optical Fiber	100	2.0	240

For the bus topology, twisted pair and both baseband and broadband coaxial cable are appropriate. At the present time, optical fibre cable is not feasible, as the multipoint configuration is not cost-effective, due to the difficulty in constructing low-loss optical taps. The tree topology can be employed with broadband coaxial cable. The unidirectional nature of broadband signalling allows the construction of a tree architecture. On the other hand, the bidirectional nature of baseband signalling, on either twisted pair or coaxial cable, is not suited to the tree topology. Again optical fibre is not now cost effective for the multipoint nature of the tree topology. Table 3.9 summarises representative parameters for transmission media for commercially available bus and tree LANs.

TABLE 3.9 : Characteristic for
Transmission Media for Local Networks : Bus

Transmission Medium	Data Rate (Mbps)	Range (km)	Number of Taps
Unshielded Twisted Pair	1-2	<2	10's
Baseband Coaxial Cable	10/70	<3/<1	100's/10's
Broadband Coaxial Cable	20 per channel	<30	100's-1,000's

The reader will note that the performance for a given medium is considerably better for the ring topology compared with the bus/tree topology. In the bus/tree topology, each station is attached to the medium by a tap, and each tap introduces some attenuation and distortion to the signal as it passes by. In the ring, each station is attached to the medium by a repeater, and each repeater generates a new signal to compensate for effects of attenuation and distortion.

The star topology requires a single point-to-point link between each device and the central switch. Twisted pair is admirably suited to the task. The higher data rates of coaxial cable or fibre would overwhelm the switches of today's technology.

COMMUNICATION SWITCHING TECHNIQUES

So far we have discussed how data can be encoded and transmitted over a communication link. In its simplest form, data communication takes place between two devices that are directly connected by some form of transmission medium. Often, however, it is impractical for two devices to be directly connected. This is so for one (or both) of the following contingencies:

- The devices are very far apart. It would be inordinately expensive, for example, to string a dedicated link between two devices, thousands of miles apart.

- There is a set of devices, each of which may require a link to many of the others at various times. Examples are ofall the telephones in the world and all of the terminals and computers owned by a single organisation. Except for the case where very few devices are available,it is impractical to provide a dedicated wire between each pair of devices.

The solution to this problem is to attach each device to a communication network. Communication is achieved by transmitting data from source to destination through a network of intermediate nodes. These nodes are not concerned with the content of the data; rather their purpose is to provide a switching facility that will move the data from node to node until they reach their destination. Figure 3.17 illustrates the situation. We have a collection of devices that wish to communicate; we will refer to them generically as **stations**. The stations may be computers, terminals, telephones or other communicating devices. We also have a collection of devices whose purpose is to provide communication, which we will refer to as **nodes**. The nodes are connected to each other in some fashion by transmission links. Each station attaches to a node. The collection of nodes is referred to as a **communication network**. If the attached devices are computers and terminals, then the collection of nodes plus stations is referred to as a **computer network**.

Three switching techniques are in common use:

- Circuit switching
- Message switching
- Packet switching

CIRCUIT SWITCHING

Communication via circuit switching implies that there is a dedicated communication path between two stations. That path is a connected sequence of links between nodes. On each physical link, a channel is dedicated to the connection. The most common example of circuit switching is the telephone network. Figure 3.18a illustrates the concept of circuit switching.

Communication via circuit switching involves three phases, which can be explained with reference to Figure 3.17.

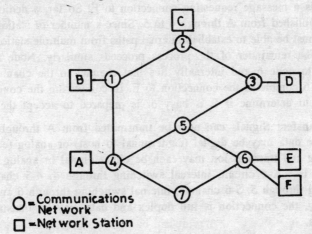

Fig. 3.17 : Generic Switching Network

O = Communications Net work
□ = Net work Station

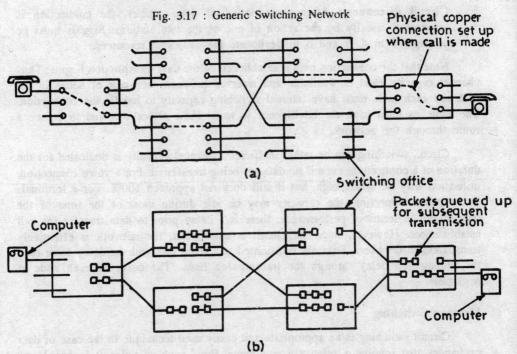

(a)

Physical copper connection set up when call is made

Switching office

Packets queued up for subsequent transmission

Computer

Computer

(b)

Fig. 3.18 (a) : Circuit switching. (b) : Packet switching

1. **Circuit establishment:** Before any data can be transmitted, an end-to-end (station-to-station) circuit must be established. For example, station A sends a request to node 4 requesting a connection to station E. Typically, the circuit from A to 4 is a dedicated line, so that part of the connection already exists. Node 4 must find the next leg in a route leading to node 6. Based on routing

information and measures of availability and perhaps cost, node 4 selects the circuit to node 5, allocates a free channel (using TDM or FDM) on that circuit and sends a message requesting connection to E. So far, a dedicated path has been established from A through 4 to 5. Since a number of stations may attach to 4, it must be able to establish internal paths from multiple stations to multiple nodes. The remainder of the process proceeds similarly. Node 5 dedicates a channel to node 6 and internally ties that channel to the channel from node 4. Node 6 completes the connection to E. In completing the connection, a test is made to determine if E is busy or is prepared to accept the connection.

2. **Data transfer:** Signals can now be transmitted from A through the network to E. The data may be digital (e.g.terminal to host) or analog (e.g.voice). The signalling and transmission may each be either digital or analog. In any case, the path is : A-4 circuit, internal switching through 4, 4-5 channel, internal switching through 5, 5-6 channel, internal switching through 6 and 6-E circuit. Generally, the connection is full duplex and data may be transmitted in both directions.

3. **Circuit disconnect:** After some period of data transfer, the connection is terminated, usually by the action of one of the two stations. Signals must be propagated to 4, 5 and 6 to deallocate the dedicated resources.

Note that the connection path is established before data transmission begins. Thus channel capacity must be available and reserved between each pair of nodes in the path and each node must have internal switching capacity to handle the connection. The switches must have the intelligence to make these allocations and to device a route through the network.

Circuit switching can be rather inefficient. Channel capacity is dedicated for the duration of a connection, even if no data are being transferred. For a voice connection, utilisation may be rather high, but it still does not approach 100%. For a terminal-to-computer connection, the capacity may be idle during most of the time of the connection. In terms of performance, there is a delay prior to data transfer for call establishment. However, once the circuit is established, the network is effectively transparent to the users. Data are transmitted at a fixed rate with no delay other than the propagation delay through the transmission links. The delay at each node is negligible.

Message Switching

Circuit switching is an appropriate and easily used technique in the case of data exchanges that involve a relatively continuous flow, such as voice (telephone) and some forms of sensor and telemetry input. However, circuit switching does have two drawbacks:

-   Both stations must be available at the same time for the data exchange.

-   Resources must be available and dedicated through the network between the two stations, when available.

An alternative approach, which is generally appropriate to digital data exchange, is to exchange logical units of data, called **messages**. Examplesof messages are telegrams, electronic mail, computer files and transaction queries and responses. If one thinks of data exchange as a sequence of messages being transmitted in both directions between stations, then a very different approach, known as message switching, can be used.

With message switching, it is not necessary to establish a dedicated path between two stations. Rather, if a station wishes to send a message (a logical unit of information) it appends a destination address to the message. The message is then passed through the network from node to node. At each node, the entire message is received, stored briefly and then transmitted to the next node.

In a circuit-switching network, each node is an electronic or perhaps electro-mechanical switching device which transmits bits as fast as it receives them. A message-switching node is typically a general-purpose minicomputer, with sufficient storage to buffer messages as they come. A message is delayed at each node for the time required to receive all bits of the message plus a queuing delay waiting for an opportunity to retransmit to the next node.

Again using Figure 3.17, consider a message from A to E. A appends E's address to the message and sends it to node 4. Node 4 stores the message and determines the next leg of the route (say to 5). Then node 4 queues the message for transmission over the 4-5 link. When the link is available, the message is transmitted to node 5, which will forward the message to node 6 and finally to E. This system is also known as a **store-and-forward** message system. In some cases, the node to which the station attaches or some central node, also files the message, creating a permanent record.

The advantages of this approach over circuit switching are:

- Line efficiency is greater, since a single node-to-node channel can be snared by many messages over time. For the same traffic volume, less total transmission capacity is needed.

- Simultaneous availability of sender and receiver is not required. The network can store the message pending the availability of the receiver.

- When traffic becomes heavy on a circuit-switched network, some calls are blocked. On a message-switched network, messages are still accepted, but delivery delay increases.

- A message-switching system can send one message to many destinations. This facility is not easily provided by a circuit-switched network.

- Message priorities can be established.

- Error control and recovery procedures on a message basis can be built into the network.

- A message-switching network can carry out speed and code conversion. Two stations of different data rates can be connected since each connects to its node at its proper data rate. The message-switching network can also easily convert format (e.g. from ASCII to EBCDIC). These features are less often found in a circuit-switched system.

- Messages sent to inoperative terminals may be intercepted and either stored or rerouted to other terminals.

The primary disadvantage of message switching is that it is not suited to real-time or interactive traffic. The delay through the network is relatively long and has relatively high variance. Thus it cannot be used for voice connections. Nor is it suited to interactive terminal-host connections.

PACKET SWITCHING

Packet switching represents an attempt to combine the advantages of message and circuit switching while minimising the disadvantages of both. In situations where there is a substantial volume of traffic among a number of stations, this objective is met. Figure 3.18b illustrates the concept of packet switching.

Packet switching is very much like message switching. The principal external difference is that the length of the units of data that may be transmitted is limited in a packet-switched network. A typical maximum length is 1000 to a few thousand bits. Message switching systems accommodate far larger messages. From a station's point of view, then, messages above the maximum length must be divided into smaller units and sent out one at a time. To distinguish the two techniques, the data units in the latter system are referred to as packets.

Again using Figure 3.17 for an example, consider the transfer of a single packet. The packet contains data plus a destination address. Station A transmits the packet to 4, which stores it briefly and then passes it to 5, which passes it to 6 and on to E. One difference from message switching is that packets are typically not filed. A copy may be temporarily stored for error recovery purposes, but that is all.

On the face of it, packet switching may seem a strange procedure to adopt, with no particular advantage over message switching. Remarkably, the simple expedient of limiting the maximum size of a data unit to a rather small length has a dramatic effect on performance. Before demonstrating this, we define two common procedures for handling entire messages over a packet-switched network.

The problem is this : A station has a message to send that is of length greater than the maximum packet size. It breaks the message into packets and sends these packets to its node. Question: How will the network handle this stream of packets? There are two approaches: datagram and virtual circuit.

In the **datagram** approach, each packet is treated independently, just as each message is treated independently in a message-switched network. Let us consider the implications of this approach. Suppose that station A has a 3-packet message to send to E. It pops the packets out, 1-2-3, to node 4. On each packet, node 4 must make a routing decision. Packet 1 comes in and node 4 determines that its queue of packets for node 5 is shorter than for node 7, so it queues the packet for node 5. Ditto for packet 2. But for packet 3, node 4 finds that its queue for node 7 is shortest and so queues packet for node 5 for that node. So the packets, each with the same destination address, do not all follow the same route. Furthermore, it is just possible that packet 3 will beat packet 2 to node 6. Thus it is possible that the packets will be delivered to E in a different sequence from the one in which they were sent. It is up to E to figure out how to reorder them. In this technique each packet, treated independently, is referred to as a "datagram".

In the **virtual circuit** approach, a logical connection is established before any packets are sent. For example, suppose that A has one or more messages to send to E. It first sends a Call Request packet to 4, requesting a connection to E. Node 4 decides to route the request and all subsequent data to 5, which decides to route the request and all subsequent data to 6, which finally delivers the Call Request packet to E. If E is prepared to accept the connection, it sends out a Call Accept packet to 6. This packet is passed back through nodes 5 and 4 to A. Stations A and E may now exchange data over the logical connection or virtual circuit that has been established. Each packet now contains a virtual circuit identifier as well as data. Each node on the pre-established route knows where to direct such packets; no routing decisions are required. Thus every data packet from A traverses nodes 4, 5 and 6; every data packet from E traverses nodes 6, 5 and 4. Eventually, one of the stations terminates the connection with a Clear Request packet. At any time, each station can have more than one virtual circuit to any other station and can have virtual circuits to more than one station.

So the main characteristic of the virtual circuit technique is that a route between stations is set up prior to data transfer. Note that this does not mean that there is a dedicated path, as in circuit switching. A packet is still buffered at each node and queued for output over a line. The difference from the datagram approach is that the node need not make a routing decision for each packet. It is made only once for each connection.

If two stations wish to exchange data over an extended period of time, there are certain advantages to virtual circuits. They all have to do with relieving the stations of unnecessary communication processing functions. A virtual circuit facility may provide a number of services, including sequencing, error control and flow control. We emphasise the word "may" because not all virtual circuit facilities will be completely reliable in providing all these services. With that proviso, we define terms. Sequencing refers to the fact that, since all packets follow the same route, they arrive in the original order. Error control is a service that assures not only that packets arrive in proper sequence, but all packets arrive correctly. For example, if a packet in a sequence fails to arrive at node 6, or arrives with an error, it can request a retransmission of that packet from node 4. Finally, flow control is a technique for assuring that a sender does not overwhelm a receiver with data. For example, if station E is buffering data from A and perceives that it is about to run out of buffer space, it can request, via the virtual circuit facility, that A suspend transmission until further notice.

One advantage of the datagram approach is that call set-up phase is avoided. Thus if a station wishes to send only one or a few packets, datagram delivery will be quicker. Another advantage of the datagram service is that, because it is more primitive, it is more flexible. A good example of this is the use of the datagram approach in inter-networking. A third advantage is that datagram delivery is inherently more reliable. If a node fails, all virtual circuits that pass through that node are lost. With datagram delivery, if a node is lost, packets may find alternate routes.

We now return to the question of performance, illustrating the techniques discussed in Figure 3.19. This figure intends to suggest the relative performance of the techniques; however, actual performance depends on a host of factors, including:

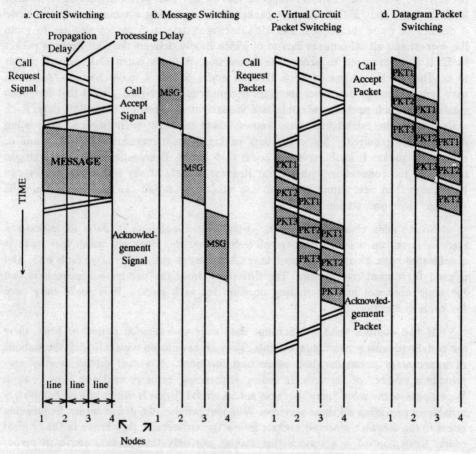

Fig. 3.19 : Even Timing for Various Communication Switching Techniques

-   Number of stations

-   Number and arrangement of nodes

-   Total load on system

-   Length (in time and data) of typical exchange between two stations

And more. Given the difficulty of comparing these methods, we hazard a few observations.

For interactive traffic, message switching is not appropriate.

For light and/or intermittent loads, circuit switching is the most cost effective, since the public telephone system can be used, via dial-up lines.

For very heavy and sustained loads between two stations, a leased circuit-switched line is the most cost effective.

Packet switching is to be preferred when there is a collection of devices that must exchange a moderate to heavy amount of data; line utilisation is most efficient with this technique.

Datagram packet switching is good for short messages and for flexibility.

Virtual circuit packet switching is good for long exchanges and for relieving stations of processing burden.

Table 3.10 summarises the main features of the four techniques that we have discussed.

TABLE 3.10 : Comparision of Communication Switching Techniques

Circuit Switching	Message Switching	Datagram Packet Switching	Virtual Circuit Packet Switching
Dedicated transmission path	No dedicated path	No dedicated path	No dedicated path
Continuous transmission of data	Transmission of messages	Transmission off packets	Transmission of packets
Fast enough for interactive	Too slow for interactive	Fast enough for interactive	Fast enough for interactive
Messages are not stored	Messages are filed for later retrieval	Packets may be stored until delivered	Packets stored
Path is established for entire conversation	Route established for each message	Route established for each packet	Route established for entire conversation
Call setup delay; negligible transmission delay	Message transmission delay	Packet transmission delay	Call setup delay; packet transmission delay
Busy signal if called party busy	No busy signal	Sender may be notified if packet not delivered	Sender notified of connection denial
Overload may block	Overload increases	Overload increases	Overload may block

call setup; no delay for established calls	message delay	packet delay	call setup; increases packet delay
Electromechanical or computerized switching nodes	Message switch center with filling facility	Small switching nodes	Small switching nodes
User responsible for message-loss protection	Network responsible for messages	Network may be responsible for individual packets	Network may be responsible for packet sequences
Usually no speed or code conversion	Speed and code conversion	Speed and code conversion	Speed and code conversion
Fixed bandwidth transmission	Dynamic use of bandwidth	Dynamic use of bandwidth	Dynamic use of bandwidth
No overhead bits after call setup	Overhead bits in each message	Overhead bits in each packet	Overhead bits in each packet

As a final point, we mention one common means of making packet-switched networks cost effective, and that is to provide a public connection service. Examples of such networks in the United States are TELENET and TYMNET. The network consists of nodes owned by the network service provider and linked together by leased channels from common carriers such as AT&T. Subscribers pay fees for attaching to the network and for transmitting packets through it. Whereas individual subscribers may not have sufficient traffic to make a packet-switched network economically feasible, the total demand of all subscribers justifies the network. These networks are referred to as value-added networks (VANs) because they take a basic long-haul transmission service (e.g., AT&T) and add value (the packet-switching logic). In some other countries, there is a single national-monopoly network, called a public data network (PDN). Circuit switching is a widely used switching technique for local networks. The types of networks that use this technique are the digital switch and the digital private branch exchange (PBX).

Packet switching is also commonly used for local networking. In many cases, however, there is only a single, direct path from source to destination. Thus, often, there is no routing or switching function in a local network. Packet rather than message switching is used, to facilitate the adoptionof techniques preventing any source from monopolising the medium.

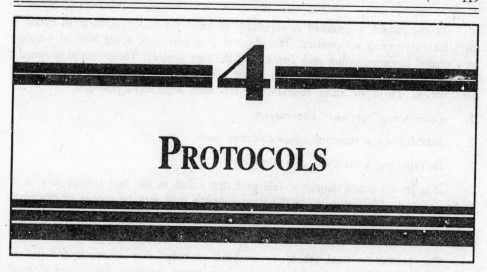

PROTOCOLS

INTRODUCTION

The word **protocol** has been borrowed from common usage to describe computer communication. In brief, the word means something similar in both instances. It describes conventional social behaviour on the one hand and the orderly exchange of information between computing equipment on the other (see Figure 4.1). One common example of the social analogy is the college classroom. If all the students spoke simultaneously, as they felt the urge, the professor would struggle to make sense of the chaos and valuable information would be lost. For this reason, classroom protocol defines a process of raising hands in which students request that they be permitted to speak, resulting in the orderly exchange of data between several different people.

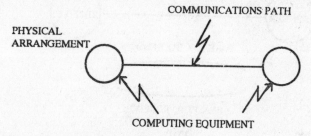

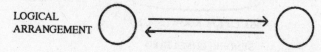

Fig. 4.1 : What is a protocol?

In computing, a protocol is necessary in order for two computers to create a path for exchanging information. The physical path may have some kind of analogy to a digital communication path connecting the two devices. The protocol is merely the logical abstraction of the process which allows two different machines to share information. There are three fundamental functions a protocol performs:

1.   Establishing necessary conventions.

2.   Establishing a standard communication path.

3.   Establishing a standard data element.

It is in the establishment of this path that errors in the data stream may need to be detected. The control of traffic flow over the path may be simple or relatively complex or it may be nonexistant. Finally, conventions are needed for starting and stopping data exchange over the path.

The protocol's final job is to establish standard data elements for use in communication over the path. In this way, the protocol creates a virtual data element to exchange between computing elements. For instance, two computers may wish to swap character streams. Sometimes, they need to deal in a simple data element, such as a letter or memo, while at other times, they deal in entire files. Or systems may be constructed for exchanging a programme or a job between the two machines. Finally, in some applications, the element which needs to be transferred may be as complex as a graphics display.

To grasp the basic elements of a communication protocol, it is necessary to understand a few basic terms. The first is **handshaking**. Handshaking is the controlled two-way transfer of data across an interface. Two devices "shake hands" with each other via a sequence of interlocking steps. In doing this, one unit of information may be transferred (see Figure 4.2).

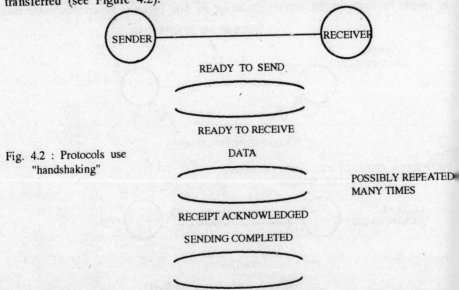

Fig. 4.2 : Protocols use
      "handshaking"

A second fundamental concept is the idea of **standards**, which can give users more flexibility in selecting and interconnecting equipment. Standardisation drastically reduce system development time and maintenance while allowing for evolution as computing needs change.

For two computing elements to communicate, **conventions** must be established. The agreed-on protocol convention determines the nature of the data representation, the format and speed of the data representation over the communication path and any sequence of control messages which are sent. A control message may be the "hello" which initiates the connection, or any other supervisory or control step. In other words, protocol conventions range from describing what a zero (0) and a one (1) look like to the control messages which "start" and "stop" data traffic.

The protocol can also build a standard communication path between computing devices. This entails translating the physical realities of the path between the two devices into a more useful **virtual communication path**; ideally, this is a medium suited to both pieces of equipment.

In establishing this virtual communication path, several items may need to be defined. For example, it may be necessary to have an addressing structure over the path which allows for communication with another device or with several others. A terminal and its connected computer may need to address other computers or printers. It is here that a level of priority may be defined. Messages flowing over the path may need to be sequenced or they may not.

Suppose you have four different kinds of information sources, such as mainframe computers, minicomputers, etc. Perhaps these source devices need to exchange data with three different types of receivers (including terminals, graphics terminals, word processors and personal computers). Unless there is a standard shared protocol, you will need 12 different protocols to permit all the possible connections. This is illustrated in Figure 4.3. Such a system demands that each protocol must serve a special purpose.

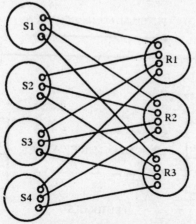

AD HOC COMMUNICATION : 12 DIFFERENT PROTOCOLS
24 PROTOCOL IMPLEMENTATIONS

Fig. 4.3 : Protocols without standards

The preferred solution for interconnecting equipment entails introducing a standard protocol which would require only 7 implementations (4 sources plus 3 receivers). This is shown in Figure 4.4.

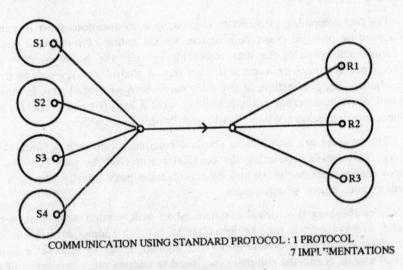

COMMUNICATION USING STANDARD PROTOCOL : 1 PROTOCOL
                                         7 IMPLEMENTATIONS

Fig. 4.4 : A standard protocol

Finally, there is a fundamental difference between protocols and interfaces. **Protocol** is the set of rules for communication between similar processes. **Interface** refers to a set of rules between dissimilar processes. Also, an interface is a physical connection between two devices or processes, while a protocol is a logical concept only. For example, there can be an interface between a host computer and a packet-switching node. In turn, there can be a host-to-node protocol as well as a host-to-host protocol. Figure 4.5 illustrates this concept.

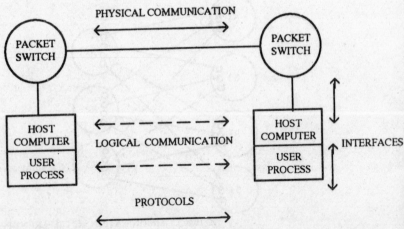

PROTOCOLS : RULES FOR COMMUNICATION BETWEEN SIMILAR PROCESS
INTERFACES RULES FOR COMMUNICATION BETWEEN DISSIMILAR PROCESS

Fig. 4.5 : Protocols and interfaces

LAN PROTOCOLS

Protocols are the formal rules and conventions governing the exchange of information between computers, defined to provide reliable and efficient transfer of information. Without protocols to guide the orderly exchange of data between points in a network, there would be chaos, not communication.

Detailed protocols are required to precisely define the format in which data and system messages are to be sent; describe how a message is addressed; and govern network traffic flow by controlling priority, routing and sequencing of messages. Only when two devices agree on the specific conventions to be used can conversation take place.

Qualitatively, protocols may be said to insure that the system is capable of "useful" work. As part of the task, the protocols must be implemented uniformly throughout the network. For computer-to-computer communication, the protocols are, of necessity, complex.

No protocol works in isolation. Rather, it functions as part of the total set of instructions which determine the operations of a device or network. Each set of protocols is designed to work under different conditions and to satisfy different requirements.

The range of possible methods for passing messages between computers is enormous. The following are specific communication protocols of interest for local area networking:

* Contention:

- Simple contention

- Carrier Sense Multiple Access (CSMA)

- Carrier Sense Multiple Access with Collision Detection
   (CSMA/CD)

-    Carrier Sense Multiple Access with Collision Avoidance
   (CSMA/CA)

* Polling

* Token Passing

PROTOCOL EVALUATION FACTORS

Precise protocol specification could fill several books with complex mathematical formulas; we will avoid mathematics in favour of general functional descriptions. When selecting a protocol, the following factors may influence your choice:

Message length: How long a message may be passed between workstations at any one time?

- Traffic volume: How many messages can be passed?

- Network size constraints: How large can a network using the protocol be?

- Performance: Under what conditions does the protocol perform well? Poorly?

- Overhead: How much traffic capacity is required to pass control messages?

- Access Delay: Does the protocol have built-in delays before a workstation can access the network?

- Station Failures: What happens to the network if a workstation fails?

- Expansion: How easily can the protocol accommodate additional workstations?

CONTENTION

Contention is what happens at a staff meeting when several people start to talk at the same time. In contention protocols, no "policeman" controls usage of the communication channels.

All workstations on a contention network share a common transmission channel. Messages are broadcast on that channel and may be overheard by all attached workstations (see Figure 4.6). A workstation responds only to messages with its address: messages intended for different destinations are ignored. When not responding to a specific message, workstations are passive, simply listening in on the channel rather than being actively involved in transmitting messages.

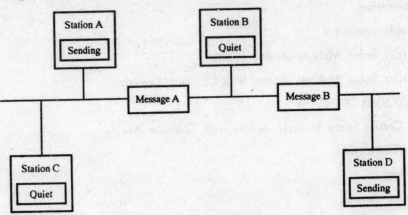

Fig. 4.6 : Contention

Messages to be transmitted are converted to packets and are sent when ready, without verifying the availability of the channel. When transmission of a packet from one workstation overlaps withthat of another, collision occurs. Colliding packets, with their embedded message, are destroyed.

While the basic contention protocol makes no provision for knowing if another message is already underway, it does provide for acknowledging the successful receipt of a packet. If the originating workstation does not receive an acknowledgement, it assumes that transmission was garbled or destroyed. The sending workstation waits a random amount of time and then retransmits the packet. The waiting time must be random or the same messages will collide repeatedly.

In some cases, the receiving workstation receives only part of a packet. The receiver may then return a negative acknowledgement to the originator, requesting retransmission.

More than any other network, the contention network is characterised by **bursty traffic**: the time interval needed for each transmission is short in relation to the interval between transmission.

CONTENTION EVALUATION FACTORS

Smooth functioning of a contention-based network is dependent upon high availability of the transmission media and a low collision rate. The network is characterised by the following:

- **Message length:** Messages are divided into short packets in order to reduce the amount of data that must be rebroadcast after collisions. Normally, the original message is also fairly short.

- **Traffic volume:** Contention protocols are designed for networks with low traffic volume, that is, one with few time. Low traffic volume implies a limited number of attached workstations.

- **Network length constraints:** The longer the network, the greater the chance of collision. Contention networks are limited by the time needed for a signal to travel the length of the transmission media and have an acknowledgement returned (that is, propagation delay).

- **Performance:** Contention networks are most effective under light to medium load. Performance under those conditions is excellent. Under heavy load, a contention network tends to be unstable, with service rapidly degrading.

- **Overhead:** Contention networks have high overhead because of collisions and the need to acknowledge the successful receipt of messages.

- **Access Delay:** Delay on the network is generally moderate to long, depending on traffic. Delay under heavy load can be significantly higher than load alone would seem to dictate.

- **Station Failures:** Because operation of the network is not dependent on the presence or absence of any one workstation, failure of a workstation inconveniences only its users. Rarely does failure of a single station disrupt service on the whole network.

- **Expansion:** Addition of new workstations is relatively easy because to be included in the network, the workstation simply must recognise its own unique address. Expansion may be achieved with minimal disruption of the network.

Refinements on contention procedures are used by many of the current micro computer local networks. These refinements are: Carrier Sense Multiple Access (CSMA) in Figure 4.7; Carrier Sense Multiple Access with Collision Detection (CSMA/CD); and Carrier Sense Multiple Access with Collision Avoidance (CSMA/CA).

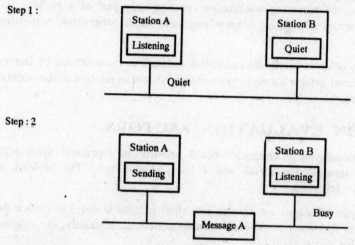

Fig. 4.7 : CSMA

Each will be discussed in separate sections. For all practical purposes, characteristics of these refinements are identical to the characteristics of simple contention.

CARRIER SENSE MULTIPLE ACCESS

Carrier Sense Multiple Access (CSMA) is a polite staff meeting, with colleagues beginning to talk only when no one else is talking. As in simple contention, members of the network share a single communication channel (see Figure 4.7).

Before information is sent, the workstation "listens" - usually on a secondary frequency - to sense whether any other workstation is using the primary transmission channel (the "carrier"). Only when the line is clear will the workstation transmit.

If a workstation becomes ready to transmit while another workstation is active, it detects the signal passing on the cable and does not send its message until the current transmission is complete. For microcomputer networks the waiting station has two options, depending on system design:

1. It can continually sense the channel while waiting for the busy signal to cease and then transmit immediately. This is called **persistent carrier sense**, as the terminal actively waits to seize the channel as soon as it becomes free. If other workstations are equally persistent, a collision may occur immediately after the busy signal ceases.

2. Alternatively, if the channel is sensed busy, the terminal reschedules its

transmission for a later time, using a random delay, and tries again **nonpersistent carrier sense**. Fewer collisions occur, resulting in higher throughput. However, delays may be slightly longer, at least in networks with low channel utilisation.

In addition to transmitting its message on the main channel, the active workstation broadcasts a carrier-sense signal on the secondary channel to inform other workstations that the line is busy.

After transmitting, the workstation waits for an acknowledgement, indicating that transmission was successful. If no acknowledgement is received or if a negative acknowledgement (indicating unsuccessful transmission) is received, the workstation assumes a collision has occurred. The workstation then waits a random amount of time before starting the process again.

In a CSMA network, collision between transmitting workstations is still inevitable. A "ready" signal on the secondary channel does not necessarily mean that the network is free of other traffic. Because of the length of time required for a signal to travel the channel (propagation delay), two or more workstations may sense an idle line simultaneously, and thus both attempt to transmit at the same time. If the propagation delay is short, the information the workstation hears by monitoring the channel is sufficiently current to permit a useful decision. The probability of success will be significantly higher than in simple contention. If, however, the information is old, that is, the propagation delay is long, CSMA offers only slight improvement over plain contention.

The secondary channel which carries the busy tone does require some bandwidth. This bandwidth is generally minimal. There is a brief delay involved in sensing the busy signal.

CARRIER SENSE MULTIPLE ACCESS WITH COLLISION DETECTION

Carrier Sense Multiple Access with Collision Detection (CSMA/CD) provides the proper etiquette for the times when polite colleagues inadvertently start talking at the same instant. At our theoretical staff meeting, both speakers would stop and wait for the other to continue. The one who resumes first would have the floor.

In CSMA/CD, in addition to sensing whether the transmission channel is in use before beginning to transmit, workstations monitor the link during transmission. When a collision is detected, transmission is halted.

As in the other contention-based protocols, the message is retransmitted after a brief interval. For CSMA/CD, the interval may be either random or pre-defined as a unique period for each workstation. Because of the ability to listen before and during transmission, the number of collisions is relatively low. Successive collisions between the same workstations is rare. Additionally, since transmission ceases as soon as a collision is detected, less delay occurs.

CARRIER SENSE MULTIPLE ACCESS WITH COLLISION AVOIDANCE

Carrier Sense Multiple Access with Collision Avoidance (CSMA/CA) is analogous to several people wishing to contribute information at a meeting, and therefore all raising their hands at the same time. At the meeting, the moderator selects the next speaker. In CSMA/CA, the protocol determines who speaks next.

A station with a message to transmit monitors the medium and waits for the line to be available. When the channel is clear, the workstation signals its intention to broadcast. If multiple workstations are waiting, the order of precedence is determined by a pre-established table.

Just as human meetings tend to be biased in favour of allowing the main speaker or resident expert the greatest opportunity to talk, most CSMA/CA schemes are biased in favour of the lower-numbered workstations. That is, after any transmission, the workstation designated as first by the table has the right to transmit. If it has no message to send, or if it fails to transmit within a pre-defined time for any reason, the next workstation has the chance, and so on.

Once any workstation transmits, the network begins again at the top of the list of precedence. Refinements are possible. Some implementations are designed to avoid having the network dominated by any one workstation: a station which has just transmitted may not be allowed to transmit again until all other stations have had an opportunity.

To accommodate multimessage dialogue, the workstation receiving a message may have the first right to transmit. If it does reply, the original sender would again have a chance. Unfortunately, two workstations may seize the medium, with one station sending messages and the other replying.

In the case when no workstation has a message to transmit, the network may reinitialise, starting again with the first workstation. In other cases, the network may enter a free-for-all period, in which the first workstation to transmit gains the channel. During the contention period, collisions are allowed.

POLLING

Polling (see Figure 4.8) involves the central control of all workstations in a network. The central, or primary, workstation acts like a teacher going down the rows of the classroom asking each student for homework. When one student has answered, the next is given a chance to respond.

A polling network contains two classes of workstations, the primary workstation (also termed the central controller or server), and the multiple secondary workstations connected to it. A buffer that can temporarily store messages is associated with each secondary workstation. When a workstation has information to transmit, the data is passed to the buffer. The message is held until the workstation is polled by the central controller.

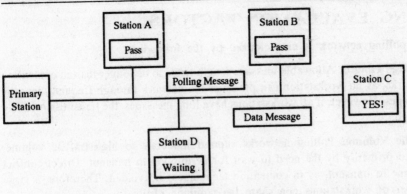

Fig. 4.8 : Polling

The primary workstation queries each secondary in turn to determine if it has a message to transmit. If the answer is affirmative, the workstation is either given permission to transmit immediately or assigned a transmission time. The amount of time a workstation may have in which to transmit once channel access is gained is determined by system parameters.

If the workstation does not have data to transmit, it still must respond with a short control message. Rather than returning a message to the primary, some networks allow a polled workstation with no data to send to pass the polling signal to the next secondary station.

Each time a workstation is polled, the primary workstation must wait for a response to be returned. After a workstation responds, the next station is polled. The primary workstation determines which workstation has access to the network at any one time.

There are two possibilities for the path of a message from source to destination workstation:

1.   All messages may be required to pass to the central workstation, which routes them to their destinations.

2.   Messages may be sent directly from the originator to their destinations.

In either case, communication between workstations is possible only under the direction of the polling computer.

Variations on polling tend to be concerned with how often workstations are queried. The basic protocol calls for all stations to have equal opportunity to broadcast. This is not always so. In some networks, workstations considered to be very active or to have priority may be polled several times within a single cycle. In other cases, an inactive device may not be polled every cycle. A third alternative is that the frequency with which individual workstations are polled may be varied to reflect their current activity level.

Polling techniques can be said to maintain a tighter control over the network than do contention-based protocols.

POLLING EVALUATION FACTORS

The polling network is characterised by the following:

Message Length: Allowable message length tends to be longer than in contention networks, as no workstation can pre-empt the network through frequent, lengthy messages. However, if all workstations have long messages, the transmission delay is high.

Traffic Volume: Polling networks support moderate to high trafffic volume, limited primarily by the need to wait for permission to transmit. Direct conflict for time to transmit, as in contention techniques, is avoided. Therefore, a large number of workstations can share the common channel.

Network Length Constraints: The distance between workstations and the overall length of the network is limited by the transmission medium, rather than by the polling protocol. As in any network, the greater the length, the longer the time required for messages to travel between sending and receiving stations.

Performance: Polling networks perform best under moderate load. Under heavy load, transmission delays may become unacceptably long. Polling is inefficient for networks with light loads. In the extreme case, most network traffic may be comprised of polling signals and negative acknowledgements, rather than actual messages.

Overhead: Administrative overhead on a polling network is high. The query and response use a measurable part of the total network capacity. Furthermore, in many polling networks, the server unit cannot be used as a workstation.

Access Delay: Delays in most polling networks are relatively long. In most implementations, a workstation is polled only once each cycle. If the network is very large, delay may be unacceptably long.

Station Failures: Little or no disruption of the network is caused by a failed secondary workstation. The inactive workstation is "invisible" to the network; that is, it simply fails to respond when polled. However, if the central workstation fails, all communication on the network ceases.

Expansion: In order for the network to be expanded, the primary workstation must be informed and the order of polling revised to reflect the addition. Therefore, expansion is more complex than expansion of a contention network.

TOKEN PASSING

Token passing can be seen as the children's game of hot potato in reverse. Like the players, the network continuously circulates a special bit pattern known as a token. Rather than being out if you are holding the object being passed, holding the token confers the right to communicate. Only the workstation holding the token can put a message onto the network. Control of the network is decentralised.

Each token contains network information, comprising of a header, a data field and a trailer (see Figure 4.9).

Empty Token :

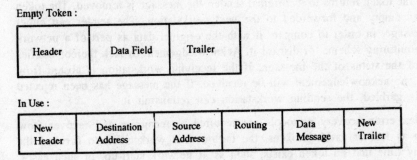

Header	Data Field	Trailer

In Use :

New Header	Destination Address	Source Address	Routing	Data Message	New Trailer

Fig. 4.9 : Token

When a workstation that wants to transmit receives an empty token, it inserts routing information, inserts the data and sends the token on a complete circuit of the network.

The workstation holding the token may transmit messages up to a specified maximum length. If it does not have anything to communicate, it passes the token to the next station in the network. Figure 4.10 illustrates token passing.

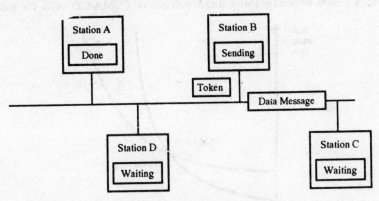

Fig. 4.10 : Token Passing

In most token passing networks, the token passes from one workstation to the one immediately adjacent. However, the token may pass from workstation to workstation in a sequence established at network implementation time, without requiring nodes to be physically adjacent. In such implementations the workstation knows the address of the next workstation to receive the token, as well as its own address.

All the workstations on the network read the address in an occupied token; if it is for a different workstation, it is passed on unchanged and unread. At the destination, the receiving workstation reads the message, marks the token as copied or rejected, and continues passing it. Only the workstation which has placed a particular message onto the network may remove that message. If a workstation is disassociated from the network, it simply does not read the message.

When the token returns to its original sender, the message is removed. The token is marked as empty and forwarded to the next workstation. The sender can either save the message, in order to compare it with the original data as part of a network reliability monitoring scheme, or discard it. Acknowledgement or lack thereof notifies the sender of the status of the message. If the receiving workstation is absent from the network, no acknowledgement will be received. If the message has been rejected because it is garbled, the sending workstation can retransmit it.

Complex error-recovery protocols are required to recognise and recover from events, such as lost or garbled tokens, the failure of a workstation to forward the token; or any time that no token exists, such as at network start-up. In such cases, a method of generating a token and beginning to circulate it must be specified. Controlled contention or a priority access scheme based on workstation address may be used to re-establish token ownership.

Token passing ensures relatively tight control over the network. The elimination of inefficiencies caused by collisions between contending units is a major advantage for users.

Figure 4.11 gives comparative performance of token rings with that of CSMA/CD. Table 4.1 lists advantages and disadvantages of CSMA/CD vis-a-vis token bus.

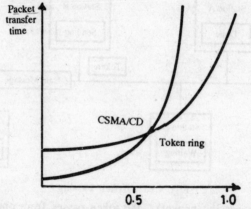

Fig. 4.11 : Performance of token rings and CSMA/CD

TABLE 4.1 : CSMA/CD versus Token Bus

Advantages	Disadvantages
CSMA/CD	
Simple algorithm	Collision detection requirement
Widely used	Fault diagnosis problems
Fair access	Minimum packet size
Good performance at low to medium load	Poor performance under very heavy load

Biased to long transmissions

Token Bus

Excellent throughput performance	Complex algorithm
Tolerates large dynamic range	Unproven technology
Regulated access	

TOKEN PASSING EVALUATION FACTORS

- **Message Length:** Token passing can accommodate moderate to long messages. Since messages are embedded within the token, multiple types of data may be handled.

- **Traffic Volume:** Traffic on a token passing network can be quite high. Because each workstation may broadcast a single message on each turn, availability of the network is equitable. There is little possibility that any one workstation will claim more than its fair share of network capacity.

- **Network Length Constraints:** Token passing networks are limited primarily by the transmission medium; not by the protocol.

- **Performance:** Token passing networks perform well under most conditions. Given a moderate to high traffic load when the network is in almost constant use, performance is excellent.

- **Overhead:** Administrative overhead on token networks is comparatively high.

- **Access Delay:** Under any given volume of traffic, line delays on the token network tend to be constant and predictable. Heavy traffic creates a moderate delay. Under moderate traffic conditions, delay is short.

- **Station Failure:** In older token rings, failure of any one workstation blocked all transmission. Recently developed token rings have eliminated this problem.

- **Expansion:** Expanding a token passing network is a complex process which may involve re-wiring the network to include the new workstations and identifying a new token circulation pattern. During expansion, service on the network may be disrupted for extended periods.

5
NETWORK ARCHITECTURE
AND STANDARDS

INTRODUCTION

Part of the power of local area networks is their ability to support a wide variety of devices. Supporting a wide variety of devices, however, can present substantial compatibility problems. For varying devices to be linked together, the hardware and software of these devices need to be compatible, or else complex interfaces have to be built for meaningful communication to take place. To facilitate this complexity, network architectures are being developed that allow complex networks to be built using a variety of equipment.

WHAT IS NETWORK ARCHITECTURE?

The term most frequently used for the overall design of a network is architecture. The goal of architecture is to achieve a high level of performance at a minimal cost. Although local area networks cannot be classified solely by architecture, the specific combination of elements determine the characteristics of a particular LAN. Table 5.1 depicts the high level objectives of network architecture.

TABLE 5.1 : High-level objectives of network architectures

* Connectivity. Permit diverse hardware and software products to be connected to form a unified networking system.

* Modularity. Permit the use of a relatively small set of massproduced general-purpose building blocks in a wide diversity of network devices.

* Ease of Implementation. Provide a general solution to network communication that can be easily installed in a variety of configurations to meet the needs of all types of users.

* Ease of Use. Provide communication facilities to network users in a way that frees them from concerns about or knowledge of network structure or implementation.

* Reliability. Provide appropriate error detection and correction facilities.

* Ease of Modification. Permit the network to evolve and be easily modified as user needs change or new technologies become available.

Specific protocols tend to be associated with specific topologies to the point that topology is often considered the means of implementing the communication protocol. The control strategy used by a network determines the number and type of connected workstations, the nature of interactions between workstations and the particular transmission link used.

No one architecture is innately superior to another: too many variables affect each individual situation. The most that can be said is that given a specific set of circumstances one network design seems to accommodate more of the user's requirements than another. Ultimately, the architecture of a network is determined by the location of the workstations to be connected, the demands of the information being transmitted, the available resources and the nature of the organisation creating the network.

Network architecture is a fancy term for the way that networking products are constructed. Networking hardware and software is implemented on systems via a mechanism called network or communication architecture. Communication architecture is the "layering" of software based upon the functionality of each layer. It is very similar to an organisation chart at a corporation. At the lowest level of the protocol layers lies the data link access, the software used to talk directly to the hardware. This is usually a cryptic interface and is difficult to implement and maintain. At the next level would be some sort of communication line handler whose job would be to keep messages sorted out and manage connection creation and destruction between machines. The next layer up would be a session control mechanism responsible for the overall message flow control and ensuring that the communication "session" between systems goes smoothly. The remainder of the upward layers is dedicated to direct user programme interaction for specific functions. For example, one layer would be used for communication with programmes desiring remote file access and manipulation, another with programme-to-programme communication, etc. Very few communication architectures do not use layered architectures, and these are somewhat antiquated. The benefits of the layered approach are many, but the most significant one is the ability to change a layer's capabilities without significantly modifying the entire architecture. This feature alone makes a layered network architecture very attractive for companies desiring inter-and intra-systems communication capability.

STANDARDS

To form a viable network, all the diverse elements - equipment, topology, communication links, protocols - must be assembled into a unified system. While the actual design of each component of the communication system can and does vary depending on the specific system involved, no single component can be selected or designed in isolation. Parts of the system must be balanced for effective communication to occur. If any one component does not interact successfully with the others or is absent, communication cannot occur.

Thousands of possible viable LAN combinations exist. Given that creative engineers love to experiment (inherent in all new technologies is an almost overwhelming desire to play, to see how many different things can be done), how do you coordinate all the pieces?

More importantly, how do you insure that a local area network is able to interconnect diverse types of equipment from multiple sources when there is no common language that computers can use to communicate with each other?

Standards that bring order to the design process are required. Currently, the work of two organisations is relevant to local area networks. They are the International

MHS CCITT X,400	MOTIS ISO 10021	DIRECTORY CCITT X.500 ISO 9594	FTAM ISO 8571	CMISE ISO 9595 (SERVICE) ISO 9596 (PROTOCOL)	DTP ISO 10026	JTM ISO 8831 ISO 8832 (PROTOCOL)	VT ISO 9040 (SERVICE) (PROTOCOL)	APPLICATION LAYER
RTSE CCITT X.226 ISO 9066		ROSE CCITT X.229 ISO 9072			CCR ISO 9804 (SERVICE) ISO 9805 (PROTOCOL)			
ACSE CCITT X.227 ISO 8649 (SERVICE) ISO 8850 (PROTOCL)								
CCITT X.226 ISO 8822 (SERVICE) ISO 8823 (PROTOCOL-CONNECTION MODE) ISO 9576 (PROTOCOL-CONNECTIONLESS MODE)				ASN.1 CCITT X.208 (LANGUAGE) CCITT X.209 (BASIC ENCODING RULES) ISO 8324 (LANGUAGE) ISO 8825 (BASIC ENCODING RULES0				PRESENTATION LAYER
CCITT X.225 ISO 8327 (SERVICE) ISO 8327 (PROTOCOL-CONNECTION MODE) ISO 9548 (PROTOCOL-CONNECTIONLES MODE)								SESSION LAYER
CCITT X.224 ISO 8072 (SERVICE) ISO 8073 (PROTOCOL-CONNECTION MODE) ISO 8802 (PROTOCOL-CONNECTIONLESS MOE)								TRANSPORT LAYER
INTERNETWORK PROTOCOL ISO 8473 (CONNECTIONLESS MODE)			PACKET LEVEL PROTOCOL CCITT X.25 (CONNECTION MODE) ISO 8208			CCITT Q.931		NETWORK LAYER
LOGICL LINK CONTROL ISO 8802.2					CCITT X.25 LAPB ISO 7776	CCITT LAPD Q.921		DATA LINK LAYER
CSMA/CD ISO 8802.3	TOKEN BUS ISO 8802.4	TOKEN RING ISO 88022.5	SLOTTED ISO ISO 8802.7	FDDI 9314	CCITT X.21/V.24	CCITT 1.430/1.431		PHYSICAL LAYER
LOCAL AREA NETWORKING						WIDE AREA NETWORKING		

Fig. 5.1 : Some of the standards contained within the OSI seven layers

Standards Organisation (ISO) and the Institute of Electrical and Electronic Engineers' (IEEE) Project 802 committee. Figure 5.1 gives some of the standards contained within the OSI seven layers. Figure 5.2 gives IEEE LAN standards.

802.1 Internetworking			
802.2 Logical link control			
802.3 Medium access	802.3 Medium access	802.5 Medium access	802.6 Medium access
802.3 Physical	802.4 Physical	802.5 Physical	802.6 Physical

Fig. 5.2 : IEEE LAN standards

The Importance of Standards

Local area network standards are following the same path as their wide area network counterparts. Increased activity in the area of standards has resulted from a recognition that computer communication is a field so complex that without rationalisation progress will be severely impeded. There are many computer equipment and system suppliers offering a plethora of communication protocols and conventions, and agreement among them on standardisation would clearly be impossible without the existence of central standards bodies, both national and international.

Users typically have a variety of computing equipment including personal computers, word processors, minicomputers and mainframe data processing systems. Only in rare cases is it possible to interconnect these pieces of equipment without using protocol conversion devices, and even then compatibility is not fully guaranteed. Consumer networks inevitably face difficulties unless there is prior agreement on limiting the choice of equipment to be used. The corporate network can often rely on a strategy to reduce the number of options which may occur and hence the cost of circumventing inconsistencies.

In this context local area networks are particularly at risk, given their intended role in interconnecting a variety of devices in many cases. Justification for purchasing a LAN or developing a new application using a LAN may depend on smooth integration with existing systems and on the ease with which new systems can be added. Particularly within a small geographical area, information can be transported physically and unless a cheap and efficient replacement for such services can be demonstrated, organisations are unlikely to change their practices. A particular example of this difficulty would be the case of two computers located in the same premises where information is exchanged using tape transfer by messenger or operator. In this case only a link offering high speed and integrity would be contemplated as an alternative. A second example concerns the use of stand-alone word processors. Typically, documents would be transferred between these machines by means of diskette exchange, so here again an electronic link would have to offer the advantages of improved speed and reliability before a capital outlay would be authorised.

At a time when it has been accepted that voice communication is a commodity and, in fact, an essential element of business life, on which large capital sums are frequently expended, it is unfortunate that the same cannot be said of electronic data and text communication. Even the physical connection of a simple microcomputer to the public telephone network can be a task requiring a great deal of effort. Even once the correct interface details have been ascertained, it is not unusual to find that the software used is incompatible with that used in the remote system.

In view of such difficulties there has been an enormous increase in the interest shown by both users and manufacturers in the importance of standards in the last few years.

The Standards Bodies

The organisations which contribute to the standards-making process are usually referred to as the standards bodies. This is an area where until recently even industry observers were confused by both the numbers of 'standards' organisations, and the mechanisms used to formulate and accept standards. Table 5.2 lists a number of acronyms, of the most important of these organisations, which may be familiar to readers of computer and trade journals.

TABLE 5.2 : Main standards bodies

ISO	International Standards Organisation

National standards bodies (member of ISO)

ANSI	American National Standards Institute
BSI	British Standards Institution
DIN	Deutsches Institut fur Normung eV (West German Standards Institute)
AFNOR	Asssociation Francaise de Normalisation (French Standards Institute)
UNI	Ente Naxionale Italiano di Unificazione (Italian Standards Institute)
JISC	Japanese Industrial Strandards Committee
SCC	Standards Council of Canada

Telecommunications standards

ITU	International Telecommunication Union
CCITT	International Telegraph and Telephone Consultative Committee (Comite Consultatif International Telegrapiue et Telephonique)

Other standards-making bodies

ECMA	European Computer Manufacturers Association
IEEE	Institute of Electrical and Electronics Engineers (USA)
NBS	National Bureau of Standards (USA)
IEC	International Electrotechnical Commission
IFIP	International Federation for Information Processing

THE OPEN SYSTEMS INTERCONNECTION MODEL

There was a time when there was no such thing as a network architecture. Companies implemented rather rude, crude and socially unacceptable software and hardware communication solutions without any thought as to layering or to the implementation of an architecture. The idea of layering really took off with the introduction of an international standard called the Open Systems Interconnection (OSI) model by the International Standards Organisation (ISO) in 1982 (International Standard 7498).

In 1978, the ISO Technical Committee 97 (this committee handles standardisation of information technology) started subcommittee number 16 (TC97/SC16) to develop an architecture and reference model that would serve as the foundation for future standards activities. From 1978 onwards, they have worked very hard at providing a flexible, reasonable communication architecture that could be implemented on a variety of systems and provide inter- and intra- systems communication capabilities in a variety of environments. Oddly enough, TC97/SC16 has not done most of the work on defining the protocols for each layer of the architecture; other ISO committees have done this, using the model specified by TC97/SC16. All protocols for all layers have not been defined yet, but the model still is highly useful in the definition of how a communication architecture is defined.

In 1978 the International Standards Organisation (ISO) proposed a broad model for mainframe wide area network communication, which they titled "The Reference Model of Open Systems Interconnection".

Open Systems Interconnection refers to the exchange of information among terminal devices, computers, people, networks and processes. The systems are open to one another by virtue of their mutual use of the standards developed from the original reference model. Openness does not imply any particular implementation, technology or interconnection means.

The Open System Interconnection Reference Model is not, by itself, a standard, nor is it a literal description of computer communication. While it defines where to perform tasks, it does not detail how to perform them. Individual services and protocols are not specified. Within the model, communication functions are addressed from the perspective of computer-to-communication network interconnection.

The Reference Model is intended to provide a common basis for coordinating the development of standards aimed at systems interconnection, while allowing existing standards to be placed in perspective within a common framework.

OSI LAYERS

As shown in the Table 5.3, each system is viewed as being composed of an ordered set of subsystems or layers. The layers of the Reference Model are separated by interfaces. Adjacent layers communicate through their common interface. Table 5.4 lists some of the well-known layers.

TABLE 5.3 : The OSI Layers

Layer	Definition
1. Physical	Concerned with transmission of unstructured bit stream over physical link : involves such parameters as signal voltage swing and bit duration; deals with the mechancial, electrical, and procedural characteristics to establish, maintain, and deactivate the physical link (RS-232-C, RS-449, X.21)
2. Data link	Provides for the reliable transfer of data across the physical link; sends blocks of data (frames) with the necessary synchronization, error control, and flow control (HDLC, SDLC, BiSync)
3. Network	Provides upper layers with independence from the data transmission and switching technologies used to connect systems; responsible for establishing, maintaining, and terminating connections (X.25, layer 3)
4. Transport	Provides reliable, transparent transfer of data between and points; provides end-to-end errror recovery and flow control
5. Session	Provides the control structure for communicaiton between applications; establishes, manages, and terminates connections (sessions) between cooperating applications
6. Presentation	Performs generally useful transformations on data to provide a standardized application interface and to provide common communications services; examples: encryption, text compression, reformatting
7. Application	Provides services to the users of the OSI environment; examples: transaction server, file transfer protocol, network management

TABLE 5.4 : Some Well-known Layers

OSI	CCITT	ISO	DOD	IEEE 802	ANS X3T9.5
7. Application		Various	Various		
6. Presentation					
5. Session		Session			
4. Transport		Transport (TP)	TCP		
3. Network	X.25	Internet	IP		

		Sublayer	
		Logical link control	
2.	Link	LAP-B	Data link
		Medium access control	Physical
1.	Physical	X.21	Physical

Each layer in the structure provides a defined set of services for the layer above and requests specific services from the layer below. Layers are defined by function: protocols are defined to control the processes managed by each layer. Relationships between layers and the information that must be passed between layers are identified.

Interfaces are located where one layer interacts with another and serve to isolate one layer from the next. Because the mechanisms and functions of the layers can be expected to change as technology develops, the functions of the interfaces are precisely defined, but the format of the data interchanges between layers is not. This permits the characteristics of a layer to change without affecting the rest of the model.

The arrangement of the layers begins with the most concrete - the physical layer, which defines cables - to the abstract - the application layer which defines user interfaces.

Layers one through four are considered system- independent. Protocols associated with these layers are relevant to all systems. Layers five, six and seven are considered system - dependent. Protocols must be defined individually for each different device. Some experts consider the first four layers to specify the communication functions: the remaining, higher, layers specify data processing functions.

To understand the OSI a little better, let us examine what each layer does. Figure 5.3 gives a diagram of the OSI model. You will notice that the model has basically

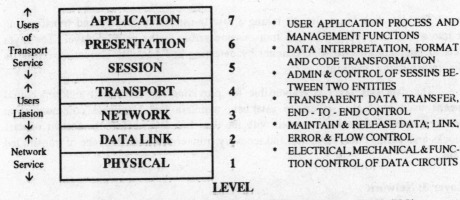

Fig. 5.3 : THE INTERNATIONAL STANDARDS ORGANISATION (ISO)
OPEN SYSTEM INTERCONNECT (OSI)
MODEL A LAYERED APPROACH TO NETWORK ARCHITECTURE

seven tiers, stacked one upon the other, that reflects a certain function at each layer. User data comes in to the top layer (layer seven) and travels through the various layers of protocols until it finally goes out over the transmission medium (hardware). It then travels to the destination node and begins its travel up the layers of protocols on the remote system until it reaches the destination programme on the remote system. This same ordeal happens on all communicating systems for the duration of communication between nodes.

The following paragraphs define the functionality of each layer of the OSI model:

Layer 1: Physical

This is the touch-and-feel layer. The physical layer provides for the transparent transmission of bit streams from one physical entity to another (or many, as in the case of datagram oriented services such as Ethernet).

The Physical Layer is concerned with transmitting raw data over a channel. It defines the mechanical, electrical, functionaland procedural characteristics necessary to establish, maintainand disconnect the physical connection. The layer is designed to accommodate a variety of physical media and differing control procedures.

Aspects of the network affected by physical layer protocols include cables and connectors; electrical signalling methods; and computer and data communication equipment interfaces. Design problems focus on making sure that when one device sends a one, it is received at the destination as a one, not a zero. Typical issues are how many microseconds a bit occupies; how many volts are used to represent a one and how many for a zero; how many pins the network connector has and what each pin is used for; and whether or not transmission may proceed simultaneously in both directions.

Layer 2: Data Link

The Data Link layer handles the transfer of data between the ends of a physical link.

The data link layer aims at taking a raw transmission facility and transforming it into a line that appears free of transmission errors to the network layer. The layer acts to maintain an error-free channel by detecting and possibly correcting errors on the transmission medium.

The data link layer is responsible for providing the functional and procedural means used by higher layers to establish, maintain and terminate communication between users. Protocols associated with the data link layer affect the format of data blocks andaddress code; detection and recovery from errors; and sequence of transmitted data.

Layer 3: Network

The Network layer handles the routing and switching of information to establish a connection for the transparent delivery of data.

The Network Layer is concerned with the transmission of data through the network. Within the network layer, data from the transport layer is accepted, converted to packet, and routed towards the destination. In some sources, this is called the communication subnet layer because it is sub-system/segment of the network as a whole.

The network layer provides the means to establish, maintain and terminate network connections between systems, and it controls routing of packets. Associated protocols cover administration and management of data; delivery of status messages; regulation of traffic flow; and the division of labour between the Network Interface Units and the host, in particular who should ensure that all packets are correctly received at their destinations.

Layer 4: Transport

The Transport layer provides for error-free delivery of data and also acts as the control area for quality of service requirements for the selected data service.

The Transport Layer provides for the transparent transfer of data between users from source system to destination systems; that is, it manages the end-to-end data flow. Its basic function is to accept data from the session layer, split it up into messages if necessary, and pass these to the network layer. It must ensure that all the pieces arrive correctly at the other end.

Layer 4 represents the vaguely defined boundary between data communication and data processing. Transport layer protocols control distribution of messages, data integrity, loss or duplicate message prevention and proper addressing of user equipment.

Layer 5: Session

Session Layer provides the coordination of communicating processes, between nodes ("virtual" connectivity).

The Session Layer establishes a connection between users: in effect, it provides the user's interface into the network. The user must negotiate with this layer to establish a connection with a process on another machine. Once that connection has been made, the session layer synchronises the dialoge and manages the data exchange; that is, it manages the session, as the dialoge between users generally is called. Technically, a session is a dialogue between two presentation layer processes.

The session layer takes the communication service of the transport layer and adds application-oriented functions. Layer 5 protocols include rules for establishing and ending connections; verifying that proper communication is occurring; and interfacing the network to the operating system.

Layer 6: Presentation

The Presentation layer provides for any format, translation or code conversion necessary to put the data into an intelligible format.

The Presentation Layer transforms information from machine format into that understandable by user. It performs functions that are requested sufficiently often to warrant finding a general solution for them, rather than letting each user solve the problem.

One major function is translation - between differing file formats, between different terminal formats and between different codes (ASCII to EBCDIC, for instance). The presentation layer is designed to represent information to communicating application-processes in a way that preserves the meaning while resolving syntax differences. Typical presentation layer services include data translation, conversion of file formats and encryption.

Layer 7: Application

The Application layer allows the end application to communicate with the communication architecture by providing the appropriate communication service(s) to the application.

The Application layer provides the user with a window into the system. All exchange of information between the user and the network occurs through this layer. Application services are the only Reference Model services directly comprehensible to users.

Layer 7 protocols are responsible for user and application programme support such as passwords, resource sharing, file transfer and network management.

At each layer, there may be one or more protocols (in the case of layer 2 and above) or communication media (in the case of layer 1) that communicate with a peer protocol or media on the complementary node(s). What this means is that, at any level, there can be more than one way to get data to and from the node; the only requirement is that there be the same peer at the destination node that understands what is sent.

At first this may all seem a bit chaotic and it is - to an extent. It is the job of the communicationarchitect and software/hardware engineers to put the right functionality in the right spots to keep throughput of the network high and the overhead of sending data back and forth low. If you consider each layer to have its own protocol or filter, it is somewhat easier to understand. We can look at communication architectures like a glorified air purifier system. One programme takes a packet of pure air and starts sending it to another programme on a remote node. To insure its purity, each layer of the communication architecture puts a special container around the pure packet of air so that it will not get contaminated on the way. This means that by the time the packet of pure air is out the node, it basically has 6 containers around it (when it is travelling, it is in container 1, the physical layer). When the packet reaches its destination, it travels up the layers, with each protocol removing the container that it knows how to remove, inspecting for damage, and if no damage is present, sending it up the next layer. If a layer finds damage, the packet is thrown away (it is contaminated) and the source node is requested to send another pure packet of air (we cannot have bad air getting to our pure air environment). This is the typical path that most data take when using communication architectures and the layered approach.

To compound misery, communication architectures do much more than send data. Nodes (systems) need to know which nodes are available for access, which services (layers) are active, and in some nodes, if routing is necessary. To do this, many communication architectures keep a database of active nodes, known nodes (nodes the system knows about but that may not necessarily be up and running or available) and nodes that are down.

OPERATION OF THE OSI MODEL IN A NETWORK

To a user, communication appears to be taking place directly between systems, with messages going directly to the destination. Communication is perceived as peer-to-peer, that is, as between corresponding layers in a connected system. Figure 5.4 gives the user's view of communication through the ISO layers. Figure 5.5 gives the system's view of communication through the ISO layers.

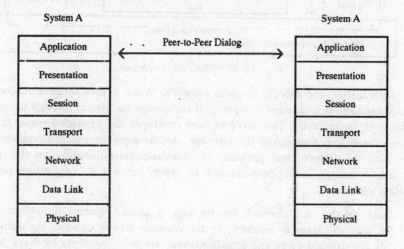

Fig. 5.4 : The User's View of Communications Through the ISO Layers

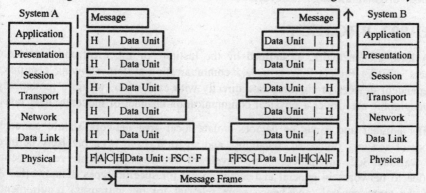

Each layer manipulates or changes the message in soem way : In System A, information is added. In System B, the added information is stripped away until the original message is revealed.

H   Message header , added by a layer for its counterpart   F   Flag   C   Control
Data Unit Original message, plus headers   A   Address   F S C

Fig. 5.5 a : The System's View of Communications Through the ISO Layers

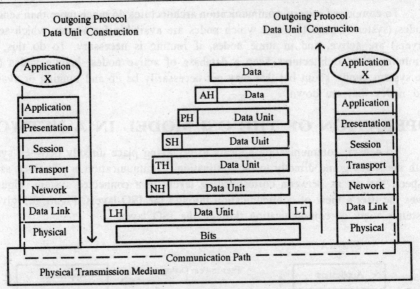

Fig. 5.5 b : The OSI Environment

In actuality, the process is quite complex. When a user sends a message, the original message is embedded in a protocol and passed downward through the interface to the next lower layer. This layer in turn envelopes the expanded message within its protocol before forwarding the message. As the message passes downward, each layer adds its protocol and performs its translation/transformation on the message received. A message must pass through all layers between its origination point and the data channel.

Once on the data channel, the message is passed upward through the layers until the requisite layer is reached. As the message moves upward, the surrounding protocols are stripped away and transformations are reversed, layer by layer, until the embedded, original message is revealed.

IEEE 802 PROJECT

A local area network, as defined by the Institute of Electrical and Electronic Engineers' (IEEE) Project 802, is a data communication system allowing a number of independent devices to communicate directly with each other, within a moderately sized geographic area, over a physical communication channel of moderate data rates.

The number and kinds of devices a data local area network should connect, the types of services supported, reliability, and so forth, have been precisely defined in the various 802 committees. Two levels of requirements exist: requirements applicable to networks in general and requirements for specific types of networks. A few of the more general (and hence more relevant for our purposes) requirements have been summarised below. This list is not of all the general requirements, however nor even of all the relevant requirements.

- **Size:** One LAN should support at least 200 devices and should be able to span at least 2 kilometers. LANs must be capable of being linked to provide service over a greater area.

- **Transmission rate:** Data shall be transmitted through the network at a rate between 1 Megabit per second and 20 Megabits per second.

- **Data communication functions:** The data communication supported should include, but are not restricted to:file transfer and transaction processing; file and database access; terminal support ("dumb" terminals, "smart" terminals, high-speed graphics terminals, etc).; electronic mail; and voicegrams.

- **Attached devices:** Devices interconnected by the LAN should include computers and terminals; mass storage devices; printers, plotters, network and site monitoring and control equipment; bridges and gateways to other networks; telephones; video cameras and monitors; photocopiers; facsimile transceivers.

- **Services:** The LAN should allow a variety of network processes to coexist.

- **Expandability:** Adding or removing devices must be easy. Changes should cause minimal disruption, defined as a transient fault lasting no more than one second.

- **Resource sharing:** When devices need to share LAN facilities, especially the bandwidth of the bus, this sharing must be fair to all devices, even in overload conditions.

- **Reliability:** The LAN should be highly reliable. No more than one packet per year may contain an undetected error.

Very early in the process of defining a LAN and developing standards, the members of the 802 project recognised that no single technology would satisfy all requirements. Specific applications, with their differing priorities, demand different technologies. Therefore, the 802 project divided into several different committees, listed in Figure 5.6, each focusing on creating separate standards. Table 5.5 gives physical layer specifications for IEEE 802 LAN standards.

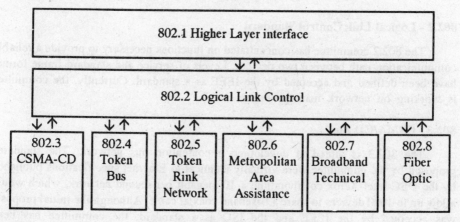

Fig. 5.6 : IEEE 802 Committees

TABLE : 5.5 Physical Layer Specifications for IEEE 802 LAN Standards

	Transmission Medium	Data Signaling Technique	Rate (Mbps)	Maximum Length (m)
IEEE 802.3 (CSMA/CD)				
Original (10 BASES)	Coaaxial Cable (50 ᴡ) (Manchester)	Baseband	10	500
Chaperner (10 BASE2)	Coaxial Cable (50 ᴡ) (Manchester)	Baseband	10	185
10 BASE-T	Unshielded Twisted Pair	Baseband (Manchester)	10	100
Broadband (10 BROAD36)	Coaxial Cable (75 ᴡ)	DPSK	10	3600
IEEE 8202.4 (Token Bus)				
Broadband	Coaxial Cable (75 ᴡ)	duobinary AM/PSK	1,5,10	a
Carrierband	Coaxial Cable (75 ᴡᴡ)	FSK	1,5,10	7600
IEEE 802.5 (Token Ring)				
Twisted Pair	Shielded Twisted Pair	Differential Manchester	1,4	b

a = not specified
b = not specified; a maximum of 250 repeaters allowed

802.1 - Higher Layer Interface Standard

The 802.1 committee is not developing standards, but has focused on issues relevant to all other committees such as addressing of messages, internetworking, network management and higher layer interfaces.

802.2 - Logical Link Control Standard

The 802.2 committee has concentrated on functions necessary to provide a reliable communication path between two devices. Levels of service and standard frame format have been defined and accepted by the IEEE as a standard. Currently, the committee is working on network management.

802.3 - CSMA/CD Bus

The 802.3 is aimed at developing a contention bus network. The standards proposed by the committee were virtually identical to Ethernet specifications published by the DEC-Intel-Xerox collaboration: a 10 megabit per second network, which would allow up to 1000 devices to share a baseband coaxial cable. Although the initial proposal was accepted by the IEEE and the ISO as a standard, the committee has been considering changing the type of cable specified to permit use of a thinner wire.

Currently, two other efforts are underway by 802.3. Part of the committee is studying low cost CSMA/CD broadband using a star topology and is in the process of defining how it would work. A second subcommittee has defined a broadband modem which will allow Ethernet to plug into a broadband cable.

802.4 - Token Passing Bus

The 802.4 committee has focused on defining a logical ring on a physical bus so that token passing protocol can be used. Broadband operation with a variety of data rates has been defined.

The specifications have been accepted and are being published as standards. One major problem affecting the usability of a token bus is that the committee is standardising protocols for a complex network that has not been yet widely implemented.

802.5 - Token Passing Ring

The 802.5 has defined a token ring using the star topology to access workstations sequentially. Baseband and broadband versions have been developed. IBM has contributed extensively to this subcommittee. The proposal of the token ring committee was accepted in the fall, 1984.

New Committees

Three new 802 committees were formed during 1984:

-   **802.6 - Metropolitan Area Network:** 802.6 is exploring the use of a variety of techniques to send data in a city-wide area. Both CATV and cellular radio are being considered.

-   **802.7 - Broadband Technical Assistance:** 802.7 was formed to define broadband LAN standards.

-   **802.8 - Fibre Optic:** The 802.8 committee is the most recently formed group. Members have begun exploring the use of fibre optics for a very high speed local area network.

802 Reference Model

Although the 802 Project committee's overall approach is based upon the structure of the International Standards Organisation (ISO) Reference Model of Open System Interconnection, it does differ from the layers defined by the ISO. Moreover, 802 is focused on the lowest ISO layers only, that is, sharing the media. No higher layer protocols are under 802 study.

The 802 Reference Model has three layers, as shown in Figure 5.7.

-   **Physical:** concerned with the nature of the transmission medium and the details of device attachment and electrical signalling.

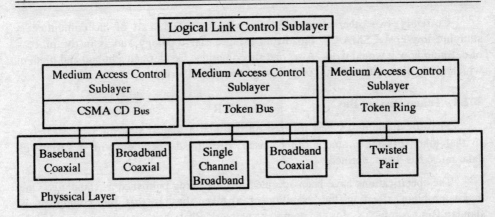

Fig. 5.7 : IEEE 802 Layers

-   **Medium Access Control:** focused on methods of sharing a single transmission medium. Typical issues centreon controlling access to the medium, capacity sharing algorithms and station addressing.

-   **Logical Link Control:** concerned with providing a reliable communication path between two devices. The relevant protocols cover the flow of frames between stations; establishing, maintaining and terminating communication between devices; and error control.

Figure 5.8 contrasts the 802 layers to the ISO layers. Basically, the 802 Physical Layer is designed to correspond to the ISO Physical Layer. However, rather than being a single layer as in the ISO model, the 802 Physical Layer is itself divided into three parts:

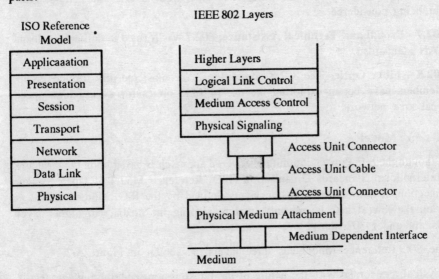

Fig. 5.8 a : IEEE 802 Layers Compared to ISO Layers

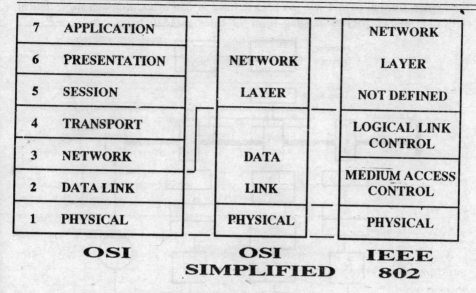

7	APPLICATION		
6	PRESENTATION	NETWORK	NETWORK LAYER
5	SESSION	LAYER	NOT DEFINED
4	TRANSPORT		LOGICAL LINK CONTROL
3	NETWORK	DATA	MEDIUM ACCESS CONTROL
2	DATA LINK	LINK	
1	PHYSICAL	PHYSICAL	PHYSICAL

OSI	OSI SIMPLIFIED	IEEE 802

Fig. 5.8 b : OSI and IEEE 802

- The physical signalling sublayer.

- Access-unit interface.

- The physical medium attachment.

This division is intended to permit the most complex part of the layer, the physical signalling sublayer, to be physically combined with the station logic in the network controller.

Jointly, the 802 Medium Access Control Layer and the Logical Link Control Layer correspond to the ISO Data Link Layer. Again, the division has been made to allow combining with other network functions.

ETHERNET

One of the best known and more successful local area networks is Ethernet (see Figure 5.9) developed at Xerox's Palo Alto Research Laboratories. The original Ethernet was designed to link a set of single-user minicomputers that were scattered throughout the research centre. Xerox's immediate goals were to enable the exchange of programmes and data and to provide access to various specialised peripherals.

Ethernet workstations are connected by a single, multidrop, baseband coaxial cable bus using CSMA/CD. As in all contention schemes, the shared channel is a passive broadcast medium with no central control. Access to the channel by stations wishing to transmit is coordinated by the stations themselves.

Workstations are attached to the main bus through a network interface module. The interface buffers and formats messages and subsequently broadcasts the data onto the cable in bursts. The data is in a fixed-length packet containing address information in the header. Current packet size has been defined as 256 bytes, although the technical specification allows packets ranging from 72 bytes to 1526 bytes.

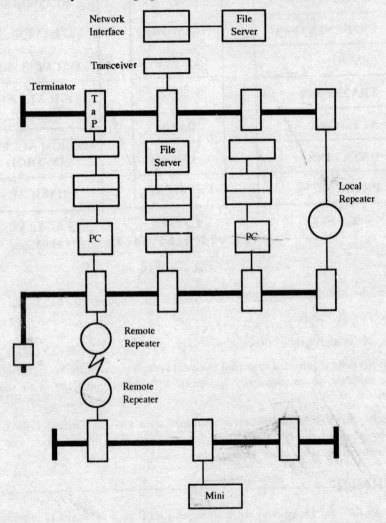

Fig. 5.9 : Ethernet Network

Each station contains address recognition mechanisms, used to identify and accept packets. Every Ethernet workstation, no matter what network it is on, has a unique 48-bit address that is assigned to it and to no other workstation. Hence, when a workstation is moved from one network to another, there is no chance of conflict. This assigning of unique identities has the advantage of flexibility: networks within a company can be physically reconfigured with minimal operating system reconfiguration.

Data on the network moves at a speed of 10 Megabytes per second, over a maximum distance of 2.5 kilometers. No more than 100 workstations can be connected in a 500 meter segment.

Ethernet's strength is that it provides efficient, high-speed resource sharing services within a limited geographic area, at a relatively low cost.

Interest in Ethernet and in local area networks in general, was focused by the 1980 announcement from Digital, Intel and Xerox of a joint project to develop specifications for a local communication network. The project's aim was compatibility, providing sufficient information for various manufacturers such that their widely differing machines could communicate with one another. In effect, the group was establishing a de facto standard.

The attempt was largely successful. The IEEE 802.3 contention bus specification is similar to Ethernet in most details. The two designs are not identical, but are extremely close.

Spurred by these factors, quite a number of vendors have announced hardware and software intended to connect microcomputers into an Ethernet compatible network. At the moment, in fact, the majority of microcomputer LANs use a variation on Ethernet.

- "Ethernet on a chip", that is, an implementation of Ethernet protocols on a single silicon chip, is available from Intel and other chip vendors.

- A fibre optic implementation of Ethernet.

- "Cheapernet", a low cost implementation of Ethernet, is close to being accepted as an IEEE 802.3 standard.

Ethernet Specification

The information in this section is based on the Ethernet Data Link and Physical Layer Specification, Version 1.0 published in 1980 by the Xerox Corporation.

Specification of Ethernet are:

Topology	-	bus
Medium	-	coaxial cable
Access Method	-	CSMA/CD
Speed	-	10 MB
Range	-	2.5 Km
Number of nodes	-	1024
Band	-	baseband

Ethernet is designed to do the following things:

1. To be simple - features which would complicate the design without improving the performance are omitted.

2. To be low cost - in order to be a suitable medium for interconnec-tion of equipment whose cost continues to fall, Ethernet itself should be cheap.

3. To allow compatibility of all Ethernet installations - the specifi-cation avoids optional features, thus allowing any Ethernet station to communicate directly with any other, at physical link and data link levels.

4. To allow single nodes, groups or the whole network to be addressed by a transmission.

5. To allow all nodes equal access to the network, on average.

6. To prevent any node interfering with the proper functioning of any other node.

7. To be high-speed - the network should operate at a data rate of 10 Mbs.

8. To be stable - the network performance in terms of data successfully transmitted should not degrade as the amount of data for transmission increases. In other words the system should not clog up as the load increases.

9. To keep delays to a minimum - no data should be kept waiting longer than necessary for transmission.

10. To have a layered architecture - the physical and data link layers specified are completely independent and correspond to the two lowest layers of the OSI model.

Ethernet does not do the following things:

1. Provide full-duplex communication. Only one device can talk at once. The appearance of two-way communication can only be provided by two devices talking alternatively in rapid succession.

2. Provide Error Control. The layers specified only detect bit errors and collisions. Recovery from these and other errors must be handled by the higher layers of the network.

3. Provide Security. There is no encryption or restricted access implied in this specification.

4. Provide variable speeds. The network operates at 10 Mbits/second.

5. Provide a priority control. All nodes have equal access rights to the network.

ARCNET

ARCNET began as a minicomputer distributed processing system offered by Datapoint. It was the first minicomputer local area network to gain a substantial user base. Since 1982, ARCNET has offered interfaces to several microcomputers.

ARC stands for Attached Research Processor Interface units; called a resource interface module (RIM), these are microprocessor-based. The RIMs monitor and control the operation of the network, particularly data transmission, buffer management, error detection, system reconfiguration and related tasks, leaving the attached computers free for user applications.

As Figure 5.10 shows, the RIM consists of four components:

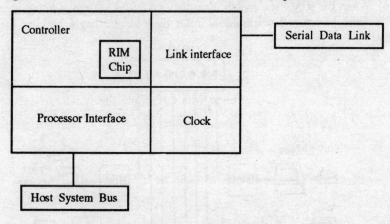

Fig. 5.10 : Resource interface Module

-   A controller, consisting of the RIM chip, node ID switch, address and data path information and RAM buffer.

-   A clock which provides synchronisation and timing for the network.

-   A link interface which connects the controller to the communication media via a serial data link and provides the transmitter and receiver capabilities

-   A processor interface which provides the address decoders, bus drivers, buffer access and other functions required to interface the controller to the system bus of the host processor.

Each workstation is connected by baseband coaxial cable to a RIM which is, in turn, connected to a port on a "hub". The hubs serve as amplifiers and connectors for the RIMs within the network. While any one hub can contain a maximum of 16 RIMs, two or more hubs can be joined for larger systems. Although physically the ARCNET resembles a compound star, logically it works as a token passing ring (see Figure 5.11).

To send a message, the workstation writes the message into a RIM buffer and issues a transmit command. The RIM sets a status flag when the token is received and the message is sent. To receive a message, the workstation assigns a RIM buffer to the RIM receiver. Acknowledgement is provided of successful or unsuccessful message receipt.

Control tokens are dispersed among the workstations of the network. All nodes share responsibility for the detection and re-creation of lost tokens, and for recreation of tokens after system reconfiguration. The user is unaware of, and has no control over, details of the token passing.

Each RIM has two addresses. The first is a fixed unique identifier. The second address is a relative one and identifies where on the ring the unit logically falls. When a new RIM becomes active, it sends a reconfiguration burst which terminates all activity on the network. The RIM that had control of the line releases it; no other RIM claims control. When the RIMs see an idle line, they know the system is being reconfigured. After a quiet period, all workstations reset their id and begin looking for network activity.

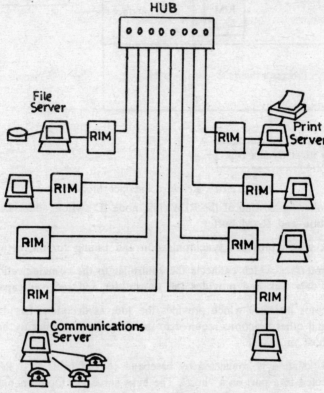

Fig. 5.11 : Arcnet Network

Communication services are restricted to a transfer between a file server and an attached computer. Actual computing is performed separately from where the data are stored, permitting more data to be stored in one location and freeing the computers to process a greater amount of data.

ARCNET imposes few restrictions on the transmission medium. Basically, the receiver at any station must be able to hear the transmitter at any other station. Any two stations must be connected by a single path. Data is transmitted on the network at 2.5 megabits per second. At that rate, the maximum propagation delay between any two stations must be 31 microseconds or less.

Datapoint has made the technical details of its protocol and communication available to the public domain as a way of encouraging other vendors to develop ARC compatible systems. Because only a few relatively inexpensive components are necessary to implement ARC, the appeal is growing.

ARCnet has the following specifications:

Speed	-	2.5 MBPS
Topology	-	Bus or Star
Cable	-	Coaxial
Number of users	-	depends upon configuration
Maximum segment		
size	-	100 feet between passive hubs,
		2000 feet between active hubs

IBM PC NETWORK

In the fall of 1984, IBM announced a single-wire broadband coaxial CSMA/CD network designed to link IBM PCs. The system is based on an existing network (LocalNet) developed by Sytek, Inc. Although targeted at IBM's three microcomputers - the PC, XT and AT - the network can support other microcomputers that supply a strictly IBM-compatible internal operating system and that are physically bus-compatible with the IBM PC.

The network, shown in Figure 5.12, has two major components:

- A network translator unit, containing a radio frequency modem and one eight-way cable splitter. The translator is the network's head end.

- PC Network Adapter, to be installed in each PC. The adapter card contains most of the network intelligence; it provides encoding and decoding services for the signals and control.

To the basic components must be added the microcomputers (you supply), and broadband coaxial cable, which IBM has thoughtfully made available in the form of cable kits containing all relevant hardware plus pre-cut cable. Short (1 foot), medium (400 foot maximum) and long (800 foot maximum) distance kits with splitters are available.

The minimal network supports up to eight PCs, each of which may be up to 200 feet from the translator's 8-way splitter. Expander kits, containing additional cable taps, are available for users who want to connect more than nine PCs. The expanded network will interconnect up to 72 micros, at a maximum distance of 2000 feet.

The IBM PC Network is, at the moment, one of the few which provides some level of network security. Although logon passwords are not required, files may be protected by a password.

The real lack is the continuing shortage of network software. Despite being based on an existing network, the network operating system is quite limited. Disk caching and print spooling are possible, system management is not.

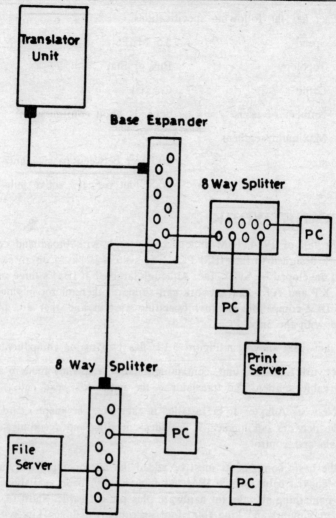

Fig. 5.12 : IBM's PC Network

The PC Network has the following specifications:

Topology	-	tree
Medium	-	75 Ohm coaxial cable
Access Method	-	CSMA/CD
Speed	-	2 Mbits/second
Range	-	304.8m to translator unit 609.6m between nodes
Number of nodes	-	72
Band	-	broadband

IBM TOKEN RING

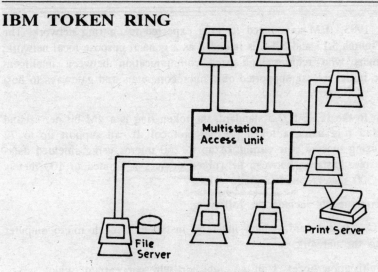

Fig. 5.13 : IBM Token Ring Network

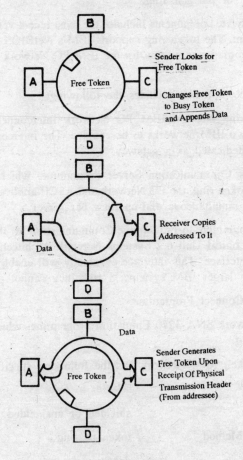

Fig. 5.14 : Token Ring

In October 1985, IBM announced its long expected token ring network. The token ring (see Figures 5.13 and 5.14) is intended as a general purpose local network, aimed at customers who require high-speed communication between intelligent workstations. The initial release supported only microcomputers and gateways to host systems.

Conforming to the IEEE 802.5 standard, the token ring is a 4M bit per second star-wired baseband ring using a token passing protocol. It can support up to 72 microcomputers using twisted pair wiring, or up to 260 micros using shielded data-grade (coaxial) cable. Distance between networked devices is limited to 100 meters on twisted pair, 300 meters on data-grade cable.

Hardware components include the following:

- Network PC Adapter card, which must be installed in each microcomputer connected to the network.

- Network Multistation Access Unit, an eight port wire concentrator which serves as the centre of the star ring.

Required software components includes the most recent version of DOS, the IBM PC operating system. The token ring supports IBM's NetBIOS (Network Basic Input/ Output System), programmes written for the IBM PC Network which will run on the token ring.

Other available software includes the following:

- IBM token ring Network/IBM PC Network interconnect programme, which enables the two IBM networks to be coupled. The interconnect programme runs on a micro dedicated as a gateway.

- Asynchronous Communication Server Programme, which provides a gateway, between the token ring, the PC Network and ASCII applications. The programme supports two simultaneous dial-up lines per server.

- Advanced Programme-to-Programme Communication for the Personal Computer, providing a Logical Unit 6.2 Systems Network Architecture (SNA) application programme interface. This interface eventually will enable PCs to communicate as peers with larger IBM systems, a task they cannot perform now.

- Series 1/PC Connect Programme.

- IBM PC Network SNA 3270 Emulation Programme, which has been tested on the token ring.

The IBM Token Ring Network has the following specifications:

Topology	-	ring
Medium	-	shielded or unshielded twisted pair
Access Method	-	token passing
Speed	-	4 Mbs

Range	-	N/A
Number of nodes	-	72 (unshielded), 260 (shielded)
Transmission	-	baseband

SUMMARY

A network architecture defines protocols, message formats and standards to which products must conform in order to connect properly with the network. Architectures are developed by standards organisations, common carriers and computer and network vendors. Network architectures use a layered approach, whereby functions are organised into groups and assigned to specific functional layers in the architecture. Network architectures define the interfaces between layers in a given network node and within the same layer in two different nodes.

OSI provides a generalised model of system interconnection. It encompasses seven layers: application, presentation, session, transport, network, data link and physical. IEEE Project 802 has developed a set of standards for local area networks. These standards specify in detail protocols and data formats for the physical and data link layers. In the IEEE approach, the data link layer is divided into two sublayers: logical link control and media access control. IEEE Project 802 documents families of standards that define the functions performed by the three layers and sublayers described by the architecture.

6

COST BENEFIT ANALYSIS OF
A LAN

INTRODUCTION

As you can see, there are potential benefits, changes and problems that accompany the implementation of a LAN. You must try to anticipate the potential impact of a new LAN. The problem for your organisation, however, is defining exactly which of the possible benefits, changes or problems will turn up for you.

Obviously, not every possible impact of networking will appear in any single organisation. Remember, too, not every impact that does appear is significant. In order to decide whether a LAN makes good business sense, you need to decide in which ways your specific business will be affected, to what extent the impact will be felt, and what the quantifiable effects will be.

Finding effects that can be quantified is one of the more difficult parts of planning for a LAN. You might feel that the LAN will help your business but not be able to prove it. In other cases, the effects are clear and so are the resulting numbers. Most LANs will have effects of both sorts.

It is important that you consider impacts that are quantifiable as well as those that are not. A company that fails to quantify the effects of any data processing installation simply is not performing enough analysis. You really do not know what the effects will be, nor will you have a way to tell if the installation has helped.

Likewise, failure to consider nonquantifiable information means ignoring part of the problem. There is really no way to break predicted impact into numbers. That does not mean that the information is immune to analysis, however.

Although LAN sales are steadily increasing, many potential users are postponing the purchase of a LAN because of confusion over network applications, benefits and standards. LAN hardware and software are rapidly maturing, and many of these early concerns are being addressed. Still, a LAN is not the only or the best solution for everyone, and you need to measure your requirements against LAN costs and capabilities. Multiuser systems offer many of the same benefits as a network, and many such systems can even be combined with networks. The discussion here provides you with a framework for analysing your own needs in order to make this important decision.

USES OF A NETWORK

Before you can decide whether to install a network, you need to understand how networks are used and how the various ways of using them satisfy your requirements. Most network installations fit into one of two categories: the first is a dedicated application system on which most users run the same set of programmes; the second consists of communication between personal computer (PC) users who each use their PCs for individual functions. Users of a dedicated system tend to view the PCs and the network as a single appliance, while users of the second kind of installation may be more interested in learning technical details and experimenting with different application packages. Each of the two kinds of installations meets a somewhat different set of needs and it is worth understanding these.

1. The Dedicated System

A dedicated network application is usually one in which sharing of information is a critical requirement. The main implementation choice is between a multiuser system and a network. For example, you may be installing PCs in a classroom laboratory in which it is mandatory that the teacher and students be able to send information back and forth immediately. In a business situation, more than one employee at a time may need to enter invoices into accounts payable, or two sales clerks may need immediate access to inventory figures. In these instances, the users only need to run programmes that are provided by the computer installer (who is often an outside consultant); no further demands are made on the system. In this case, the system configuration may remain fairly static and require little managing.

The hardware you choose for a dedicated installation may be less expensive than that intended for networked PC users. For example, your applications may all run from the network disk drives, allowing diskless PCs to be used as workstations. The pattern of use of the network itself may be more constant and predictable, allowing its peak needs to be handled with fewer server hardware components. Hard disk usage is easier to estimate and control, since the number and size of software applications are fixed and the data storage space needed is a function of business activity.

A dedicated system at a given site may be either a totally new installation of PCs or an enhancement to an existing PC installation. Each of these cases has a different set of problems that you should consider before installing a network. If you are designing a new PC installation, you have a chance to select a complete set of applications on the basis of their ability to share information over a network. This should result in consistent use of the network and good control over data. The negative side to an all-new installation is the larger number of new hardware components and software programmes to install, get working and train people to use.

If you are considering adding networking capability to a group of PCs already running dedicated applications, you need to decide whether to install networked versions of the existing applications or to try to convert the system over to new applications. In both cases, you not only must train people to use the new network software, you also must consider how you will get the old data converted for the new applications. Even using network versions of old applications introduces new questions of security and controlling access by multiple users to the same file.

2. Communication Between PC Users

The second category of useful network application is for a group of PC users who want to share hardware and information. This class of users may be working in a small business and using PCs for a variety of word processing and accounting chores; they may want to add a fast printer that everyone can use or set up a new accounting system that smoothly integrates functions previously done separately. Or such users may be managers in a medium-to-large corporation; they may be doing project management and financial analysis and would like to be able to send electronic mail or directly import information from the corporate mainframe. They may be programmers developing software on PCs and wanting to share common subroutines or control source code updates on a large project that many programmers are coding in parallel.

This group of users is likely to be using many applications and their needs are usually much less predictable and controllable than those of dedicated applications users. Consequently, the job of networking is more challenging. Fortunately, there is usually at least one knowledgeable user at such a site who can handle the network management job.

Most such users are already experienced, productive PC users who must perceive a network as enhancing their productivity or they will reject it. They may be used to having their own machines, having total control over the way they are used and having no need to share them with others. A network introduces a new requirement for cooperation. If the network is poorly chosen or installed and slows things down instead of providing benefits to the users, you will be faced with an unpleasant situation: millions of rupees worth of unused networking hardware and an uncooperative group of users. If you find yourself in such a situation, you have to review your installation and uses of network. It may turn out that the system you selected is suitable to your needs and can be made efficient and productive through some simple configuration modifications that better balance the use of the network. If you still have problems, consider enlisting the help of an experienced consultant who can provide references of successful installations. Sometimes the initial set-up is better done with the aid of an experienced hand.

COST BENEFIT ANALYSIS

You have seen this term before, may be in a report from a consultant or possibly when you took business in college or university. In any case, a cost benefit analysis is simply a way of looking at the pluses and minuses of any decision as it affects the economics of a business.

While a thorough cost benefit analysis is a comprehensive, detailed, voluminous document, you will rarely need to be that thorough when deciding whether you want to have a LAN become part of your business. Normally, a decision of this sort is fairly clear cut: it is usually easy to see if it makes good business sense.

All that is really required is for you to lay out the costs and benefits of the LAN. In small LAN installations, this can be done by simply listing the costs on one side of a sheet of paper and the benefits on the other. Simply draw a line down the centre of a page and label the left side Costs and the right side Benefits.

Be careful to consider all of the costs and do not overstate the benefits. Some costs are frequently overlooked because they are not very obvious. The cost of training is often underestimated. Likewise the potential benefits are often exaggerated. For instance, you might come to believe that a LAN will solve all of your organisational problems — it would not. Be critical when you list the benefit side of the paper.

When you are calculating cost/benefit comparisons in a complex situation, more study will be required. While it is still possible to do the comparison on a sheet of paper, it is more difficult to be accurate that way, and the chances of being wrong are greater. Unless you know your operation unusually well, you will need to do some research, and you will need to describe the cost and benefit items more completely.

Really large installations are beyond the scope of a quick cost/benefit analysis. When your prospective LAN starts including access to external systems or requires mainframe services, or when it reaches sufficient size that it calls for multiple file servers, you are entering the area where the study needs to be completed by a consultant or an internal service group that will perform a similar function.

Even in large installations you will probably know the major cost elements, but there is a good chance you will miss some significant ones. As the size of the proposed LAN grows, so do the risks. Still, it does help to know what the cost elements and the benefits might be. Remember, every installation is different, and every organisation is unique. The details of your analysis are just as unique.

THE COSTS

Hardware and software are the most obvious first cost items. This includes the cost of the networking software, the file server(s), any other gateways or servers, the network interface cards, power conditioning equipment and the cables. Added to this are training costs, administration costs, and the time lost to organisational matters and disruption of work. Most companies find that the cost of hardware and software is smaller than the labour costs required to make the LAN part of your organisation.

HARDWARE AND SOFTWARE

Network Operating System. Depending on the network, this may or may not be a major cost item. For example, Apple Macintosh computers come with Appletalk networking software as a part of the package. At the other extreme, Novel NetWare 386 costs about eight thousand dollars retail per file server. Sometimes network software is bundled with other hardware, including network interface cards.

Electronic Mail. Many network operating systems include electronic mail at no charge. Often, the e-mail software is worth the cost. For this reason, a number of companies, including WordPerfect, will sell you software that will handle your electronic mail and perform other functions including scheduling. These packages are priced using vastly different methods, but if you start by figuring about $200 per workstation, you will be safe.

Application Software. Some applications come ready for networks, but most require additional licenses or special LAN add-ons. If you plan to use your software on the LAN, you will want to get the LAN version. You will need to price this yourself.

File Server. Not all LANs require a file server, but most do, and many of the LANs that do not require file servers will still use one if it is available. The file server is usually an IBM PC/AT compatible computer or an IBM PS/2 that has been equipped with extra memory and big disks. You can plan on the server costing you between six and ten thousand dollars, depending on the number and size of the hard disks being used. Larger hard disks cost more money than smaller ones do. If you plan to have your file server use an additional disk as a back-up, then you will have to pay for that as well.

Gateways and Other Servers. You may or may not need additional support devices such as asynchronous communication servers or IBM 3270 gateways, but if you do, you will also need to provide a computer for each one of them to run in. Each gateway communication server, or print server is really an IBM PC/AT-compatible computer with a disk drive and a special board that operates as the gateway. You will need to provide the PC, the gateway or server device, a network interface card and a monitor. You do not, however, normally need an expensive machine for this duty. An inexpensive IBM PC/AT or compatible computer is generally adequate for this duty.

Network Interface Cards. These are the circuit cards that allow you to connect to the network. In some cases, such as the Apple Macintosh, a network interface is built in. In others, you must supply the interface device. Normally this is a plug-in card that installs inside the machine.

Uninterruptable Power Supply (UPS). While not strictly part of the LAN itself, this device prevents possibly catastrophic damage to the LAN due to loss of power. Essentially, it is a standby battery-operated electrical supply that will take over for a few minutes when the AC power fails. UPS devices that are designed to support network equipment will come with a special signal cable that is used to notify the network software of the power failure. When the network detects the power failure message from the UPS, it begins shutting down the network by closing open files, saving data and making sure the network is ready to be turned off. While it is doing this, the network software will be telling users to log off if they can. Not all network software is able to handle the signals from a UPS, and some of those that are capable of handling it require the support of third-party software.

Cabling. The wiring that actually carries the signals between computers can turn out to be the most expensive part of the network. The reason for this is the amount of labour that is involved in pulling the coaxial cable required by some networks through walls. It can be especially expensive in the case of a building that is already built and occupied, especially if the building is old. Newer buildings are designed for electrical and telephone cable runs, and running network cable through these is easier and therefore cheaper.

Some buildings were built with sufficient extra wire in the phone system to support a LAN. In cases like this, there are ways to run your LAN on the telephone cabling already in the walls. Normally this requires the addition of some hardware called a concentrator to support this type of cable, but the cost of the concentrator is much less than the cost of installing coaxial cable. The use of telephone wire to support the LAN requires either the use of special network interface cards or of devices called transceivers, which add an extra one hundred dollars or so to the cost of each workstation installation.

PERSONNEL COSTS

In addition to the cost of buying the hardware and software, there are also indirect costs related to a LAN installation. In general, these are the costs of time required for your employees to help in the planning and implementation, as well as the time for learning how to use the LAN.

Planning Costs. If you plan to have a LAN that meets your needs, you and your employees will need to be involved in the design from the beginning. You will need to be able to describe your requirements to the LAN designers in detail, and you will be required to answer detailed questions about what you plan to use the LAN to do, how often you will use it, and how much information transfer you will be responsible for handling. Your employees will also need to provide this information, and you will need to review the installation company's plans to make sure they are supporting what you need to do.

Disruption. Once the LAN installation begins, your work day and that of your employees will be interrupted. Some of the interruptions will be minor, involving something simple such as a request to move for a few minutes while a cable is installed above your desk. Others will be much more demanding, such as being willing to have the power to the office cut off for an hour or two, or being willing to make room for an installer who wants to take your computer apart, install a network interface card, and then test it. More disruptions will come once the LAN is installed and testing begins, because the installation company will want to test everything from every workstation. They will also come back with more requests when something does not work and they need to figure out what it is.

Training. The major single interruption is training. There is no question that training is required, but it still might take several days from each person's working time. The exact number of days required depends on the training course, the nature of the network operating system, and the abilities of the employee. Once the formal training is over, informal training will continue until all users are proficient in the use of the network. There are two aspects to training costs. Most business managers understand that the training course itself costs money, one way or the other. The other cost is the employee time the training takes, and the time that is lost before the employee begins training.

BENEFITS OF A NETWORK

After that long list of costs, you are probably wondering to yourself why any sane business operator would consider a LAN. The reason is, of course, that the benefits usually outweigh the costs. This is especially true if you assign a value to such things as accuracy, speed and effective internal communication. The most important benefit, and the one that is relatively easy to measure,at least roughly, is security of the information the business needs to stay in business.

For some reason, it never fails to surprise people when they are told that one of their business's greatest assets is the information the business maintains. Think about the information in your business. How much is your customer list worth? How much is your supplier list worth? How about your list of accounts receivable? While it is possible your business does not need this information, most do, and they would be hard pressed to stay in business without it.

When a business begins to depend on a computer, whether it is a personal computer or a mainframe, it comes to depend on the proper operation of the computer for the business to run properly. If you were to find that your computer had stopped working, you could be in for a problem. Of course, if you had backed up your information, you would simply have to take it to another computer and resume operations there.

The same concept works for a LAN. The advantage is that since all or most of the information your business needs is in one place, it is much easier to make sure it is backed up. In fact, this is one of the primary duties of your LAN administrator.

With the LAN, you have a much better chance of finding critical information on the file server, especially if it is the sort of information people are likely to need to share. Even if it is not getting the person who is responsible for the critical information,to copy to the file server is fairly easy, since it only takes seconds. In fact, the entire process can be automated. This way, you can ensure that the important data your company needs to continue in business is always backed up. You are not betting your company on the continued operation of a thirty thousand rupees hard disk.

Like most investments, a network should be assessed on the basis of costs and benefits. Table 6.1 lists some of the typical costs and benefits of a network. The obvious items of major expense are the network hardware and software. You can do a rough analysis without a specific network vendor in mind, but you should repeat it once your choice is narrowed to one or two vendors. People's time is also a factor, not only during the installation and training period, but also over the long - term, because you will need a network manager: the person in-charge of the network, responsible for allocating its resources and authorising people to use its various parts. For a small-to moderate-size network that does not change much, the network manager's job may be minimal and can probably be absorbed as a part-time activity by a knowledgeable user. In a large installation with many servers and a constantly changing user community, this job grows in significance and may become quite time-consuming.

Some of the benefits of a LAN are tangible, such as the savings in hardware costs achieved by having many users share one piece of hardware instead of each using a separate device. Your present hardware may also be better used, since different people will probably want to use it at different times, keeping it in use more often than when it was dedicated to a single user. Network application like electronic mail can boost organisational communication, with beneficial results: increasing the amount of programme and data sharing reduces redundant individual efforts; presenting the same file to many users at once provides a consistent picture of organisational data; assigning the responsibility for backing up data to a single person increases the likelihood that this vital function will be regularly performed.

After you build the cost/benefit list that is correct for you, you must quantify each category the best you can. You will find help with many of the common costs and benefits mentioned here. Some of the other benefits, such as increased control over backups and data security, are difficult to quantify.

The analysis takes a different form if you know that your needs cannot be met by establishing communication among isolated personal computers but instead require a network or a multiuser computer system — as, for example, when real-time access to data must be shared. In this case, the cost/benefit analysis can still be done, but the conclusion is a foregone one. Your application needs change the terms of the question. It is no longer a question of whether or not to use a network, but of whether to select a network or a multiuser system. You should do a cost/benefit analysis for each selection and compare them. Multiuser computers and networks are discussed later.

FIGURING VALUE

How much is the information worth? Because every company is different, and because their data is handled differently, it is impossible to generalise; but here is how to figure the value for your business.

You have to look at two areas: first is the cost to recreate the information, and second is the cost of interruption to your operations. If you depend on the information in your computer to conduct your business, and you have no other way to do it, then you can simply add up the amount lost per day of down time. Of course, you will have to add the damage to your good will as well. Meanwhile, you will have to pay someone to create all this information again. They will do this from written records, possibly records from customers and suppliers, and it can take quite some time. You might find that you can never recover all the information.

TABLE 6.1 : Some network costs and benefits

Costs	Benefits
Hardware	Financial
Workstations	Shared hardware
Additional memory	Improved Hardware: use
Additional disk storage	Increased productivity
Network connectionboard	Organisational
Cables	Improved communication
Servers	Increased sharing
Disk servers	Data consistency
Print servers	Backup control
Gateways	People
Other servers	Access to better hardware
Software	Sharing managed by system
Workstations and Servers	
DOS upgrade	
System software	
Network applications	
People	
Installation time	
Network management time	
End user training	

As you can see, the cost to a business of loss of information can be considerable. It can be avoided, however, if you make sure that you keep a copy of the information, preferably somewhere outside of the place where you do business. That way, even if you lose the computers in a fire, you can be back in business as soon as you recover the copy.

Performing these backups with a LAN is simple. For the most part, the entire process can be automated, and if you are careful to take the tapes to a safe place, your business records are protected. There are companies that specialise in safe storage of computer records, but you can accomplish the same thing by keeping the tapes in a safe or a bank vault. The result is that your information is safe.

Now that you have seen the value of protecting your information and your LAN's role in making that possible, there are other areas to consider as benefits. Most have to do with making information available to all users at a reasonable cost.

Earlier, when many people needed to have access to the same information, you bought a mainframe or a minicomputer. If you did not need a lot of access, you might have bought time on such a machine. Either way, you would spend a great deal of money to get access to the computer that would support your needs. A LAN offers a much lower cost alternative that has the advantage of usually offering much better performance. You store the information on a file server or a database server, and access it with personal computers.

The net cost of using a LAN for shared data access is only a small fraction of the cost of buying and running a minicomputer or a mainframe. The fact that the performance is better (because each user has a dedicated CPU) helps the equation also. The difference in cost between the mainframe or minicomputer alternative is the amount of savings, and thus the cost benefit.

Shared access is a productivity benefit in itself in most organisations. This is because groups of people can have access to the same information when they need it, rather than having to wait until one person is finished with a file. Shared access helps to ensure that information stays up-to-date as well. The common files are updated as they are used, so there is no cause for worry if one person's copy of company information was updated while another's was not.

Improved communication is also a significant benefit, especially in larger organisations. Without the electronic mail and the scheduling capabilities available on most LANs, your employees will remain in the trap of telephone tag and missed meetings. While it is hard to quantify the cost of telephone tag, it is very real and can be very expensive both, in time and missed opportunities.

ALTERNATE SYSTEMS

One of the areas in which you can quantify the differences between a planned LAN and the status quo is when you have a computer system that the LAN will replace. If you are already using a minicomputer or a mainframe, you can compare the costs of the existing system with the costs of the LAN. This is usually pretty easy to do, since you will already have records of what the current system is costing.

If you do not have such a system but are considering a mainframe or minicomputer as another alternate, the same considerations will hold true as if you owned it, although you will have to research the costs. In either case, there are two areas of difference that are the more significant. The first is the cost of the machinery itself, and the second is the support staff.

Most companies do not buy a mainframe or minicomputer outright. Instead, they sign a lease for a number of years. While there are companies that also lease their file servers and other LAN equipment, this is less common. To compare the two, you should project the costs of the minicomputer or mainframe over the period of the lease. These costs should include the leasing charges, of course, but they should also include all other costs that are likely to be incurred over that period of time.

If the lease runs for five years, for example, you should include the costs of leasing for five years, as well as five years of staff support, maintenance, training, and the like. Then, you should do the same for the LAN equipment you will be buying, alongwith staff costs, maintenance and training. Compare the figures, keeping in mind that the purchase costs are all up front, which means you do not have the use of your money for the period of time in which you would be making lease payments.

Frequently the difference in cost, especially for systems that are of moderate size, is considerable. A LAN nearly always gives a company more for the rupee than does a centralised minicomputer or mainframe. This is not true in every case, though, so you should do the analysis for the specific situations in your company.

SHARING HARDWARE

One of the most tangible benefits of a LAN is that it requires fewer peripherals per user than a stand-alone PC environment, since LAN users can share hardware. A worksheet like the one shown in Table 6.2 can be helpful in balancing the cost of installing a LAN against the savings in shared peripherals. In this example, an installation containing 10 PCs is under consideration. Without a network, each PC needs a 80-megabyte hard disk and a 40-megabyte tape drive for backups. The two laser printers will be shared by the 10 users, introducing some operational difficulties since the printers are directly accessible from only 2 of the 10 PCs.

TABLE 6.2 : Peripheral sharing cos analysis

Peripheral	Unit Cost ($)	Number needed without LAN	Cost without LAN ($)	Number needed with LAN	Cost with LAN ($)
Laser printer	3,500	2	7,000	1	3,500
80 MB disk	500	10	5,000		
300 MB disk	1,500			2	3,000
40 MB tape	1,000	10	10,000		
150 MB tape	2,000			1	2,000
Peripheral cost without a LAN			22,000		
Peripheral cost with LAN					8,500
LAN peripheral cost savings					13,500

If a LAN is used, the same productive efficiency can be obtained from one laser printer, two 300-megabyte hard disks and one 150-megabyte tape drive for back-up. This set-up represents a saving of $13,500 in the cost of peripherals. If the LAN costs $700 per workstation and $7,000 for a network server, the $14,000 apparent LAN cost is reduced to $500 by the peripheral cost savings, and now all users can access the laser printer without leaving their PCs.

If on the other hand, your hardware needs are considerably less, for example, you do not need a hard disk and you need only a $400 dot matrix printer per PC, savings from peripheral sharing would not justify the cost of a network.

A consideration that is separate from peripheral cost savings but perhaps equally important is the operational benefits of sharing hardware on a LAN. More convenient access to shared hardware may mean higher productivity. For example, in the absence of a LAN a user may copy a file to a floppy disk and carry it to the PC attached to the laser printer, interrupting the work of the person who normally uses that PC; then both people wait while the printing is done. By contrast, each LAN user has access to the printer as if it were connected to his own PC. It is easier to make sure your hard disk back-ups are done when the whole network can be backed up on a single drive than when 10 people must remember to do their own individual back-ups on separate drives.

Having fewer devices may lower maintenance costs. In the preceding example, 10 disk drives in a stand-alone configuration are replaced by 2 on a LAN, 10 tape by 1, and 2 printers by 1. This reduction from 22 devices to only 4 may sufficiently reduce maintenance costs to easily cover the last $500 of initial LAN cost figured in that example. There is, however, the consideration that having fewer devices increases the number of people who depend on each device. A failure of, say, the one network printer means nobody can print until it is fixed. However, having fewer devices to cover by a maintenance contract may enable you to justify a higher cost contract with faster guaranteed repair time, reducing the loss of productivity from hardware problems.

Sharing hardware helps to justify the installation of faster, more expensive peripherals on the grounds that the additional speed can increase productivity. But that increase may be offset by the increased number of users sharing the device, which in some situations may mean that users spend more time being unproductive while waiting their turn. Whether fewer, faster devices mean a net gain, loss or neither depends on your particular patterns of use.

Every installation must be analysed in its own context since there are an infinite number of possible variations. Of course, before you can do such an analysis you need to know how to estimate the number of peripherals required with and without a LAN.

SHARING INFORMATION

Information sharing is less tangible than hardware sharing but in many cases may be more important. Business was transacted and people communicated before there were personal computer networks, so obviously there are other ways to get the job done. A network should offer some improvement over the system it replaces, provide a new service that saves time or money, or so enhance the work environment as to increase productivity and efficiency. Your job is to determine what that improvement, innovation or enhancement is and how to measure it.

At this point in your decision-making process you perform a pay-back analysis. You need to understand what information is transferred today in your present system, how much the information transfer costs and what the benefits of such transfers are. You then need to answer each of these same questions assuming a network is available. The term information transfer is used in a very general sense to mean any use of the network (since what networks basically do is transfer information). You need to factor in your own circumstances and use the right unit of measurement for your case

The cost of transferring information in a network should exclude initial network purchase and installation costs, and should consist solely of the operating cost — the cost of running the network to transfer information. The benefits minus the cost of each transaction represent the profit or loss. If the network figure represents a higher profit or lower loss, then that increment, times the number of transactions per year, represents the net benefit of having a LAN each year. Divide the cost of purchasing and installing the LAN by this yearly benefit and you get a rough estimate of the network's payback period measured in years. If you found a saving from sharing hardware on a LAN, substract this from the purchase cost of the LAN before entering the cost in the preceding equation. Of course, this estimate is unadjusted for depreciation or investment tax credits; if you need to increase its accuracy in these or other areas you should consult an accountant. Table 6.3 gives the template for pay-back analysis of a LAN.

TABLE 6.3 : Payback analysiss of a LAN

Type of information transfer	Without a LAN			With a AN		
	Number per year	Cost fo each	Cost per year	Number per year	Cost of each	Cost per year
1.						
2.						
3.						
n.						
Cost without a LAN	A					
Cost with a LAN							B
Savingss from LAN							C=A-B
Payback period =	$\dfrac{\text{Installation cost - Other savings}}{\text{Annual savings}}$					

You may find it difficult to quantify the costs and benefits of information transfers. Do not be discouraged — just going through this exercise forces you to think about your business or organisation in a new way that is beneficial if you decide not to purchase a network, and is of fundamental importance if you do. Analysing information flow can help you see better ways to do things and uncover wasteful or redundant movement of data, be it on paper or electronic media. Consider the following potential improvements:

1.   Time saved trying to reach people on the phone if electronic mail is available as an alternative.

2.   Increased sales possible if clerks can handle more people through faster computer response.

3.   Improved control of your business if data can be gathered in real time from many control points and analysed at any moment.

4.   Protection from losses if data is stored centrally where it can be kept secure and backed up.

NETWORK APPLICATION SOFTWARE

Whether a network can do useful work for you depends on whether you can run the right software applications. There are two broad categories to investigate:

1.   Single-user software written for stand-alone PCs but able to take advantage of a network.

2.   Software written especially for a network and requiring some feature of a network to function.

If you are considering a network to enhance the environment of a group of stand-alone PCs, you will probably consider the first category most seriously; if you want to set up a new installation and networking seems important to achieving your aims, you are probably interested in the second category. Of course, you may have mixed requirements and need to consider software in both categories.

Network vendors have taken steps to ensure that most single-user software can be used in some fashion with their products. The reason is that most software on the market is written for the single-user PC —by a considerable margin the most prevalent type of machine. A PC network typically lets single-user software access the network printers and hard disks, and perhaps other shared peripherals as well. The ability to do this well is of key importance if you are considering adding networking to a group of existing PCs with applications that you have a financial investment in and that your users have spent time learning.

New software written specifically for a network often takes advantage of the network's ability to send data between PCs. In this class of software you will find electronic mail systems that let network users send messages to one another. Another use of this capability is to send files from one PC to another, a more direct and quicker form of sharing information than the non-network alternative of copying data to floppy disks and mailing or carrying it to another PC user.

Most network system software has controls that let programmers store data on a network server where it can be accessed by two or more network PCs at a time. A number of multiuser-shared database systems are appearing for networks that provide not only all the features of single-user data base systems but also extra controls for use in the network environment. If you use a database management system on a stand-alone PC and would like to be able to share databases with other PC users, this is the type of software you need. If you write your own programmes for your database manager, you will need to learn some multi-user database update rules, which should be provided by the vendor of your network database management system.

Although its use seldom justifies the cost of a network, another popular application of networks is a multiuser personal calendar manager. This type of software lets you maintain your own daily appointment calendar, which can be read and updated by others on the network; and you or any of several network users may even schedule meetings for all who use the calendar manager to keep their appointments.

CONNECTIONS TO OTHER NETWORKS

A gateway is a hardware device that connects two networks together and lets users on either network communicate with those on the other network. If the gateway happens to connect you to a public access network, you can communicate with other computer users who have access to the same public network. This capability is often used to send messages and files, or to log on to a remote computer using software that lets your PC act like a terminal.

Gateways are also used to connect with corporate mainframes, such as IBM systems networked with IBM's SNA. Many software packages let you access data on the mainframe (with proper authorisation) and import selected information to your PC for local processing. The most common uses of mainframe data include putting it into a database or spreadsheet for manipulation, analysis, graphing and reporting. If you have a number of users who need to do this occasionally, a single gateway on the network can give them all access to the mainframe, perhaps more economically than if everyone had individual connections to it.

CENTRALISED CONTROL AND DISTRIBUTED COMPUTING

A network can also help you to establish centralised control over some important aspects of computer use in your organisation, while still maintaining the benefits of distributed computing. A centralised, shared database is easier to manage than many small databases stored on individual PCs. And such a database is more appropriate for holding information that applies to or is used by more than one person. For example, if you store the names and addresses of customers in one centralised database that all your users can access over the network, a customer address need be updated only once, in the central database, and all users will see the latest version of the address the next time they access the database. If the address was stored in many different users individual PC databases, they would all need to update it, requiring much extra effort and increasing the likelihood of error or omission of an update. The same principle applies to many other types of information stored by every organisation.

Another advantage of centralised control of data is the ease of assembling information and analysing and reporting it. If data that needs to be compared or merged is stored on many different PCs, gathering it can take much time and effort. Often, as a consequence, opportunities that require such an effort are simply bypassed.

Storing data in one place also allows security to be increased. Most network software lets you control who can access data and what they can do to it. If someone needs to view a file or a part of a file, the network manager can grant the person access to that data as necessary. Without a network, the entire file may have to be copied and given to the user, running the risk that it will travel further than intended or that parts of it will be updated and then not merged in the original file, resulting in the creation of several versions of the file. It may be impossible later to reconstruct a consistent, accurate set of information. Networking does not by itself eliminate the problem: the network manager must set up the proper security controls for the benefit to be felt. If network users can freely copy files to their own PCs, the exact opposite scenario could take place, with many versions of the same file again in existence across the network.

While providing the benefits of centralised data storage, a network still retains the attraction of distributed processing. Each user having his own computer allows for consistent, predictable response time as long as all processing is being done on that local computer. If you add networking to a group of existing PCs, you should try to configure the system so that people can use their PCs just as before and get the same response times, or use new features provided by the network at its performance level. Since some parts of the network can be used by only one user at a time, access to the network is subject to delays — you may have to wait your turn to use the network disk or printer. Most waits for any single operation take only some thousandths of a second, but if many users stack up many requests, a delay can be several seconds or more.

SHOULD YOU WAIT TO BUY A LAN?

A local area network can represent a sizable investment, and many potential LAN purchasers have taken a "wait and see" attitude while they watch LAN hardware mature and LAN applications increase in number and capability. For a long time, LAN installations seemed best left to the pioneers, but many of the reasons behind people's decisions to wait have been addressed by today's PC networks.

SIZE OF INVESTMENT

Large organisations have been especially hesitant to install networks for whole facilities or even the entire corporation. There is a very real concern that installation of the "wrong" network on such a large scale could be an enormous waste of money. Many customers in this category have been installing smaller trial networks as learning experiments, seeing how the network solution fits their needs. You may want to consider doing something similar, if you have enough time to make a decision.

On the other hand, managers of a small organisation that needs a few PCs connected together to do a specific job may make their decisions under a different kind of pressure. Their goal may be to select a cost-effective network that gets the known jobs done, rather than making a choice that will be right for hundreds or even thousands of users, doing unanticipated things with the network for many years in the future.

STANDARDS

The more you anticipate growth in the types of things you will do with connected PCs, the more important standards become. While a proprietary, non-standard system may do the job perfectly well, a network that adheres to a published standard gives you the benefits of increased competition on its price, may give you a larger selection of vendors for hardware and software components, and is more likely to be the subject of long-term development attention from many vendors.

Some of the benefits of having industry standards are being realised through a combination of de facto standards for networking software, such as Microsoft's MS-DOS and IBM's NETBIOS, and published standards for networking hardware, mostly from the IEEE 802 committees. Selection of an IEEE 802 standard network does not guarantee that you can easily intermix software and hardware from different vendors and achieve a working result. The IEEE standards are an important part of the picture, but taken alone they do not address enough of the total network system to facilitate such a mix and match of components.

The IBM and Microsoft industry standards go a long way toward filling the software gap in the networking standards story. Many major PC network vendors are providing these standards for their networks, so software vendors can put their products on a large variety of networks by writing to the IBM and Microsoft interfaces. You should check to make sure the software you purchase will work on the hardware you have, but things are getting much closer to the state of single-user software on the IBM PC, where vendors know that by writing to MS-DOS and BIOS interfaces their software will run on many compatible systems. Another significant software standard has been set by Novell with their NetWare networking software, which runs on the hardware of a large number of vendors and provides a uniform user and programming interface.

PRICES

The networking industry has recognised that price is an important part of any buying decision, and has worked hard at making LANs more affordable. The Ethernet system is a good example. The original Ethernet standard dictates an expensive hook-up scheme that requires a heavy bus cable and an electronic transceiver box for every workstation and server. When combined with the network interface circuitry itself in each network node, the result was a high cost for every connection (well over $1,000), plus an expensive cable strung throughout the installation.

It was recognised that this cost was keeping many people from installing networks, so an alternative system was developed. Called Cheapernet, it offers connection costs under $700; uses thinner, less-expensive coaxial cable; and requires no transceiver. The new system runs software written for the original Ethernet, transmits data at the same rate (although over shorter distances), and can be connected to a LAN based on the original Ethernet cable. StarLAN by AT&T, which supports the Ethernet standard, can use even less expensive twisted-pair cable (which is already installed in many buildings) to connect telephones to a local switchboard.

In addition to cheaper cabling schemes, LAN hardware is benefiting from custom VLSI (very large scale integration) circuit technology. This approach replaces dozens of discrete parts with a single large custom integrated circuit, increasing reliability and decreasing manufacturing costs because there are fewer parts per network connection circuit.

The entire networking industry is also enjoying the usual advantages that come with increased sales volumes, and the entry of major firms such as AT&T and IBM can only help this trend. The resulting economies of scale tend to lower LAN prices further; lower prices lead to more sales, and for a while at least the benefits should be felt all around. If you wait, you may pay less, but one disadvantage of waiting is that you postpone the benefits of networking. If you decide that a network is right for your organisation but you do not want to pay more than is necessary, try to choose a network system that can expand sufficiently to meet your needs several years down the road, and buy only what you need today.

SOFTWARE

The limited availability of network software has also been given as a reason to postpone installing a LAN. Good software has been available for networks for some time, but much of it has come from smaller firms with lower advertising budgets, so it does not have as obvious a market presence as the major single-user PC software. The large software vendors have delayed making their software available on networks not because of technical problems, but rather because of struggles over how to license software for a LAN. The problems are twofold: how to deal with a system on which the number of users may be constantly changing, and how to administer a scheme that charges fairly but does not put undue restrictions on end users.

Most vendors are settling on one of two schemes: either a flat-fee site license covering all users in one installation, or a charge per active user coupled with a software lock that lets only the licensed number of users run the product at a time.

Two other factors have helped increase the variety of software available for networks: standards and the increasing number of LAN installations. Software standards such as NETBIOS and MS-DOS give software vendors a single interface that enables them to write their software for a large fraction of the installed network base. A bigger market usually attracts more vendors, and software developers are no exception. Even the major vendors who had deferred offering network versions of their software are starting to recognise the importance of the market and are offering network software.

The pioneering phase of networking PCs is over. Standards have emerged, networks have become affordable for many and software for accomplishing many useful tasks is available. Although you still should make sure that the benefits of a network justify its cost, most of the earlier reasons to wait before purchasing a LAN have been largely overcome.

LANS AND MULTIUSER SYSTEMS

Many of the problems that are addressed by a local area network can also be solved by a multiuser time-shared computer system. The typical multiuser system has one central computer connected to several terminals, as shown in Figure 6.1. The system is called time-shared because the processing time of the central computer is shared among all the terminals. All application software on a multiuser system runs on the central processor and the terminals are used for keyboard input and screen output only. By contrast, in a PC network each user's workstation is a full-fledged computer capable of running software on its own.

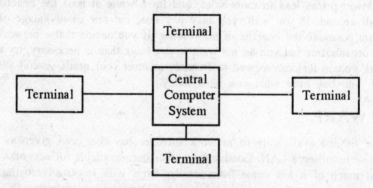

Fig. 6.1 : A Multiuser system

Each approach has its own advantages, and there are cases where a combination of the two approaches works best. In a combination approach, multiuser systems may be networked together, allowing easy transfer of information between them while retaining the benefits of multiuser systems where needed.

It is typically less expensive to add a user to a multiuser system than to a network — a terminal costs substantially less than a personal computer and a network connection (although that price gap is narrowing). The problem with this generalisation comes when the performance limits of a multiuser system are reached. For example, it costs much more than the price of 4 terminals to add 4 more users to a 16-user installation based on a multiuser system that only handles 4 to 16 terminals. Replacement of the central computer itself may be required if the performance or the physical connection capability of the original central processor has been exceeded.

Adding workstations to a network tends to degrade performance more gradually than does adding terminals to a time-sharing system— as long as each workstation does a lot of local processing and does not drain the network servers as much as terminals do a central processor. However, networks also can have discontinuities in their cost-per-user curves. A discontinuity occurs at the point at which the network server is saturated and needs to be replaced or augmented by another server. Things can get very expensive if it is difficult to add a new network server and coordinate its use with an existing server. A multiuser system is more likely to be expandable with less impact on software, as long as there is some way to replace or upgrade the central computer with a more powerful system that can run the same software as the old system.

For some purposes, there is more software available for multiuser systems than for networks, especially software customised for specific vertical market segments such as law offices, wholesalers, construction businesses, and the like. On the other hand, PCs have fostered the development of excellent personal productivity software such as word processors, spreadsheets and personal data managers, and many of these packages have built a strong following among end-users, who may not want to give them up for the benefits of a pure multiuser system.

While use of the popular single-user software on a network is still the subject of investigation by many software vendors, multiuser systems have forced software vendors to deal with the multiuser licensing issue. In most cases the approach taken is to license for a single computer, but one that is a multiuser computer so that all the users connected to that machine can use the software.

Consistent response time is one of the personal computer's greatest attractions, and a network maintains this feature for software that runs on the workstation. In a multiuser system, since all the applications software runs on the central computer, response time varies according to the number of users active at its terminals. A network puts processing power in each workstation, buffering the end user from network data transfer times under many conditions.

Networks also may give each user more control over the placement of files than do multiuser systems. Files that must be kept secure can be kept on floppy disk and loaded only at the workstation, while a multiuser system requires everything to be loaded on the central computer. This reliance on a central computer can affect downtime, too. If the central computer needs repair, no user can use any of the terminals. A network can usually function in a degraded fashion, letting each user run any application that run totally on the workstation until the server or network is repaired.

A network is most needed when a group of existing PCs need to communicate, or when the ability to run PC software that can not be used on a multiuser system is required. A multiuser system is a better choice when low-cost expansion up to the limits of the system is mandated, or when a specific software package that is not available on a network provides the best solution. You should also keep the coexistence approach in mind, since it may let you benefit from the best features of each approach.

CONCLUSIONS

The decision to use a networking approach is a major one and should be driven by your needs and analysis of the costs and benefits of installing a LAN. The conditions for purchasing a LAN are favourably and continually improving.

A cost benefit analysis sounds worse than it really is. All that is really required for most businesses is a careful look at all of the factors. Often, the analysis will show some overwhelming factor that dictates a specific choice, regardless of the other factors. In many other cases, the analysis will serve to illustrate what the planners already suspected. Sometimes, though, a careful analysis will turn up a surprise, showing that a previously unsuspected alternative is the most cost effective.

While a LAN is nearly always more cost effective than most other multi-user alternatives, it is not always so. In addition, there are some jobs that a PC-based LAN simply can not handle. If you are dealing with a huge database with millions of records, you might find this to be the case for you. Likewise an installation with thousands of users sharing common data might find a mainframe or minicomputer more likely to meet their needs.

The only way to be sure of this, however, is to do the analysis. Such an analysis is also a good way to make sure you remember to consider all of the costs and benefits of any such installation. Even if it does not change your mind about which one to choose, it will help keep you from being surprised by the outcome.

EVALUATING AND SELECTING A LOCAL AREA NETWORK

INTRODUCTION

As you analyse the features of candidate LANs, you need to consider their ability to handle not only your present needs but your future needs as well. An accurate assessment of present needs requires a detailed understanding of the problems you are trying to solve. Assessing future needs requires that you put your networking requirements into the context of your business or organisational plan, especially with regard to the need to transfer and process information. A network represents a sizable investment and should be one that can grow with your computer applications. Think about growth in areas such as the number of network nodes, capacity of disk storage, number of print servers, and the size of the physical area covered by the network. Also, if you will be using off-the-shelf software, how much software is available for the network you choose? The network vendor or your dealer may be able to provide you with a catalogue of currently supported software applications.

GENERAL

Cost is always an important consideration. PC networking is a competitive business, and advances in electronic technology are currently driving costs down. Highly integrated designs are reducing the number of parts required on a network interface card. Follow two rules of thumb: choose a vendor who is actively working with new technology so that expansion of your LAN in the future will benefit from reduced costs, and do not buy more hardware than you need as long as prices continue to fall over time.

Ease of installing and using the network should be a major factor in your selection. The software used to initialise and manage your network is the biggest factor in this respect. Do not be fooled by the simple appearance of the floppy disk your network software comes on, compared to the pages of impressive-sounding specifications describing the hardware. The hardware must be right for you, but the software is even more important. The discussion here will help you learn what to look for in network software and you should plan to spend more time evaluating the software than the hardware in your network purchase.

You should evaluate your network vendor and its local representative to assess the support you will get during the planning, installation and use of your network. Truly useful service requires expertise and time, so be wary of assurances that all the help you need is free. A certain amount of consulting and assistance may be covered in the cost of the sale, but free long-term assistance is probably either nonexistent or of low quality, or the assurance of such assistance a signal that the provider is new in business or would not be around very long. Reliable references from previous sales should be requested and checked. You should also request references before hiring a consultant to help with any phase of your network installation.

Once the network is installed, you and your end-users will need training. You should evaluate your own situation and decide if you your staff and your users need to attend classes. If so, see if your dealer offers them, how much they cost and when they are given. Unless you have considerable in-house expertise or a lot of patience, you should not plan to depend entirely on reading the manuals, figuring it out for yourself and training your end-users. If your programmers are going to be modifying software for the network, consider the availability of technical documentation and training for them. Your network dealer or vendor should be able to assist you in locating these.

Maintenance of your system may be a critical factor. More productivity depends on your network being up and running, hence it is vital that you have fast, dependable service for it. The same consideration also applies to any other computer equipment. If you are used to a single-user PC environment, you may not be prepared for the way a network increases the dependency of many users on a single piece of hardware. For example, if several point-of-sale computers or a classroom full of student PCs all depend on a network disk server, the failure of that disk server may require that service be quicker than would the failure of a single PC. Many service options exist, ranging from on-site service within a couple of hours of the failure, through mailing the suspected component away for a couple of weeks. You must consider the options and make sure the appropriate ones are available for the system you select.

APPLICATIONS

The most important consideration in selecting a network is its ability to solve a problem, increase productivity or enhance the operation of your organisation. The first step in choosing a network has little to do with the network system itself. You must carefully determine what you want the network to achieve and what application software can be used to meet these goals. It may be off-the-shelf software from a third-party vendor or it may be custom written by your programmers or a consultant. Your PC network should be chosen for its ability to run this software.

EXISTING SOFTWARE

If you are networking a group of PCs that are already in use, you need to analyse how existing software will function in the network environment. Even if you decide that existing software will be used in the same way as before and will not take special advantage of the network environment, you must still be sure it does not conflict with the network in any way. In some cases a software package or hardware card may be unable to run at all on a workstation that is equipped with a network connection. You dealer, network vendor or application software vendor should be able to tell you what will and will not work together.

If you want to take advantage of the network with existing software, you should check the same sources to see if the version you own supports the network you want to install. You may have to purchase an upgraded version of the software that incorporates network support. Make sure the software works with the network in the way that you need it to.

If your applications are written by your own programmers, you need to understand how this software will function on a network. The same considerations apply as for outside-developed software, but you cannot turn to an outside vendor for answers. It may be necessary to consult with the vendor of the programming language your applications are written in. Some implementations of programming languages work with networks, while others have problems. In any case, if you decide that achieving the desired results requires that your applications be modified, you or your programmers must first review the network to make sure that it supplies the functions you need. This phase of network selection is very technical and must be done by someone familiar with your applications and with multiuser programming environments, which present a new set of problems compared to single-user environments. You must perform a similar analysis if you need new, custom-written applications for your network. You may have more freedom of choice for a programming language for a new application.

NEW SOFTWARE

If one reason for buying a network is to run new applications such as shared database applications or electronic mail that require a network, you may find a suitable off-the-shelf package from an outside software vendor. The vendor can tell you what networks the package supports, and you can evaluate the features of the package rather than its ability to run on a network.

LAN EVALUATION

The LAN shopper has many networks and a wide range of features, components and prices from which to choose. This variety tends to complicate the selection process but also enables users to design systems ideally suited to their particular needs. Before the network is actually up and running, many components must be evaluated applications, software peripherals, workstations, servers and LAN hardware. We concentrate on the components of the basic system. In most cases, the selection process should be based on the intended applications and environment in which the network is used. The first stage in the evaluation process, therefore, should be a careful description of the LAN functions and the physical site.

Any network you evaluate has three main components: workstations, servers and connections. Most networks support only a limited number of choices in these three areas, so although you must evaluate your network selection in all three dimensions, you will probably have to make trade-offs in deciding which network system most closely meets your requirements.

Following is a list of questions that should be answered:

PHYSICAL SITE

1. What is the maximum distance between workstations?

2. Can you use existing cable?

   A. No requirement

   B. Telephone wire (twisted pair)

   C. 3270 cable (RG-62)

   D. Others (specify)

3. What is the workstation distribution?

   A. Clustered

   B. Distributed

4. What types of workstations will be used? (brand and model)

FUNCTIONS

1. How many workstations?

2. How many hours will each workstation be in use?

3. List each workstation's applications (word processing, data entry, and so on).

4. List the percentage of workday devoted to each application.

PERFORMANCE

1. What is the desired response time? (Select comparable)

   A. XT floppy drive

   B. XT hard disk drive

   C. AT hard disk drive

2.   Which is the primary consideration?

A.   Cost

B.   Performance

Answers to these questions will help determine the right LAN system for a particular site. Following are some examples of how the site definition is used.

THE PHYSICAL SITE

Physical site requirements help determine what network cable and topology are best. Each type of cable has inherent distance limitations. Twisted pair supports short runs. Baseband coaxial supports longer runs. Broadband coaxial and fibre optics support extremely long runs. Transmission speed is limited by cable, too, with fibre optics being the fastest, followed by baseband coaxial, broadband and twisted pair.

Matched against the cable characteristics are the types of available cable. You may be able to take the cable that is already installed and use it on the LAN. Twisted-pair and 3270 cabling (RG-62) are often available and can be used for LANs, provided that the cable meets the transmission speed requirements.

Before you decide to use installed telephone wire (twisted pair) for a LAN, you should carefully test its condition and suitability. Voice transmissions are much more tolerant of media imperfections than are data transmissions. Barely audible noise on the line that is only annoying during a telephone conversation often prevents successful data communication. Telephone systems often are a collection of old and new wiring and switches and this medium frequently fails during high-speed data communication. The higher the data transmission rates (in excess of 1 Mbs) and the longer the distances between communicating devices, the more likely the failure.

But telephone wire systems are being used successfully for LANs in many buildings - and with a considerable saving in cabling costs. Do not reject the idea without testing its feasibility.

Existing broadband cable systems can be used for new LAN installations, provided that the existing installation supports two-way communication. Many corporations and campuses have a broadband cable system that was installed for cable TV transmissions. Converting a cable TV system to support broadband data transmission is seldom practical because the initial cable TV installation was designed for one-way communication only. LANs are two-way communication systems. Installing new broadband cable usually is cheaper than converting the existing system. Due to the large potential savings of using an existing cable system, its feasibility for a particular site always should be analysed by an expert.

Cable selection has long-term implications that are especially significant in large installations. If properly chosen and installed, LAN cable can give satisfactory service for 10, 15 or more years before it has to be replaced or upgraded. Because the cable and cable installation costs typically are 50 percent of the cost of the entire installation, careful planning is well worth the effort.

Network topology should be matched to the site layout. Topology affects the amount of cable that must be purchased and installed. Even the cable bulk should be considered. Some cable trays may not have room for three or four more wires that may be required by some topologies. If workstations are clustered, a star topology is ideal. If they are distributed through individual offices, a linear bus topology is good. The distributed star topology is a natural choice when connection must be made to small clusters of workstations distributed through several offices. The star-wired ring (IBM cabling system) was designed as a wiring scheme for large buildings, so this system uses a star topology for individual floors and connects the floors with a single high-speed cable - a good strategy for large buildings.

NETWORK FUNCTIONS

Network functions and performance are closely related. Looking at the checklist, you may realise that the proposed network has a current need for eight workstations. If you add three more workstations within a few months, include those also as current workstations.

Long-range growth should be considered and included in your overall network strategy. But because of the flexible architecture of networks, you usually do not need to install a high-performance system in anticipation of a future need.

The number of workday hours a workstation is in use (question 2 on the checklist) is a factor in determining the station's impact on the network. For example, a workstation may be used by outside salespeople for an average of three hours a day, or it may be used a full eight hours a day. The types of applications and their percentage of the day's activity also will affect the network. Word processing is a light user of a network because most processing is done locally. Database work is a heavy user of a network because data continually must be sent back to the network to update the shared hard disk.

WORKSTATIONS

If you need to use non-IBM PC workstations on your network, you must select a network vendor that supports different types of computers on a single network. Make sure you understand how the different kinds of computers need to share such network resources as disk storage and printers, and be sure that the network you choose permits the right degree of sharing. For example, some networks may let you connect two different kinds of personal computer workstations to the same cable, but may require that each have its own separate disk server, and there may be no way to exchange data between the two computers.

The workstation hardware requirements that you need to evaluate include:

*   Amount of random access memory (RAM) required.

*.   Amount of local disk storage required.

*   Compatibility with other workstation hardware.

You should also consider whether the number of workstations supported by the network meets your current and projected needs. Your greatest evaluative effort should be spent on the workstation software, concentrating on such things as:

* Ease of installation and use.

* Number of needed functions supported.

* Ability to run application software.

* Performance.

* Flexibility and ease of modification.

* Security.

EVALUATING NIC

All the components in a LAN have the potential to affect the LAN's performance, yet no classification scheme is commonly available to rate LAN component performance. Because performance ratings are not available, you have to use what statistics are available to estimate performance.

The network interface card (NIC) has four characteristics that typically are used to predict NIC performance. These are:

1. Bit rate

2. Access method

3. On-board processor

4. NIC-to-host transfer

The bit rate often is referred to as the speed of the LAN. LANs are rated according to the speed of data crossing a clear piece of cable. Most of the LANs have bit rates from 1Mbs up to 10Mbs. Actual throughput is never 100% of the bit rate because of other LAN performance factors. And because of individual NIC design factors, one 10Mbs NIC may have very high throughput, whereas another may have very low throughput. Therefore, bit rate is a poor way to compare LANs, especially when the bit rates of the systems being compared are close.

Bit rate, however, should be considered in the selection process. Although a high bit rate does not guarantee high throughput, a low bit rate does guarantee low throughput. A 1Mbs LAN might get 80 percent of the bit rate as throughput. But that amount is only 0.8Mbs or 100 kilobytes per second throughput. A 10Mbs LAN might be much less efficient, getting perhaps 40 % of the bit rate as throughput. Yes that 40% would amount to 4Mbs throughput.

The cable access scheme of a NIC tells virtually nothing about its actual performance. Theoretically, a token-passing access scheme is more efficient in high-traffic situations than a contention scheme (CSMA-CD, and so forth), but the NIC's design can overcome limitations in the access scheme.

The on-board processor is another poor way to judge NICs. Logically, an on-board processor should make for a faster, more efficient NIC. In practice, though, the firmware used to control the on-board processor often is inefficient and that factor increases system overhead.

The NIC-to-host transfer method - the fourth of the NIC evaluation features - is the most valuable for making comparisons. The width of current transfer buses usually is 8- or 16- bits. A NIC with a 16-bit-wide bus interface transfers data twice as fast as an 8-bit-wide interface.

Three methods are used to transfer data: shared memory, I/O port and direct memory access (DMA). Shared memory is the fastest because it involves no data transfers. DMA is the slowest because all data must be transferred into a contiguous area of memory to be read.

One other criterion that should be considered when evaluating NICs is the types of workstations the NICs support. The IBM PC bus is a standard, and most of the NICs can be plugged into PC or PC-compatible buses. Additionally, many LAN companies make NICs that also support one or more different buses. If your company wants to network different types of PCs, bus compatibility becomes an important issue.

EVALUATING SERVERS

Many computers can act as network servers. Most are AT-compatible machines; however, several machines have been designed especially for use as network servers. The criteria used to describe network servers are the primary ones used in evaluation. They are:

- Processor

- Clock cycle speed

- Wait states

- Memory (max)

- Expansion bus

- Bus width

Processor is the most commonly understood performance factor. Anybody who has ever used an 8088 workstation and then switched to an 80486 workstation knows the effect of faster processors.

Processor speed is rated according to how much data a processor can process and transfer in a single block. The Intel 8088 processor, which is used in the PC- and XT-compatible machines, processes data 16 bits at a time and transfers data 8 bits at a time. The Intel 80186 processes and transfers data in 16-bit blocks. Intel's 80286, used in AT-compatible machines, also is a 16/16 processor. The Motorola MC68000 processor processes data 32 bits at a time and transfers 16 bits at a time.

The processor is driven at a set speed by a component called a clock crystal.

Faster clock cycle speeds result in faster performance. An 80286 machine with a 16 MHz crystal, for example, might be able to perform a task in one second but, with an 20 MHz crystal, could do the same task in 0.6 seconds.

In computers, circuitry performance and processor/clock crystal performance must be balanced. A processor that runs faster than the circuits can support must be slowed down. This is accomplished by placing wait states between the processor and the circuitry. One wait state is a period of time equal to one cycle of the clock crystal. Wait states cause a delay in the delivery of data to the circuitry so that the flow of data matches the capability of the circuitry. A machine with one wait state is slower than a machine with zero wait states, all other things being equal.

Memory maximum refers to the total amount of random-access memory (RAM) supported in the machine. Available RAM can be used in a server to cache or store temporarily, data in electronic memory. Because accesses to electronic memory are much faster than accesses to a physical disk, available RAM does affect performance.

Expansion buses, which allow computers to adapt to changing technology, affect both performance and adaptability. Machines with expansion buses, such as AT-compatible machines, generally transfer data slower than machines that use proprietary buses. But expansion buses often are desirable. For example, new generations of NICs generally outperform old NICs. The old NICs can be replaced provided that the machine has an expansion bus. Moreover, an expansion bus permits the machine to serve multiple networks when that capability is supported by the network operating system.

The bus width involves the same issue as the NIC-to-host transfer width discussed under network interface. A 16-bit-wide bus transfers data twice as fast as an 8-bit-wide bus.

Most vendors of IBM PC networks let you use IBM PCs as servers as well as workstations — at least to provide disk and print service to the network. Many vendors also provide proprietary hardware-based servers, usually claiming higher performance than can be had from PCs. Your choice of server can, therefore, extend beyond the issues mentioned under workstations to include the choice of the hardware itself.

Some networks offer you a choice between dedicated and non-dedicated servers. A dedicated server is useful only as a server, while a non-dedicated server can also be used simultaneously as a workstation. This is a cost/performance trade-off, for such use of a server as a workstation almost always diminishes its performance as a server except possibly if it was being given very light use in either capacity. Another consideration is the vulnerability of a server used as a workstation: the workstation user should be running only well-tested software in a stable configuration, since any crashes or "hang ups" of this software can adversely affect a whole community of users with work in progress on the server.

Another choice must be made between multipurpose and singlepurpose servers — between, say, use of a single PC/AT as both a disk and print server and use of two PC/ATs, one functioning as a disk server and the other as a print server. Again, this choice usually presents a cost/performance trade-off. Two PC/ATs cost more than one but if both functions are used heavily enough you will get better performance from two than if you try to implement both these functions on a single PC/AT. If you decide to try a multipurpose server or a nondedicated server, you should set up an experimental configuration and see if the performance meets your needs before you order a full network configuration based on that choice.

Disk Servers. Some of the factors to consider when evaluating network disk storage servers are:

* Number of mass storage servers supported.

* Number, capacity and speed of hard disks per server.

* Method of splitting disks up between workstations.

* Provisions for multiuser file sharing and locking.

You may have to choose between a file server and a disk server. The difference between the two is pretty technical, and you need not be too concerned about it as long as your applications work properly and you are satisfied with performance. The distinction has to do with the nature of the information that passes between a workstation and the server. Figure 7.1 shows a simplified view of a workstation application package accessing a disk drive through MS-DOS (Microsoft Disk Operating System). The goal of any PC network is to allow the application to access the disk on a remote computer as if the disk drive were on the local computer. Thus, network software must first intercept the application's request to read or write a local disk file and send that request to the remote disk or file server for processing; it then must get the result that is returned from the remote server and pass it to the application, just as if it had come from the workstation's MS-DOS.

Workstatiion

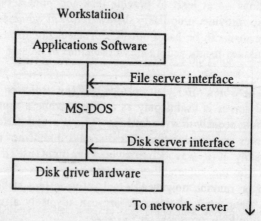

Fig. 7.1 : Difference between file server and disk server

With a disk server, interception occurs between MS-DOS and the local disk drive. When an application requests a block from a file that is on a network disk server, the workstation MS-DOS does most of the work. MS-DOS computes the location of the disk block and requests it from what it treats as a local disk drive. The network system software intercepts this request and sends it to the disk server, which reads or writes the appropriate block on the server's disk.

With a file server, the workstation MS-DOS does not become involved with a network disk file access. The network system software intervenes before MS-DOS can receive a network disk file request. Instead, the entire request is sent over to the file server, which processes it and sends back the results.

Sometimes a single application request to read or write a file block can result in several disk input or output operations between MS-DOS and the disk drive. In such cases, using a disk server may generate more network traffic than using a file server; the file server sends the initial request from the workstation to the server and the server sends back only the final result; by contrast, the disk server sends the intermediate results back and forth, since the MS-DOS on the workstation must process the extra disk blocks.

You should try to find objective performance information comparing data access speeds for the networks you evaluate. The performance of the network disk or file server will have a strong effect on the performance of many applications and on the number of workstations you can connect.

Print Servers. Print servers, like disk servers, may be implemented on proprietary hardware or on IBM PC compatible computers. Some considerations when selecting a print server are:

* Number of printers supported.

* Interfaces supported, serial or parallel.

* Printer models supported.

* Print server software.

In addition to letting you share a printer among several workstations, a print server usually stores print output on a server disk drive and sends it to the printer as fast as the printer can accept it. This capability, called **print spooling**, means that the print server must have adequate disk storage to handle the volume of files your users will send to be printed. You will probably need a hard disk and perhaps should consider using a disk server as a print server too. The software used to control the print server may vary from vendor to vendor and you should be sure that it provides the functions you need.

Other Servers. Disk and print servers are the most widely used network service, but there are others that your applications may require. Some of the most common are:

* Backup servers.

* Gateway servers.

* Remote communication (modem) servers.

You must plan for the backup of your network mass storage. Tape cartridges are a popular medium for storage, since you can often back up an entire hard disk on a single cartridge. You may prefer cartridge disk servers, or even a duplicate hard disk server that can hold as much as your primary network disk.

Gateways, used to connect dissimilar networks, are discussed in more detail later. Remote communication servers are useful if the network needs to be accessed from a remote site over a phone line using a **modem** (modulator-demodulator), a device that converts data into tones that can be transmitted over the phone. Two computers connected to the phone with modems can send files and other information back and forth. A good remote communication server lets you use the network from a remote site just as if you were connected with a local workstation. Peformance is usually slowed down by the limits of the phone lines. Another seeming use of a modem on a network, for sharing information among workstations, usually does not work out well because little of the PC communication software is adapted to this environment.

EVALUATING OPERATING SYSTEMS

The choice of network operating system, perhaps more than any other LAN component, will determine the success of the LAN. Some of the important criteria for judging network operating systems are ease of use, data safety, support for standards, cost, performance, security, and functionality.

The relevant standards today are DOS 4.1 and NETBIOS. An operating system must support these application-to-network interfaces to have access to the large number of software packages and hardware devices being developed for the standards. People with non-standard products argue that you usually need no more than a few applications, not thousands. That is true. If, however, the products you choose are standard products, they will offer you a better migration path and probably lower cost.

Cost also applies to the network operating system itself. Cost should be considered closely with performance. A high-performance network operating system can support more workstations and is, therefore, more cost effective for large or growing installations.

PC Network Programme is the slowest operating system because it uses DOS as an integral part of the network operating system. DOS's performance is adequate in a single workstation, but it cannot provide high performance in a multiuser network environment.

3+ is faster than PC Network Programme. 3+ gains the speed advantage by using a DOS-emulation programme instead of DOS itself, and the emulator is enhanced with performance features.

Netware is the fastest of the DOS-compatible operating systems by a factor of 200 to 300 percent. Rather than using DOS or emulating it, Netware is built on a special operating system designed specifically for network and shared disk management. This strategy has a limitation in that some hard disks are not compatible with NetWare. NetWare supports all IBM PC-compatible drives and many other major drives. If you already have a non-IBM PC type disk drive and want to use it on your network, however, you should verify the disk drive's compatibility.

Network system security is implemented through one of two methods. Security is based either on a name/password that's associated with network objects or on user profiles. In a name/password system, every directory must be accessed with a name and optional password. With user profiles, after the login name and password are entered, all directories authorised to that user can be accessed with normal directory and path commands.

The name/password system is more difficult to set up and maintain than the user profile system. Both security schemes, however, are easy to use. In the name/password system, you can store names and passwords in a batch file to eliminate the need to remember them at each log-in. Unfortunately, when the names and passwords are stored in batch files, they can be accessed at the workstation and read with simple DOS commands, so the system loses its security.

Functionality is different among the network operating systems. A quick way to evaluate functionality is to compare the lists of network commands.

CONNECTIONS

It is ironic that the components most readily identified with a network cables and network interface hardware are in many respects the least important components. The applications supported by the network and the network-management software are what you use the most. The performance limits of the server software or hardware are usually reached before the limits of cable bandwidth (which is the data transfer speed) or network-interface hardware design can be approached. Still, there are many important choices to make with respect to connections, especially relative to costs.

There are three main areas to consider in choosing a network connection scheme: the cable type, the topology (or physical layout)and the low-level network protocol used to transmit data. Each LAN vendor usually bundles together a solution that addresses each of these three areas, so you do not have to decide on them individually.

Cable Types. The choice of a LAN limits your cabling options. Many LANs are designed to work with only one type of cable, although some can accommodate two or more types. In many cases the wiring is the most expensive part of installing LAN, and the importance of this aspect of the cabling choice is clear. You must be sure you know the details of each LAN's requirements before you estimate cabling costs. The most common cables are twisted-pair and coaxial cable commonly called "coax". Each of these is available in different grades at different costs per foot.

Twisted-pair, the least expensive medium, is simply two wires twisted together and covered with an insulating sheath. Twisted-pair has another cost advantage over coax — most buildings are already wired with twisted-pair for their phone systems. Networks that can use this existing cable can often be installed at significantly less cost than systems that require new wiring. The disadvantges of twisted-pair include greater sensitivity to noise, possibly resulting in the repeated transmission of network messages to correct transmission errors; shorter distance coverage than coax for some networks; and lower data rate than coax on some networks.

Coaxial cable is very commonly used in LANs and it comes in several varieties, offering a range in terms of:

* Cost per foot.

* Thickness and flexibility.

* Ease of installation.

* Usable lengths.

* Bandwidths.

Network connections can be categorised as **baseband** or **broadband**. Baseband supports fewer channels of information than broadband; the connection is usually less expensive and the installation less critical. Ethernet and the IBM token-ring are examples of baseband networks. A broadband network cable is physically capable of carrying other signals such as video, voice and security information as well as network data traffic. However, appropriate hardware and software is needed to take advantage of this low-level physical capability. The IBM PC Network is an example of a broadband network.

Fibre optic cables are by far the most expensive medium, but they are also the most resistant to noise and interference and thus have a very low error rate. There are fewer vendors of fibre optic LANs than there are of electrical wire-based systems, but commercial products do exist and are in use. If very high noise immunity is important to you, it may be worthwhile to investigate this choice further.

Repeaters. Cabling distances vary with cable and network card choices. If you expect to expand your network you should determine whether the maximum cable length supported is enough for your needs. Some networks can employ repeaters: hardware devices that considerably extend the maximum usable length of the cable. A repeater works at the physical level; that is, to the network software it is not distinguishable from the cable.

Bridge. Another way to extend networks is with a bridge. A bridge connects two identical networks and passes messages between them. However, it is a bit smarter than a repeater; it only sends messages to the other network that are destined for it, while a repeater transfers everything back and forth, just like a cable. Bridges can cut down on total network traffic by splitting up your network into clusters of those workstations and servers that most often talk to one another. Since the messages local to the cluster stay within that part of the network and do not go past the bridge, the amount of irrelevant network traffic on the other side of the bridge is reduced. However, a bridge can become a bottleneck if it is slower than a simple piece of cable or a repeater and if you put it in the wrong place, such as in between two or more network nodes that communicate heavily.

Topologies. Your choice of a network also involves selecting a layout of physical connections, or topology. The most common PC LAN layout is the **bus** structure, shown in Figure 7.2: a single cable is routed everywhere a connection is needed, and workstations and servers are connected to it. Some networks, such as Ethernet, let you make the connection with a tap that does not cut the wire in two. You can connect a new workstation to the LAN or remove an existing one without disturbing the workstations on either side or shutting the LAN down during the operation. A bus usually results in a shorter total cable length than the other topologies. It has the disadvantage that a single break in the cable may bring the entire network operation to a halt.

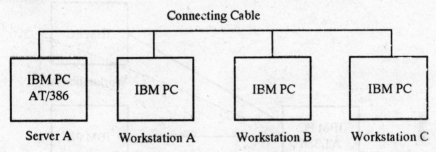

Fig. 7.2 : Bus network topology

The second major cable layout, the **ring**, is like a bus structure with its ends tied together, as shown in Figure 7.3. One of the technical disadvantages of a ring is that at some level each node in the ring has to handle all the data being transferred in the network. For example, in Figure 7.3, for A to pass a file to C, B must handle the file as an intermediary. Failure of a single node can disrupt the entire network's operation. The main advantage of this topology is that it is more deterministic than a bus (explained below under the discussion of protocols).

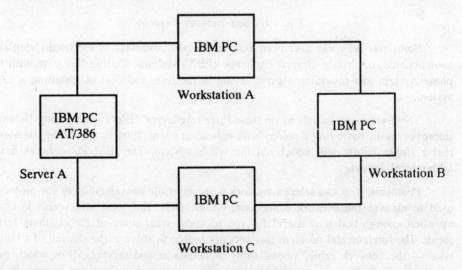

Fig. 7.3 : Ring network topology

The **star** topology, shown in Figure 7.4, resembles many traditional multiuser or time-sharing systems: a central computer with separate lines to each workstation. This layout usually requires more total cable length than the bus or ring. Star networks often terminate each line with a cluster controller, a specialised computer capable of handling several workstations, thus improving the economy of the wiring. Furthermore, star configurations often use twisted-pair — the least expensive cable. Since each line is dedicated to carrying information between only two nodes, it can be of a lower bandwidth than a bus, which must handle traffic for all the nodes.

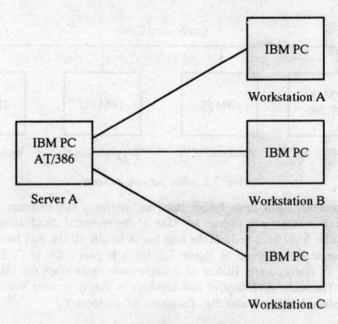

Fig. 7.4 : Star Network topology

Some star networks have been designed to take advantage of electronic telephone switchboards, or Private Branch Exchange (PBX) systems, sharing this wire with the phone system and providing a great saving in the time and cost of installing a LAN system.

There are many variations on these three topologies. IBM's Token-Ring Network improves on the basic ring topology with redundant connections to reduce the likelihood that a single failure will knock out the whole system. The IBM PC network has a hierarchical layout.

Protocols. You can select a network with very little consideration of the protocols used to manage the network connection. Nevertheless, this topic still seems to come up often enough that it is useful for you to know what some of the common terms mean. The fundamental problem that network protocols solve is the sharing of a single wire — the network cable, among many workstations and servers, all of which may need to use it at any unpredictable time. The most popular network protocols are **token passing** and **carrier sense multiple access/collision detection** (CSMA/CD). In brief, token passing is an orderly method of sharing a cable, while CSMA/CD lets every node use the cable when it needs to and handles collisions on the cable when they occur.

In a token-passing system, information is passed around the network from node to node. Messages are linked together and the last message is followed by a special message called the **token**, which signifies the end of the group of messages. As each node is passed, it removes from the group any old messages that it sent, since if it is seeing them again, they must have gone all the way around the network. the node reads any messages addressed to it and marks them as having been read, then passes them on to the next node. When the token is seen, any new messages to be sent are added to the end of the group, then the token is passed.

The CSMA/CD protocol is an entirely different means of regulating message traffic on the cable. Each node monitors the network and waits to transmit until the level of network traffic has subsided. If two nodes try to talk on the network at the same time, a collision occurs — it is sensed by the transmitting nodes, and they wait a randomly selected interval before trying again. To avoid continuous collisions, each node waits for different amounts of time before retransmitting.

CSMA/CD is used widely in PC LANs, the best-known example being Ethernet-based systems such as 3COMs. It is also used in the IBM PC Network product. Its main advantage is ease of reconfiguration — you can add a new workstation or server to a bus-based system at any time without shutting the network down. It is efficient under light use, but starts getting bogged down under heavy use because of the time spent recovering from collisions.

Token passing's main advantage is that it is "deterministic": each node gets a chance to transmit a message within a fixed amount of time. This feature is especially important in many manufacturing applications where a guaranteed response time is critical.

Token passing is also efficient under heavy use. Since there are no collisions, the bus cannot be overloaded. However, you cannot remove a workstation or server from the system without shutting down and reconfiguring, since removal of a node breaks the ring and the token stops in its tracks. It also takes some clever network software to recover from the loss or garbling of the token; in this respect token passing is more vulnerable than CSMA/CD.

In most cases, topology and protocol are not nearly as important factors as systems and applications software. Figures 7.5 to 7.8 presents comparative analysis of various network features by topology, media and protocol.

	Small	Medium	Large	Very Large
Topology :				
Bus	X—————————————		X	
Ring			X———————	—X
Star		X—————	X	

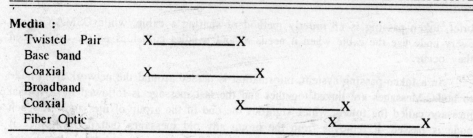

Media :

Twisted Pair	X————————X		
Base band			
Coaxial	X———— ————X		
Broadband			
Coaxial	X————————X		
Fiber Optic	X————————X	

Fig. 7.5 : Distance Compared by Topology and Media

	Low	Moderate	High	Very High
Media :				
Twisted Pair	X			
Base band				
Coaxial	X————X			
Broadband				
Coaxial		X————X		
Fiber Optic			X————X	
Protocol :				
Contention	X			
Token Passing			X	
Polling		X		

Fig. 7.6 : Network Traffic Capacity by Media and Protocol

	Easy	Moderate	Difficult
Topology :			
Bus	X		
Ring		X	
Star			X
Media :			
Twisted Pair	X		
Base band Coaxial	X		
Broadband Coaxial		X	
Fiber Optic			X
Protocol :			
Contention	X		
Token Passing		X	
Polling		X	

Fig. 7.7 : Expandability by Topology, Media, and Protocol

	Low	Moderate	High	Very High
Cable:				
Twisted Pair	X			
Base band				
Coaxial	X			
Broadband				
Coaxial		X		
Fiber Optic		X	X	
Installation :				
Twisted Pair	X			
Base band				
Coaxial	X			
Broadband				
Coaxial		X		
Fiber Optic			X	

Fig. 7.8 : Media Cost Comparison

ESTIMATING HARDWARE PERFORMANCE

Performance on a network is best expressed as throughput: How long does a request take to make its way from the workstation through the network to its destination? The two key hardware elements in that throughput are the NIC and the server.

A particular NIC-server combination can develop a maximum amount of throughput for a LAN. If that throughput is expressed in kilobytes per second, the NIC-server combination can put only a certain amount of kilobytes per second on the network.

Each network user shares that network throughput. If your NIC-server combination can deliver 300 kilobytes per second throughput and you are the only active user on the network, then potentially you could receive data at 300 kilobytes per second. If two other people are using the network at the same time, the total throughput now is divided among three users. Each could get a maximum of 100 kilobytes per second.

One other factor is significant: how much throughput a single workstation actually can handle under a particular NIC-server combination. Because of workstation limitations, that figure usually is going to be less than maximum NIC-server throughput.

Therefore, to calculate the probable throughput available to each workstation for a given NIC-server combination, you need to know three things:

1. The maximum throughput

2. The single station throughput

3. The number of users

Of these variables, quantifying the number of users is the most difficult. The type of application and the number of hours per day devoted to that application will decide the actual load on the network. For example, you might have a ten-station network, but one workstation is in the boss's office and is never used. Obviously when you are calculating the number of people that divide up the available NIC-server throughput, you divide by nine workstations, not ten, even though the network actually is connected to ten workstations.

But that example is rudimentary. The number of users needs to be defined much more carefully. For an accurate approximation of user activity, categorise users into five groups. The physical site questionnaire mentioned earlier will help in user definition.

A type 1 user uses the network very lightly, mostly for local processing applications, that is, word processing and spreadsheets. This person is classed as a 1 to 5% user of the network, depending on how many hours a day the user spends utilising the network.

A type 2 user is more active, utilising applications that require more disk access. This type of work includes light database activity or mail merge. This person is a 5 to 10% network user.

A type 3 user must frequently access the shared disk for such applications as heavy database or mail-merge work. As a general rule, applications for this type of user spend about the same amount of time accessing the shared disk as they do manipulating the data at the workstation. This person is a 10 to 20% user of the network, again depending on the number of hours spent using the application.

A type 4 user is a very heavy user of the network, doing applications that require a great deal of disk access. Such applications include reservation systems. The type 4 user is a 20 to 40% user.

A type 5 user is someone who constantly demands as much throughput as the station can deliver. Continuously copying files from the shared hard disk, as in a back-p operation, or performing compiles in a programme development environment are examples of this type of user's applications. A type 5 user is a 40 to 100% user.

The formula for estimating system throughput is

$$T = M/U$$

T stands for available throughput per-workstation , M for maximum network throughput, and U for 100% users. A 100% user is a person running an application that uses the network to the maximum possible from a single workstation.

The figure for 100% users is developed by adding the percentages together for all users on the system. A sample site might have the following users:

			Total
5 Type 1 users each with a weight of	.04		.20
10 Type 2 users each with a weight of	.10		1.00
1 Type 3 user with a weight of	.20		.20
		Total	1.40

STANDARDS

Depending on your needs, standards can be of the greatest importance or may be only a minor consideration in your choice of a network. Standards are likely to be of more importance if you:

* Plan to expand your network.

* Need to connect to other networks.

* Plan to run applications from several vendors.

Standards are of least importance if you are buying a small configuration that will remain fairly static and will not need to be connected to other networks, use devices from other vendors or run many different applications programmes.

There is more standardisation among network hardware components than among software applications. You can probably find many more hardware products from different vendors that can physically coexist than software products that can share information. For example, you could buy a workstation and a print server from two vendors that claim. Ethernet compatibility, find that they can be connected to the same cable without physical interference, but discover that you cannot use the print server from the workstation because the two are incompatible in ways the Ethernet standard simply does not address. You must check very carefully for compatibility before you select network components from more than one vendor.

SOFTWARE

The ISO Open Systms Interconnect (OSI) model is a framework for describing network standards, rather than a standard itself. If you want to mix network components from different vendors, they must be compatible at some common OSI layer. Most of the current standards address only the lower levels of the OSI model. Applications software generally interfaces to the network at the highest levels, where there are very few widely accepted standard interfaces. This is one reason why applications software often needs to be modified for a specific network before it can run on it.

MS-DOS 6.0 and MS-NET. Although formal standards for network applications software may still be in the future, there are some promising de facto standards. Support for these standards may be important in your choice of a network, especially if you require wide availability of applications software.

Microsoft set a major standard in the personal computer world by releasing the

MS-DOS operating system, called PC-DOS on the IBM PC. MS-NET, Microsoft's network software, appears to be having a similar impact in the networking world. IBM PC Network provides an implemention of MS-NET, and many computer and LAN vendors are adding MS-NET or MS-NET-compatible interfaces to their products. MS-NET is accessed via a set of system calls provided in MS-DOS Version 6.0, and these calls provide several important network programming functions. More and more software is being adapted to run under MS-NET and MS-DOS 6.0, so the increasing support for these interfaces may influence your choice of a network.

NETBIOS. Another important PC networking software industry standard is the OSI session level NETBIOS interface, first presented by the IBM PC Network system. Many other LAN vendors have since provided a compatible interface with their systems, and IBM itself has provided this interface to its Token-Ring Network.

Application packages are more likely to use the simpler, higher-level MS-NET and MS-DOS 6.0 interaces than NETBIOS. The NETBIOS interface is especially important for systems-level network software, such as programmes for network servers. Unless you need to run a specific application that requires NETBIOS, it may be of slightly less importance to you than MS-NET compatibility. However, because it is supported in several IBM products, it is likely to be used more as time passes.

HARDWARE

Hardware standards are most important in the fundamental parts of your network such as cable type and the low-level network protocols. If you choose a non-standard, proprietary cable and protocol offered by only one vendor, you may be locking yourself into that vendor for all your future networking needs. A network conforming to one of the IEEE 802 standards opens the door to a broader choice of vendors.

IBM. IBM offers three networking hardware choices. The industrial token bus is designed for factory automation and process control. The PC Network uses broadband technology. The Token-Ring Network is an evolving system intended for use in large corporate networks, and is the basis for the IEEE 802.5 standards committee work.

IBM has suggested that, in an office environment, the broadband PC Network should be used to connect a small number of PCs together. The token-ring is seen as the building-wide network used to tie a large number of machines or clusters of machines together. A gateway product provides the connection between the broadband LAN and the token-ring. You can also use the token-ring as a local PC network, omitting the broadband network entirely. The Token-Ring Network runs the same software as the broadband PC Network. It supports the MS-DOS 4.1 and NETBIOS interfaces mentioned earlier. It can run over IBM's coax or the less expensive twisted-pair that meets telephone installation standards. Both wiring choices provide a bandwidth of 4 million bits per second, although you can connect more nodes and go a greater distance using coax.

The Token-Ring Network may be appropriate if you are planning to connect a large number of systems, including other IBM computers. IBM has expressed its intention to provide a complete corporate computernetwork hook-up, although the details for connecting together more than just PCs are being released very slowly.

Ethernet. The Ethernet standard is supported by many computer vendors, and several variations in cabling have evolved to reduce the relatively high cost of the original specification. Electronic devices called 'transceivers' can be used to connect the different cabling schemes. The choice of cable generally has no impact on applications software, and is a trade-off between cost and performance, with respect to speed and maximum cable length.

Standard Ethernet requires a heavy trunk cable and a transceiver for every workstation. The transceiver connects to the trunk cable, and a wire runs from the transceiver to the workstation or server. Cheapernet uses lighter, less-expensive cable and has the same 10 million bits per second capacity as Ethernet, but does not use an outboard transceiver and cannot support as long a cable as Ethernet.

StarLAN. AT&T's StarLAN is a competitor to IBM's token-ring in the coporate network arena. It uses a standard Ethernet trunk cable connected by a device called a 'hub' to clusters of workstations. The workstations connect to the hub with standard telephone company twisted-pair. You can connect hubs to hubs, increasing the number of workstations supported in a cluster and giving you more flexibility in wiring them together. StarLAN operates at a bandwidth of 1 Mbs.

MAINFRAME CONNECTIONS

If you are selecting a PC network for use in an installation where there are other computers (especialy minicomputers or mainframes), you should think about how you could connect your network to them even if you see no immediate need to do so. There are several classes of connection that may be important for you:

* Message and file transfer.

* Terminal emulation.

* Programme-to-programme communication.

* Remote job entry.

Making a good selection requires technical expertise. You need to understand the host computer application, data-file structure and communication connections, as well as the gateway connection between the host and the PC network, the PC network hardware, and the software that runs on the PC workstations to access the host.

GATEWAYS

Figure 7.9 shows one means of connecting a mainframe to a LAN. The interconnection is via a gateway, which is a server designed to pass information back and forth between two dissimilar networks. In this case, an Ethernet PC LAN is connected to a 4300 series IBM mainframe with a gateway processor. The gateway translates low-level protocols and handles the speed differences between the two networks. Since all traffic between the two networks must pass through the gateway, you must carefully evaluate the performance capability of the gateway in the light of the amount of the data you expect to transfer through it. If it does not have enough capacity it will become a bottleneck.

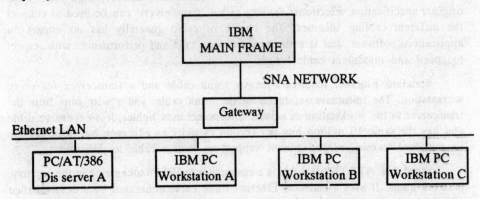

Fig. 7.9 : A geteway connecting a LAN to a mainframe

Most major PC network vendors offer gateways to IBM SNA networks, and some offer gateways to other popular PC networks. You may have a choice between a dedicated gateway server computer and an add-on board for a PC. The trade-offs are similar to those between a proprietary disk or file server and the use of a PC to do the job. You should examine price and performance as you make your evaluation, as well as the software provided to make the connection between the two networks.

DIRECT CONNECTION

An alternative means of connecting to a minicomputer or mainframe host is to run a direct connection from each PC on the LAN to the host computer. Many add-on cards are available to connect to host computers via most of the communication protocols available. However, this approach usually costs much more than the gateway approach and it makes little or no use of the PC LAN. For the extra cost, you may get more performance or more consistent performance when you access the host, since there is a dedicated connection rather than a shared connection through a gateway.

MESSAGE AND FILE TRANSFER

Message transfer and file transfer refer to electronic mail and document transfer, respectively. Many different kinds of electronic mail systems are in use today, and there is not yet a standard. Some systems cover only workstations connected to a common network and others connect also to public electronic mail services to cover a very wide area. The usefulness of electronic mail increases with the increase in the number of people you can communicate with, so be sure to consider ways to connect your PC workstations to electronic mail systems if appropriate.

There is not yet an official standard for document transfer either, although IBM's DISOSS standard is widely supported. If you need to share documents with a DISOSS system, examine whether the network of your choice can do so.

TERMINAL EMULATION

Terminal emulation is a very common approach to connecting a PC to a host computer. To the host your PC appears to be a terminal, and the host lets you do whatever a terminal can do on it, such as accessing existing applications on the host which is often very important. But with straight terminal emulation you cannot do anything that takes advantage of the fact that you are using a PC. If you want to do terminal emulation, you should examine the available options with respect to:

* Faithful emulation of desired terminal.

* Ease of use (how keys are mapped onto PC keyboard).

* Performance (how fast the emulator can receive data from host).

DATA EXTRACTION

Another way of accessing the host from a PC on a LAN is to extract data from host databases and move it to the PC for processing. This is another highly technical area, and to do a proper evaluation you need an excellent understanding of the software that runs on both ends of the connection. The software that extracts data from the mainframe database must have a detailed understanding of the host data-file layout, and it is possible that a revision in host software will change something in the layout and cause the extraction software to stop working. If the data extraction software is not updated for a period of time, you may be unable to run your application until it is updated. If you can find data extraction software from the same vendor as for the host database-management software, it may be more likely that the extraction software will be updated concurrently with the database software — although there is no guarantee.

REMOTE JOB ENTRY

Submitting jobs for processing on the host computer is another common need of PC users. A gateway or direct connection can provide the necessary data link for this remote job entry to take place, but PC software is also needed to do the actual job submission and control. Ease of use and match-up of functions against your needs list are the most important criteria.

PROGRAMME TO PROGRAMME COMMUNICATION

A relatively new area is programme to programme communication. IBM has introduced a standard called LU 6.2, and the full implications are still unfolding. Not much PC software is available that takes advantage of programme-to-programme communication, but as more software gets written for networks, this capability will grow in importance. The goal is to let a programmer set-up two or more programmesthat can execute on two different computers and pass information back and forth as they are running.

SECURITY

You should closely examine the security provided by software used to connect networked PCs to a mainframe. In most cases the mainframe data files were created before the PCs has access to them, and security may not have been a big consideration when the files were first stored. It is very easy to miss a security problem when security is an afterthought rather than something designed into an application. In addition to straightforward security issues, such as who can access which files, there are more complicated ones to consider, such as the ability for any authorised user to access host data and store it on the local network hard disk. Without the appropriate additional security, other network users may be able to access your data. If any PC on the network has a modem and is used to receive incoming calls, then anyone who can call the PC may be able to "break into" your mainframe.

HARDWARE COMPATIBILITY

Before choosing your mainframe connection equipment, be sure any hardware cards that must be added to network PCs are compatible with other cards that you plan to have in the PCs. Communication cards are among those more likely to have imcompatibilities with network interface cards than other types of cards. A complete list of the cards going into the workstations and servers should be checked out with your dealer and the board manufacturers.

WHAT DO YOU WANT FROM A LAN?

LANs serve a wide variety of functions and it is important that the prospective user is clear about what he requires from a LAN. For example it may be used to provide any or all of the following functions and many others:

File serving

Print serving

Process control and monitoring

Electronic messaging

Distributed processing facilities

Remote links to mainframe processors

Conferencing

Video transmission

Electronic office functions

LAN applications are limited solely by the imagination of the user. Very few systems can do all of these, and some LANs because of their nature will only perform a few of the functions well, so it is useful to examine the system requirements for each type of application. In general the following rules hold:

1. **File and print servers:** These are installed to spread the cost of expensive peripherals for groups of micro-computers and mini-computers; low interconnection costs are very important, with speed of operation being less so, particularly in the case of print servers.

2. **Process control and monitoring:** The vital factor in this application is the speed of the system response. The delay between the initiation of a command and its execution, or between the monitoring of an event and its acknowledgement by the process controller must be short and fixed, so that the controller can make allowances for it. Thus a network with guaranteed access and short transmission delays is essential. Interconnection costs and equipment costs are not the overriding factor when the plant to which the LAN connects costs a great deal - much more than the LAN itself.

3. **Electronic messaging:** This function will normally be an addition to local functions provided by small business computers and so must be compatible with them. Network traffic will be light compared with other applications and so a low speed network without guaranteed immediate access is indicated, as a time delay of a few seconds is not important in this application.

4. **Distributed processing:** This is common in scientific and engineering work, where terminals, workstations and various sizes of computer are connected together in order to share software and hardware facilities. As programmes and large batches of data need to be transferred from device to device at regular intervals, high speed bulk data transfer is the network's primary aim. Interconnection costs are not of primary importance, as the value of the attached equipment is usually relatively high.

5. **Remote mainframe links:** If this is the main purpose of the network, and a number of terminals wish to gain access to a single mainframe, network usage by each individual terminal will be low, and mainframe response time is likely to be much greater than network access time. A low speed network with variable access time will suit the application.

6. **Conferencing:** This application implies transmission of voice signals, as well as data, and therefore requires a network where speech can be transmitted in an analogous form, e.g. PABX-based network, or one where speech can be digitised and then transmitted, without interrupting data transmission, e.g. broadband network.

7. **Video transmission:** If video signals are to be transmitted as well as data, and possibly voice signals, the network must have a very high bandwidth and the ability to separate the various types of signals or the video signal will be of unacceptably poor quality. This requires some sort of broadband system.

8. **Electronic office functions:** This covers a wide variety of functions including some mentioned above and so needs a reasonably high performance network to fulfil its requirements.

In addition, system limitations will affect the choice of LAN for many applications. For example, the following questions must be kept in mind when examining a LAN:

1. Can it support the number of nodes required? Most LANs have an upper limit on the number of devices that can be simultaneously attached to the network.

2. Can it cover the physical area of the site? Most types of LAN have an upper limit on the lengths of connecting cables. Some can be extended with repeater units but this will be an added expense.

3. Can the LAN cope with the maximum amount of traffic envisaged for the system in an acceptable manner? This question is less straightforward to answer than the previous two but ignoring it may prove more costly to rectify.

4. Can it be connected easily to the equipment with which it is to be used? LAN suppliers normally offer a variety of plug-in interface units for popular computers and peripherals, which make interconnection much simpler than would otherwise be the case.

SPECIFYING A LAN

So far, we have thought about the purpose of the LAN and the types of system that will fulfil a particular purpose, but in a very general, broad way. It is now important to specify, in detail, without reference to any available commercial system, the network that is required. This is necessary at this stage to ensure that the network eventually purchased will meet the requirements of its users.

The best way to start is to follow this set of rules:

1. Draw up a list of the physical and logical requirements of the system:

    Number of nodes

    Area covered

    Maximum rate of data transfer

    Types of devices to be connected to the network

    Number of each type of device

It is also worth drawing a plan of the lay-out to give a clearer idea of possible difficulties.

2. Find out from the potential users what they intend to do with the network and sort their responses into two types - essential requirements and optional extras.

3. Have a clear idea of the funds available, and the possibility of further funds for upgrading the LAN system at a later date.

Following these rules should provide clear specificationsto present to any supplier of LANs and this is the most important stage in finding a system to suit your specific requirements.

However, at this point it is wise to consider whether a true LAN is the answer to your problems, or whether one of the various types of devices performing related functions might be a more cost-effective solution. It is unnecessarily expensive to pursue a high-tech solution when there is a low-tech one available.

For example, if the requirement is simply for a number of terminals or similar devices to be connected together, so that one device is only connected to one other device at any one time, in the manner of a telephone system, then an Intelligent Switch might be the answer, particularly if the physical distances are small.

A LAN is probably the right answer if one or more of the following points are valid:

1. A wide variety of connections which change with time are required.

2. Cabling costs look like being a substantial portion of system costs. LANs use the transmission medium efficiently and do not require multiple cables.

3. A large percentage of nodes in the system require regular access to other nodes, i.e. most of the nodes have something to say at regular intervals.

4. Both point-to-point and broadcast data transmission are required within the network. LANs need no alteration to physical connections to provide both.

MATCHING LANS TO USERS

We may split LAN users into the following groups:

Scientific and engineering

Office automation

Industrial automation/process control

Education

Home/interest

We now examine their requirements and see which types of LAN serve them best. It is important to note that no two applications are alike and that the network should serve the user, rather than dictate what the user can and cannot do. For example, a network used for scientific or engineering purposes may well need to provide some services associated with office automation work, such as printing from a control station.

The three Tables 7.1 to 7.3 give comparisons of features for LANs assessed by transmission medium, accessing method and topology. Table 7.4 lists the features you must look for while evaluating a LAN. By listing the features most important for a particular application, it is possible to go a long way toward picking the most suitable type of LAN. The following two examples illustrate the process.

TABLE : 7.1 : Comparison of transmisssion media

Trans-mission Medium	Band-width	Ease of Connect-ion	Distance	Suitability for different Topologies	Ease of Install-ion	Noise Immun-ity	Cost
Twisted Pair	Low	Good	Low	High	Average	Low	Low
Baseband Coaxial	Ave-rage	Good	Average	High	Good	Average/ Good	Average
Broadband Coaxial	High	Good	High	High	Good	High	Average/ High
Optical Fibre	Very High	Poor	Very High	Poor	Average	Very High	High

TABLE : 7.2 : Comparison of Access methods

Access method	Nature	Bandwith	No. of Nodess	Distance	Delay	Cost per Node
CSMA/CD	Random	High	Average	Average	Unlimited	High
Token Passing	Deter-ministic	Average	High	High	Low	Average
Register Insertion	Dete-ministic	Average/ low	High	High	Average/ low	Low
Empty Slot	Deter-ministic	Average	High	High	Low	Average
Time-Division Multiplexed	Deter-ministic	Low	High	Average	Low	Low

TABLE : 7.3 : Comparision of topologies

Topology	Cost	Complexity at interface	Flexibility and Expandability After Installation	Reliability
Bus	Low/Average	Average	Good	Good
Ring	Average	Low	Average	Good
Star	High	Low	Poor	Average

TABLE : 7.4

What features you must look for while evaluating a LAN ?

*	**Topology**	-	Bus, Star, Ring etc.
*	**Protocol**	-	Token Passing, Carrier Sensing Time Division, Multiplexing
*	**Max No of Nodes**	-	Normlly 64-255.
*	**Cabling Technology**	-	Co-axial, Twisted Pair, Fibre Optics etc.
*	**Data Transfer Rate**	-	Expressed in Million Bits/second (1-2.5)
*	**Distance**	-	Normally 1.2 Kms-64 Kms.
*	**O/s Compatibility**	-	Whether multiple o/systems can be suported simultneously (eg. DOS and UNIX)
*	**Security Features**	-	By Password, by User, by Directory etc.
*	**File Server**	-	Whether dedicated or can also be used as a node.
*	**Driverless Workstations**	-	Availability of Nodes without peripherals.
*	**System Supported**	-	PC/XT/AT/386/68000 Series etc.
*	**Lan cost**	-	Cost Per Node
		-	Cost of cabling
		-	Cost of Dedicated Resource Server, if any.

Example 1: A network based in a college classroom, connecting a number of personal computers to a master computer, and to a print-serving device and a file-serving device and operated by the teacher in-charge. The master computer would not be in continuous communication with the rest but would need to access any of them from time to time. All would use print and file servers. The desired characteristics would be:

Transmission medium bandwidth - low/moderate

    no. of nodes   - low/moderate

    distance   - low

    ease of installation   - low/moderate

    noise immunity   - low/moderate

    cost   - low:the most important factor

Accessing method control   - distributed (all intelligent nodes)
    bandwidth   - low/mediu

no. of nodes	- low/medium (dependent on class size)
distance	- low
degree of contention	- low
degree of determinism	- high
degree of flexibility	- low
delay time	- low/moderate
Topology interface complexity	- low (to keep costs low)
flexibility	- low
expandability	- low
reliability	- moderate to high
cost	- low: most important item

Comparing the requirements with the tables suggests a bus or tree system with some sort of deterministic accessing scheme using twisted-pair cables. However, the evaluations in the tables are relative and it may prove that because of the relatively short distances involved, the extra cost of a different type of transmission medium may be negligible in comparison with the system cost. Similarly, the time delays involved in using a non-deterministic access method may be acceptable when considered in comparison with the speed with which the users interact with the various computer/ nodes in the network.

Example 2: A network for a modern business office, where the current requirements are mainly linking an assortment of workstations, word-processors, print and file-servers but provision must be made for possible future expansion, and where links to the company mainframe and a video network are envisaged. Bearing in mind the final functions the LAN may have to perform, the desired characteristics would be:

Transmission medium bandwidth -	high (to accommodate video)
no. of nodes	- high (future additional nodes)
distance	- moderate (except for main-frame connection)
ease of installation	- moderate
noise immunity	- moderate
cost	- low: not most important factor
Accessing method control	- distributed
bandwidth	- high
no. of nodes	- high

distance	-	moderate
degree of contention	-	moderate
degree of determinism	-	low
degree of flexibility	-	high
delay time	-	low and fixed (because of video)
Topology interface complexity	-	can be high
flexibility	-	high
expandability	-	high
reliability	-	high
cost	-	low (in comparison with system)

The network fulfilling most of the conditions in this case would be a broadband coaxial, random access, bus or tree system, such as the commercial Ethernet LANs now being sold for office automation by a number of suppliers. There is however one problem: video transmission would require low, fixed time delays in transmission, to avoid unacceptable degradation of the reconstituted video signal at the receiving station. This factor suggests that a deterministic access method i.e. some form of token-passing system, should be adopted to ensure future video compatibility despite the reduced performance of the LAN in other areas that this choice of accessing method would imply.

On the subject of cost, cheaper is always better, but must be considered in terms of the cost of the system the LAN is to serve. One LAN may cost twice as much as another for a limited increase in facilities, but where this extra cost is only a few percent of the total system cost, it may well be acceptable.

Having decided which types of LAN will suit the specification, it is important to balance the trade-off between costs and features of suitable networks. It is rare that a LAN will provide everything its prospective users want at a price they are willing to pay and so some order of priority should be given to the various features in the specification. Beyond this point it is unwise to be specific as each application has its own pitfalls. The only sure result is that the final system will have some unnecessary features and not have some necessary ones, so allow for a certain amount of flexibility in your specification.

PURCHASING A LAN

Having discovered a number of networks which seem to fulfil most or all of the specifications, the problem of choosing one to buy arises. A number of practical points can affect this decision.

1. **Complete package or components?** In other words, do you buy a 'turnkey' system from one supplier or various bits and pieces from different people and

then try to make them work yourself? The first course should guarantee a working system without too many problems, but will undoubtedly cost a great deal more than the latter option. Self-installation, in comparison, could be fraught with practical difficulties. In brief, do-it-yourself is only recommended if every penny counts, and there is adequate technical back-up to solve the problems.

2. **General compatibility:** This is really part of point 1, but worth looking at separately. A number of manufacturers supply LANs complete with workstations of their own design but do not provide interfaces for other popular makes of computer (e.g. IBM PC) or standard peripheral connections (e.g. Centronics interface, RS232C port, etc.) Purchasing this type of LAN is a quick way to get a network up and running but may make your current equipment redundant, or tie up expensive workstations as interface units to the equipment you wish to keep. In general, these packaged LAN-and-workstation systems are a good thing if an installation is being built from scratch, rather than networking existing devices. Most such LAN packages offer a standard operating system, such as CP/M or MS-DOS, on their workstations and so a certain amount of software compatibility is catered for.

3. **Timescale for delivery and installation:** This can vary widely from supplier to supplier and a more expensive or less versatile LAN may be a better buy if it can be installed now, when the delivery time for your first-choice LAN is six months or a year.

4. **Where more than one LAN seems to fit the specification:** Try to get the competing systems installed for a short time for evaluation purposes. Most suppliers will consider this if they feel it will lead to a sale. Despite matching your specifications to the suppliers', there is no substitute for the 'suck it and see' approach in assessing the usefulness of any piece of equipment.

5   **Component costs may affect a decision:** For example, if two LANs, one with coaxial cable and the other with fibre optic cable, suit your application and cost approximately the same amount, the component costs for future expansion are likely to be much greater for a fibre optic system than for a coaxial system. In this case, the coaxial cable system would be a better solution.

LAN ACQUISITION STRATEGIES

When seeking the perfect fit for your network, ponder on these questions before you decide where to buy:

1. What problems do you wish to solve with the LAN?

2. What are the design requirements?

3. What sort of functionality do you intend to provide to the user?

4. Are you building a PC-only LAN or an Enterprise Wide Network?

5. What are your performance expectations?

6.   What are the availability expectations?

7.   Flexibility. Is your organisation stable or in constant movement?

8.   What is your management strategy? Autonomous or Centralised?

9.   Security. Highly sensitive data?

10. What is the size and complexity of your network?

11. How many locations do you have?

12. How fast does your network have to grow?

13. Is it heterogeneous or homogeneous?

14. Is the nature of the problem physical or logical?

15. Do you need to make LAN-to-WAN connections?

16. Do you need to make LAN-to-host connections?

17. What are your uptime availability requirements?

18. What are your security needs?

19. Do you have a network management strategy?

20. What are your staff resources?

21. How are your current supplier relationships?

22. What are your time and price requirements?

23. What do you need in the way of on-going service and support?

8

EVALUATION AND SELECTION OF SOFTWARE PACKAGES

INTRODUCTION

Computers have already had far-reaching effects in almost every sector of industry. Rapid technological developments in computer hardware has heightened the desire by businesses to purchase mini-and microcomputers. Small computer systems have become more attractive because of the relatively lower cost of acquiring computer hardware. Once a computer is purchased, however, a company must either develop or purchase the required software to process the input data and produce the desired information.

A plethora of software packages are available today. Businesses are tempted to purchase these packages without evaluating the alternative of developing the needed software in-house. To make an informed choice, an evaluation of the costs of the available alternatives is needed, and this requires a well defined plan. One has to take care, since buying a package is often considered a long-term investment, involving a good amount of money. Spending enormous amounts of money on inadequate software packages results in an inadequate or useless computerised system. Issues, concerns and approaches for software package evaluation and selection are discussed here.

TRENDS IN SOFTWARE EVOLUTION

In studying the continuing evolution of computers, it becomes amply clear that while there are dramatic developments in both hardware and software, there is a qualitative difference in these developments. While hardware improvements concentrate on higher speeds at lower costs, with lower energy consumption and in a smaller size, the thrust of software is in making computers easier to use, or user-friendly as manufacturers prefer to refer to this feature. We are also beginning to see more and more reasoning power being built into the software — a trend that is bringing the terms Artificial Intelligence, Knowledge Based Systems, Expert Systems and Decision Support Systems into the foreground. But the developments in software do not necessarily share the cost-reduction, and quite often imply clear increases in cost.

In making computers more user-friendly and menu-driven rather than command-driven, substantial amount of software needs to be added, and this concept creates an ironical situation where the user finds that while software is becoming simpler and easy to use, it is becoming more expensive. Between the hardware and the computer user, more and better layers of software are being padded with the objective of achieving user-friendliness as well as higher levels of independent reasoning (see Figure 8.1). It is these layers of software which give a purpose as well as ease and functionality to the hardware. These layers are further examined more closely.

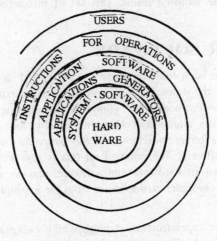

Fig. 8.1 : Layers of Software

1. Systems Software

Systems software is the layer closest to the hardware, and since it is specific to a particular computer model, is supplied by manufacturers along with the computer. In the early days, computer scientists interacted with hardware through a similar software layer, and a high level of skill was necessary to deal with the technicalities of that layer of software. Obviously, a need was felt to build interfaces that would make it easier to use computers. Furthermore, each model of computer required different types of skills and this was becoming an additional hindrance to the widespread use of computers.

2. High Level Languages

High Level Languages emerged as a solution to the problem. Programming languages like COBOL, FORTRAN, etc were developed, with which it was very much simpler to use computers. Further, programmes written for one computer could run on another computer provided an appropriate layer of software was available on both. Over the years, programming languages have gone through significant evolution, and we are currently using Fourth Generation Languages (4GLs) which are a short step away from the natural languages like English. The second layer of software, then, is that which enables programming languages to operate on the hardware.

3. Application Software

Application software is the set of programmes that are written to get a specific application, e.g. Payroll and Invoicing,to work on a computer. Obviously, these would be different from application to application, and also from organisation to organisation. Thus applications software could be viewed as the third layer. Once an application package has been implemented, what the operating staff (or the end-users, in the case of on-line, multi-terminal systems) would need to know is the sequence of interaction with the system to get the required result. This set of instructions could be viewed as the fourth layer.

THE NEED FOR SOFTWARE

Hardware costs have been tumbling over the years, and this reduction is likely to continue. Software, on the other hand, is becoming more expensive. In the early days of computers, it was common to see computer manufacturers offering software free with the hardware. The situation is changing rapidly and one can expect that a point will come when a buyer will be given the hardware free, if he buys more than a certain value of software. The point of all this is that we need to underscore the opposite trends in costs of hardware and software, and we also need to realise that the real benefits from computerisation comes from the appropriate software, rather than hardware alone.

Software is often the superstructure through which anorganisation's goals and objectives may be accomplished. Purchasing software is an important task that deserves proper planning and consideration. It is analogous to the procurement of plant or equipment facilities. Selection of software should be approached with the same care. However, because of the highly abstract nature of software and its function, it can be difficult to follow these steps, particularly when determining costs. Also, writing software is an art still in the embryonic stage. It lacks any generally accepted principles for development and testing, and this increases the difficulty in evaluating the benefits of the package.

Two sources for obtaining software exist. In-house development, particularly of application systems, has been the traditional approach. Now, software packages are emerging as a viable alternative to the in-house development. The perceived costs — both direct and indirect,of in-house development have been the major impetus for the trend in purchasing commercial packages.

SOFTWARE PACKAGES

Various terms exist to describe packages — application packages, application software, standard systems or software packages. Regardless of the terminology used, what is being considered is a package of facilities and services that is designed to cope with some commercial, statistical or scientific job, for example, stock control, payroll, etc. Technical packages, covering such matters as design and stress calculation, also exist but these are not discussed here.

There are two main categories of software packages. Systems software packages and application software packages. For example the packages Operating Systems (OS), Translators, Simulators andJob Accounting are system software packages while the packages like Payroll, Inventory and PERT/CPM are application packages.

System software packages are used to enhance, extend or drive computer hardware. Although system packages currently represent only 25 percent of the total number of software packages available, they account for approximately 50 percent of the total revenue from software packages. Figure 8.2 illustrates the two main categories of software and their subsets. Utility packages or programmes are a special set of software routines, normally supplied by computer manufacturers, to perform certain standard functions for all users. They fall into two categories, those designed to be used in the operational environment, and those used to assist programmetrials. Examples of the former are sort programmes, merge programmes and standard printing programmes. In the latter group, examples are store dumps, disk and tape edits and programme diagnostic routines.

Systems Software		Applications Software	
-	Computer dependent	-	Organisation dependent
-	Supplied by computer manufacturer	-	To be arranged by the buyer
*	Operating Systems	*	Payroll Systems
*	Translators, Compilers	*	Financial Accounting Systems
*	Utilities	*	Accounts Payable Systems
*	Data Base Management Systems (DBMS)	*	Accounts Receivable Systems
		*	Fixed Asset Accounting
*	Job Accounting Systems	*	General Ledger Systems
*	Telecommunication Systems	*	Capital Project Accounting
		*	Forecasting and Statistical Packages
		*	Medical and Health Care Systems
		*	Developing and Maintenance Aids for EDP Department
		*	Purchasing and Materials Management
		*	Inventory Control and Accounting
		*	Production Planning and Control

Fig. 8.2 : Categories of software systems

Applications software packages are special-purpose systems designed for business, scientific, medical, academic or other uses. Thus, applications software packages are designed to perform more specific functions, while systems software perform general functions and are typically made available with the purchase of the hardware. Accordingly, we will deal primarily with application software packages.

Typically, a commercial package consists of a computer programme or suite of standardised computer programmes, programme documentation, user's manuals, procedures. instruction booklets, implementation assistance and possibly some formal tuition in the use of the package. The underlying theme of all packages is to provide a more or less readymade system that will cope with individual user's problems.

A software package is a computerised application system,e.g. payroll, accounts payable or bill of materials. Typically, a package is developed by a specialised computer application company for outrightsale to organisations needing a specific data processing (EDP) system. One successful software package could be used by several thousand organisations. By purchasing the package, an organisation eliminates the need to design its own EDP system. It is usually safe to assume that a well field-proven package is highly reliable and performs according to the documentation provided by the software vendor. While the decision to buy a software package is analogous to many make-or-buy decisions, buying a software package does not imply elimination of all in-house systems and programming efforts but rather substitution of some of the tasks in the standard systems development and programming life cycle for another set of tasks that, in theory, is easier, less time-consuming and less expensive.

Packages are available from computer manufacturers, specialist software houses, data processing consultants, computer bureaux or ordinary users who are capitalising on hard-won expertise. The concept of packages seems first class in that itspreadsthe development costs over a number of users to become operational that much more quickly, but there are problems. To be usable by a variety of organisations, packages have to be designed forgeneralised use. They must be able to handle many more situations,types of input and output and processing requirements, than any one user would probably ever need. This tends to make them complicated and difficult to use, at least initially. A more serious problem is the uniqueness of some aspect of the organisation's activities which may not be covered by the package. Nevertheless, if a package can be found that suits some applicationsit may be an excellent proposition, both financially and operationally.

SOFTWARE PACKAGES AND IN-HOUSE SOFTWARE

Whether a software package or in-house developed software is chosen, the basic goal of the organisation remains the same: to provide a computerised system that meets a definite application requirements. However, these two types of programmes have several distinct differences which are discussed below. Figure 8.3 depicts the differences in acquisition or development of software.

OFF THE SHELF PACKAGES
*   Hardware dependent
*   Proprietary product
*   Inflexible and rigid
*   Least expensive

CUSTOMISATION OF PACKAGES
* Need experienced manpower
* Need continual maintenance
* Some limitations will persist

TAILOR MADE APPLICATION DEVELOPMENT
* Accepted mode in most countries
* Complete satisfaction of user requirements possible
* Takes longer time and effort
* Most expensive
* Needs greater user involvement
* Requires skilled manpower

Fig. 8.3 : Acquisition/Development of Software

Software Package

1. Acquired from an outside vendor, it constitutes a legal contract concerning price and functional capabilities.

2. It is usually installed in multiple organisations, each withthe same set of vendor-supplied software.

3. A full set of documentation is available for each management level of the organisation.

4. It is usually field tested prior to public sale.

5. Maintenance is performed by the vendor via a software maintenance contract.

6. It can usually be enhanced over time with DP state-of-the-art improvements.

In-house developed software

1. Design, programming and implementation aspects are developed to suit the needs of one organisation.

2. Maintenance is the responsibility of the organisation's data processing department.

3. Design may or may not consider the latest state-of-the-art software techniques, and is dependent upon the capabilities and expertise of personnel in the organisation.

SOFTWARE DEVELOPMENT COSTS

Cost is the main reason for purchasing a software package rather than developing an in-house system. Developing in-house software system isexpensive. Costs include the salaries for programmers, systems analysts and project managers and these costs are increasing faster than the cost of hardware (see Figure 8.4). Developing software is a labour-intensive activity, and it is becoming more difficult to locate and retain experienced, qualified individuals for systems development. In-house software development also requires systems teams to use some computer time. Disk space, paper costs and CPU time also add to the development cost. If hardware utilisation is at, or approaching the saturation point, computer time is much more valuable; thus, it becomes much more costly for the systems team to use the hardware.

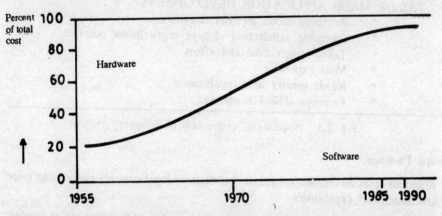

Fig. 8.4 : Trends in Software and Hardware Costs

Studies indicate that (1) software development costs several times the cost of an IC (Integrated Circuit) chip, (2) approximately 70 percent of the total cost of a software product occurs after the product is delivered, and goes into debugging and maintenance, and (3) software maintenance alone takes 50 to 80% of the data processing budget at a typical installation. The increasing importance of software is readily apparent from Figure 8.5. About 80% of the costs was attributed to hardware in the mid 1950s. This ratio is on the verge of reversing by rapidly decreasing hardware costs and by the increasing rate of labour-intensive software costs.

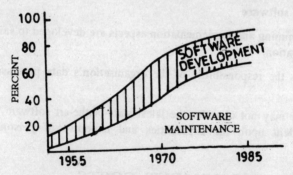

Fig. 8.5 : Hardware Software Cost Trends

Software maintenance plays an important role in computer based systems. Its cost is continually rising and reflects the high labour-intensive effort. The price and performance of hardware have improved by leaps and bounds, but improvement in programmer productivity has been low. This is reflected in the high cost of software development and also gradual increase in the software maintenance cost.

Time can be the other critical cost factor involved in an in-house system. In-house software often is delivered late. If there is a needfor virtually immediate delivery, then a software package is more likely to be operative in a short-run time frame.

Currently, there are no precise studies that compare the relative costs of in-house development versus purchasing or leasing a software package. Also, it is important to evaluate the alternatives before making the decision of whether to buy or develop the software.

SOFTWARE PACKAGE COSTS

A software package also involves certain expenditures. Total software costs for package can include the following:

1. Lease or purchase price.

2. Cost of modifying the package to meet internal requirements.

3. Cost of modifying operating procedures.

4. Cost of modifying the operating system so that it is compatible with the package.

5. Cost of modifying or adding computer hardware.

6. Cost of training programmers, systems analysts and other EDP personnel so that the package can be used efficiently.

Many of these costs will be incurred regardless of whether the software is internally developed or purchased (e.g. cost of modifying operating procedures, cost of modifying or adding computer hardware). However, there are many costs unique to purchasing the software package (e.g. the lease or purchase price).

The most frequently encountered cost after the purchase of the package is the cost of modifying a package so that it fulfills the organisation's needs. There usually are unique information and procedural requirements that have to be met. An earlier study on this topic revealed that nearly three-fourths of the application software packages required significant modifications before they were operative. If a software vendor can make the modifications, these costs can be easily identified. If the modifications are to be made internally then determining costs is difficult since part of the cost is an allocation of fixed EDP costs. When modifications are significant, these costs are higher than for internally developed software because the systems team will be less familiar with the software package. This will increase the time, effort and costs for modifying the package.

When packaged software is maintained by in-house programmers, systems analysts and project managers, there also training costs are to be considered. For an in-house system, this training is an integral part of the systems development cycle. When a software package is acquired, time will have to be spent training EDP personnel on the mechanics of the system.

SOFTWARE QUALITY

Before we take up the question of software selection it would perhaps be necessary to know as to what constitutes good quality software package. A good quality software may have a proper mix of the following strongly competing attributes:

-   Clear definition of purpose

-   Simplicity of use

-   Ruggedness

-   Early availability

-   Reliability

-   Extensibility and improvability

-   Adaptability and extension to different configurations

-   Suitability to configurations of the range

-   Brevity

-   Efficiency (speed)

-   Operating case for the operator

-   Adaptability to wide range of applications

-   Coherence and consistency with other programmes

-   Minimum cost to develop international standards

-   Conformity to national and international standards with respect to character codes, tape formats, languages, etc.

-   Clear, accurate and precise user's document

ASSESSING A PACKAGE

To make a realistic appraisal of the suitability of a package is a lengthy process but even so it takes far less time than the investigation, design, programming, testing and implementation of a tailor-made system. The following steps are necessary:

1. Determine the reporting facilities and routine outputs necessary to meet the organisation's requirements.

2. Determine the types and formats of the inputs available within the organisation.

3. Determine all relevant volumes (transactions, reports, outputs, amendments),current and for the future. Step 1 to 3 are normal in any systems investigation and design, whether or not packages are being considered.

4. Determine essential requirements and useful additional facilities.

5. Consider packages available and assess suitability for the application being

considered. The assessment of the package is covered in steps 6-13.

6. Coverage - What is the general coverage of the package? Is it for very narrow area of the organisation's activities or does it encompass many functions?

7. Flexibility - Is the package capable of revision and modification without substantial difficulty? Are a number of exits provided from the standard package for users to create their own additions? Can different reports be generated on demand or reporting requirements be easily inserted into the package?

8. Restrictions - What restrictions on coding, input formats, the organisation's clerical systems, will be caused by the use of the package? What information, if any, will have to be foregone?

9. Assistance - Is full documentation of all aspects of the package provided? What on-site assistance is given during the implementation of the package? Is any formal training given in the use of package?

10. Reliability - What is the source of the package? What do existing users, if any, say about the package itself and the supplier? If the package is not yet developed, what is the record of the package suppliers? Do they have a record of producing high quality, tested material to a definite schedule?

11. Hardware Requirements - What are the memory/peripheral software requirements of the package? Can you use it on your installation?

12. Performance - How well does the package perform? What timings are available? Is a benchmark test possible? What do existing users say about its performance? If package is being developed, does the specification include anticipated performance details?

13. Costs - Will the package be paid for by outright-purchase, lease or by some form of usage charge? How do the costs compare with alternative packages? How do the costs compare with the projected costs of developing a tailor-made system?

WHEN TO SELECT A PACKAGE

There are two predominant reasons for selecting a software package. First, individuals in charge of selecting or using the system are relatively naive with respect to computer programming, computer technology and their specific application. Secondly, the total cost of in-house development (which includes systems analysis, design, coding, testing, implementation and hardware utilisation) exceeds the total cost of leasing or purchasing a software package.

Obviously, in the first instance where the individual or organisation has little experience with programming or computer hardware or even their target applications, they would be well advised to go the software package route since the costs to develop the necessary expertise would be prohibitive. These organisations usually should purchase or lease a complete systems package. So called "turnkey" systems are available from original equipment manufacturers (OEM). If a user or organisation is in this .category, it would be prudent, if not imperative, to hire a consultant to aid in the selection process.

If an organisation is relatively sophisticated with respect to the target application and computer technology, then the comparison of the relative costs of the software packages and in-house development is necessary to get the most from the software package. In doing so, the organisation must make a comparison of the total costs involved in each of the alternatives.

Many of these costs will be comparable regardless of whether the organisation purchases a software package or develops it in-house (e.g., cost of modifying operating procedures). To expedite the analysis, an organisation should focus its analysis on the critical costs.

Software packages are most advantageous when the software is needed soon, the software package can be implemented with only minor modifications and the organisation does not have to maintain the software. Conversely in-house development is preferable when existing packages are not readily compatible with the system, when software packages will require extensive modification by the user organisation and when users are taking total responsibility for software maintenance.

Since time can be critical, the first decision to be made is how soon the software will be needed. If the software will be needed very quickly, or if the hardware is being used at or near capacity for current operations, in-house development will be cost prohibitive. As shown in Figure 8.4 labour costs are increasing rapidly, and to quickly develop the in-house software, an organisation would have to devote a large amount of time and energy to the project, increasing its cost. Also, if the hardware is currently being used at or near capacity, significant indirect costs for in-house software development result because of interruption of operations.

If time is not critical, choosing between purchase and in-house development is not as clear cut. Most software packages require a significant amount of modification before they are fully operational. This is not true of software developed in-house, since it is specifically tailored to specific needs. If the modification must be done by EDP

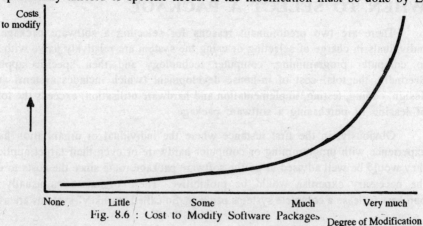

Fig. 8.6 : Cost to Modify Software Packages

department rather than a vendor, the cost of the software package should be increased accordingly. Obviously, as the degree of modification increases, the cost increases and this is not a linear relationship (see Figure 8.6).

The remaining critical factor to consider is the maintenance of the software. If the supplier is to maintain the software, the cost is the agreed upon price which the supplier charges for the service. But, if the organisation plans to maintain the software, there can be hidden costs implicit in that decision. The EDP personnel must be trained so that they can provide efficient maintenance of the system. As a consequence, maintenance is likely to be more costly in terms of the organisation's human resources. However, there is a cost saving that will partially offset the human resources cost. By providing maintenance, the organisation has instantaneous access to maintenance personnel which in the long-run can be quite cost-effective. Figure 8.7 depicts the cost trade-off between acquisition and development of software.

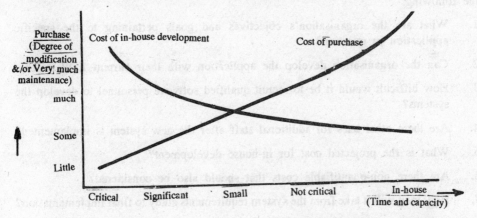

Fig. 8.7 : Relative cost of purchases vs in-house development of software

In general, therefore, packages can be worthwhile in three situations:

1. Where an existing proven package more or less exactly fits the requirements of one of the organisation's applications and is a cost effective proposition.

2. Where an organisation is a new computer user and personnel at all levels are unfamiliar with data processing, then the interim use of packages may be beneficial. Such use will help the organisation gain data processing expertise and refine their requirements' definitions without massive expenditure. Also, the installation is likely to become productive more quickly.

3. The third situation is where an organisation has many of the basic foundation applications operational, using tailor-made systems but wishes to develop the use of more sophisticated techniques. The use of many of these techniques (e.g. linear programming, simulation and PERT) is likely to be only occasional and a package may be the ideal answer, either on the organisation's own computer or at a bureau.

AREAS OF CONCERN FOR MANAGEMENT

The decision to buy/select/make software requires an evaluation process recognising both direct and indirect costs and benefits. Implications relating to in-house development, such as utilisation of data processing staff, work priorities, risk and track record of previous in-house efforts of a similar nature, must be compared to the gamut of factors relating to software package acquisition, e.g. contractual arrangements, vendor selection and goodness-of-fit between user needs and package capabilities. The choice is not always obvious, and further more, it requires a deep consideration of many detailed factors, which are sometimes even harder to determine.

In the make or buy software decision, management is faced with a series of questions that requires understanding of management policies and system implementation goals. These questions provide a focal point for management to decide whether to make or buy the software package. The decision should answer questions such as the following:

1.   What are the organisation's objectives and goals pertaining to the specific application in question?

2.   Can the organisation develop the application with their current EDP staff?

3.   How difficult would it be to recruit qualified software personnel to develop the systems?

4.   Are there other uses for additional staff after the new system is implemented?

5.   What is the projected cost for in-house development?

6.   Are there non-quantifiable costs that should also be considered?

7.   How long will it take from the system requirements study to final implementation?

8.   Are the new system expectations only for the short range say less than 3 years?

9.   Can the organisation's long term needs be identified and included in the new system?

10.   What impact will the in-house development have on organisation's resources?

11.   What is the anticipated effect of systems maintenance — its costs, duration and resources?

12.   Are there software packages that meet the organisation's need?

13.   What is the range of cost for acquiring a package that meets identified needs?

14.   Do the software packages function on the current hardware?

15.   Are there plans to change the hardware configuration? If so, when, and will the package operate on the new configuration?

16.   What is the source language of the proposed package?

17.   What is the impact of the package on the current hardware?

18. If additional hardware is required, what will it cost and what is the order lead time?

19. What is the performance record of the proposed vendor?

20. What is the performance record of the proposed package?

ADVANTAGES AND DISADVANTAGES OF ACQUIRING A SOFTWARE PACKAGE

In evaluating the alternative method of implementing a software application, the decision-maker should be aware of the advantages and disadvantages of acquiring a software package. Some of these are discussed here.

Advantages

1. Eliminates reinventing the wheel. In many instances,packages provide basic capabilities that are more then sufficient to accommodate an organisation's needs. Often packages have been designed for a specific industry and functional use, i.e. construction industry accounting package or manufacturing bill-of-materials (BOM) software.

2. Often costs less than in-house development. The following table provides a buy versus make matrix for a hypothetical package. The values included in the matrix typify the costs and time required for a package equivalent to a Rs.80,000 software package. As the matrix shows, both investment cost and payback period indicate economic advantages in acquiring a package.

Economic evaluation matrix : buy versus make software.

ESTIMATE	MAKE	BUY
A. Cost of Evaluation Study	Rs.5,000	Rs.15,000
B. Duration of Evaluation Study	1 month	3 months
C. Development Time	18 months	6 months
D. Cost of in-house Development/ Acquisition	Rs.200,000	Rs.40,000
E. Conversion Time	3 months	3 months
F. Conversion Cost	Rs.25,000	Rs.25,000
G. Annual Savings	Rs.100,000	Rs.100,000
H. Projected Payable Time Period	*27 months	10 months

* Sum of (A+D+F)

Rs.8,500 (=Rs.100,000/12 months)

3.   Releases software personnel for other projects. Most data processing departments have substantial backlog of user-requested data processing systems. The ratio of personnel and implementation time period is dramatically in favour of the acquisition route. As such, DP personnel become available sooner for other projects. While the ratio in the above mentioned table is 3:1, this ratio can be even higher.

4.   Has high reliability and performs according to stated documentation. Packages have been implemented in a large number of installations. Thus, the package is generally field-proven andoperates as described in the documentation.

5.   Assures that the system is documented. Part of the package acquisition decision involves review of vendor supplied documentation. Unfortunately, when a package is developed in-house, documentation is usually low on the priority ladder. As a result, final documentation is incomplete and too often is not updated during the software maintenance process.

6.   Minimises risk usually associated with large-scale system development effort. System development efforts generally have had bad performance records. Management have experience with projects being overdue and over the budget. A package reduces the probability that this situation will occur and places some reasonable constraints on anticipated costs.

7.   Provides improved opportunity costs. Since packages are known to be less expensive, the economic advantage offers management the chance to redirect some financial and manpower resources to other projects.

Disadvantages

   With all the pluses, software packages can still bring problems which are of following nature:

1.   May not adequately meet user's requirements. This is probably the major drawback of acquiring a software package. Too often the organisation's needs are not clearly defined, so the selected software package does not adequately meet processing requirements.

2.   Modification of base system results in loss of vendor support. If the selected system requires changes, the purchaser can lose its guarantee by modifying the software code. An alternative is to use the package interface files to develop alternative processing not supplied by the system. These are generally known an Add-ons.

3.   Additional hardware may be required. The selected package may involve additional computer resources that would not otherwise be required. Although selection of another package could be an alternative, this choice may not be available.

4.   Purchase of packages involves large cash outlay. This substantial investment can be conceived as an added expense since the use of in-house personnel is often

considered a fixed cost. Since many organisations have in-house systems and programming personnel, the problem involves determining how to allocate personnel to the project of highest priority, rather than deciding whether to incur an expense.

5. Implementation responsibility still lies with the organisation and not with the vendor. While software package vendors provide reliable products with some implementation assistance, sole responsibility still lies with the purchaser. Therefore, acquisition of a package does not automatically imply successful installation.

SOFTWARE VENDOR CHECKLIST

Many questions you would ask prospective application software vendors do not differentiate one vendor from another. The similarities between suppliers are not what's important — it is the differences that count. Here are questions you should ask prospective application software vendors before making your selection.

1. Can the application software you are considering be easily delivered in a variety of data processing environments (operating system, teleprocessing monitor and data base) to permit easy migration and allow system software environmental independence?

2. Can the application software be delivered for VSAM and all popular data base management systems, rather than being tied to the application vendor's data base system - one which could be outmoded by new data base products developed by another vendor in this rapidly changing high-technology industry?

3. Is the application software implemented using a "native" or direct approach to the operating system, teleprocessing monitor and data base manager, without the inefficiency associated with "bridges" or the vendor dependencies on a "black box" approach?

4. Is the application product coded in an efficient, widely used and industry-standard language such as COBOL or C rather than a vendor-dependent language unknown to the general data processing community?

5. Can the application product be "tailored" or streamlined to meet the specific functional and operational needs of a company through purchase of a basic package and selected optional features, thereby avoiding delivery of useless code?

6. Does the vendor retain a source version of each customer's uniquely tailored application software for emergency back-up, problem determination and client assistance?

7. Does the vendor have a broad, completely integrated line of application software which can be demonstrated on a single system instead of merely described?

8. Have all of the vendor's products been integrated by design and developed by a single organisation, thus eliminating the need for inefficient interfaces and unknown "black boxes" to tie together unrelated or acquired applications?

9. Does the vendor clearly demonstrate a full commitment to the complex business of application software, rather than offer an incidental addition to its main product line?

10. Has the vendor been in the application software business a minimum of ten years with a successful track record of sustained profits and a strong financial posture?

11. Does the vendor have sufficient capital liquidity to develop enhancements to its product line and to meet unexpected cashflow requirements, and little or no debt to assure its long-term staying power in the event of economic difficulties?

12. Is the vendor's product line not only broad enough to satisfy the product needs of your immediate project, but also broad enough to satisfy the product needs of any subsequent project extensions?

13. Can the vendor provide you with a complete listing and demonstration of integration points between functional systems, as well as plans for specific additional integration points in subsequent releases?

14. Does the vendor routinely provide for a pre-installation planning meeting to prepare the client for the installation steps to be completed?

15. Does the vendor provide educational and training support in the form of public workshops and private, individualised education?

16. Does the vendor provide 24 hours, seven-day-a-week 'hot line' telephone support for service and trouble-shooting?

17. Does the vendor have a formal independent users group which is organised with application interests in view and which meets regularly?

18. Does the vendor enjoy a position of leadership within professional organisations recognised in each application field?

19. Does the vendor provide a comprehensive security system built into the application which dynamically adjusts the system for the user, based upon the capabilities specified in the user's unique security profile?

20. Does the vendor have a maintenance plan available which routinely provides enhancements and corrections on a regular basis?

21. Does the vendor provide source language code for all programmes and routines thereby permitting better user understanding, modification and maintenance?

22. Are all programmes written using top-down, structured techniques with good on-line documentation?

CONCLUSION

To summarise, before your organisation embarks on the development of a tailor-made system, are you sure that no package exists that will cope with the work? When one considers how many people have independently and expensively solved the same problems in sales accounting, credit control, pay roll and the like, it is enough to make an accountant shudder. When an organisation has a well developed EDP group, the choice between in-house development and purchase of new software is not always clear cut. The advantages of purchasing a software package are that it can be implemented quickly and the initial costs (purchase or lease price) are much lower than the costs to develop the software. However, in-house development provides the advantages of flexibility, compatibility with the existing hardware and lower cost at training personnel. Organisations with a sophisticated EDP department should consider the relative cost of in-house development before looking for a software package to purchase or lease.

9
PLANNING AND INSTALLING A LOCAL AREA NETWORK

INTRODUCTION

Installation of the physical components of a LAN is the single, most time consuming, expensive and difficult part of making a local area network part of your business. If you are installing a LAN into an existing office, you can expect disruption at the very least. While the steps involved are not much different from thosefor the installation of any other data processing equipment that requires cable linkto each workstation, that only means they are roughly equal in the amount of trouble thay cause.

Fortunately, with proper planning and some application of technology, the disruption and difficulty can be reduced significantly. The fact remains, though, that the LAN's support equipment will still require space, and the cable will have to be somewhere. How difficult the process is depends on you, to some extent.

Once you have selected a network vendor and system, you need to make a detailed plan of your specific configuration and then install the system according to the plan. The discussion here deals with planning and installing a local area network. After it is installed and running, you can use it and must manage it. Most of the work involved in managing a network is similar to the installation process; some additional management responsibilities are discussed later.

Although the installation process of each local area network is unique, there are many similarities among networks from different vendors. Hardware installation varies the least from one network to another; methods of cabling are generally the area of greatest difference. Software installation varies in its specifits, but several general concepts hold across most networks, and understanding these concepts helps smooth planning and installation. The discussion here provides an overview of the installation process so you can decide whether you want to attempt it yourself, and if so, to give you hints to make things go more smoothly.

If you plan to install a moderate-to-large network using hardware or software that is new to you, it is recommended that you build a very small experimental network first. Many network vendors sell "starter kits" containing everything you need to connect two PCs together. A few days of experience with a couple of workstations and a server can teach you a lot about your particular situation. This small-scale experiment can also help you during the planning phase to make a better detailed plan and to purchase the right equipment when you order the bulk of your network hardware and software.

If your potential network users, who will share peripherals and information, are well familiar with the use of PC, try setting a couple of them up with a server and your intended software configuration. If your network will be used to manage the operation of a business, it may be harder to set up a trial network. Use recent or dummy data for your network applications and have some of the eventual network users spend a few hours working with this data as they would with the real thing.

Figure 9.1 shows a sample checklist of things to evaluate after finishing the network trial. Note that it is only a sample — you should tailor it to your own environment and needs. When considering the items, also discuss them with the network users.

Disk storage
  Performance
  Responsiveness (delay from request to action)
  Transfer speed (time to load and save files)
  Consistency (variation in performance)
File placement
  Convenience (ease of locating and accessing)
  Usability (able to access disk from all applications)
  Volumes (correct things on public and private volumes)
Print service
  Performance '
  Usability (print from all applications)
  Spooling (time workstation is tied up while printing)
Job management
  Sharing (distribution of printers to users)
  Separating (distinguishing different users' print-outs)
  Forms (need to change print forms often)
Systems software
  Operating environment
  Understanding (quality of training)
  Ease of use (ease of doing necessary tasks)
  Functionality (can do all necessary tasks)
  Reliability (as compared to single-user PC)
Security
  Functionality (keeps unwanted users out)
  Convenience (not cumbersome for authorised users)

Application software
    Personal programmes
    Usability (can use programmes on network as desired)
    Licensing (do users understand license issues)
Multiuser network applications
    Sharing (any problems with concurrent data access)
    Functionality (does intended job)

Fig. 9.1 : Checklist for trial network evaluation

You will probably modify several aspects of your network configuration after the trial run. If this experiment seems to use more time than you would like to spend, consider the likely results of implementating a full network without the benefit of a trial. Unless you are exceptionally skillful or lucky, you will lose time in many ways:

* Users' time wasted running in a suboptimal configuration

* Your time spent reconfiguring all the servers and workstations

* Users' time wasted while you reconfigure the network

Even worse problems are possible from an improperly installed network, especially if it is used to run a business — you could lose money, irritate customers and upset employees. Of course, none of these potential problems is unique to local area networks; they can arise from any change in data processing equipment or procedures.

PLANNING THE INSTALLATION

There is an old saying that if you plan to go nowhere in particular, you are bound to get there. Although your needs — the components and how you should arrange them — may seem obvious to you, writing them down into a plan will probably reveal additional things you will need.

The complexity of your plan and the time you should devote to it will vary with the size of your network. A few hours to a day of planning may suffice for a network composed of four or five PCs run by knowledgeable computer users sharing a network disk and printer, while it may take months to plan for a hundred or more workstations running several different multiuser applications sharing a dozen network servers and linked to a corporate mainframe. If you are faced with such a complex task, do not hesitate to engage an experienced consultant to help with your planning.

Modern programming practices generally stress the importance of planning "top-down" and implementing "bottom-up." Planning and installing a network should be approached the same way. Briefly, top-down planning means starting with a high-level description of the overall task you are trying to perform. This description should help you see the separate components of a large, complicated problem. It is easier to deal with these components separately than trying to solve the whole problem at once. If the interfaces and connections between the components are well-defined and understood, you should be able to work out the details of each separate component by itself without concern for the details of the other components until you get to them.

Each individual component can be treated the same way: broken down into smaller pieces that can be separately considered. This process is called "successive refinement." You eventually reach a level of detail that cannot be further refined, and you have solved the problem. You are then ready to implement the solution — in this case, purchase and install the network.

Bottom-up implementation means you install the simplest, lowest-level pieces of your design, test them to see if they work as planned, then add the next level and test it, repeating the process until the entire network has been installed. Each successive level of implementation adds more function to the network, and is built on a previously tested foundation. This approach is very important, since problems are more easily found than if you wire an entire network together, load all the software, then try to determine why something does not work.

The discussion here is oriented towards the above approach to planning and installing a network. The highest-level description of the network is at the applications software level. What are your end users going to do with the system? This question generates a list of needs, from which a description of the required application and system software configuration follows. The software configuration in turn suggests your server and workstation requirements, from which it is fairly simple to see how to cable them together.

This whole process requires that you have a good understanding of your application needs and use that understanding to select the right network software and hardware. Two critical skills may require a consultant's help: one is studying a system and turning that analysis into the right applications software set-up — the job of a systems analyst; the other is determining a good network hardware and software configuration to support the applications software — best done by a local area network specialist (who could very well be the same person as the systems analyst). Make sure your in-house person or consultant has the right mix of experience and skills to make your installation a successful one.

SOFTWARE PLANNING

Although the analysis of your application needs from a systems viewpoint cannot be covered here in its full scope, some of the special needs from a network perspective will be discussed. Before you start planning your network installation, you should have selected the applications software for your network on the basis of the considerations listed in Figure 9.2. Without a good understanding of the applications you will run, you cannot possibly plan the requirements or configuration of your network.

Business
    Problems to solve
    Improvements sought
    Conservation from existing system
    Financial resources to purchase system

People
    End-user computer sophistication
    End-user need and ability to modify applications
    In-house or outside custom programming availability
    Network management responsibility
Software
    Applicability to problems at hand
    User interface suitability
    Integration with other applications
    Shared database access across network
    Custom programming requirement
    Ability and need to modify source code

Fig 9.2. Application software selection considerations

Your hardware and software plans are interdependent. As you work through your software plan, you will gather information that will shape the hardware plan. You may need to make a couple of passes through both plans, modifying earlier decisions as you gain a greater understanding of the interdependencies. For example, the number of servers you need in order to support your workstations depends on the applications software that will run on your network, and also on how that software is installed and used in conjunction with the network. Some software can be set up to make very little demand on the network, while other packages use the network constantly and heavily.

Figure 9.3 diagrams a piece of a network from a user's perspective. This viewpoint is helpful to guide in top-down planning of your LAN. You must determine:

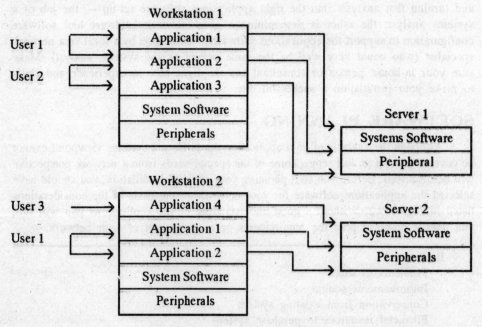

Fig. 9.3 : Network Usage Diagram

* Who your network users are?

* Which applications each user runs on each workstation?

* Which servers each application uses from each workstation?

As you can see in the diagram, the relationships may be complicated. A workstation may be used by more than one user, and a user may use more than one workstation. A workstation can run more than one application, and an application may be run on more than one workstation. The applications may use one or more servers.

To simplify this picture, identify the major components of your network and study each individually:

* Users

* Applications software

* Systems software

* Workstations

* Servers

* Connections

Figure 9.3 also shows peripherals, such as disk drives, printers and modems. They should be considered part of the workstation and server plans.

Refining your understanding of each of these areas will yield insights that will help improve your understanding of the others. To best use this information, you should keep notes as you go; a worksheet helps to keep things organised. Figure 9.4 is an example of a worksheet that you can use for each user of your network. In addition to name, network log-on ID and password, you need to know which applications this person uses, and from which workstations they are run. This use pattern, together with knowledge about the applications themselves, determines the workstation configuration you will need.

User Information Worksheet

Name_____,_____System Manager Privilege (Y/N):_____
Network log-on ID:_____Password:_____
(Repeat log-on ID and password for each account used if more than one)

Network Usage

List each application used by this individual along with the workstation number it is used on :

Application Name   Workstation Number

_____   _____

_____   _____

_____   _____

_____   _____

Fig 9.4. User information worksheet

Applications Software. You need to understand the demands that each of your applications places on the workstation, on the servers and on the connections between workstations and servers. Figure 9.5 shows a basic applications software information worksheet that you can use to analyse your applications. It does not address connection requirements, since the larger context of applications, workstations and servers determines these. This worksheet concentrates on the individual application characteristics, independent of context.

Application Software Information Worksheet

General Information
  Application programme: _____ Version #: _____
  Vendor : _____

Workstation Requirements

Microcomputer verdor and model: _____
DOS version #:
  Lowest: _____
  Highest: _____
Display adapter:
  (monochrome, graphics, special): _____
Monitor type:
  (monochrome, B&W composite, colour composite, colour RGB): _____
Random access memory:
  Shared memory in kilobytes: _____
  Unshared memory in kilobytes: _____
Disk storage:
  Floppy drive A: storage needed in kilobytes: _____
  Floppy drive B: storage needed in kilobytes: _____
  Hard drive C: storage needed in kilobytes _____
  Number of files used: _____
Printers:
  Type of printer 1: _____ Forms for printer 1: _____
  Type of printer 2: _____ Forms for printer 2: _____
Plotter:
  Type of plotter: _____
Modem:
  Type of modem: _____
Pointing device:
  (mouse, digitiser): _____
Other peripherals: _____

_____

Server Requirements

Server vendor and model: _____
DOS version #: _____

Random access memory:
Shared memory in kilobytes: _____
Unshared memory in kilobytes: _____
    Disk storage:
    Shared read-only in kilobytes: _____
    Shared read/write in kilobytes: _____
    Unshared read-only in kilobytes: _____
    Unshared read/write in kilobytes: _____
    Number of files used: _____
Printer:
    Type of printer 1: _____ Forms for printer 1: _____
    Demand on printer 1 (% of capacity): _____
    Type of printer 2: _____ Forms for printer 2: _____
    Demand on printer 2 (% of capacity): _____
Plotter:
    Type of plotter: _____
Modem:
    Type of modem: _____
Other peripherals:

(Repeat server information for each server accessed by application)

Fig. 9.5 : Appliction software information worsheet

You should fill out one of these worksheets for every application you will run on your network. Some applications may be thought of as a single large unit that may be run as a collection of separate smaller components. For example, your accounting system may have been purchased as a single software package, but it may contain separate modules for accounts payable, accounts receivable, general ledger and payroll; different users may run different subsets of this accounting package, perhaps not even all on one workstation. If the modules put different demands on the system, each should be considered separately.

Often, the same workstation can satisfy many requirements of both single-user PC and multiuser versions of an application. The DOS version number you use should be within the range you have marked on the worksheet to indicate the lowest and highest revision of DOS that the application can run under. The need to display graphics or text and the subsequent choices between display adapters and monitors are familiar problems faced by all PC buyers. Some applications can run on any monitor; if this is the case, indicate so by writing "any" in the blank. Application memory requirements are mostly independent of use in a network, although some applications may require additional space to manage multiuser access to data. Indicate the minimum memory required by your application, or if you know from experience that you need more than the minimum to obtain satisfactory performance or functionality, use that amount.

Disk storage questions must be reviewed in light of the network environment.

Many applications can be run completely from the network's disk storage and need no local storage. Some of the most common reasons for requiring local workstation storage are listed below:

* Copy protection requires local disk drive to start programme.

* Programme is incompatible with the network software and can only be run locally.

* Programme is hard-coded to use local drive letters. A: or B:

* Security considerations prohibit putting data on network disk drives.

* Performance is improved by local storage of data or programmes.

Performance considerations are hard to generalise, but how long it takes to access data depends on where it is stored. The storage options considered here are RAM disks, hard disks and floppy disks. A RAM disk uses random access memory to emulate a very fast disk drive. Some networks support all three options in both the workstation and the server; others support a subset of them in one place or the other.

The graph in Figure 9.6 shows the relationship between network load and the data access speed of these storage options. No one graph can accurately depict the performance relationships under all conditions. For example, on a particular network, it may always be faster to get data from a local hard disk than from a server's RAM disk. Nevertheless, the following rules usually apply:

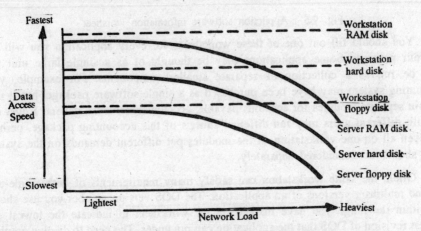

Fig. 9.6 : Access speed versus Network Load

* Workstation storage access speed is independent of network load.

* Given equally fast floppy disk drives and hard disk drives, data can be accessed more quickly from a local device than from across the network, even when the network is lightly loaded.

* Network data access slows as network loads increase.

The last point is critical, as Figure 9.6 demonstrates. Network load refers to the drain on the server from all the competing workstations. If you stored frequently accessed data on a network hard disk and the network load was light (on the left side of the graph), performance would be somewhere between that of a local hard disk and a local floppy disk — probably quite adequate. But if the network load turns out to be heavy (on the right side of the graph), the data access speed may be considerably slower than a local floppy disk — possibly inadequate. In most cases, the limits of the server will be reached long before you use all the bandwidth of the connecting cable.

Performance considerations encourage storing not only some data on the local hard disk, but other software elements as well, including programme overlay files. The WordStar word processor, for example, includes two such files, WSOVLY1.OVR and WSMSGS.OVR. Overlay files contain programme subroutines that various applications commands require. The application (in this case WordStar) loads part of the file to get the appropriate subroutines. If these must be loaded over the network each time they are used, there will be a delay of several seconds each time while the overlays are read into memory from across the network. If this delay is not acceptable, consider storing the overlays locally, or copying them from the server to a local RAM disk at the beginning of each session with the application. An MS-DOS batch file should be used to automate the process. Remember, however, that some software licenses prohibit this practice.

You also need to know the maximum number of disk files your applications have open at any one time. The workstation must be set up to allow for the right number of files, which also affects the amount of workstation random access memory you will need. There is more information about this topic later. You should carefully evaluate the application's use of printers with respect to how your network is used. The trade-offs between attaching a printer to the workstation and using the network printer are mostly between cost and convenience. A local printer may be needed if your application requires:

*   Immediate printing

*   A specialised printer not suitable for other users

*   Preprinted or multipart forms that must stay loaded in the printer

For example, if your workstation is used as a cash register and prints multipart invoices while the customer waits, it may be best to dedicate a printer to that workstation. On the other hand, use of a shared printer on a network server may be in order if your application specifies:

*   Infrequent use of a printer

*   That delays in printing are acceptable

*   An expensive printer (which must be shared to justify cost)

Plotters and other output devices can generally be analysed by the same methods as printers. Some applications require modems — devices that connect your computer to a telephone line for transferring data between the workstation and a remote computer not on the network. If your application requires a mouse, digitiser, or any other workstation peripheral, note that on the applications worksheet, too.

Next you need to determine the requirements each application places on network servers. If a specific type of server is required, that fact should be noted. Many applications can be used with any network server, but some require specific server features — such as an application that is split into two parts, one running on the workstation and the other on the server. Such an application may also make a demand on the server's random access memory, and that requirement should be noted.

Server disk requirements depend on the decisions made earlier regarding how the programmes and data will be partitioned between the server and workstation. Network server disks may be the storage option of choice when:

*   Many users use a programme or data file

*   Only one user needs the file, but from different workstations

*   Network disk capacity is greater than local capacity

*   Network disk speed is greater than that of local disks

Once you have decided what to place on the server, you also must decide whether to place it in shared or unshared, read-only or read/write storage. Most network systems require you to categorise the server's storage according to these or similar terms. If the data is accessed by more than one user at a time, it must be stored as shared data. If it is not only read but also modified, it must be read/write. Shared files may include applications programsme, DOS utilities, network utilities and multiuser databases.

It is usually only necessary to keep one copy of a shared file on the server. For example, the network software may include utility programmes to display and modify the print queue for network printers. Rather than storing copies of this utility on every workstation, you can place one copy of it in shared storage on a network disk. Unshared storage is typically used to hold files pertaining to a single user, such as:

*   Private data files

*   Single-user licensed applications

*   User profile information

*   System management files

. *   Software under development.

On the worksheet estimate the shared and unshared, read-only and read/write server disk space required under each of these categories. If your applications require a certain number of files to be open on the server, note this fact also. Refer to your network documentation for more details, since some network servers handle network file opening independently of the MS-DOS file system, and the MS-DOS CONFIG.SYS FILES parameter (explained soon) is not the way to control this operation.

Next you must determine print server requirements for the application. In the previous discussion you saw that your application needs guide your choice between a local printer and a shared printer. If this application will use a network printer, you should estimate the percentage of the printer's capacity that the application will use from each workstation. For example, if a printer can print 100 plane tickets an hour and a ticketing agent's workstation can handle 20 customers per hour, each workstation may use up to 20% of the printer's capacity. You would expect that the printer could handle a maximum of five workstations. It may be appropriate to perform a more detailed analysis taking into account such things as the time it takes to turn the printer off-line while removing a ticket, reloading forms, and so on.

You should fill out an application software information worksheet for every application that will run on the network. Be sure to include network utilities and special applications such as electronic mail. From your information about all the applications that will run on the network, and about which users will run which application, you can derive the system software, workstation and server configuration of your network.

Systems Software. System software integrates the applications software with the network hardware. Your systems software plan is determined by the applications you will run, the needs of the users who run the application, and the exact configuration of servers and workstations you choose. Since you have planned only the first two items so far, you can not complete the systems software plan until you have determined the workstation server configuration. Since doing so is easier if you understand the basic principles of your network's systems software, it is important to review the documentation and make sure you understand the areas discussed in the following sections as they are implemented in your network.

One piece of important systems software probably does not come from your network vendor. Most PC networks use the MS-DOS operating system on the workstations and on the servers. In most respects MS-DOS is used in a LAN environment exactly as a stand-alone PC, but some issues should be considered, especially performance and ease of use.

The exact details of how to configure MS-DOS for your LAN PCs vary from network to network, and you must follow the directions supplied by your vendor. Two important MS-DOS system files usually come into play: CONFIG.SYS and AUTOEXEC.BAT. These files contain plain ASCII (American Standard Code for Information Interchange) text and can be created and modified by most text editors, such as the EDLIN programme that comes with MS-DOS.

CONFIG.SYS contains system configuration information that can affect network performance. One important entry is the BUFFERS parameter. A line in the CONFIG.SYS file like:

BUFFERS=20

tells MS-DOS to allocate 20 buffers in RAM for storage of disk blocks. These buffers fill up with blocks read from disk. If a programme accesses a block that is already in memory, that data is available at memory speeds much greater than disk speeds. However, allocating too many blocks can have a detrimental effect, since the blocks must periodically be written back to disk for permanent storage, and there can be quite a pause while this happens if you allocate a large number of buffers. Additionally, each block takes 512 bytes of workstation memory, which is subtracted from memory that would otherwise be available for applications and systems software.

Another important CONFIG.SYS file entry is the FILES parameter. Structured like the BUFFERS entry, it tells MS-DOS how may files can be open at a time. For example,

FILES=20

tells MS-DOS to allocate enough local memory and DOS file control information to allow 20 files to be open at once. To set this parameter correctly, you must understand the needs of your application and systems software.

The AUTOEXEC.BAT file is used to automate the set-up of a workstation or server running under MS-DOS. All the commands it contains are automatically executed every time you start the PC. Each LAN vendor's software puts different requirements on the contents of this file, and some vendors even custom-build the file for you automatically. Using this file enables all the network software to be loaded and an application to start running before the end-user touches the keyboard.

During planning you must also determine what version of MS-DOS you will run on your workstations and servers. Many networks let you mix different revisions on the same network, but the safest course is to use only one version everywhere. Using the applications software information worksheets, you will determine the lowest and highest acceptable revision levels for MS-DOS on your system, it is advisable to use the highest revision level uniformly across the network.

Most of the new systems software you have to deal with controls the network itself. It is easiest to plan to install this software as two components: the workstation component and the server component. In each case there are two further major subdivisions to consider: resident operating software and utilities. The operating software is the part that must be configured and installed. It controls the network hardware for you while you are using the network, just as MS-DOS controls your PC's disk drives and other devices. The utilities are used to configure, extend and maintain the network. They are programmes that you run briefly to do a specific operation, like the MS-DOS FORMAT command.

Which systems software to install on the workstation varies from vendor to vendor. Generally, you need to know which network resources, especially disks and printers, you will be using from each workstation. In some cases, you just install an all-purpose software driver, and the resources you can use from that workstation depend on the user account established for you on the server. Occasionally you need to know whether the users of this workstation will be using such network applications as electronic mail, and adjust the workstation software accordingly.

In any event, you need to consider this software in the light of overall workstation requirements. The application software information worksheet (Figure 9.5) contains most of the relevant questions that you need to answer. Your network docu nentation probably describes how much overall software support, with respect to memory, disk and printer, is required by the network software that runs on the workstations. Using this summary information, fill out an applications software worksheet so the needs of the network software can be factored into the workstation configuration. This single sheet can probably be used for most of your workstations. If workstations differ in the applications they run (for example, some have electronic mail privileges and some do not), you may consider those applications separately, creating a worksheet for each.

Most LANs come with a variety of utilities used to configure and operate the network. Referring to the network documentation, determine what is offered and what your network users need. This software is a prime candidate to load into network disk storage, since it will probably be used at most workstations. In most cases it includes, at a minimum, software to:

*   Connect and disconnect to network disk storage.

*   Connect and disconnect to network printers.

*   Monitor and modify network print queue status.

You must decide whether it is appropriate for your users to have access to these utilities. In some cases, you may want to provide a batch file that executes the utility in a predetermined way. Consider the sophistication of your users and the possible damage that can be done by accidental or malicious misuse of these utilities. Software that you probably should not make widely available includes network utilities to:

*   Create and modify user accounts or user profiles.

*   Create and modify network disk volumes.

*   Alter network security.

These utilities should be used only by you or the designated system manager, and they should be stored securely so they cannot be misused.

Network software for the server can also be treated during planning as two parts: operating software and utilities for managing the server. The operating software handles workstation requests for server devices such as disks and printers; utilities set up the server so that its resources can be shared with the network. Again, consult your network documentation to see what options are available for configuring the server operating software. In some cases, you simply load it and answer a couple of questions. For other systems you have to make many configuration decisions to suit the type of hardware attached to the server.

If your server is also used as a workstation, make note of any special restrictions in the way it can be used or the software it can run. When configuring the hardware, consider the demands of both workstation and server software. For example, there must be sufficient random access memory to support the memory-resident software of both the workstation and server.

Most LAN software controls network disk allocation by means of **volumes** or **directories**. Among the many reasons for grouping files in volumes are the following:

* Security.

* Write protection.

* Ease of finding and accessing files.

* Application software requirements.

* Providing personal disk storage.

You must understand your applications with respect to each of these categories. Also relevant is the previous discussion about grouping files according to their being shared or unshared, or read-only or read/write. In many systems these paired categories are mutually exclusive: an entire volume or directory must be declared, say, shared and read-only, or unshared and read/write. Some systems allow a finer level of differentiation, letting you assign these attributes to individual files instead of to the volume or directory. Read your system manuals to see what your network software supports. You should thoroughly understand your applications software needs and systems software capabilities in this area, since making a change usually involves redoing major portions of your installation. The applications worksheets should be re-examined to see if the server disk requirement sections are adequately filled out.

Next examine the network provisions for print service to assess flexibility. In some systems you identify your printer by name and the basic set-up is done automatically. Others require you to use printer control codes to make your printer do things like go to the top of the next page or reset to standard character pitch. You must understand your application's printing requirements, your network software's printing options, and the relationship between the two. Consider the amount of memory that the software on the server needs to drive the printer. Sometimes you can specify a print buffer size; a large buffer may speed network printing but also takes memory away from other server software.

Your network security requirements depend on your user community, the sensitivity of your data, your applications software and your network software. In some cases you may plan to install the network with security turned off. For example, an elaborate security system may be more trouble than it's worth in a software development environment where the users are computer knowledgeable, code under development must be shared among all users, and network-licensed compilers are uniformly used. By the time you give everyone the appropriate privileges, everyone may have access to everything anyway.

Even in such an open environment, you may help prevent accidental damage if you use read-only volumes or directories to store compilers and archived copies of the code you are developing. In a different setting, such as a retail store where the network holds the business's accounting system, point-of-sale workstations, and electronic mail between branch stores and the home store, elaborate security may be necessary.

Since the security provided by each network varies, it is difficult to create a planning worksheet that is generally useful. Base yours on the type of security your network offers and fill it out during the planning process. Your network security arrangements could address the particular user on a specific application; or you could save time and effort by assigning the same security arrangement to all users who fit in a similar class, for example, all secretaries may have the same security level, check-out clerks another level, and bookkeepers a third.

HARDWARE PLANNING

Once you have a good understanding of your users, applicationsand systems software, you can derive your needs for workstations, servers and connections. You need to determine the workstation and server hardware configurations and the connection scheme you will use to tie the workstations and servers together.

Your user information worksheets identify all the applications each workstation uses. Collect this information on a workstation configuration worksheet so that you can determine what hardware the workstation needs. By analysing all workstations, you determine the number of servers needed to support your workstations and the hardware configuration of each server. Finally, on the basis of your network's data dependencies — that is, which workstations communicate with which servers — you must build a connection plan for your cables and network transceiver cards. This plan is usually the most straightforward and is dictated by the architecture of the network system you choose.

Workstation Planning. The configuration of your workstations is determined by the applications and systems software that run on them. Your user information worksheets tell you who uses what applications software on each workstation. Your analysis of systems software reveals the hardware dependencies it imposes. You now combine this data to determine the workstation hardware configuration.

One approach to collating this information is to use a workstation configuration worksheet, shown in Figure 9.7; it identifies the major hardware requirements of each piece of software that will be run on each workstation. You need such a worksheet for every workstation, although, of course, you can duplicate the same information for workstations with identical requirements. The first two worksheet entries are for the MS-DOS and network software requirements; fill them in now or as soon as you have enough information.

Workstation Configuration Worksheet
Workstation Requirements by Application

Appli cation	Memory Unshared	Usage Shared	Disk A:	Drive B:	Usage C:	Files Used	Display Type	Printer Type	Dos Version Low High	other Devices
MS-DOS										
Network										

Workstation Hardware Summary
Memory:
Floppy disk drive(s):
FILES= in CONFIG.SYS:
Display(s):
Printer(s):
DOS version:
Other devices:
Serial ports:
Parallel ports:
Expansion slots:

Fig 9.7. Workstation configuration worksheet

The user information worksheets you completed earlier contain entries for applications and workstations. For each workstation, extract the name of each application run on it and put an entry in the left-hand column of the worksheet. From the applications worksheets transfer the relevant information to the proper line of the workstation configuration worksheet. If you are proficient with a PC database management package, you can automate this process, especially if your package can handle relationships among multiple databases.

Once you have all the information about all the applications that must run on this workstation, you can see what your workstation hardware configuration must be. Analyse the data in each column and enter the results in the summary table at the bottom of the worksheet.

1.   RAM must be at least as much as the sum of all the unshared memory plus the largest shared memory requirement that must be in use concurrently. Typically this is the sum of the memory requirements of your network driver software, any memory-resident utility programmes, MS-DOS itself and the largest application programme you run.

2.   Some applications may require one or more floppy disk drives. (If this is a hardware expense you would rather avoid, substitute a network shared disk, if possible.) Your total floppy disk space requirements gives you an idea of how to load software on each diskette and how often your users will have to swap them.

3.   Some applications may require a hard disk. The minimum disk size needed equals the sum of disk space requirements of all the applications. Again, add this expense to each workstation only after you are sure the network drive is not an option.

4.   The total number of files opened by all the software that must run currently gives you the value for the MS-DOS FILES= entry in the CONFIG.SYS file. Consult the MS-DOS manual to determine how much RAM is thus consumed and make sure that figure is included in the MS-DOS memory requirement on this worksheet.

5. For each workstation you assign a video display of the type required by most applications. Determining this demands some non-network PC hardware expertise. If any of your applications require graphics, you will probably need a graphics display adapter and monitor. Most such display devices can also handle your text requirements, although often the quality of text is not as good as on a text-only monitor.

6. If any of your applications require a printer, it must be allocated here. If several of your applications require different kinds of printers, you may want to limit the number of printers you must purchase for each workstation by reallocating applications and users among workstations.

7. The DOS version needed is one between the maximum of the low entries and the minimum of the high entries listed in the workstation configuration worksheet. If the first number is higher than the second number, you have a conflict in DOS requirements and must separate the conflicting applications. Check with the vendor of the software that requires an older DOS revision and see if an upgrade is available for the newer version.

8. Any other special peripherials (such as modems, mice, digitisers or plotters) should be entered in the last column. You will probably need only one each of these but make sure choice is compatible with any two or more applications that require them. For example, if you have two different graphics applications, choose a plotter they both support.

9. Depending on the types of devices you attach to your workstation, you may need one or more serial or parallel I/O ports. This information can be derived from the documentation for the peripherals and your workstation itself. There are many ways to add these ports, and some PCs include them as standard equipment.

10. You must also make sure your workstation has enough expansion slots to hold all the peripherals you want to attach to it. Consult your owner's manuals for the workstation and the peripherals. Most network attachments take up one expansion slot. Make sure you account for slots needed to supply serial and parallel ports and to connect special devices such as mice.

At the completion of this exercise, you should have a good idea of the hardware configuration you need for each workstation. Review the systems software configuration needed to support that hardware, and factor any additional demands on the workstation back into the worksheet. If you can do so without being wasteful, be liberal enough in your figures to make sure your configuration will not fail if some piece of software needs a bit more memory than its documentation states. In performing this analysis for all your workstations, you may also decide that a different grouping of applications on the workstations can reduce cost with no loss of function. But be careful not to sacrifice the problem-solving goals that motivated your installing a network.

Server Planning. The next stage in your plan is the determination of network server configurations. Figure 9.8 shows a server configuration worksheet. If your network is small enough to function with a single server, planning is fairly simple.

If you have dozens of workstations, determining your server requirements not only requires careful analysis but may benefit from some creativity as well.

Server Configuration Worksheet
Server Requirements by Application

Appli- cation	Number in Work- station	Memory Usage Unshared Shared	Disk Usage Unshared Shared R-O R/W R-O R/W	Files Used	Printer type	% Capa- city Used	Other Devices

MS-DOS
Network
Workstation Hardware Summary
Memory:
Floppy disk drive(s):
FILES= in CONFIG.SYS:
Display(s):
Printer(s):
DOS version:
Other devices:
Serial ports:
Parallel ports:
Expansion slots:

Fig. 9.8 : Server configuration worksheet

To minimise cost, you will probably want to use as few servers as possible. Naturally, you need to know how many workstations a server can support. The right number depends heavily on the type of applications you are running, your pattern of using them and the ability of your network software and hardware to support that pattern. You derive your estimate from experience with your applications and form the network vendor's information. Figure 9.9 gives some very rough estimates of the number of PC workstations that can be typically supported by some of the more common types of servers under varying network loads. Actual rates of use are subject to wide variation according to individual circumstances, so these figures should not be used as the only basis for your estimate.

	Light Use	Moderate Use	Heavy Use
PC/AT server	12-18	8-12	4-8
High-performance server	18-36	12-18	6-12

Fig 9.9 : Typical number of workstations supported by different
types of servers under different loads

A light load might consist of word processing or spreadsheet processing during which only data file resides on the server, or execution of an electronic mail programme. A moderate load could consist of interactive database queries and interactive transaction processing. A heavy load would comprise software development or batch database work such as report generation.

These examples are intended to give you a feeling for the problem. The true criterion is really the amount of server access required per minute. If the server is accessed only occasionally and most of the processing is local to the workstation, there is only a light load on the server and it can handle more workstations. If almost every command given on the workstation sends a request to the server, this represents a heavy network load, and the server can handle fewer workstations.

You need to know how many workstations a server can handle for each application you will run. If you need more than one server, you must decide what files and print service to place on each server. There are several reasons for grouping programme and data files on a single server:

*   The applications software requires it

*   Network loads suggest the configuration

*   Redundant storage of the files on other servers is reduced

*   All the server resources for a group of workstations are provided, and cabling costs are minimised for that group.

From these and other factors that are important in your environment, you must come up with a trial server configuration, deciding the workstation/application pairs that will use that server for network resources.

After you fill in all the information about your applications and the network software, you can analyse the worksheet in Figure 9.8 and at the bottom write your estimate of the server hardware required. Note that this worksheet tells you only what is necessary, not what is sufficient. Performance considerations determine the latter. Here are some things to consider during your analysis:

1.   Server memory should be at least equal to the sum of unshared memory times the number of workstations requiring it plus the largest programme that can use shared memory at any one time. If more than two or more shared-memory programmes can run at once, you must sum their memory requirements together. Your network software documentation should help you determine this requirement.

2.   Network disk capacity must be large enough to hold all the unshared files,times the number of workstations requiring them plus the total amount of shared disk storage used.

3.   The maximum number of files in use at any one time determines the FILES= parameter in the MS-DOS CONFIG.SYS file. Some network software opens multiple-user files as a single MS-DOS file, so you should consult your network documentation when computing this value.

4. Your server needs one printer of each type required by the workstations. The printer's use rate is the sum of the percent of capacity used by each application, times the number of workstations running that application at once. If your use rate exceeds 100%, either your server needs more than one of that type of printer or you need another print server.

5. Other devices such as modems, tape drives and communication gateways should be noted in the server configuration. Make sure you have a way to back-up the disk storage for the server.

6. Using your projected configuration, you can ascertain the number of serial and parallel I/O ports your server needs, and you can determine the number of expansion slots required to hold all the peripheral adapter cards.

If the summary turns out to be a realistic configuration, go on to the next server. If you find you require more of some resource than can be configured on a single server, you need to rethink your allocation of servers to workstations.

Connection Planning. The final major step in your plan is usually the most straightforward. You need to determine how you will connect the workstations and servers of your network. Connections are needed whenever data must flow between two network nodes. For example, a connection is needed if an application needs to get a data file from a disk server, send output to the printer on a print server or send a message to another workstation by electronic mail.

A connection can be physical or virtual: a physical connection is a direct one by connecting cable; a virtual connection is one achieved by routing the data through one or more intermediate nodes. Be sure you understand the possibilities implicit in this distinction, since virtual connections add no cabling costs, although they may extract more of a performance penalty than a direct connection.

Different networks have different connection rules. The exact details of your network must guide your choices. In any case, you should start with a logic diagram showing the data dependency paths of your network, such as in Figure 9.3. From this diagram, your network cabling rules and your physical site map, you can construct a connection blueprint for your LAN.

Site planning for the workstations and servers themselves is usually no more complex than planning for stand-alone PCs. Adequate power typically requires no more than a convenient wall outlet with stable power, and adequate cooling usually requires only comfortable temperatures. Cable stringing is another matter, and can quickly get you involved with local safety and building regulations. Your best bet is a good electrical contractor with some previous experience in installing LANs. In addition to following electrical codes for safety, LAN cabling needs to conform to the vendor's rules regarding:

*   Minimum separation between connections to the cable.

*   Maximum lengths of cable runs.

*   Proper termination at the ends of the cable.

* Use of drop cables from the trunk to a workstation or server.

* Repeaters to boost the signal over long distances.

* Routing away from sources of electrical interference such as AC wiring, motors and fluorescent light fixtures.

Finding the problem with an improperly laid cable can be frustrating and time-consuming, so you are well advised to learn the rules of the LAN in advance and make sure you follow them. A carefully worked out map of your site drawn to scale and showing all workstations, servers and connecting cables is a must. Study the map and make sure all the length constraints are met. Leave some room for expansion in your cable runs. For example, allow a workstation to be moved from desk to desk within a room if possible. Run bus cables near enough to potential future network node sites so you can easily add the node later.

You must also be sure to follow the cable length rules that pertain to the exact type of cable you are using. Different cable grades with compatible basic electrical characteristics may have different signal-loss rates, meaning that you may be able to use 5000 feet of one type of cable but only 2000 feet of another. Different network topologies can result in radically different cabling diagrams for the same siting of workstations and servers. For example:

* A bus may require one cable strung past all the nodes.

* A bus with drop cables sends a single cable into each office; one not using drop cables may appear to send two cables into each office (it's actually the same cable entering and leaving the node).

* A star may require much more wire than a bus, especially if the workstations are closer together than to the server at the hub

Once your cable diagram is drawn, you can decide whether to use precut cables or custom-made ones. You must balance the cost of the unused lengths of the precut cables against the labour costs of making exact-length custom cables. In many areas this difference may be slight, since the labour costs of running a single cable far exceed the material costs. If you decide to use precut lengths, be sure they also meet your cabling rules — as far as the network rules go — 20 feet of excess precut cable in a 1-foot diameter coil still counts as 20 feet.

DOING THE INSTALLATION

If you have built a trial network to learn about your system and carefully analysed your network as described here, the actual installation is a matter of executing your plan. You should build your network in testable sections, making sure each one functions according to your expectations before continuing with the installation. For example, you may install one server and its workstations and make sure they work together before adding another server.

The order of installation may be dictated by your network vendor, but it typically follows a sequence such as:

1.   Set up the server and workstation hardware.

2.   Make sure the combination works stand-alone.

3.   Install the network cards and cables and connect them.

4.   Install the system software on the server and test it.

5.   Install the system software on the workstation and test it.

6.   Bring up your applications and test them.

You can see that the order of implementation is practically the reverse of the order of planning and design. You start implementation with the lowest-level components of your network, make sure they work, and then build on that foundation, testing each successive layer to make sure it works too.

HARDWARE AND SOFTWARE INSTALLATION

If you are reasonably sure about your network layout you can run cables at the same time you set up workstations and servers. Make sure that the cables you need first for system testing are installed early enough. If you are unsure about your network in any way, for example, whether it will have adequate performance, run only enough cables to perform a test. String more cables when you are satisfied with your design.

Set up the servers following the instructions provided by the server and network software vendor. Connect all the peripherals identified in your server worksheet and make sure the minimum requirements for memory and disk storage are met. Workstations should be set up the same way. In most cases you can test the workstations to see if they function as stand-alone PCs. You can frequently also test the server this way, especially if it is a PC/AT.

Next, the system software should be installed on the servers and workstations configured as the documentation and your worksheets suggest. The worksheets should greatly assist you in the areas that might otherwise require a lot of guesswork, such as allocating server storage to volumes or directories, making different network resources such as printers available to your end users, and setting up system security.

Cable your server and workstations together and start testing the system. Your LAN documentation probably suggests some simple tests you can perform to make sure the basics are functioning before you start trying you applications. When you are satisfied that all is well you can start loading and testing the applications.

DIAGNOSING PROBLEMS

If all does not go well, consult your network documentation and look for an explanation of common problems or interpretation of error messages. Building and testing you network in small pieces should help you to locate the point at which things stopped working. Like most system problem-solving, half the battle is isolating the problem to a small part of the system, then fixing the faulty part or replacing it with a good part. A network has many parts, possibly strung out across a large area, and can be formidable to debug. Some techniques for isolating problems follow:

1. Make sure every workstation and server works alone, outside of the network environment.

2. Test network connection cards with loopback plugs, if they are available, or hardware diagnostic software.

3. Test cables for short circuits with an ohmmeter. There should be no direct connection between the network cable conductors. Short circuits may be induced by a kink or pinch in the wire.

4. Test applications software on local disk drives and printers, if possible.

Try to narrow down the number of system components whose working status is unknown. Do this by swapping in components known to work. Consider using this technique with server and workstation PCs, network connection cards, cables, and even application packages that use the same or similar server resources as the suspect applications. It may be difficult to swap a cable strung through the wall or ceiling, so if you suspect it is bad, try moving the workstation or server to another location with a known good connection on the network and see if it works there. If it does, your suspicions about the cable should be heightened.

TRAINING NETWORK USERS

Once you are satisfied that your applications are installed and working, you need to train the users of your network,tuning the training to their needs. Technical users may just want copies of the network documentation and they will learn what they need to know when they need to know it. End-users who do not care at all about system implementation or utilities may only need to be trained on the applications. In any case, you should plan for some time to be spent on training and if your system is installed by or with a lot of help from a consultant, plan for that consultant to spend several days at your site to answer questions and make adjustments in the initial configuration.

MANAGING THE NETWORK

Every network needs a manager who is responsible after the installation. If your network is fairly static in the applications it runs and its configuration of workstations and servers, it may be enough to assign a non-technical user who can handle daily back-ups of the servers, answer questions about the applications and assign new user accounts as needed. A consultant can be called in when network management needs go beyond these simple ones.

If your network environment is dynamic (new applications are frequently brought up, new workstatons and servers added, security requirements undergo change, and the like), you may need an experienced person in-house or a consultant on call. Many management tasks can be handled by someone who is not a computer expert but who has received the proper training on the network.

COMMON PROBLEMS IN PHYSICAL INSTALLATION

Despite the best intentions and efforts of everyone involved, the installation and use of any high technology item of equipment rarely goes as planned. The variation between theory and practice can be a small nuisance or a huge, expensive disaster.

In this section, we will look at some of the more common difficulties encountered when installing a LAN and try to indicate how these can be avoided. Many of the problems described are common to all sorts of high-technology equipment and may well be worth remembering in other circumstances.

The gap between theory and practice occurs when the assessment of technical suitability fails to take into account the problems involved in installing the particular hardware (and possibly software in a modular system) which is required by the LAN, or when the operating conditions of the LAN deviate from the original specifications.

The problems break up into two main groups, as previously mentioned. The most common group is that produced by an inadequate original specification for the system. It is important to remember that items such as cabling are an integral part of the system and should be investigated and specified properly before a network is purchased. The main problem areas relating to poor specifications are:

1. Cabling: In the area of cabling, the physical constraints imposed by the premises become immediately apparent. The network cables, either twisted pair, coaxial or fibre optic, must be routed to conform with current provisions for cables and in the case of the electrical conductors, be well clear of any electrical noise sources. This may well mean that it is difficult or impossible to have the cables emerging where they are required. Some of the coaxial cables, e.g. Ethernet, are very stiff as they have a solid outer conductor, and are therefore restricted in the amount they can be bent. This may cause difficulties in installing them in standard cable ducts.

Positioning for the cable tap points, where the network nodes are attached to the cable, must be considered carefully to avoid problems. They should be placed as close to the networked equipment as possible, without interfering with associated equipment. However, spacing between the cable tap points may need to be maintained, depending on the type of network, and so more than one node may have to share the same cable tap point. Where a number of networked devices stand in the same area, they may overload the physical connection facilities of the network at that point.

At the other end of the scale, some nodes may be too far from the main network to be connected without exceeding the allowed distance for cabling. In some networks, this problem can be overcome by adding an extra length of cable and a repeater to boost and reconstitute the network signals but in others, it may be necessary to have the remote node as a separate system with a special connection to the main system. In either case, connection will be expensive, but there are ways of getting round these problems if they can be identified at the planning stage.

The distance limits set by manufacturers and suppliers for the full extent of their standard networks (typically 1/2 - 1 km) may seem much greater than the user's needs, but the practical difficulties involved in installing a network will very quickly use up the available cable. By planning the optimum layout for the cable, the user can include a much greater area within the network. See Figures 9.10 and 9.11 for an example of optimising the cable layout for a bus LAN within a single multi-storey building.

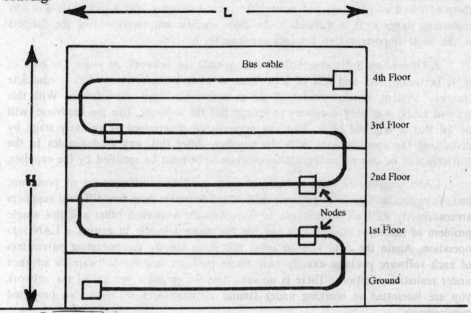

Fig. 9.10 : Cable layout for five-storey building

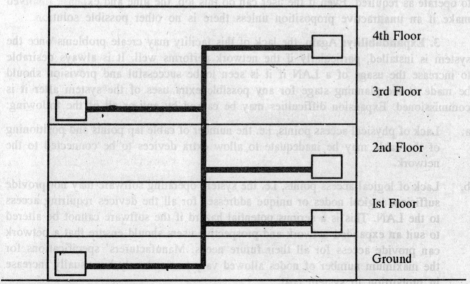

Length of cable = 2.5L + H

Fig. 9.11 : Alternative cable layout to Figure. 9.10

Finally, on the subject of cabling, there is the matter of the robustness of the cable. In some situations, the cable may be exposed to damp and extreme temperatures, particularly where the network connects separate buildings. More commonly, it may be prone to mechanical damage where it is not protected by suitable cable ducting. The only answer in both these cases is to determine the possible dangers, minimise them as much as possible, and protect the cable or ensure that it can withstand any remaining dangers. It is difficult to be more specific but awareness of the dangers is the most important step towards averting them.

2. Operating Software: Software to operate the network, or rather the lack of it, is becoming less and less of a problem as more manufacturers offer a complete 'turnkey' system, which includes all the necessary hardware and software. With this type of LAN, it is only necessary to ensure that the software, like the hardware, will do all that is required of it. This can normally be determined at an early stage by discussing the specifications with the supplier. After this, any inadequacies in the software will be due to inadequate specifications, or must be rectified by the supplier.

LANs constructed from component parts produce a different set of problems, and are particularly prone to software difficulties. Software from two different suppliers are notoriously difficult to persuade to communicate with each other and this single problem of incompatible software may be the greatest hurdle in getting a LAN into operation. Again the only way to avoid this is to specify the operating parameters of each software package exactly and, where possible, test the software in advance under realistic conditions. There is no substitute for seeing a version of the network you are interested in working under similar circumstances to your own projected requirements.

In general, it is best to avoid any system where the software must be tailored to operate as required. Even if the user can do this job, the time and expense involved make it an unattractive proposition unless there is no other possible solution.

3. Expandability: Again, the lack of this facility may create problems once the system is installed, particularly if the network performs well. It is always desirable to increase the usage of a LAN if it is seen to be successful and provision should be made at the planning stage for any possible extra uses of the system after it is commissioned. Expansion difficulties may be caused by any or all of the following:

a.   Lack of physical access points, i.e. the number of cable tap points and positioning of the cable may be inadequate to allow extra devices to be connected to the network.

b.   Lack of logical access points, i.e. the system operating software may not provide sufficient logical nodes or unique addresses for all the devices requiring access to the LAN. This is a serious potential hazard if the software cannot be altered to suit an expanded network and prospective users should ensure that a network can provide access for all their future needs. Manufacturers' specifications for the maximum number of nodes allowed vary tremendously but usually increase in proportion to system cost.

c.   Lack of data-carrying capacity, i e. the network may be able to support extra devices but adding them to the LAN degrades its performance to an unacceptable level. This will happen in any LAN as the actual combined data transmission rates of the attached nodes approaches the quoted data transmission rate of the network. As this point is reached, more data is being generated by the nodes than the network can transmit, and so the data must join a queue until the network is ready for it. This phenomenon is familiar to users of large mainframe computers, and when the computer is overloaded serious delays can result which makes the system difficult to use.

All three points mentioned here must be noted if the network is to be expanded successfully in the future. Additionally it should be possible to add extra cabling to the system without unnecessary expense or difficulty. This will allow both for expansion and for alternative uses of the network, when equipment is moved and used in new locations.

4. Standardisation: Where the LAN is supplied complete with workstations, standardisation of interface will not be a problem. If however, you are looking for a LAN to interconnect existing equipment, it is vital that the LAN nodes should be capable of connecting to the equipment without difficulty. This implies some sort of standard interface unit compatible with the interface units on the existing equipment.

There are a number of standard, or rather generally accepted, forms of connection available on the types of equipment likely to be used as workstations, file servers or print-servers in the network. The most common will be some form of serial data link using RS232C/V24 protocols, simple 8-bit parallel data links like the Centronics interface standard, or more complex 8-bit parallel data links like the IEEE488 interface bus. The last is very common in programmable test and measurement equipment.

If the LAN under examination is to be used for a variety of equipment and does not provide interfaces for some or all of the standards mentioned above, it is unlikely to be suitable.

A number of commercially-available LANs are designed for use with specific microcomputers, such as the Apple or IBM PC, and include interface units that plug directly into the expansion sockets in the microcomputer. These networks normally allow other devices to be attached via interfaces in the microcomputer and are thus versatile in terms of the range of compatible equipment. However, each extra device attached to the network requires a microcomputer to act as an interface unit; and so adding new items is an expensive proposition, as extra microcomputers will be tied up in servicing these. See Figure 9.12.

In general, standardisation of interconnections can be a serious problem for modular LANs used to interconnect existing equipment, but is unlikely to be a significant installation and operation problem in turnkey systems.

As use of the network changes, other difficulties may arise. Matters such as expandability and overloading have already been touched upon as consequences of poor specifications but they will become acute if the way the network is used changes

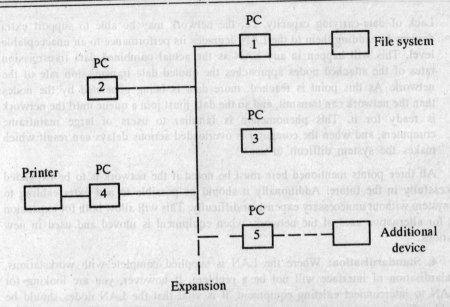

Fig. 9.12 : Problems inherent in LANs dedicated to single types of microcomputers

with time, particularly as more potential users see the advantages of applying the installed LAN to their requirements. It is therefore vital that manufacturers and suppliers provide technical support both during installation and operation of the LAN. A good supplier should be happy to have a representative on-site throughout the installation period and to continue to make engineers available if there are any problems after installation is complete.

10

UTILISING A LOCAL AREA
NETWORK

INTRODUCTION

There are a variety of ways in which a local area network can be used. A LAN can reduce hardware costs if an expensive peripheral such as a laser printer is needed by more than one PC user. It can provide a means for passing information between users, eliminating the need to send floppy diskettes, or replacing a hard copy inter-office mail system. These applications are for convenience and efficiency, and are among the most common uses of LANs today.

There are also many applications that simply cannot be implemented through the use of several isolated PCs. Any time more than one user needs instant access to the latest version of a particular piece of data, such as an inventory count or the status of a reservation list, a multiuser application package is required. A network is not the only way to satisfy the need for instant access, since a shared central computer may also be used. But as far as networks are concerned, this type of application is the most sophisticated and the least likely to be available off the shelf.

This chapter looks in a little more detail at what LANs are used for in practice. It begins with a recap of the motivation behind developing LANs. It then lists both the advantages that are to be gained by their use and the problems faced in actually achieving those advantages.

MOTIVATION

The main motivations behind the development of LANs, and, more important, their increasingly widespread use, are as follows:

1.   The decreasing cost, and consequent increased use, of computers;

2.   Rapid improvements in communication technology;

3.   The marriage of these two distinct disciplines, computing and communication, together.

Other considerations which make this area even more fruitful pertain to the nature of computing that is being performed. Two strong trends are emerging. Firstly there is one towards personal, user-friendly, interactive computing. Examples are full screen editing, word processing with graphics, etc. The emphasis here is very much on fast and friendly, I/O (input/output). Secondly there is a trend towards using dedicated processors to perform specific tasks, for example, real time control of devices in factory automation.

Neither of the two cases is suited to large mainframe systems; but both are useful for personal or dedicated workstations. Thus over the past few years there has been a large increase in the use of workstations to cater for these situations. There are, however a number of desirable properties of centralised systems which are not present when there is widespread use of small workstations. A LAN provides a mechanism whereby nodes can be interconnected, thus combining the flexibility of small machines with the advantages of large mainframes.

The following section examines the supposed advantages of a LAN-based system; it is followed by a discussion of the nicer properties of traditional systems, and finally a look is taken at how these much- quoted advantages of LANs can be actually attained in practice and at what cost. Then, we look at sharing and at some of the different types of facilities that can be provided using a LAN.

ADVANTAGES OF LANS

There are two ways of viewing machines connected to a LAN. They can be

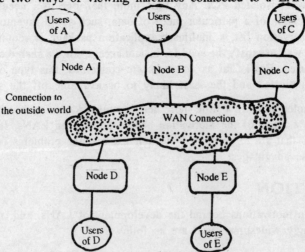

Fig. 10.1 : a :The user's view of a WAN

Note : Users regard the node to which they are directly connected as their computer system. The rest of the world is contacted over the WAN treated as distinct computer systems which occasionally exchange information across the network; this is very much the way WANs are regarded. A second approach is to treat the resulting configuration as a single computer system, which is made up of a number of nodes (see Figure 10.1). The following is a list of some of the potential advantages of a LAN-based system.

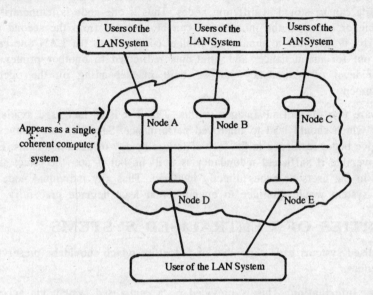

Fig. 10.1 b : The user's view of a LAN-based sysstem
Note : The system can be regarded as a single unit with all the nodes acting in cooperation

1. **Sharing:** This is the key to the attractiveness of LANs, i.e. the ability to share resources between users of the network. Ideally, if a user is connected to the network, all the resources on it, hardware or software, are available to him.

2. **Incremental growth:** A computing system based around a LAN has the ability to expand easily, and to contract. New resources can be added on to the network as they are needed or become available or, as is often the case, the finance to purchase them becomes available.

3. **Placing power where it is needed and used:** Computing power, be it processors or peripherals, can be physically placed where it is needed and used.

4. **Autonomy:** By placing resources where they are used, it is possible to give responsibility for the control and administration of that resource to the people who use it directly. These are the people with the greatest awareness of its needs. This differs from centralised systems where decisions on availability, division of resources, etc., are made in a broader context.

This point, while not being technical in nature, is a very strong motivation towards a LAN-based system. Centralised computing centres are quite often kingdoms in themselves. Users are rarely allowed access even to see the computer on which they are working. Services are provided by the 'computing centre' as best they can, often to the inconvenience of a particular section of users. In a LAN-based system, where each node can retain as much local autonomy as it pleases, these issues do not arise.

5. **Redundancy:** This can be easily built into the system, e.g. two copies of the same file can be stored at different nodes. Thus if one node is temporarily not available or overused the information can be obtained from the second copy. Similarly, if there are a number of printers connected to the LAN one can be taken out for maintenance, and print-outs redirected to another printer. Any desired level of redundancy can be built in, depending on the operating environment.

There are two distinct advantages to this. The first is in increased availability of resources which should lead to improved performance. Secondly, redundancy can be used to give better resilience in the face of failure by any of its components. Errors may be recoverable if sufficient redundancy is built in, but if not, the effect should be localised to the users or nodes directly involved. Thus any individual node may fail but the system would continue to operate or at least degrade gracefully.

PROPERTIES OF CENTRALISED SYSTEMS

Centralised systems have a number of properties which should be preserved in LAN-based ones.

1. **Sharing information:** This is provided on a centralised system via access to shared files or a common data base.

2. **Communication:** Human users may communicate with each other via electronic mailing and, at a lower level, operating system processes communicate using some type of 'inter-process communication' facility.

3. **Expensive peripherals are easily shared:** All the users have access to any of the peripherals connected to the system.

4. **Powerful number crunching:** For CPU-intensive applications, access to a powerful 'number cruncher' is essential. This is typically not available on personal workstations.

PROBLEMS WITH LANS

None of the potential advantages of centralised systems outlined above comes free of charge. A large amount of software must be developed to achieve even some of the possible advantages. The following is a list of some of the problems encountered.

1. **Backup:** As there is no centralised control in a LAN-based system automatic taking of backups cannot easily be carried out.

2. **Security:** Centralised systems have their own security problems, but using a LAN introduces additional ones. Firstly, if key resources are not located in the same

place, supervision becomes a problem. Secondly, there is a new window of vulnerability to confidential data. This occurs while it is being transmitted over the network. It is all too easy for a malicious user to listen to the network traffic and eavesdrop on sensitive data. The normal solution is to encrypt the data before transmitting and decrypt it on reception.

3.   **Creation of standards:** Standards have to be imposed, not only within a network but also across networks.

4.   **System failure:** Failure is a problem in any system but particularly so in a network-based one. Failure covers not only hardware faults but also errors in software and problems arising from local autonomy. An extreme example of the latter might be the administrator of a node withdrawing it from the network while a user is doing a file transfer!

SHARING

To exploit fully the potential advantages of LANs it is necessary to provide an easy and flexible means of sharing. There are three distinct types of sharing and they are looked at in order of increasing complexity. All are provided, in some form, by centralised systems and must be catered to in a network environment.

1.   **Peripherals:** These are often expensive. It is impractical for each processor to have both its own letter quality and high-speed printer. A mainframe may have one of each connected to it allowing all users controlled access in a cost-effective manner.

2.   **Information:** Users of a multiuser system can share and exchange information in a number of ways. Examples are sending electronic mail or having controlled access to the same files or data base.

3.   **Control:** In a traditional time sharing system, all control is performed centrally, if the processor fails then the entire system fails. In a network system this need not (and should not) be the case. To support incremental growth, graceful degradation and flexible service, it is essential that control is not centralised in one particular location. The failure of one node should not have a 'domino' effect on the rest. This is called distributed control and is a very lively area of research at present.

SPECTRUM OF LAN USAGE

Figure 10.2 illustrates the broad spectrum of network uses, ranging from sharing hardware to sharing and modifying information. As you move to the right, along this axis, the sophistication of network systems and applications software increases, as does the amount of interaction among network users. The simplest use of a network is sharing hardware. In this environment, no one network user is very aware of the others. Each user can view the network pretty much as consisting of his own machine with its own collection of programmes and data files. Users become aware of other network users primarily through their impact on shared devices, such as printers and tape drives, that can be used by only one user at a time. If someone else is using a device that you want to access, you must wait your turn. You may also notice a slowdown in response from shared hardware that can be accessed by more than one user at a time, such as disk drives, communication gateways, or the network bus itself. In this case, the network software makes the shared peripherals appear to be attached to the workstation as if they were a local device. In a sense, the network is nothing more than an intelligent extension cord, in that it provides some measure of conflict avoidance. Usage requests for devices that can only be accessed by one workstation at a time may be queued up, or an error message returned indicating that the device is in use and you must try again later.

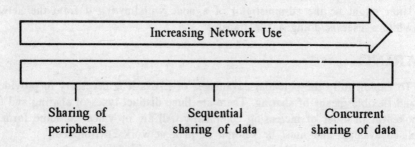

Fig. 10.2 : Spectrum of Network Use

Concurrently accessible devices like disk drives are partitioned by the network software into separate logical devices, each of which is a self-contained system that can be accessed without interference from other workstations. The next stage of network software sophistication permits users to share information electronically but not concurrently. This use is analogous to passing diskettes around in a non-networked, multiple-PC environment. Network users are aware of other network users, but they still operate mainly in a private environment, passing information to each other by the network instead of manually. Using the network to transfer information is more convenient than passing diskettes around, but it introduces two new problems. Consider that when someone hands you a diskette and says, "here's the latest copy of the budget, add your department's data to it" you automatically know two things:

1.   You have the latest information

2.   Nobody else is going to modify the data on that diskette until you are finished with it.

The first problem of network information transfer is version control; when you are handed a diskette, unless the person has made a mistake, you are assured you are being given current information. The second problem is concurrent update control; when you are the only one who can physically modify the data file, you can be sure that it does not contain partial information from several different users that results in an inconsistent picture. When you replace this manual system with an electronic system, such as a LAN, you need some new means of providing these controls. You need some way of informing other users which files to access and when. If several versions of the data are in a shared volume that everyone can access, you must prevent different workstation users from accessing different files and making their modifications in an uncontrolled order. You can still use single-user MS-DOS software for this type of application, but some extra care must be taken in setting up the network and in establishing use procedures. Some networks are better than others at providing automatic safeguards against accidental damage to data files.

The most complex network application is one in which many network users must have simultaneous access to the same information, both to read it and modify it. Many real-life business applications fall into this category; reservation systems, sales from inventory, banking systems and manufacturing control operations are just a few examples. The user's view of this system is more unified than in the previous scenarios. Many workstation users are simultaneously using the network to manage and control a single application or process.

Each user may interact with one, two or even all the other users from moment to moment. Two reservation agents may try, only seconds apart, to reserve the last room in a hotel; the first one should get the reservation, and the second one should see instantly that the room is no longer available. The systems and application software needed for this kind of application must be carefully designed. Most PC networks provide some support for this type of environment, but the level of support varies, and it requires a knowledgeable and experienced systems analyst to evaluate a particular network's suitability for a specific application. The applications are likely to require custom programming, as perhaps are the systems. This need is especially likely if the end users of the network are not computer-knowledgeable, and the application must be easy to use and reliable and its data must be relatively safe from accidental damage. For example, in this type of environment it is probably not sufficient to require users to type in manual commands to lock data files before updating them.

SOFTWARE ISSUES

Since network hardware for personal computers was developed before network application software, the network operating software was designed to allow most existing MS-DOS software to run without modification, even though that software was developed for the single-user PC. Programming functions were provided so that new multiuser software could be written, or single-user programmes could be adapted to the multiuser LAN environment.

There are degrees to which you can successfully run single-user software on a LAN; the range of adaptability runs along that same axis shown in Figure 10.2. At the left end is software most similar to that for a single, dedicated PC. The network provides some additional peripherals and the software to manage them and make your application see them as local peripherals. This configuration presents the least risk and extra work on the part of the system manager and users. Most single-user MS-DOS programmes can run in this environment.

The middle range of the scale in Figure 10.2 represents the use of single-user programmes with carefully controlled resource sharing. The sharing mechanisms are outside of the application software. Procedural mechanisms include a previously agreed-upon method for creating or updating shared information and coordinating access among users. Network commands to lock files for access or update can also be manually typed by the user.

This sharing is not "transparent" to the end-user; that is, it is not managed automatically by the application. A single-user application is being used in a multiuser environment. If the established procedures are not followed, there is a risk of data loss or damage.

The right side of the scale requires the use of software written specifically for the network environment. When properly designed, this is the safest environment, since the application and systems software together prevent accidental data damage by system users. Such network software is discussed later.

Many existing MS-DOS applications run without modification on a network. The following sections examine their use and suggest ways to best configure them for a LAN environment. First, it is important to look at some of the problem areas that restrict function or even prevent some packages from working at all.

COPY PROTECTION

Many of the best-selling personal computer software packages are copy-protected to prevent purchasers from making copies of the disk and sharing the software with unlicensed users. You cannot load such copy-protected software to a network disk and have all your workstation users access and run that software. Even if you could, it would probably be in violation of the license under which you are using the software. However, there are still ways you can make use of many such packages in conjunction with a LAN; you can run the software on your workstation and use the network for disk and print service, or you can load the software to the network disk and run it from a single workstation just as if you had loaded it to that workstation's hard disk.

Most current software lets you access network disks and printers. You can use the network's disk or file server to hold the programme and data files. Only one workstation is licensed to use the programme, however, and that workstation may need the original programme disk in order to start the software, depending on the type of copy protection used. Before hard disks increased in popularity, almost all copy-protection schemes required the use of the original distribution diskette, called a key disk, to start the software. The programme checks to see if the key disk is in drive A:, and if it is not the programme does not start. The normal MS-DOS disk-copying utilities cannot copy the key disk, so only one user can run the package at a time.

As the number of PCs with hard disks increased, users complained about key disk copy-protection schemes, since they wanted to load their software to the hard disk and take advantage of its speed and convenience. Software vendors responded with new copy-protection schemes that allow users to load the software onto a hard disk and run it.

Using this type of copy-protected software on a network disk is much riskier than the key disk scheme. The copy-protection apparatus uses low-level details about a PC's hard disk organisation that may not be duplicated by the network environment. It may directly access the hard disk controller, bypassing MS-DOS and the network software, guaranteeing that it will not work on the network disk drive. This type of copy-protection scheme may also depend on the exact placement of the protected programs on the hard disk. If the system manager makes a backup of the network disk, then reloads it later, it may come back in a different place on the disk. The package's copy-protection scheme will sense that the software has moved and make it fail to run.

Even if you find that a package does install successfully on your network hard disk, the burden is on the system manager to enforce the single-user, single-machine license restriction. The key disk enforces this restriction for you, but software installed on the network hard disk may be accessed from more than one workstation. If you want to use such a configuration, a password or other security mechanism should be used to restrict access to the software. If you have any questions about the licensing issues involved, consult the software vendor.

DISK ACCESS

Unintentional multiuser update of a file can occur during shared use of programs that write system information to the disk during the program's execution; such information can be about program configuration, user profiles, or internal data structures.

If a software package is loaded to a network disk and run by several users, not only data files can be unintentionally updated. For example, you may store your desired default word processing settings in a program configuration file. If this file is stored in the directory that the word processor resides in, your settings can be overwritten by another user's the next time they are changed.

There are two ways around this problem of accidental change to data and program files. First, if the application package lets you specify the name or directory of the system file, you can set up separate files for each user. This approach is the most conservative of disk space. If this cannot be done, your second recourse is to provide each user with his own copy of the software in a private network directory.

The single-user program's documentation may not state whether the program can be written to disk (since this may not be an important concern in the single-user environment). You will have to find out for yourself. If the program saves any information between executions, such as user profile or program configuration data, it is writing something to the disk. If you are not sure, consult the software vendor. If you can not obtain this information, you can experiment by putting the programme in a write-protected or read-only directory or volume on the network disk. Do not try to create or modify any critical data while you do this experiment, since the application's handling of a write-protect error, should one occur, may cause you to lose the data file. Most packages will not lose your data, since they may be run on write-protected floppy disks, but you should not count on this. If you can execute the programme's functions without problems, it does not need to write to the disk, and you can share it over the network among multiple users.

More and more network software now require MS-DOS Version 3.2 or higher. If your software requires lower versions of MS-DOS, check with the network vendor to make sure that the system supports that version. In any case, it is a good idea to use only one version of MS-DOS throughout your network, both for servers and workstations. You may be able to successfully mix versions, but it is not recommended.

Some programmes also depend on certain disk-access features that survive from the CP/M operating system. These are technical and have to do with direct manipulation of operating system data structures or dependence on undocumented operating system behaviour related to opening, accessing and closing files. Most network systems software has been modified to handle the common violations of operating system protocol, but if an application bypasses the operating system completely, there is no way the network software can prevent problems.

PRINTING

Most applications can be made to work successfully with a network printer, but you may run across one or more of the following problem areas:

- Direct hardware access by the application.

- Network software filtering of control codes.

- Network software interjection of control codes.

- Conflict between the network and application print buffering.

- Non-release of shared printers by the application.

- Setting of printer parameters by different applications.

Do not let this list alarm you, since you may not hit any of these problems. However, printing problems can be especially frustrating, so it is worthwhile to go over some of the more frequent causes and solutions for them.

Nearly all network systems software that provides sharing of printers can redirect print output that the application sends by an MS-DOS call to the MS-DOS PRN: or LPTx: device. Many networks can also intercept print output sent to the PC's BIOS, a lower-level programming interface. If, however, the application software directly accesses printer port hardware on the local PC, there is little that can be done to get that application to use a network printer.

Fortunately, this most common problem area is also often remediable by a user configuration option. Many application packages use the hardware interface directly when configured to print a serial printer, but use an MS-DOS or BIOS (Basic Input Output System) interface when printing to parallel printers. If your application does not seem to work on the network, check to see whether you have chosen COM1:

or COM2: as the printer port. Even if this designation identifies the physical port that the printer is connected to on the server, you may be able to make your printing instructions work by telling your application that the printer is connected to LPT1:, or PRN:, or that it is a parallel printer and following the network instructions for redirecting that device to the network printer.

Less frequently, you may have a problem even when you have selected a parallel printer from your application. Some programmes check the hardware directly for printer status information that is not available from MS-DOS or BIOS. This is especially likely if your program has a built-in print spooler. If you can disable the spooler, try to do so; you may then be able to start printing on the network printer.

Many applications let you print to a disk file instead of to a printer. In other words, the print output is stored as text in a file. The command to do this varies from application to application. You can then print this text file either by using the network print command, or by using the MS-DOS COPY command to copy the file to the network printer:

COPY file LPT1:

(This example assumes that the network printer is redirected from the local printer named LPT1:).

The second command printing problem occurs when your application needs to send special control codes to the printer and your network software either filters them out or interprets them as having special meaning for some network function. For example, say your network software supports a command to immediately stop whatever is printing on the network printer; when you issue that command from your workstation, the network software sends a certain character sequence to the print server, and upon seeing that character sequence, the printer server software stops the printing process. The problem arises if, by coincidence, your application programme sends that same character sequence to the network printer, intending a different result but stopping the printer instead. For example, an application printing high-resolution graphics to a graphics printer may send practically any character sequence to create a complicated graphics image. In addition to graphics images, control character sequences are generated to control special printer functions such as microspacing, superscripts and subscripts, or to print simple character graphics or foreign language characters.

If the network you choose does not implement print commands as described, you may have nothing to be concerned about. On the other hand, if your application prints perfectly when connected to the local printer but has problems on the network printer, character sequences are an area to investigate. You should note the exact function in process when the problem occurs and check with your network vendor for a possible solution.

A companion problem occurs when the network print software tries to be helpful and adds formatting control to your print output at the same time that your application programme is supposed to be in control of the printer. The result is a poorly formatted print-out, the most common symptoms being extra linefeeds, formfeeds or slowly creeping output that starts lower and lower on each successive page. The simplest solution to this type of problem is to turn off the network print driver's control of output format. If there is no single command or configuration choice for doing this, look for settings in the network print control software like:

- Page length

- Line length

- Skip over perforations?

- Margins

- Borders

- Page offset.

Make these settings equivalent to the physical limits of the paper you are using. For example, for 8 1/2- by 11-inch paper, you would want the following settings: page length of 66 lines, do not skip over perforations, top or bottom margin of 0, left and right borders of 0 and page offset of 0.

Another possible source of problems is conflict between print buffers. It is common for print buffering to take place in:

- Your application programme.

- The workstation (if an installable print spooler is used).

- The network print server.

- The printer itself.

Sometimes these buffers work together, but at other times one buffer gets hung up waiting for input from another. You may also have a problem such that the last line or few lines of a file never get printed. In any event, it is seldom efficient to have more than one print buffer working on the same print output. All that extra handling of the print output may use extra system resources with no net reduction in waiting time. The solution is to reduce your print buffering software to the minimum and see if the problem goes away. Even if you are not experiencing a problem, try disabling your application's print spooler if you can, or do not load the workstation print spooler, and see if there is any noticeable difference in printing performance or in the delay between the start of printing and the time you regain control of your workstation. If there is no degradation, leave the print spooler disabled or unloaded.

There is also the general problem of having a shared printer instead of a dedicated printer. When you are the only user of a printer, there is no need to know when you are through with it, since nobody else is waiting to use it. Your software can send it data continuously or at a leisurely pace and the next character sent to the printer will follow the previous one exactly, with no intervening data from other users. Programmers have written their applications with this in mind, and very few programmes use MS-DOS system calls to release or "close" the printer when they are done printing.

In a network environment it is necessary to know whether you are truly finished with a particular print job or are just pausing to instruct the computer about the next thing to be printed. Every network provides one or more ways to release the printer, such as:

- An explicit user command.

- A software sequence.

- A printer inactivity time-out.

Your network system documentation should provide adequate information on how to use this printer-release feature, and you should be aware of the need to use it on your network. If you do not, you could have seemingly random problems with network printing. For example, if your system provided a time-out value of, say, 30 seconds, and 95% of your printing never paused for more than 30 seconds but 5% of your printing did, 5% of the time the network printer would appear to mysteriously stop in the middle of one print job and start one on behalf of another workstation.

Similarly, if a software character sequence is used to release the printer, you could have problems similar to those with network software filtering of control codes. Your application could coincidentally send the control code sequence that releases the printer, when in fact it was attempting to control the printer in some other way.

Finally, in a shared environment, you must manage the use of different printer settings by different application software packages. Modern printers are capable of many fancy printing operations, and an application package can set the printer up to use different fonts, character widths, lines per inch, and so on. You should establish a default condition for the printer, and if an application programme changes the printer configuration, it should set it back when it is finished. Some network print server software allows you to establish a character code sequence that is sent to the printer before starting every new print job. If your print server software supports resetting the printer, you should enter the character sequence that resets the printer to the condition expected by your network users. No matter what each user's individual print job does to the printer configuration, the printer is then restored to a known state before each new print job, independently of what the application programme does.

If your print server software does not have such a feature, then you must be sure that your users send the equivalent sequence from their applications whenever they have changed the printer configuration in the course of a print job.

Another common cause of user complaints is related not to network software but to operating procedure. Whenever you remove output from the printer, be sure to turn the printer back on-line so that it can be used by other workstations. If the printer is out of earshot, a long time may go by before the user realises that his or her print job is not ready because the printer is off-line, not because some other user's output is printing.

SHARED SERVERS

When a network server is also used as a workstation, it is especially vulnerable to system crashes caused by application software bugs or user errors. When a server is also a workstation, the safest user software to run is an application programme that is also running on the other workstations. For example, a cash register programme that has been in use for a period of time and appears to be fairly stable is not likely to cause the server to crash. When the server also acts as a workstation, the riskiest thing to do is to allow the user to run many different programmes, including some that have not been tried on that workstation before. The IBM PC environment offers no hard protection against an application programme crashing the system, and one that behaves well on a single-user PC may have a conflict with the server software that shows up only at the most inopportune moment.

Some programmes that work well on a stand-alone PC may have a problem on a shared network server, so be sure to try them in a non-critical environment first. You should be especially careful about memory-resident programmes that are activated from within another programme by an unusual key sequence. Even if they don't crash the server PC, these programmes may shut off the server's interrupt system and result in temporary suspension of network service. If network response time seems to suddenly slow down by a very large factor, make sure no one is running such a programme on a shared server.

It almost goes without saying that trying to develop software on a PC that is also acting as a network server is a sure recipe for disaster. New software invariably has bugs that can hang up or crash the system and bring the network server down at the same time. Likewise, software that is self-booting or runs under an operating system other than MS-DOS certainly cannot be used while the PC is acting as a server.

If the application running on a shared network server appears to be hung up - that is, there is no response from the keyboard - you should try to salvage the most you can out of the situation. In some cases, the server software may still be running and only the application package is hung up. Have all the workstation users of the network server finish what they are doing and log off the server before you shut it down and restart it.

USING APPLICATIONS

Taking advantage of the network environment, the most popular PC application categories include word processing, spreadsheets, database management, accounting systems and graphics packages. For each of these applications there is a different common-use scenario, with different requirements for sharing and modifying data.

As more PC LANs are installed, more software is being written specifically for the network environment. The majority of software running on LANs today is single-user software, but several of the application areas mentioned above are seeing a steady growth in network versions. Other applications are, by their nature, unique to the network environment. Foremost among these is electronic mail, a system for sending messages and files to other users on the network.

WORD PROCESSING

One of the most common uses of personal computers is word processing. Seldom does more than one person using a word processor need to update the same file at the same time, so single-user word processors generally work well in a network environment. The network's disk or file server should be used as you would use a local hard disk: for storing the programme and document files.

Another advantage of a network for word processing is that you may be able to afford a faster, more-expensive printer if it can be shared by many users. Some of the new laser printers are especially well suited for such uses, and they combine text output of typeset quality with graphics output capability. Not only can they improve the professional appearance of your firm's correspondence, presentations or documentation, they may further justify their cost by allowing you to make less use of some outside services for jobs such as typesetting of advertising copy.

Many installations share several common document formats, often referred to as boiler-plates. You should take advantage of this commonality wherever possible and establish a shared public volume or directory containing the frequently used boiler-plates. This saves disk space and painlessly enforces consistency among many users.

Finally, the network provides an easy means for users to share finished documents. Simply place a document in a shared directory and inform the intended recipient of its location. Users can read or print the document right from its storage location without creating another space-consuming copy. An electronic mail system makes it even easier to inform network users of the documents and their location.

SPREADSHEETS

In their patterns of use spreadsheets present many analogues to the word processors. A spreadsheet is created and modified by a single user, then perhaps shared with others. The network is a fast and convenient way to share a spreadsheet among several users - far superior to making many diskette copies and carrying them to the other users.

Consider using shared volumes or directories to store commonly used spreadsheet templates or macros. Most spreadsheet users spend a fair amount of time developing special routines to handle dates or some locally unique data such as supporting tables for sales forecasts. Share these with other network users by saving them on the disk server.

A major trend in patterns of PC use is to extract data from corporate mainframes and load it into spreadsheets to generate "what-if" scenarios. A network with a gateway or bridge to the mainframe should work with this strategy; if your users need such a capability, make sure the network software and hardware provide it.

DATABASE MANAGEMENT SYSTEMS

There is more likely to be a natural need for several users to simultaneously

read and modify the same database than to access a document or a spreadsheet. Databa
applications fit into the LAN, being natural candidates for using shared network storag
printersand other services. The caveats and procedures already discussed apply to the
as well, with emphasis on the need to control access to data files, especially if y
use a single-user database system with manual controls over file access. Make s
that any manual protocol to be followed is well understood by your users, and consi
using safeguards such as storing data files in private directories where the netw
automatically restricts access to one workstation at a time.

ACCOUNTING SYSTEMS

Many applications are used for accounting, including point-of-sale, invent
control, general ledger, accounts receivable and payable and payroll. If more than
user needs to access the same accounting file at the same time, you need to inv
in a good multiuser accounting system for your business. It is especially crucial
guarantee data security, integrity and recovery. You should not rely on error-pr
manual controls over any of these critical areas.

Data security requires that your network software provide adequate protect
against unauthorised reading or modification of accounting information. The lar
the number of users and types of applications running on the network storing y
accounting data, the more critical protection becomes - and the less able a sim
security scheme is to provide enough flexibility to allow authorised users to do t
work, without unauthorised users tampering with vital data. In many cases, you
want to provide several levels of access to the same file; for instance, the assist
bookkeeper may be able to read the values of salaries, but only the head bookkee
can change them.

Data integrity refers to the freedom of data from corruption. The damage d
by the failure of two users to synchronise their access to a word processing docun
pales by comparison to the possible damage done by a corrupted accounting data

Even if you have done your best to prevent data loss or corruption, you sh
plan for its occurrence. You must be sure you can recover from it when, not i
happens. Do not be among the majority of users who start worrying about reco
after disaster strikes. In most cases, planning simply means that you back-up
network disk files as often as necessary so that if you lost everything but the b
ups you should have to re-enter no more than one business day's worth of transacti
You should, of course, have hard copy or some other suitable back-up of the d
transactions so you can re-enter them.

GRAPHICS SOFTWARE

Like word processors and spreadsheets, there is not much call for multi
concurrent update of a graph or the data used to generate a graph. A LAN can contri
to the usefulness of a graphics package in several ways, though. You have alr
seen how a LAN makes it easy to share information between PC users. Grap
packages generally only need to read a data file to produce a graph, and thus

n unobtrusively retrieve data from common network databases for graphing. Graphics tput devices such as plotters and 35 millimeter slide makers may be difficult to stify for a single PC, but easy to justify when an entire department can share one a LAN.

ELECTRONIC MAIL

A good electronic mail system is both useful and addictive. The term "electronic ail" is somewhat misleading, since the system not only transmits information that ould otherwise be sent through inter-office, but also replaces short telephone calls th electronic messages sent back and forth. Every user on the network has a network me or address, and the mail system lets you compose a message and send it to other user or users. The message is stored on the network server, and the user notified that it is waiting for retrieval. If a user is not logged on when a message ives, the system stores the fact that a message is waiting and notifies the user the xt time he or she logs on. Some systems are less automated and require users to rt the mail software on the workstation to check the status of waiting mail.

There are many desirable features of an electronic mail system; for example, u can:

Send and receive messages and files.

Forward incoming messages.

Save, print and reply to messages.

Retrieve, edit and re-send saved messages.

Send messages and files to lists of users.

Temporarily forward mail to another user.

Access external networks.

Access public electronic mail systems.

Sending and receiving messages and files should be quick and easy, requiring inimum of keystrokes. You can send more than one file at a time by specifying MS-DOS filename template. You should be able to forward a message to another work user, adding comments to the message to explain the reason for forwarding Replying to a message should also be very easy to do; the system should automatically ply the name and address of the sender as the recipient of the reply, rather than ing you to remember it and type it in.

You should be able to save messages and files on any convenient disk as well being able to print them locally or on a network printer. You should be able to messages by pulling up an old message from the disk, modifying it and sending ff to a new destination. The electronic mail system should make it easy to maintain ribution or mailing lists and to share such lists among network users. In other ds, you should be able to mail a message or a file to a group of users all at e by simply giving the name of the list you created.

Temporary mail forwarding is useful if you are going to be away from your desk for an extended period of time while someone else, such as a secretary, watches your mail for urgent messages. Finally, access to users outside the local area network obviously extends the benefits of the system to whatever size group you can access. A uniform electronic mail system across an entire division or corporation can be a great productivity boon. An even wider circle may be accessed if you can use your electronic mail system to interact with a public electronic mail system.

The benefits of electronic mail include:

- Reduce "telephone tag".

- Increased speed of disseminating information.

- Lower direct and indirect mailing costs.

- Improved corporate communication.

In a typical business environment, an inordinate number of phone calls result in "telephone tag" - the leaving of messages to call back rather than completion of the communication. Often the message is brief, (it could be written in a page or less) but is too long to dictate to the secretary or whoever answers the phone. Although not all business use of the telephone falls into this category, a great deal frequently does. If the party you need to converse with can be reached over the network, and has access to the electronic mail system, the exchange of "please call back" messages can be drastically reduced or even eliminated.

Electronic mail is very fast, operating practically at the speed of data transfer over your network. Combined with the reduction of telephone tag this is a double benefit. Not only is your message more likely to get to its destination, it does so more quickly than it could through the normal mail or even an express courier service.

The sources of savings from electronic mail are several. There are direct savings in paper, envelopes, postage and telephone costs. There are indirect savings in the reduced labor of handling paper mail, and productivity is increased because less time is wasted on unsuccessful telephone calls.

Improved corporate communication is a major intangible benefit, for which the electronic mail system must be extended beyond the local area network to cover a large number of people, such as a division or corporation. The most common business problems can be traced to poor communications. Most of the people that each employee needs to communicate with daily should be reachable over the network. You may quickly discover that the benefits of electronic mail outweigh those of any other single use of the network.

ECTRONIC CALENDER

Electronic calendar applications are slowly gaining a popularity among local area network users. An electronic calendar is a specialized database application that lets you enter and retrieve your daily appointment calendar. Among other things, a good electronic calendar system allows you to:

- Enter appointments quickly and easily
- Schedule meetings based on someone else's calendar
- Search for appointments by time, day, and description
- Reschedule appointments without reentering data
- View and modify another user's calendar
- Print or view calendar for entire day, week, or month
- Store appointments that recur daily, weekly, monthly, or annually
- Determine scheduling conflicts among all participants in a meeting
- Schedule reservations of meeting rooms.

It is important that entry of appointments be fast and easy. It's hard to beat a calendar on the desk for quick view and entry of appointments, so the software that provides this function must be usable with a minimum of keystrokes and delay. Recall of appointments must be equally quick, although here the system can have some advantages over a paper system, especially for someone with a very full schedule. Appointments are frequently changed, and the system must handle this quickly and with a minimum of typing. The system should automatically reschedule appointments that recur on some regular basis.

It should be no surprise that the benefit of a LAN in conjunction with an electronic calendar is the ability to use other people's calendars when you schedule a meeting.

Intelligent calendar systems can handle requests like "schedule a one-hour meeting Thursday afternoon between Taneja, Lal, Suresh, and Basandra." If all these users keep their calendars updated, the system can check the calendars for a common one-hour slot and, having found one, add that meeting time to all their calendars. Of course, if no common time is available, the system must report this and allow you to try another time.

Some calendar systems can schedule other resources such as meeting rooms - another example of how a network provides a big improvement over a system of isolated PCs. If all users can access the schedule of your meeting rooms from the PC in their office, there is no need for anyone to wander around the building looking for an available room.

Remote access via a telephone connection and modem is also very desirable if you are often on the road. You can check your calendar to see what new appointments have been made for you and you can let people back at the office know where you will be and when you will be there.

MULTI-USER SHARED DATABASES

Another major use of PC networks is multi-user shared database management. A multi-user system should provide all the features of a single-user system, and allow convenient but controlled access by more than one user to the same database. A LAN database system may be used alone or as the basis for a multi-user application such as an accounting system.

Different network database systems control shared access to different degrees. All such systems provide basic locking mechanisms, but they differ mostly in how much responsibility they place on the user to lock in the correct sequence in order to prevent errorneous database updates or deadlocks between database users. The least control is offered by a system that simply provides the lock and unlock commands but does not integrate them into the database access operations. In such cases, any user can execute all the database access commands even if another user has issued one or more lock commands. Clearly, the integrity of such a database depends totally upon everyone's proper use of the lock and unlock operations.

A more sophisticated system may detect the fact that one user has locked a certain file and will not allow other users to access that file until the first lock is released. The same protection applies to individual data records. Deadlocks occur when each of two or more users holds something locked that another needs. Each user ends up waiting for a resource held locked by the other, and nobody gets any further. Automatic detection of such a situation is possible but is complicated and unusual in microcomputer database systems. Security is often more of an issue for a multi-user database than for many other network applications. Its importance depends on the contents of the database, but you should carefully evaluate the security provided by the combination of your underlying network software and the database system's own security features. A database system can assign security safeguards much more precisely than the network software. For example, the network may provide security at the directory or file level, but you may want to limit some users' update privileges to certain fields in a database record while letting them read a larger set of fields or perhaps the entire record. The network software can't help you assign security measures selectively, but a good multi-user database package can.

BACKUP STRATEGIES

The need to back up a network's disk storage has been stressed already. Part of the benefit of a network is that is is usually one person's responsibility to make sure the backup gets done, and that data stored on the network server by everyone and anyone is backed up when the network is backed up. If the network server is lost and the backup has not been done, everyone loses data, potentially causing a major disaster. The system manager should set up a backup procedure and make sure it gets implemented.

As a general rule, you should consider the effects of losing the network disk server at any given time. If you wouldn't want to have to manually recover the information stored or modified since the last backup was done, it means that another backup should be scheduled. As a practical matter, you should back the system up at least once a day.

It is not imperative to save the entire contents of the network disk drives, since many if not most files do not change daily. The MS-DOS BACKUP utility, and most other network backup programs, allow you to specify that only files modified since the last full backup need to be saved. This utility should make your daily backups go much faster. If they do not go faster, examine the files being backed up. It may be that some extremely large files are being backed up in their entirety although only a portion of each file is modified each day. Consider whether such a file can be split up into smaller portions and whether such a change might speed up the daily backups.

Restoring a disk server from a loss of data requires one of two possibilities:

1.   The last full backup and all the partial backups must be restored

2.   The last full backup and the last partial backup must be restored.

The first case holds if your backup program saves all files that have been modified since the last backup, be it a complete backup of the disk or a partial one. In this case, you should do a full backup once a week or so, since the number of backups you must restore gets larger every day. In the second case, your backup program can keep track of files that have been modified since the last full backup and save all of them. This may be done by specifying the date of the last full backup and saving all files modified after that date. Here you need only restore two backups, the full one and the last partial one. The trade-off is that this partial backup is cumulative and thus gets larger every day, while in the first case the sizes of the partial backups are proportional to the amount of data modified since the last partial backup. In the second case, you will want to do a new full backup when the partial backup starts taking too long or approaches the size of the last full backup.

SOFTWARE LICENSING

Using applications in a network environment raises the important issue of licensing. Most software vendors have well-established policies regarding the use of their products on single-user systems but are vague about how their software fits into a multiuser network. Of course, a vendor who sells software specifically written for a network environment usually has a well-defined policy. But personal computer networks have caught many vendors by surprise, and you will discover policies ranging from progressive approaches with liberal discounts for multiple users and one-time site licenses, to "head-in-the-sand" policies that don't address local area networks at all.

Single Licenses

Most MS-DOS software is sold with a single-user, single-machine license, meaning that it is intended to be run by one user on one PC. If you purchase software like this to run on a network, you cannot use it from more than one PC at a time without violating the license agreement. Some licenses prohibit the use of the software on more than one PC at any time, even if it is never used on two PCs at once.

Multiuser Licenses

As more multiuser PC software appears, vendors are establishing licensing procedures to cover its use. One common approach allows you to pay by the number of users. Some policies consist of an honor system whereby you agree that your installation does not have more than the specified number of users of that particular application. Other vendors have installed "counting locks" in their software, allowing the specified number of users to run the package at one time. When a user over the limit tries to run the package, an error message is returned explaining that the limitation has been reached. If you find the limit too restricting, you can usually purchase the right for additional users. to run the package concurrently.

Site Licensing

A new approach among PC software vendors to the multiuser licensing problem is site licensing. You usually pay a fixed fee for the right for an unlimited number of users to use the software at a particular installation. This approach is gaining in popularity as major corporations, faced with spiraling software expenses, are making strong demands for it. A site license for a package can save money in the long run, and it appeals to a central data processing department in that it provides some measure of control over the software in use on the company's personal computers. If a corporation purchases a site license for a particular software package, it is more likely that all the users in that company will standardize on the package. There is a side benefit to the company that purchases a site license: there need be no more worrying about lawsuits arising from employees' making unauthorized copies of single-user packages.

EXAMPLES OF LAN USAGE

This section gives a brief overview of what LANs are being used for in practice.

File transfer: A LAN provides a means whereby files can be transferred between any machines on the network. It involves running some file transfer utility on both of the nodes, and typically requires setting up some sort of virtual circuit between the two ends. LANs however can be used for much more than file transfer and this is the reason for their increasing popularity.

Office automation: This is another area where LANs can have an impact. Computers can play a much larger role in an office than just word processing or spreadsheet calculations. The processing and retrieving of all sorts of information are being automated. This includes not just standard text, like most documents, but unstructured documents, hand-written letters, photographs, voice and video. As the use of computers in offices increases, LANs will play an important role in enabling information to be exchanged and shared.Industrial control: A LAN can also be a very useful tool in a factory environment. A typical working organization might consist of a number of small or dedicated processors performing real-time monitoring functions. These would periodically communicate with a central node to perform status updates etc, or with each other to exchange information. A LAN is ideal for such an arrangement because of its flexibility and speed.

Distributed systems: A LAN-based system can be regarded as a single computing facility rather than a collection of individual ones. A distributed operating system is an attempt to provide support for applications that are network based. It does so by imposing a large degree of order on the components connected to the network. Ideally, the user of a distributed operating system should not be able to tell the difference between a centralized system and a distributed one. Networking and all other underlying issues are taken care of by the distributed operating system.

11

MAINFRAME CONNECTION

INTRODUCTION

A major benefit of networking is that microcomputers and the work performed on them is no longer are isolated. Information can be passed from one computer to another and read and updated as needed. The process of linking PCs and combining their capabilities creates a flexible new computing resource. In the corporate environment the next step is to link this new resource with an established one: the mainframe computer.

It is likely that at some point you will need to communicate with one of the larger computers, called mainframes. Perhaps it will be a small departmental computer used by your work-group. It may be it be a larger one, run by your division's MIS department. Or it might be a corporate computer thousands of miles away. Herewe will discuss:

*   reasons for communicating with a mainframe.

*   a brief history of IBM's data communications.

*   methods of connecting personal computer networks to larger computers.

*   problems that can occur.

*   prospects for the future.

The IBM PC first entered the corporate world by the back door. The PC was quietly brought in on purchasing orders for typewriters. And when it arrived, most of the work the PC was given probably could have been done with typewriters, calculators and pencils and paper.

Quickly, the PC began to achieve respectability. First-rate application programmes came along for word processing and spreadsheets. These programmes were easy to learn and use. Often they were a distinct improvement over comparable mainframe programmes. But the PC remained isolated from the mainframe and unable to access corporations' primary data banks.

Then devices began to appear that let the PC communicate with the mainframe and manipulate mainframe data (see Figure 11.1). PC-to-mainframe communication was a prerequisite to making the PC part of large-system computing. Now that the PC is established, the door is open to explore fully the other applications of an intelligent desktop workstation in a mainframe world.

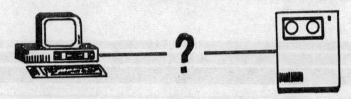

Fig. 11.1 : Micro to mainframe

Incidentally, PCs can communicate with larger computers made by manufacturers other than IBM. Some of these non-IBM computers function so much like IBM's computers that they are known as plug-compatible computers, which means you can plug anything into them that you can plug into an IBM mainframe. Because plug-compatible computers are essentially equivalent to IBM's, anything written here about IBM mainframes applies to plug-compatible computers as well.

WHAT IS A MAINFRAME?

For the many computers that are not plug-compatible with IBM, there is a thriving business in hardware and software that lets IBM computers and non-IBM computers communicate. This will doubtless continue to be true for local area networks. So if your mainframe is not IBM or IBM-compatible, you will need to check with various dealers and users for details on the products available and how they interface to the IBM network. However, much of the information here is still applicable even for mainframes that are not IBM-compatible.

Not long ago, there were three distinct types of computers: mainframes, minicomputers and microcomputers. Microcomputers could support one person, mainframes could support hundreds of people, and minicomputers fell somewhere in between. IBM so dominated the mainframe market that to some people "mainframe" meant "made by IBM". Until recently, however, IBM had few products in the minicomputer category.

Now, demarcation is more difficult. Computer power has increased dramatically. Some children's toys have more computing power than ENIAC, the first computer, which filled an entire room and dimmed city lights when it was switched on.

Similarly, in many cases today's so-called "personal" computers are more powerful than yesterday's minicomputers and mainframe computers. Some personal computers are now so powerful that more than one person can use them at a time. So simply defining a mainframe as "any computer that can support more than one user at a time" is no longer sufficient.

For the purpose of discussion, we will define a mainframe as a multiuser computer running an IBM proprietary operating system. Computers running MS-DOS or a form of UNIX are not included in our definition of mainframe because IBM does not own the rights to these operating systems. After all, if the mainframe ran MS-DOS, it could be connected through the LAN just like a big PC. In a similar way, a UNIX computer usually cannot communicate with MS-DOS unless a special hardware bridge product is used.

Some might object that this definition of mainframe includes smaller computers such as IBM Series/1 and IBM System/36 mainframes, which are often referred to as minicomputers. Rather than get bogged down in a discussion of the dividing line between minicomputers and mainframes,we will avoid the problem by calling all of them mainframes, unless we are referring to a specific computer model. Here, we are more concerned with which computers can communicate with each other, rather than with their relative capabilities.

WHY TALK TO A MAINFRAME?

When the notorious 19th-century criminal Willie Sutton was arrested, legend has it that someone asked him why he robbed banks. He replied, quite logically, "Because that's where the money is". Similarly, people need to communicate with mainframes because, in most cases, that is where the data is. Despite the technological advances of personal computers, mainframes are unsurpassed in their ability to manipulate huge amounts of data. You can think of a mainframe as a giant disk server, providing a large amount of hard disk storage that can be shared.

Whereas an IBM PC/AT/486, for example, can support a single 300- megabyte hard disk drive, a mainframe can easily support over six 1000-megabyte drives. And, as many users are discovering, a single file, such as a large database, can easily fill an entire 300-megabyte drive. No matter how powerful a PC is, it simply cannot support that amount of data. Moreover, mainframes are most often used by large corporations, so many people will want access to the mainframe's vast amount of data storage. Although no PC can support more than a few users, a large mainframe can support dozens, even hundreds, of users.

In the same way that a mainframe can act as a large disk server, it can also act as a large print server. But instead of supporting a $5,000 laser printer, as a PC print server might, a mainframe would support extremely expensive peripherals. For instance, IBM makes a large, high capacity laser printer that costs over $100,000. Other peripherals might be typesetting machines, flat-bed plotters several feet across, or line printers that print hundreds of lines per minute.

Mainframes also have much more computing power than PCs. Computing power is measured in MIPS, or million instructions per second. A PC can usually perform around one MIPS, but a mainframe can perform ten or more MIPS. The difference in power is not significant if you are balancing your checkbook, but it can make a big difference if you are calculating a complicated equation.

Mainframes can also make life easier for PC users by automatically backing up files. Nearly everybody has forgotten to make a back-up copy of a file. If you are lucky, you only lose a few minutes' work: if you are not, you lose 300 megabytes of data that took weeks to accumulate. With a connection to a larger computer, you can set up a system whereby PC files are automatically backed up onto the mainframe.

Finally, a mainframe can act as a gateway to another mainframe or network. It is analogous to large airlines. You do not fly from Calcutta to Srinagar directly; instead, you might fly from Calcutta to New Delhi, then from New Delhi to Srinagar. If your destination is less frequented, like Leh/Ladakh, you would break up the flight even further by flying from New Delhi to Srinagar, then from Srinagar to Leh/Ladakh. It is the same with gateways. You do not have to communicate directly with a particular computer; it is sufficient to communicate with another computer that can, as shown in Figure 11.2.

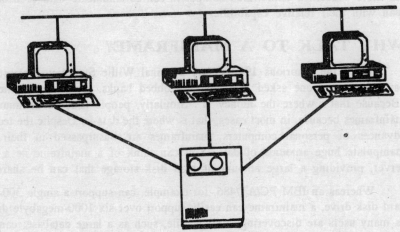

Fig. 11.2 : Terminal emulation

BRIEF HISTORY OF IBM DATA COMMUNICATIONS

To understand the techniques used for communicating between PCs and mainframes, we need to see how IBM data communication developed. In the early 1970s, when data communication began to develop, there were two kinds of devices: computers and terminals. Terminals functioned only as input/output devices; they could not store information or manipulate it in any way. Consequently, all data communication were set up in a hierarchical fashion. The computer was the "master" and the terminal was the "slave". The master computer started and stopped all transmission, and governed what information was sent. The slave terminal could respond only if information was coming too fast, or if the transmission was garbled.

The master-slave hierarchy was fine back when terminals truly had no computing power (sometimes referred to as intelligence; terminals with no computing power are called dumb). Few computers had to communicate with intelligent devices such as other computers. When they did, one computer would revert to a slave status (usually through a programme) to accept the data.

But as the industry matured, computers in a range of sizes became available. Small terminals became as powerful as the master computers. Large organisations, and organisations with many branch offices, found they wanted to transfer information between their computers more often. The master-slave relationship was limiting, and wasted the power of the slave computer.

The proliferation of devices spawned another problem. IBM's data communication products like VTAM and SDLC had been gathered under the umbrella term of SNA (Systems Network Architecture). Much of SNA consisted of programmes developed specifically to communicate between two particular devices. Each combination of new devices required a new set of rules (a protocol) to specify how the two devices would communicate.

Consequently, every time a new device became available, it had to imitate an existing device or IBM had to write a series of data communication programmes following a new protocol so that the new device could communicate with existing devices.

Then came the introduction of the personal computer. Here was a device with significant computing power, but so small and relatively cheap that it blossomed on desks everywhere. People wanted to send data from their PCs to the mainframe, and take data from the mainframe for further manipulation on the PC. But mainframes could only communicate with a PC if the PC "pretended" to be a dumb terminal (terminal emulation). So users had a choice. They could print the data from the mainframe and then retype it on the PC. Or they could write a programme to transfer data between applications. Unfortunately, each combination of applications required writing a different programme.

LU 6.2 - The Final Solution

As might be expected, users were not thrilled about either of these options. They wanted to transmit data directly from the mainframe to their PC applications. IBM's solution was to develop one last set of protocols. Unlike other protocols, which were device specific, this protocol set defined a way that two intelligent devices could communicate; neither had to be a slave to the other. This kind of communication is called peer-to-peer communication, because the two devices communicate as equals. Either machine can start, stop and control transmissions.

The protocol set is marketed by IBM under the term APPC, for Advanced Programme-to-Programme Communication. Following traditional IBM practice, APPC consists of one physical unit (PU 2.1) protocol and one logical unit (LU 6.2) protocol. These terms equate roughly to hardware and software; thus, the PU 2.1 protocol essentially defines peer-to-peer communication between actual hardware devices, and the LU 6.2 protocol defines peer-to-peer communication between the software and application that run on the devices. Users whose computers are connected to a network running APPC can write programmes that can communicate on a peer-to-peer basis with each other.

Specifically, LU 6.2 defines a group of verbs (subroutines) that programmers can use for communication. Programmes using these verbs have a common interface. The programe can perform any function, run on any computer and be written in any language, as long as it uses the verbs in the accepted way. The advantage of using common verbs is that each programmer does not have to programme the actual connection; IBM's communication products take care of the actual connection.

Just defining these protocols does not solve the communication problem. Because programmes do not use these protocols as yet, users cannot usually communicate directly with mainframes. The act that they have been defined, however, means that peer-to-peer software can be developed and will be available. In the meantime, terminal emulation is still the most common method of communication between PCs and mainframes.

OFFICE SOFTWARE PROTOCOLS

Another set of protocols is used between IBM's office software products rather than between hardware devices. DCA, Document Content Architecture, specifies the internal structure of a document, or how the document is stored in the computer. DIA, Document Interchange Architecture, specifies how documents can be moved, stored and retrieved.

The product DISOSS (Distributed Office Support System), follows the DIA and DCA standards. It uses a central mainframe computer to store and distribute documents. With DISOSS, users can communicate with users on other computers through electronic mail, store documents in a "host library", and retrieve documents for later use. Eventually, the distribution portion will be replaced by SNADS (SNA Distributed Services). The advantage of SNADS is that it does not require a central computer; instead, as with APPC, users can send, file and retrieve documents on a peer-to-peer basis.

TERMINAL EMULATION

Host computer systems, whether they are mainframes or minicomputers, are designed to support workstations commonly called "dumb" terminals. A dumb terminal does none of its own application processing, but must rely on the host system for its intelligence.

The simplest way for a PC to access a mainframe system is by emulating a dumb terminal. In emulation, one device assumes the characteristics of another device. That is, after an emulation package is installed in a PC, the PC becomes a functional replacement for the terminal. Emulation may require software only or a combination of hardware and software.

Several types of terminals, including the DEC VT100 series and the IBM 3101, are widely used. Suppose that a host system is running an application that interfaces with VT100 terminals, in this case, mainframe access can be easy. Communication software containing a VT100 emulation programme is loaded at the PC. A connection is made to the host through dial-up telephone lines, and the PC, which now emulates a VT100, can access the host as a dumb terminal.

One of the most popular types of mainframe terminal systems is the 3270 series from IBM. The 3270 terminals are used in on-line (interactive) sessions with an IBM host computer. These highly functional terminals support such features as text insertion and deletion and automatic cursor movement.

Through emulation hardware and software, the PC workstation can perform the same functions as the 3270 terminal. In addition, the PC can receive and store data from the host computer, modify or reformat display data, run local application programmes, and send the output to the host.

The host can be an IBM System/370, IBM 308X or 43XX processor. The PC can be connected via coaxial cable to a channel-attached IBM 3274 or 3276 cluster controller, or remotely to a bisynchronous or SNA/SDLC 3274 cluster controller (see Figure 11.3).

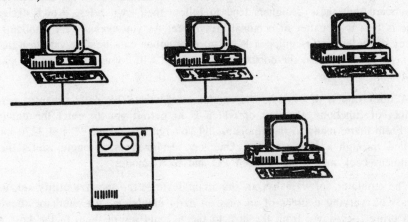

Fig. 11.3 : Gateway connection

A 3270 emulator is a type of gateway. Through it, virtual circuits are established between host and terminal devices, and go to a bisynchronous or SNA network and the IBM host. The emulation package includes a circuit board, which supports the physical connection between the PC and mainframe system. Also included is software, which runs on the PC and provides its 3270 functionality.

Emulators are available to make the PC look like either the 3278 or 3279 terminal, although accommodations must be made for some models. The 3278 Model 2 display is PC compatible, with 24 lines by 80 characters. Model 3 has a 33-line display; Model 4, a 43-line display. You cannot put more than the standard 24 lines on the PC screen, so to handle large displays, the emulators enable you to use the PC's PgUp and PgDn keys to scroll the screen.

The 3279s are colour terminals. Again, emulation is not perfect because the 3279 resolution is higher than that of the PC colour monitor. The alternatives are either to use only the text mode of the 3279 and forego the graphics, or to purchase a graphics monitor.

The IBM PC keyboard provides all the special functions of the 3270 series keyboard, although some adaptation is needed because the numbers and positions of the keys differ. Many companies, including IBM, provide 3270 emulation packages.

HOW TO EVALUATE AN EMULATOR?

The first step in evaluating a 3270 emulator is to check that it is both hardware and feature-compatible with your system, beginning with the PC. All emulators will not work with all IBM PC compatibles The emulator board should fit any slot and be used like any other circuit board. Other parts of your existing system, such as cluster controllers, may be "IBM-compatible" but not compatible enough to support a particular emulator without some modification.

After you check compatibility, the next step is to look at emulation quality and how it is achieved. All emulator designers make accommodation for the screen and the keyboard, but these designers tend to follow their own rules. Which designer's scheme is best is a matter of personal preference. As you evaluate the emulator, test each key of the emulator-equipped PC. You may notice considerable variation in what a key actually does, what the documentation says it will do, and what the comparable key on a 3270 does.

A third step is to evaluate the emulator software. This software must perform a number of functions, the first of which is to permit you to enter the emulation mode. From there, many of the emulators let you run concurrent PC and 3270 modes, controlled through a toggle switch. One key, designed as a toggle, shifts the PC environment back and forth between PC and 3270 modes.

The emulator software has an important feature, the transfer utility set, which appears with varying degrees of success on early emulators. An emulator should be able to bring files down from the host to the PC and return them to the host when processing is completed. The transfer utilities should support whatever environment is necessary. The key-point is you must make certain that the software supports not only the two-way transfer, but also the desired mainframe environment - TSO or VM/CMS or both.

How the information is displayed should also be taken into account. Compare the emulated display with the 3270 to see that status lines or comments, are the same and that all the characters are compatible. Some differences can occur in the character sets, so designers must choose representative characters.

The emulator should be totally compatible with your present system. You should be able to disconnect the coax and connector from the 3270 terminal and plug the cable directly into the emulator board on the PC. Then, when you turn on the system and start the emulator software, you will be connected to the mainframe.

THE EMULATOR ON THE NETWORK

As part of a LAN, a terminal-emulation package can serve individual users who need to access the mainframe. The only concern is that the emulator settings should not conflict with any other devices within the PC workstation.

For example, if you have a modem in a PC, a 3270 emulation board and a network interface card, you must know the interrupts and all the I/O (input/ouput) channels being used by each. If some of the interrupt settings are identical for two or more boards, the system would not function properly.

Most emulators permit the concurrent use of other communication software, including networking software, as long as the interrupts and channels are not duplicated. The emulator software should permit the changing of channels so that conflicts can be avoided. If a specific address is already used for communication, you should be able to reset the emulator address to an alternative address so that the communication programmes do not "collide" with each other.

The network sets up its own communication system, managed by the network interface card and network software. The network does not affect the PCs' three parallel ports (LPT1, LPT2 and LPT3) and two serial ports (COM1 and COM2). But other devices, such as printers, modems and emulators, use these ports and must be directed properly.

MAINFRAME GATEWAYS: ALTERNATIVES TO TERMINAL EMULATION

The mainframe gateway is an alternative to the terminal emulation package. Instead of serving an individual PC as the standard emulation package does, the mainframe gateway can serve all PCs attached to the network. Although gateways are available that support such protocols as X.25 and asynchronous communication,the SNA gateway is becoming the primary LAN-to-mainframe link.

In most configurations, the gateway emulates a 3274 cluster controller (see Figure 11.4). PCs attached to the LAN can initiate a 3270 session with the mainframe through the gateway. To start the session. the PC must load an emulation programme, the PC requires no special emulation hardware.

Gateways have a fixed number of ports, each of which supports a mainframe session. Gateways come in 8-, 16-, 24-, 32-and 64-port versions. One of the gateway's advantages is that it usually supports as many as 5 or 6 simultaneous mainframe sessions on a single PC. Each session takes up the entire screen, and users can switch from one session to another.

Functionally, the gateway and the emulation board solutions are basically the same. Both let the PC function alternately as a 3278 terminal and a microcomputer. The primary reason for opting for the gateway-type link is a significant saving in cost.

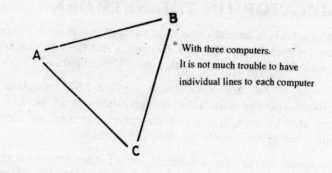

With three computers.
It is not much trouble to have
individual lines to each computer

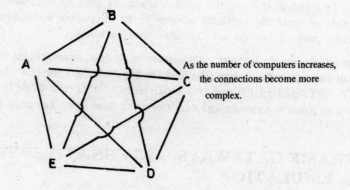

As the number of computers increases,
the connections become more
complex.

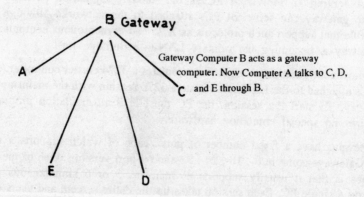

Gateway Computer B acts as a gateway
computer. Now Computer A talks to C, D,
and E through B.

Fig. 11.4 : Reason for gateway

A port for a PC on an SNA gateway costs upto $400. Providing the same connectivity with an emulation board costs approximately $1,000 for the emulation board and another $500 or so for a port on the 3274 cluster controller.

Additionally, the gateway approach requires only one connection between the

LAN and mainframe. With emulation boards, each emulator-equipped PC must be furnished with its own dedicated 3270 cable, usually at a cost of several hundred dollars each.

The resulting cost difference between the two solutions is considerable. Compared to the emulation board solution, the gateway method saves well over $1,000 per PC workstation.

Another important advantage of the gateway is that it permits better management of communication and mainframe processing resources. Emulator-equipped PCs can place a heavy burden on a mainframe communication system because of their capability to download large files, run multiple sessions and use mainframe storage areas through virtual host storage (VHS).

A gateway enables many users to access the mainframe. But the number of simultaneous sessions from the LAN to the mainframe can be limited by restricting the total number of gateway ports available. A 15-workstation departmental LAN, for example, may have an 8-port gateway, which reduces the potential load on the mainframe system. As the network grows, and needs additional mainframe ports, more gateways can be added.

PCS AS MAINFRAME WORKSTATIONS

For an analyst or for anyone else whose position requires that many jobs be done concurrently, the terminal-emulating PC can be effective. Perhaps an analyst works on the mainframe, writing and maintaining programmes. In addition, the analyst may be needed to support local PC users and their application software. With a LAN-attached PC that can emulate a mainframe terminal, the analyst can work in both the PC and mainframe environments and reach out to many physical locations — all from a single workstation.

Suppose that the analyst is working on a project on the mainframe in a 3270 mode and somebody comes in with a question about a spreadsheet. The analyst presses a couple of keys and brings up the application. After assisting the person, the analyst returns the mainframe to 3270 mode. With electronic mail this process is even better. A question can be asked through a PC-conveyed memo. The sender references the appropriate files, which the analyst can call up from the central hard disk. The analyst can then send back a response. Although the two users may be miles apart, the interaction is the same as if they were sitting next to one another.

Another interesting feature of the PC and terminal emulator is that you can capture a complete session. Later, at the end of the session, you can decide whether to keep it. But at the end of a session on a dumb terminal, the session is gone. If you want to know what you did or you want to remember a particular piece of information, you have to run the session again from the start. With the PC, you capture the session and review it as you wish. And you can store the whole session for later viewing or analysis.

Many terminal operators — the people in planning, finance, accounting and inventory — extract bits and pieces from large files. Typically, these operators look through thousands of pages of output but actually manipulate just a few pages of it. With a 3270 emulator, the operators are able to extract information and manipulate it locally on their PCs. The small computational work is taken down to the local level. This set-up reduces the workload on the mainframe, which can then support more operators and be more accessible to them.

With this arrangement the host system is benefited by downloading menial tasks that do not require mainframe power. The mainframe is best used to store very large files and databases. Of course, the mainframe excels at running large programmes and handling extensive computational tasks, such as executing large compiling jobs. All other work should be run on the PC, if possible.

At the local level, operators can manipulate the data with personal computer programmes. These are usually much easier to use than comparable mainframe programmes. And PC software is not only easier to use but often more powerful as well. Usually, mainframe programmes lack the sophistication of the smaller programmes that are written for the PC.

Engineers can bring down subroutines from their files and manipulate these subroutines on the text editor, may be even run a compatible compiler on the PC level. When a subroutine checks out, an engineer can put it into the mainframe and do the final run that costs many thousands of rupees per hour of computation time. The user saves time in manipulating the programme, which, of course, saves money too.

Sometimes, part of the processing is done on the host mainframe, and another part is downloaded to the PC for processing. Suppose that you have a computer programme which generates all its numbers in English engineering units, such as pounds, feet, inches, and so on. You are doing work for a government agency that has decided to convert to metric. The agency wants the report printed in metric units.

You have several choices. You can do all the calculation by hand. Or you can modify your primary programme that generated the numbers. You can leave the primary programme alone and run a conversion programme on the mainframe to put the file into proper form. Or you can let the PC handle the work. You can capture the output onto your PC and write a conversion programme that reads that output, then gives the metric equivalents. Using the PC in this way is good management of resources. You can take data in its original form and have it manipulated for a special purpose by your local machine. You can reformat data and merge it into a document or spreadsheet, all done locally on your PC.

BACK-UP ON THE PC

In a corporate data processing environment, the mainframe computing system provides the primary data storage facility. But even with all' the mainframe's sophisticated data protection and back-up procedures, sole reliance on this system has some drawbacks. Mainframe hard disk devices are reliable but not immune to head crashes. Nothing is quite as horrifying as to find out that a head crash occurred on the track where your data happened to be located. Of course, everything is archived or backed up regularly. But suppose that the major editing which you did yesterday was wiped out by a head crash, shortly before the data was due to be backed up.

Besides head crashes, mainframe data is subject to other threats. Disk space on mainframes is always a scarce commodity. Invariably, the amount of data expands to fill the disk faster than new disks can be installed. In one instance, a company moved its computing resources from one computer to another. By mistake, all the archived tapes from the old machine were placed on scratch status, which means that they could be erased and reused. Consequently, vast amounts of important data were lost.

After the arrival of PC, with a handful of floppies, a user have both control and back-up and not be concerned with how the mainframe data is handled or mishandled. Obviously, personal archiving can get you into trouble. You should always work with the programme that is on the mainframe, not with your personal back-up. Otherwise, local back-up systems create the risk of having multiple versions, overwriting other people's work, and experiencing many of the multiuser problems. Then, too, personal archiving may violate company security. Nonetheless, a system of personal archiving, when properly used, can be an important benefit of the PC-to-mainframe connection.

RELIABILITY OF MAINFRAME CONNECTION

Many multibillion dollar corporations have trouble maintaining reliable communication between terminals and host mainframe computers. Downtime may have any number of causes. In one instance, a backhoe operator dug through a cable and shut down a data processing department for two days. Most problems tend to be less radical, involving only a few hours of downtime now and again. But accumulated downtime is a serious mainframe-related problem. One study in a major corporation showed that the host computer was unavailable for 10 to 20% of the time. A more representative figure may be as low as 5%. That 5%, however, seems to be concentrated during peak hours, therefore magnifying the effect.

The costs of downtime can mount up with an unreliable communication network. Companies often do not see these costs because they do not show up on any ledger sheet. Nevertheless, the costs are real.

In contrast, the PC rarely has downtime, certainly nothing like that of mainframe systems. If the mainframe goes down, you will probably have an entire staff sitting around with little to do. But if you have copies of mainframe files and programmes sitting on a network server, the real effect of mainframe downtime can be minimised.

CONNECTING MAINFRAMES TO LANS

In 1986, IBM released dozens of software products for their local area networks. The networks themselves provided connections between devices; the software products continue the process by providing connections between applications.

In this section, we will discuss the products available for connecting each kind of mainframe to each kind of LAN. Keep in mind that some of the products are not sufficient for the average user's needs. What exist are the physical hardware connections and some of the general software connections. But you cannot yet run Lotus 1-2-3, for example, and get data directly from the mainframe.

In general, IBM's Token-Ring Network is a better bet than the PC Network if you plan to communicate with mainframes. For example, the Token Ring Supports two programming interfaces: NETBIOS and APPC. Although not much software is available to take advantage of APPC, the fact that it is supported by the Token Ring is, as IBM would say, a strategic statement of direction. NETBIOS does not support the LU 6.2 protocol at all. Consequently, Token-Ring Network users must choose between running NETBIOS to be compatible with existing PC networks, or APPC to be compatible with future mainframe communication.

MAINFRAME PRODUCTS FOR THE TOKEN RING

Communication products for the Token Ring are divided into three categories, depending on which mainframe is being used:

- System/370 and 370 compatibles

- System/36

- Series/1

We will discuss each computer family in turn, first covering the hardware products available, then the software.

System/370 Hardware for the Token Ring

The System/370 is IBM's flagship mainframe computer. Computers in this family are more popular than any other mainframe computer. They are most often used 'for administrative duties, such as budgeting, storing personnel records and managing large databases.

Terminals and computers communicate with System/370 machines through hardware devices called communication controllers. These devices are like the control units on expensive stereos. Communication controllers have connections for devices such as terminals, networks, consoles and modems. Most of the ways to communicate with a System/370 involve the 3725 Communication Controller. In addition, PCs can communicate with the System/370 indirectly through the System/36; this is discussed in the section on System/36 communication.

3725 Communication Controller

The 3725 Communication Controller has been around for several years. In general, it is used to communicate between terminals and the mainframe. With a special attachment, up to four Token-Ring Networks can be connected to a Model 1 or Model 2 3725; by adding an expansion unit called a 3726, a total of eight Token-Ring Networks can be connected.

To connect the LANs to the 3725, you first need a unit called a Line and Token-Ring Attachment Base [LAB] Type C. The LAB has a twofold purpose:

-       to hold the TICs [Token-Ring interface couplers - these are what actually communicate with the Token-Ring Network by transmitting and receiving messages].

-       to funnel the information from the TICs to the mainframe.

Each LAB unit can contain four TICs; this means the LAB can communicate with up to four Token-Ring Networks. Each TIC can connect to one Token-Ring Network with a shielded twisted-pair [type 6] cable. A 3726 expansion unit can be connected to the Model 1 3725 controller. Combined, the 3725 and 3726 can contain two LAB Type C units; that is, the 3726 can hold two if the 3725 has none, or the 3725 and 3726 can each hold one. The TIC can transmit data at rates of up to four million bits per second. Speed in actual use, however, depends on factors such as system load.

3720 Communication Controller

The 3720 is a small communication controller in the 3725 family. Like the 3725, it is used to communicate between terminals and the mainframe.

Four 3720 models are available; the ones we are concerned with are the Models 11 and 12, which can each support upto two Token-Ring Networks. The Model 12 is designed for remote locations connected to the mainframe by telephone lines. They do this through the same TIC connector that the 3725 uses; LABs are not needed. Each can also communicate with upto four System/370 computers through connections known as TPSs for two-processor switches. As the name implies, one switch can connect two mainframes, and the 3720 can support two switches. Like the network adapter cards used to connect PCs to the LAN, the TICs and TPSs are optional cards that are inserted in the 3720.

Performance of 3720 is supposed to be about one-third that of the 3725's;consequently, one might expect the maximum transmission speed to be slightly over one million bits per second. As with the 3725, in-use speed depends on system load.

3174 Subsystem Control Unit

The 3174 Subsystem Control Unit connects 3270-type terminals to System/370 mainframes through a 3720 or 3725 Communication Controller. Because of the 3270-type terminal's high intelligence, the 3174 is required to manage data transfer between the terminal and the System/370. Through the 3174, PCs on a Token-Ring Network can also communicate with the high-priced, high-performance 308X and 3090 mainframes.

There are two varieties of the 3174, the large cluster and the small cluster, with several models of each variety. Token-Ring Networks can be connected to one model of each variety. The large cluster model that supports the Token-Ring Network is called the 3R, and supports up to 32 terminals. The small cluster model that supports the Token-Ring Network is called the 53R, and supports up to 16 terminals.

3270 Emulation

The final hardware communication method to a System/370 is also the oldest: terminal emulation. One PC emulates a different type of communication controller, the 3274, while up to 32 other PCs emulate 3278 [monochrome] or 3279 [colour] terminals. It is called 3270 emulation because all these devices are members of the 3270 family.

Although this method has the advantages of simplicity and low cost, it has all the inherent disadvantages of terminal emulation. Moreover, the PC emulating the 3274 controller must be dedicated to this task; it cannot be used for any function other than as a terminal controller. If one PC is emulating the 3274 terminal controller, a card called an SDLC adapter is installed in that PC. This card is similar to the network adapter card.

System/370 Software for the Token Ring

The hardware connection between the System/370 mainframe and the Token-Ring Network is only half the story. To do useful work, there must be a software connection as well. Three kinds of software can connect Token-Ring Networks and mainframes; most of the software supports several kinds of hardware connection. In addition, the communication controllers usually have some supporting software. Support for the Token-Ring Network is usually included in the latest release of the software, so selecting the proper software is not an issue.

APPC Software

No APPC software exists as yet. Nonetheless, it is almost certain that software using the APPC standard will be developed both by IBM and by other vendors. Software written to this standard will be supported on the 3174, 3720 and 3725 hardware connections.

Personal Services/PC Software

You use Personal Services/PC software when you are communicating with the previously described DISOSS on the System/370. With Personal Services/PC, you can access and manipulate documents from a Token-Ring Network just as you can when you are using a terminal on the System/370. For example, you can store, retrieve and delete documents in the System/370 host library. You can also search for particular documents, and then print them on printers attached to the mainframe. Finally, you can send documents to other users with the electronic mail portion of Personal Services/PC.

Most models of the IBM PC support Personal Services/PC. Unfortunately, Personal Services/PC for the System/370 is supported only when the PC is emulating a 3270 terminal. This means that the programme cannot take full advantage of the

PC's intelligence, for reasons we mentioned previously when discussing terminal emulation. The Personal Services/PC software can be used when the PC is connected with a 3174, 3270, 3725 or 3720 hardware controller device, as long as the PC is emulating a 3270 terminal.

3270 Emulation Programme

The IBM PC 3270 Emulation programme is used when PCs connected to the Token-Ring Network need to emulate 3270 terminals to communicate with the System/ 370. Several versions exist; all versions of the software let users run System/370 programmes by emulating a 3270 terminal.

This software is used when a PC is emulating a 3270 terminal, either when a PC is directly connected to a 3274 terminal controller or when a PC is emulating a 3274 terminal controller. In addition, PCs connected to either a 3725 or 3720 Communication Controller can run this software, rather than APPC, if you need or prefer terminal emulation - for example, if you want to run Personal Services/PC.

System/36 Hardware for the Token Ring

The System/36 is a small computer that IBM calls a "departmental computer"; it can satisfy the computing needs of a department, whereas the System/370 can satisfy the needs of an entire company or a division. Several models of the System/36 are available. IBM has called the System/36 the primary office departmental system; the machine's support of the Token Ring bolsters this.

5360/5362/5364 System Unit LAN Attachment

The 5360, 5362 and 5364 are all different models of the System/36 computer. The 5360/5362/5364 System Unit LAN Attachment devices connect the Token-Ring Network to System/36 machines. In the case of the Token-Ring Network, the connection is through a dedicated IBM PC/AT — that is, the only function the PC/AT can perform is that of a communication controller. When connected to the 5364 model of the System/ 36, the IBM PC AT can run System/36 workstation applications, but cannot run IBM PC programme. A System/36 can communicate with upto two Token-Ring Networks.

With the 5360 and 5362 models of the System/36, an additional device called the System/36 LAN Attachment Feature is required. This product includes a System/ 36 LAN Attachment Adapter card, which is installed into the IBM PC/AT like any typical card. The 5364 can communicate directly with the dedicated IBM PC/AT, so the System/36 LAN Attachment Feature and LAN Attachment Adapter card are not required.

3174 Subsystem Control Unit

With the 3174 Subsystem Control Unit, you can connect a Token-Ring Network directly to the System/36 mainframe. As with the System/370, the 3174 connects 3270-type terminals to the System/36. Because of the 3270-type terminal's high intelligence, the 3174 is required to manage data transfer between terminals and the System/36.

There are two varieties of the 3174, the large cluster and the small cluster, with several models of each variety. Token-Ring Networks can be connected to one model of each variety. The large cluster model that supports the Token-Ring Network is called the 3R, and supports up to 32 terminals. The small cluster model that supports the Token-Ring Network is called the 53R, and supports up to 16 terminals.

PC Adapter II for the IBM PC

A PC Adapter II card must be installed in the dedicated IBM/PC AT for each Token-Ring Network connection to the System/36. That is, if the maximum of two Token-Ring Networks are connected to the System/36, two PC Adapter II cards are required. This is true whether the 5360, 5362 or 5364 models of the System/36 are used.

The PC Adapter II card can also be used to connect IBM PCs to the Token-Ring Network; it is the equivalent of the PC Network adapter card with an additional 8K of RAM. The additional RAM lets you send longer network messages and, when installed in a server, support more PCs.

The PC Adapter II card can be installed in the IBM PC, Portable, PC/XT, PC/AT and models 5531, 7531 and 7532 of the Industrial Computer. To act as a controller to the System/36, however, an IBM PC/AT is required. As with the PC adapter card, the PC Adapter II supports both the APPC and NETBIOS programming interfaces.

System/36 Software for the Token Ring

Three kinds of software are involved in the System/36 connection to the Token-Ring Network. Two of them are sold together under the name LAN Communications Licensed programme; one component runs on the System/36 and one component runs on the IBM PC/AT used as a gateway between the System/36 and the Token-Ring Network. The third kind of software, Support/36, runs on the PCs communicating to the System/36.

System Unit LAN Communications Licensed Programme

The System Unit LAN Communications Licensed programme comes in two versions: one for the 5630 and 5632 models of the System/36, and one for the 5634 model. You do not run this programme, as such; it just has to be available on the system unit. The programme supports communication with upto two Token-Ring Networks.

The component that runs on the gateway IBM PC/AT is stored on the System/36. When communication start, the System/36 downloads this component to the IBM PC/AT, where the programme automatically runs.

Support/36 Programme

The Support/36 programme is what lets PCs on the Token-Ring Network communicate with the System/36. The optional Support/36 Workstation Feature lets the PC emulate a System/36 workstation as well. With the Workstation Feature, each PC can emulate up to four System/36 workstations; although only one System/36 session can be displayed on the screen at a time, any other sessions continue running. However, a PC session cannot continue running. One of these sessions can emulate a 5219 or a 5256 printer.

Even without the Workstation Feature, PCs can use the System/36 as a virtual disk (disk server) and virtual print (print server) device. Essentially, the programme gives any PC on the Token-Ring Network the same capabilities as a directly connected mainframe PC. With this software, PCs can also emulate a 3270 terminal and can communicate through the System/36 to a System/370.

Series/1 Hardware for the Token Ring

No products, specifically for the Token-Ring Network, are available to communicate with the Series/1. Several products that can run on the PC Network, however, can run on the Token-Ring Network tooif the Token Ring is running NETBIOS. See the following descriptions.

MAINFRAME PRODUCTS FOR THE PC NETWORK

In general, fewer products are available for the PC Network than for the Token-Ring Network. For example, the PC Network has no way to communicate with the System/36. Although some products are available, it is better to buy a Token-Ring Network if you need to do large-scale mainframe communication. All products mentioned in this section will also run on the Token-Ring Network if it is running NETBIOS.

System/370 Hardware for the PC Network

PCs on the PC Network can communicate with a System/370 only through terminal emulation. Terminal emulation is an inefficient way to communicate between PCs and mainframes. For this reason, IBM is recommending that LAN users, who often need to communicate with a mainframe, use the Token-Ring Network.

3270 Emulation

The only communication method from the PC Network to a System/370 is also the oldest: terminal emulation. It can be accomplished in one of two ways. First, one PC can emulate a different type of communication controller, the 3274, while upto five other PCs emulate 3278 (monochrome) or 3279 (colour) terminals. It is called 3270 emulation because these devices are all members of the 3270 family. Second, a PC can be connected directly to a 3274 terminal controller.

Although these methods have several advantages, namely their simplicity and low cost, they all have the inherent disadvantages of terminal emulation. Moreover, the PC emulating the 3274 controller must be dedicated to this task; that is, it can not be used for any function other than acting as a terminal controller. In a PC emulating the 3274, you install a card called an SDLC adapter. This card is similar to the network adapter card.

System/370 Software for the PC Network

3270 Emulation Programme

There are several versions of the IBM PC 3270 Emulation programme. All versions of the software let users run System/370 programmes by emulating a 3270 terminal. In addition to running System/370 programmes, you can run Personal Services/PC to access DISOSS features.

Personal Services/PC Software

You use Personal Services/PC software when you are communicating with DISOSS on the System/370. With this product, you can access and manipulate documents just as you can when you are using a terminal on the System/370. For example, you can store, retrieveand delete documents in the host library. You can also search for particular documents, and then print them on printers attached to the mainframe. Finally, you can send documents to other users with electronic mail. Most models of the IBM PC support Personal Services/PC. Because communication to the System/370 is supported only when the PC is emulating a 3270 terminal, Personal Services/PC can not take full advantage of the PC's intelligence.

Series/1 Hardware for the PC Network

The traditional role of the Series/1 has been that of a factory processor - controlling robots, industrial manufacturing machines, and so on. IBM has begun adding office functions to the Series/1, to the extent that some analysts think it will eventually replace the System/36. But the fact that the Series/1 does not support the Token-Ring Network (other than in NETBIOS emulation) might be an IBM signal that it will not be enhanced much further.

Series/1 PC Connect Adapter

As with the System/370 connection, you can connect to the Series/1 by dedicating an IBM PC/AT or XT for use as a gateway to the PC Network. Then, any PC on the PC Network can communicate with the Series/1 mainframe, including using its disks and output devices. The adapter is much like any other PC card, and you install it the same way.

Series/1 Software for the PC Network

As mentioned, IBM recently began adding office functions to the Series/1. For example, the machine now supports the DISOSS protocols. Consequently, PCs on the PC Network can access documents on the Series/1 with the Personal Services/PC package. PCs connected to the Series/1 mainframe can communicate with System/370 DISOSS, but because information is transferred using SNADS and other IBM data communication connections, rather than with the PC Network or the Token-Ring Network, it will not be discussed here.

Series/1 Office Connect Software

Office connect includes software for the PC as well as the Series/1. With Series/1 software, the machine can provide the document distribution and library services. With PC software, PCs can communicate with Series/1 software using Personal Services/PC (described next).

Personal Services/PC Software

Personal Services/PC software is used to communicate with Office Connect on the Series/1. With it, you can access and manipulate documents just as you can when you are using a terminal on the System/370. For example, you can store, retrieve and delete documents, and then print them on printers attached to the mainframe. Finally, you can send documents to other users with electronic mail. Most models of the IBM PC support Personal Services/PC.

FUTURE OF MAINFRAME AND LAN COMMUNICATION

By now, you may have come to two conclusions. First, mainframe to LAN communication is complicated. Second, it will be a while before all the pieces are in place for complete mainframe-to-PC networking.

Although a base for peer-to-peer communication is there, you are still limited to terminal emulation with existing products. But by the end of the decade, you should have your choice of products that support peer-to-peer communication between mainframes and LANs. Now we will discuss the future of mainframe and LAN communication, including problems that must be solved and where the first software products will come from.

What does peer-to-peer communication really mean? How will it affect your life? What good will it do you? Let usstart with an example. Suppose you want to get some of your company's budget information out of the mainframe and into a Lotus 1-2-3 spreadsheet. Most likely, you cannot do it directly (and if you can, you can bet that somebody in the MIS department spent a few busy weeks writing a programme to enable you to do it).

So how would you do it? First of all, you have to run a programme on the mainframe to extract the data you want from the budget, and place that information in a separate file on the mainframe. Second, you have to transfer the information from the mainframe to the PC, which probably requires running a terminal emulation programmeand either downloading the file or logging it to disk. Finally, you have to convert the mainframe data into a form that Lotus 1-2-3 on the PC can read and that is in the same format as your spreadsheet.

By now you have probably concluded that it would be easier to retype the spreadsheet information. But let us look at how this scenario might work with APPC-compatible applications. First, you run Lotus 1-2-3 and call up your spreadsheet. Next, while you are still running Lotus 1-2-3 with the spreadsheet, you look at the budget data on the mainframe. It would automatically be converted to a format that Lotus 1-2-3 and your spreadsheet could read. Finally, you select the data you need and it is automatically transferred to your floppy disk.

When you have finished, the software might automatically update the information in the mainframe's files. Or you might want to check it first; in that case, the software could save a copy of the file on the mainframe to protect you from power and disk problems.

But what if your company's budget was so large or so disjointed that it was spread over several computers. In that case, the software might find out which computer contains the information, set up a session on that computer, and transfer the information. All of this would happen without your doing anything, or even without your noticing. This feature is called transparent access, because you cannot see it happening. APPC has other potential advantages. Currently, most information has to pass through a mainframe computer. In the office product protocols, all distribution goes through a central computer.

But what happens if that computer fails? Anybody who has ever needed to fly into a hub city that is having problems knows what happens - air traffic backs up all over the country. The same thing happens with the computer network. In the future, however, things will be different. Computers will know several routes for transmitting information, so if a certain route goes down or is overloaded, data can simply be transmitted by another route.

Vendors of computers other than IBM, such as Apple and DEC, are looking at APPC too. With it, computers that are not compatible with IBM, such as the Macintosh, could transmit data to IBM PCs without having to be fully IBM-compatible.

This intercomputer communication may require time. Fortunately, APPC supports multitasking (doing several things at one time). Consequently, if it is taking a long time to get your data, you can continue writing your report or revising your spreadsheet. Perhaps a window in the corner of your PC screen will inform you of the progress of the data transfer.

These examples are just a sample of what APPC-compatible programmes might be able to do. Probably the first programmes to support the APPC interface will be new products, or products that are already popular, such as Lotus 1-2-3. Eventually, products that do not support the APPC interface will be ignored, as tapes in Betamax format are now.

POTENTIAL ROADBLOCKS TO PEER-TO-PEER COMMUNICATION

Before this idyllic scenario can take place, several issues need to be settled. First, IBM has not finished the final APPC specifications yet. This definitely slows development; you can not write a programme to fit a standard if the standard itself has not been defined.

Second, it will be many years before mainframe applications can be converted to peer-to-peer applications, because so many mainframe programmes are still written in COBOL and assembly language. MIS departments can not rewrite programmes fast enough. And until those programmes are converted, users will be stuck with terminal emulation and master-slave communication.

Then there is the question of how users will manage all the data that is suddenly available. Any organisation with more than one PC and more than one copy of Lotus 1-2-3 has probably experienced the multiple spreadsheets problem. One of these days, a scientist will win the Nobel Prize by explaining how several users, starting with the same data, can reach different conclusions - some of them flawed. And the more access users have to data, the more faulty conclusions they can come up with.

Worse still, users could take data produced by their faulty conclusions and transmit it to the mainframe, where it would replace the correct data. Organisations need to set up procedures and guidelines to prevent this.

Transactions also need to be defined so one user does not rewrite a record just as another user is reading it. Until these data management issues are settled, application programmers have to incorporate the precautions into their programmes. But if each programmer devises a different way to incorporate data management, we could again have incompatible programmes.

Then there is network management. Everyone certainly has heard of the Postal Service's Dead Letter Office, with its storehouse of letters that are addressed to unknown places or have illegible addresses. In the same way, if a computer does not know how to reach the destination computer, the message never gets to the recipient. Whenever computers are removed from, added to or moved within a network, their addresses change and there is chance for messages to be lost.

Keeping track of computer whereabouts is already a problem in traditional SNA networks, which are set up so that most routing information is contained in a few computers. This is equivalent to having all your letters go to New Delhi before they can go to their destination across town. Every time a computer is added to or removed from the network, for example, the entire network has to shut down to change the address tables.

A peer-to-peer environment would be worse, because it cannot be centrally configured. Instead, each computer must know the addresses of all the other computers, including how to get there. It is as though a cross-country letter has to include the names of all the cities through which the letter might travel.

This information grows geometrically. Every time a computer is added to the network, it must be configured with the addressing information about all the other computers in the network.

Fortunately, IBM is developing an extension to SNA called LEN, for Low Entry Networking. When this extension is fully developed, network configuration will be easier. Moreover, it may implement dynamic routing, which means that the route from one computer to another can change depending on network conditions. If traffic is slow or a computer is down, for example, the route can be changed to handle the situation.

This brings up another problem, however. When there is no central computer, how do you know when a computer or a communication line is not working? The malfunctioning computer cannot tell you. Existing central computers can run diagnostics on other computers, but with APPC, there will not be any central computers.

After enough messages are lost, someone may finally realise that there is a problem, but that could take days. It might be like the movie, the Andromeda Strain, in which the scientists did not receive any important messages for several days simply because a piece of paper was blocking the bell on the teletype machine ! IBM and third-party vendors need to develop diagnostic hardware and software that can deal with LANs.

INTRODUCTION

Security for microcomputer LANs has increased in importance, and more vendors are supplying LAN security systems. As end-users become more aware of the value of the vast amounts of data being accumulated and the need to protect that data, more users adopt such systems.

Newspapers carry stories almost every week about some computer network being penetrated, either for financial gain or as a prank. Most of these break-ins involve large corporate networks and wide area networks. As local area networks proliferate and tap into national and international data communication systems, these local networks will also become targets.

Companies tnat do sensitive work, such as those with defence contracts, are often heavily involved in data security. Other companies may be aware only of the threat, but not of their own vulnerability. Most analysts agree that businesses and institutions, such as schools, will have to suffer a loss through theft or vandalism before they actually establish measures to protect their data.

A computing network, like any other valuable, shared resource, is subject to breaches of security. Such breaches can be accidental or intentional, and their effects on network operations can range from harmless to irritating to devastating.

Security is a critical issue to those planning, managing or using a LAN. It is also a very complex issue. Security is a component of overall network reliability. However, reliability depends largely upon the dependability of network hardware, software and technology. In contrast, the security of a network depends almost exclusively upon the behaviour of that network's authorised users, managers and their guests.

Security, like reliability, is best addressed as part of an overall network strategy. Security concerns must be balanced by other factors that affect the network and its users. Users and managers must therefore discover and implement methods that improve network security without infringing upon users' work patterns or implying that all users are suspected violators of security.

Users have other concerns that network security methods must address as well. Users must be reassured that they can collaborate on projects and share information without being spied upon by managers or other users. Well-implemented password protection schemes can provide much of this reassurance. Managers must also demonstrate to users that procedures for tracking user work patterns on the network are used to improve security and reliability, and not merely to keep a closer eye on users or their activities.

Security methods must be selected with care and implemented with the full cooperation and knowledge of authorised users if security is to be assured (see Figure 12.1). A first step toward these goals is a definition of network security.

LAN Security

1. Security cannot exist without a management policy

2. LAN users should be positively identifiable before they have access to network resources.

   Prevention : passwords, passkeys authorization measures.

3. Data, hardware, and software should be protected from unauthorized and/or accidental, modification, destruction, theft, or disclosure.

   Prevention : locks

4. Data should be reconstructible.

   Prevention : frequent, regular backup of files.

5. Equipment must be protected from fire, dirt, and natural disasters.
   Prevention : smoke detectors, sprinklers, air conditioning

---

Fig. 12.1 : Essentials of LAN Security

WHAT NETWORK SECURITY MEANS

All the features of electromagnetic media that are desirable to a user also make this media vulnerable to theft and damage. Information stored on disk is easily copied, altered and erased. As larger amounts of critical data are stored in this way, the significance of the problem grows.

A stand-alone personal computer is easy to secure. You simply put your diskettes in a safe and store your computer in a locked closet. But when you attach that computer to a network of computers, security becomes more complicated. Even a "local" network probably will spread out through several offices, with connecting cables running in ceilings and floors, and in halls and basements. A thief or vandal can tap into any one of a dozen or more spots on the network, many secluded from normal observation. But tapping into the network from some secluded spot on the cable is not usually necessary. A person can simply log-on to a convenient PC and steal or damage data at will. Unfortunately, the easier a system is to use, the easier it is to misuse.

Like any other kind of insurance, data security involves trade-offs. You must weigh the cost of the potential loss against the cost of protection as well as any inconvenience the security measures may cause. The first thing to do in planning your data security programme is to put a value on the data you are going to protect.

In general, a secure network is one that is resistant to disruptions caused by unauthorised network use. Such a network is designed and operated to minimize unauthorised use and can recover from disruptions easily and completely should unauthorised users evade safeguards.

Network security can be defined as the protection of network resources against unauthorised disclosure, modification, utilisation, restriction or destruction. Security has long been an object of concern and study for both data processing systems and communication facilities. With computer networks, these concerns are combined. And for local networks, the problems may be most acute.

Consider a full-capacity local network, with direct terminal access to the network and data files and applications distributed among a variety of processors. The local network may also provide access to and from long-haul communication and be part of an internet. The complexity of the task of providing security in such an environment is clear. The subject is a broad one, and encompasses physical and administrative controls as well as automated ones.

This general definition of a secure network is the foundation upon which you must build a definition that fits your work group's specific requirements and constraints. An effective definition requires careful assessment of needs by you, your colleagues and your managers.

RISK ANALYSIS

Before you can realistically decide how much time and money to invest in data security, you must quantify the risk. Risk analysis has been elevated to a precise discipline. For our purposes, we would not need to examine formulas or other exact methods of quantifying every risk associated with networked data. But we can look briefly at some of the elements of risk analysis. These can help you to develop a preliminary description of your data's value and potential for loss.

First, you will want to determine two values, in rupees, for the information stored in your data system. One is the cost of re-creating the data; the other is the value of lost business if a competitor should gain access to your data.

These two figures should be easy to obtain or at least to estimate. Many smaller companies have never considered the potential loss of their stored data. If nothing else, such an appraisal should encourage the use of data back-up and the insistence on serious password security procedures.

Next, you should identify any possible threats to your data. If your data has little or no monetary value to a competitor, then there is probably little risk of theft. On the other hand, the value of your data to a competitor may be great, with the risk of theft proportionally high.

The physical volume of valuable data is another element to consider. If the volume and diversity of the data are extensive, the chance of a total loss by theft is reduced. A related calculation is the frequency of potential thefts. This figure can be difficult to predict unless you have compiled a history of losses over some period of time. Law enforcement agencies and some trade associations keep extensive records of thefts, defined by type of business, kind of penetration and value of loss. Contacting these groups may turn up sufficient data to allow you to make an intelligent prediction of risk. In addition, you should make a detailed study of any active attacks on your data so that you can estimate the cost of countering a similar attack.

Vandalism is another threat, possibly more serious than theft because the frequency of vandalism is often greater. A discontented employee may decide to "get even" by destroying or altering important files. Or an act of vandalism may be done simply as a prank or game, just to see if it can be done.

After you calculate the value of your data and the types of risks, the final element in risk analysis is the data's vulnerability. Remote access is one factor that causes data to become more easily available and vulnerable. When people can access your network remotely, the potential for loss increases.

On a local basis, the risk to data goes up when the network's contents are generally known. The capability to see those contents (for example, files servers, and other resources) is controlled partially by the operating system and partially by the site administration.

Making a risk analysis will enable you to answer many questions about where risks are greatest and how much money and procedural inconveniences are necessary to thwart these threats. Next, you should consider steps for building a secure data network.

TYPES OF THREATS

A publication of the National Bureau of Standards identified some of the threats that have stimulated the upsurge of interest in security:

1.   Organised and intentional attempts to obtain economic or market information

from competitive organisations in the private sector.

2.   Organised and intentional attempts to obtain economic information from government agencies.

3.   Inadvertent acquisition of economic or market information.

4.   Inadvertent acquisition of information about individuals.

5.   Intentional fraud through illegal access to computer data banks with emphasis, in decreasing order of importance, on acquisition of funding data, economic data, law enforcement data and data about individuals.

6.   Government intrusion on the rights of individuals.

7.   Invasion of individual rights by the intelligence community.

These are examples of specific threats that an organisation or an individual (or an organisation on behalf of its employees) may feel the need to counter. The nature of the threat that concerns an organisation will vary greatly from one set of circumstances to another. Fortunately, we can approach the problem from a different angle by looking at the generic types of threats that might be encountered.

Table 12.1 lists the types of threats that might be faced in the context of network security. The threats can be divided into the categories of passive threats and active threats (see Figure 12.2).

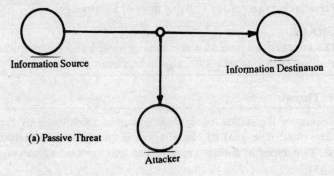

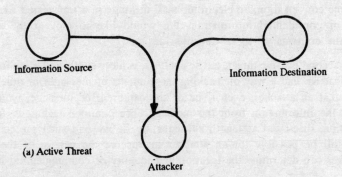

Fig. 12.2 : Passive and Active Communications Security Threats

TABLE 12.1 : Potential Network Security Threats

PASSIVE THREATS

The monitoring and/or recording of data while the data are being transmitted over a communication facility.

RELEASE OF MESSAGE CONTENTS

Attack can read the user data in messages.

TRAFFIC ANALYSIS

The attacker can read packet headers, to determine the location and identity of communicating hosts. The attacker can also observe the length and frequency of messages.

ACTIVE THREATS

The unauthorised use of a device attached to a communication facility to alter transmitting data or control signals or to generate spurious data or control signals.

MESSAGE-STREAM MODIFICATION

The attacker can selectively modify, delete, delay, reorder and duplicate real messages.

The attacker can also insert counterfeit messages.

DENIAL OF MESSAGE SERVICE

The attacker can destroy or delay most or all messages.

MASQUERADE

The attacker can pose as a real host or switch and communicate with another host or switch to acquire data or services.

1. Passive Threats

These are in the nature of eavesdropping or monitoring of the transmissions of an organisation. The goal of the attacker is to obtain information that is being transmitted. Two types of threats are involved here: release of message contents and traffic analysis.

The threat of release of message contents is clearly understood by most managers. A telephone conversation, an electronic mail message or a transferred file may contain sensitive or confidential information. We would like to prevent the attacker from learning the contents of these transmissions.

The second passive threat, traffic analysis, is more subtle and often less applicable. Suppose that we had a way of masking the contents of messages or other information traffic so that an attacker, even if he or she captured the message, would be unable to extract the information from the message. The common technique for doing this is encryption, discussed at length subsequently. If we had such protection in place, it might still be possible for an attacker to observe the pattern of these messages. The attacker can determine the location and identity of communicating hosts and can also observe the frequency and length of messages being exchanged. This information might be useful in guessing the nature of the communication that is taking place.

Passive threats are very difficult to detect since they do not involve any alteration of the data. However, it is feasible to prevent these attacks from being successful. Thus the emphasis in dealing with passive threats is on prevention and not detection.

2. Active Threats

The second major category of threat is active threats. These involve some modification of the data stream or the creation of a false stream. We can subdivide these threats into three categories: message-stream modification, denial of message service and masquerade.

Message-stream modification simply means that some portion of a legitimate message is altered, or that messages are delayed, replayed or reordered, in order to produce an unauthorised effect. For example, a message meaning "Allow J. N. Saxena to read confidential file accounts" is modified to mean "Allow F. C. Bansal to read confidential file accounts."

The **denial of service** prevents or inhibits the normal use or management of communication facilities. This attack may have a specific target; for example, an entity may suppress all messages directed to a particular destination (e.g. the security audit service). Another form of service denial is the disruption of an entire network, either by disabling the network or by overloading it with messages so as to degrade performance.

A **masquerade** takes place when one entity pretends to be a different entity. A masquerade attack usually includes one of the other two forms of active attack. Such an attack can take place, for example, by capturing and replaying an authentication sequence.

Active threats present the opposite characteristics of passive threats. Whereas passive attacks are difficult to detect, measures are available to prevent their success. On the other hand, it is quite difficult to absolutely prevent active attacks, since this would require physical protection of all communication facilities and paths at all times. Instead, the goal with respect to active attacks is to detect these attacks and to recover from any disruption or delays caused by the attack. Because the detection has a deterrent effect, this may also contribute to prevention.

DETERMINING WHAT SECURE MEANS TO YOU AND YOUR LAN

To arrive at a specific definition of security for your LAN, you and your colleagues must first examine your current network or network plans to identify points of vulnerability. Where points of vulnerability occur depends greatly on the work and network use patterns of every member of your work group. An initial challenge, thus;is to determine these patterns accurately without interfering with them.

If you already have a network, your group will have to decide whether written surveys, personal interviews, software that tracks network access by user, or some other method is best for gathering this information. If you are still in the planning stages, you and your group will have to gather the same information about each independent personal computer (PC) user and use the data to hypothesise points of network vulnerability. A consultant may be helpful with this step.

Every network environment is different, with a different list of specific points of vulnerability. However, most environments have certain vulnerable points. Be sure not to overlook these areas in determining your own environment's particular potential weaknesses.

SECURING WORKSTATIONS AND SERVERS

Like LANs themselves, strategies that address security begin on users' desktops, with their workstations. To protect against both accidental and intentional breaches of network security, users must develop good workstation-protection habits.

One simple habit is turning off workstations when leaving for the evening or weekend, so the screens do not attract wandering eyes and hands. Keeping boot (start-up) disks in a non-obvious drawer instead of on a desk or in the workstation's floppy drive also reduces the likelihood of unauthorised access via an authorised user's workstation.

Physical locks are also available for disk drive doors, keyboardsand workstations or PC system units. Some of these locks impede both access and theft. LAN users in large or open-office environments should be encouraged to use these additional security measures and not to defeat them by keeping the keys in their unlocked desks.

It is important to note that in many organisations, the most serious threat to workstation security is not unauthorised users with malicious intent. A larger problem is unauthorised access to user workstations by guests or children of authorised users. These legitimate users often sit their charges in front of an absent user's workstation, to play or explore while the worker works.

This problem is most acute during off hours, when network supervision is minimal or absent. Some companies report a similar problem with after-hours office cleaning staff bringing in and playing unauthorised games on PCs connected to a network. Practices like these must be detected and discouraged to prevent serious network problems caused by well-intended but untrained people.

Servers represent another point of potential vulnerability, especially if they are non-dedicated and also used as workstations. A single-user problem on a combined workstation-server can become a network-wide problem. In addition, even a dedicated server can be mistaken for a workstation if it has a keyboard, floppy disk drive and a screen attached.

The more critical your network is to your business, the more seriously you and your colleagues must work to secure your servers. Removal of the keyboard from each

PC-based server is a good first step. You may also want to put warning signs on servers or to secure them behind locked doors, depending upon their configuration and susceptibility to unauthorised access.

SECURING NETWORK PASSWORDS

Another point of vulnerability under direct user supervision is the passwords that allow access to the network itself, as well as to specific resources, such as particular servers, programmes, or files. Users remember their passwords better when they choose their own, so assignment of random passwords is to be avoided in most situations. However, users must be encouraged to use a bit of creativity when selecting their passwords to make them difficult for unauthorised users to guess or discover accidentally.

You and your colleagues should choose as passwords random numbers or word combinations that are not obvious, but have enough personal significance to be remembered easily. Such a password is less likely to be guessed or discovered and is a more effective security measure than a password based on your telephone number, your birthday or a loved one's name.

You and your colleagues must also implement routines for changing your passwords regularly. Some network managers automatically invalidate any passwords more than 30 days old, forcing users to select new ones at least once a month. Your network's security and reliability could be enhanced simultaneously if you and your colleagues changed your personal passwords each time you made complete back-up copies of your network files.

Needless to say, some users write down their passwords or store them in some electronic note file. If these users leave thenotes where others can find them, all the security you and your colleagues are trying to implement can be rendered useless. Encourage your co-workers to treat their network passwords like credit card numbers or access codes for automated teller machines and to protect them with at least as much vigilance.

SECURING FILES AND PROGRAMMES

Users can also help protect against unauthorised access to network files and programmes. Keep master and boot copies of programmes on write-protected disks and, if possible, use passwords to protect your work group's network or application software. When copies of important files are stored on easily removable media such as floppy disks or tape cartridges, restrict access to these media by using locks and keys, sign-in and sign-out lists, supervisor monitoringor other measures. These practices reduce the possibility of accidental or malicious erasure or modification of important files.

Files must also be protected while they are in use on a network. Users must strive always to open and close files according to the procedures required by their network and application software. Otherwise, network file directories can become incorrect or corrupted, and larger problems can result. Most network software offers some protection against these problems, but good user habits are the best safeguards.

Some network programmes require the insertion of key disks into workstation floppy drives to qualify legitimate users for access to programmes and files. Where these disks are in use, they must be protected and not widely distributed or duplicated. The use of third-party programmes that eliminate the need for key disks must also be weighed against the increased security risk that these disks can represent.

Networks must also be protected from unauthorised programmes, such as game programmes or other personal software. Unauthorised programmescan contaminate your network with annoying or highly destructive software viruses.

You and your colleagues should avoid bringing unauthorised software into contact with your network. Whether a harmless game or your own copy of a programme your work group uses, any software not supplied through your network's usual channels should be viewed as a potential source of harm to your network.

LEVELS OF SECURITY

There is no such thing as 100% security. With enough skill and enough time to complete the job, a perpetrator can defeat any security measure.

Of the two security elements of skill and time, the most dependable protection is time. If you can make certain that a break-in will be a time-consuming project for a thief, you have gone a long way in protecting your data. Therefore, all serious security systems are layered with not one but several security measures (see Figure 12.3). For a local area network the following strategies should be considered:

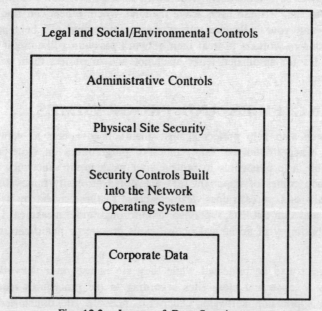

Fig. 12.3 : Layers of Data Security

1.   Physical security

2.   Access Control

3.   Personal identification

4.   Encryption

5.   The diskless PC

6.   Protection against cable radiation

7.   Call-back security

1. PHYSICAL SECURITY

Data security can take many forms. The simplest is physical security, which may be a lock on the computer or a guard at the door. With physical security, a would-be thief must attack and defeat your security measures before becoming a threat to the data.

Locks can set up barriers from the back door to the office door to the computer itself. Key locks are now provided for IBM PC/ATs and compatibles. The lock interrupts the power to the display and keyboard, while still allowing the terminal to remain on-line. Turning the key powers up the user interfaces; the key cannot be removed while the system is on. This kind of physical security is available for personal computers.

An alarm system works in partnership with your physical security measures. Locking devices are designed to increase the time needed for penetration. Alarms put an effective limit on the amount of time available. Professional criminals do not run when they hear an alarm or when they think they have tripped a silent alarm. Most know precisely how much time they have before the police arrive. If they cannot get through the security system's physical barriers in the time available, then the criminals will abandon the effort.

2. ACCESS CONTROLS

The purpose of access controls is to ensure that only authorised users have access to the system and its individual resources and that access to and modification of particular portions of data is limited to authorised individuals and programmes.

Figure 12.4 depicts, generically, the measures taken to control access in a data processing system. They fall into two categories: first those associated with the user or group of users and, second, those associated with the data. In what follows, we elaborate on these concepts and extend them to the local networking environment.

The control of access by user is referred to as authentication. A quite common example of this on a time-sharing system is the user log-on, which requires both a user ID and a password. The system will only allow a user to logon if that user's ID is known to the system and if the user knows the password associated by the system with that ID. This ID/password system is a notoriously unreliable method of access control. Users can forget their passwords, and accidentally or intentionally reveal their password. Also, the ID/password file is subject to penetration attempts.

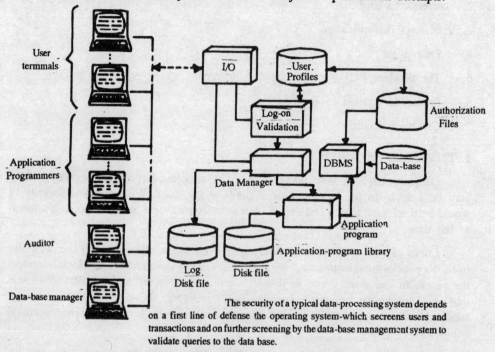

The security of a typical data-processing system depends on a first line of defense the operating system-which secreens users and transactions and on further screening by the data-base management system to validate queries to the data base.

Fig. 12.4 : Data Processing System Security

No cost-effective method of overcoming this problem exists. Exotic techniques such as voiceprints, fingerprints and hand geometry analysis may be foolproof but are at present prohibitively expensive. Simple measures that can be taken now are to change passwords frequently and to maintain tight multiple measures of security over the ID/password directory. One additional measure that is cost effective is to associate ID's with terminals rather than users and hard wire the code into the terminal. This changes an administrative/software security problem into a physical security problem. However, if it is desirable to allow one-to-many and/or many-to-one relationships between users and terminals, this technique is ineffective.

The problem of authentication is compounded over a multiaccess medium LAN. The log-on dialogue must take place over the communication medium and eavesdropping is a potential threat. One approach to protection would be to certify that each NIU can capture only data addressed to it. This is no easy task. Another approach is to encrypt the ID/password data. User and user group authentication can be either centralised or distributed. In a centralised approach the network provides a log-on service. Distributed authentication treats the network as a transparent communication link, and the usual log-on procedure is carried out by the destination host. Of course, the security concerns for multiaccess media must still be addressed.

In fact, in many local networks, two levels of authentication will probably be used. Individual hosts may be provided with a log-on facility to protect host-specific resources and applications. In addition, the network as a whole may have protection to restrict network access to authorised users. This two-level facility is desirable currentlyfor the common case, in which the local network connects disparate hosts and simply provides a convenient means of terminal-host access. Future integrated networks (in the OSI sense) may require only a network-level scheme.

Following successful authentication, the user has been granted access to one or a set of hosts and/or processes. This is generally not sufficient for a system that includes sensitive data in its data base. Through the authentication procedure, a user can be identified together with a profile that specifies permissible operations and file accesses. The operating system can enforce rules based on the user profile. The database management system, however, must control access to specific portions of records. For example, it may be permissible for anyone in administration to obtain a list of company personnel, but only selected individuals may have access to salary information. The issue is more than just one of level of detail. Whereas the operating system may grant a user permission to access a file or use an application, following which there are no further security checks, the database management system must take a decision on each individual access attempt. That decision will depend not only on the user's identity but also on the specific parts of the record being accessed, and even on the information already divulged to the user.

A general model of access control as exercised by a data base management system is that of an access matrix (see Table 12.2). One axis of the table consists of identified subjects that may attempt data access. Typically, this list will consist of individual users or user groups, although access could be controlled for terminals, hosts or processes instead of or in addition to users. The other axis lists the objects that may be accessed. At the greatest level of detail, objects may be individual data fields. More aggregate groupings, such as records, record types, or even the entire data base may also be objects in the matrix indicates the access rights of that subject for that object.

TABLE 12.2 : Data Base Access Matrix

In practice, an access matrix is usually sparse, and is implemented by decomposition in one of two ways. The matrix may be decomposed by columns, yielding access control lists. Thus for each object, an access control list lists users and their permitted access opportunities. Decomposition by rows yields capability tickets. A capability ticket specifies authorised objects and operations for a user. Each user has a number of tickets and may be authorised to loan or give them to others. Because tickets may be dispersed around the system, they present a greater security management problem than access control lists.

Network considerations for access control parallel those for authentication. Encryption may be needed to provide secure communications on a LAN. Typically, access control is decentralised, that is, controlled by host-based data management systems. However, if a network data base server exists on a LAN, access control becomes a network service.

3. PERSONAL IDENTIFICATION

A local area network presents some additional security problems because of its dispersed nature and because many people have access to the network. Remote access through modems and telephone lines is used widely on LANs, which makes dispersion essentially infinite. Dispersion thwarts one of the best types of personal-identification security systems.

On most networks the first line of security is personal identification. You physically recognise people who are authorised to be in your office, sitting at a PC. With remote access this kind of identification is impossible. Companies must rely on passwords and classified access schemes to protect their data.

Several techniques can be used to restrict access to authorised users. All these techniques are based on some kind of identification: personal, such as ID badge; key word such as a log-in name and password; or key number.

Badges and personal recognition may not be successful in large companies where everyone is not personally known. In a company with many employees, a counterfeit badge may, in fact, be all that is necessary to penetrate a security system based widely on identification.

PASSWORDS

Password security adds no cost to the network and is potentially a useful security measure. After logging onto the network, the user must type a password. Theoretically, if users must give a password, unauthorised access is prevented. But often the password system is misused and ineffective.

Passwords usually are chosen because they are easily remembered. This, however, also makes them easily guessed. Common assignments include first name for log-in name and last name or title for password. The value of passwords is further diluted when employees give their passwords to others in the organisation. A password often is given out because another employee needs to read a particular file or to perform some task for an absent employee.

Password protection can be improved through both systematised procedures and more sophisticated operating system password utilities. Passwords should be assigned by a network manager, not by the individual. This assignment method reduces the likelihood that someone will identify the password in half a dozen guesses. Many network operating systems have a password utility that allows authorised users to change their own passwords. Such a utility should be deleted from all users' directories and given only to the network supervisor.

Over time, passwords will become generally known, particularly within a small office or department. This decaying security can be stopped by periodically issuing new passwords, say, on a monthly basis. One additional advantage of changing passwords regularly is that employees will take more seriously both the password system and the subject of security.

SECURITY IN LOG-IN

The network operating system should be designed to thwart attempts to break into the system. For one thing, the password should not be "echoed" back to the screen when the user types it in during log-in. The number of times that a password can be attempted should be limited to no more than three tries. After that, the log-in name should be invalidated temporarily, and the network supervisor notified of a failed log-in. An audit trail can also be provided to record the number of password attempts from a given user or station. The presence of the audit trail utility that monitors the password system is a deterrent in itself, especially to malicious or casual vandals.

A sophisticated thief, however, can collect log-in routines and passwords as they are entered often simply by tapping into the network. The network operating system can be enhanced to make this activity more difficult for the thief. Passwords can be encrypted at the workstation and decrypted at the central processor so that the data on the cable is unusable through a tap.

As part of security planning and implementation, an independent analyst should evaluate the security measures, even to the extent of attempting to steal or corrupt a prearranged target file.

4. ENCRYPTION

Earlier, we referred to one of the major security risks on LANs, which uses a multiaccess medium - the risk of eavesdropping. Eavesdropping can be accomplished by programming the NIU to accept packets other than those addressed to it or by physically tapping into the medium. One countermeasure that, properly used, is very effective is to encrypt the data in each packet (i.e. send the data in code).

Encryption is the process of changing intelligible data into unintelligible data; decryption reverses the process. For most local area networks, data encryption is used only when the security threat is substantial.

Ensuring that data is secure in a network environment is more difficult than ensuring the security of physical documents. Typically, data in a network is held in a common storage facility, and anyone authorised to use the central storage has the potential to access classified files. The best solution to this potential problem is to store the data in an encrypted form. Then, any unauthorised person accessing the file would not be able to read its contents.

Encryption techniques cover a broad range, from simple encryption that guards against accidental disclosure to sophisticated methods which protect against all but the highly trained criminal with an in-depth knowledge of cryptanalysis and considerable deciphering equipment.

Most encryption schemes are based on mathematical operations that are "computationally infeasible". That is, they are based on prime numbers which are so large that even the computational power of a mainframe computer cannot break the code within a practical time period.

Two primary types of encryption exist: link and end-to-end. Link encryption used to make data unreadable while it is on a point-to-point link, such as between two PCs. Link encryption prevents the casual reading of data.

End-to-end encryption protects data anywhere on the system. This type of encryption corresponds to Layer 4 (the Transport Layer) in the OSI Model. Because Layer 4 is end-to-end, encryption here can provide protection to any number of communication links or intermediate networks.

ENCRYPTION KEYS

Encryption key systems are commonly found on dial-up networks but are also available on LANs. A key is essentially a formula for coding and decoding a message. Keys are carefully distributed to authorised users. In fact, the security of the distribution channel for keys often establishes the security level of a system.

Such a system of secret keys is very difficult and expensive to maintain, especially as the number of participants increases. To overcome these disadvantages, a new key called a "public key" was devised. Public keys may be published openly, and they permit virtually any individual to use a personal public key to code a message and send it to another person. To decode the message, however, the receiver must use a secret key. A secret key consists of two prime numbers that are not published.

One other application of public keys is to authenticate messages. You can use your secret key to encrypt a message and send it to a second person. That person will take your public key and use it to decode the message. If your public key decode an encoded message, presumably sent by you, then proof has been provided that you did indeed send the message. In other words, the public key is an electronic signature.

All keys are factorable and, therefore, limited in their level of security. Over the last few years, a debate has been going on about how complex a key should be. Generally, any encryption system provides file privacy against casual perusal. But encryption systems can go far beyond providing file privacy. The Data Encryption Standard (DES) is an encryption system designed by IBM and adopted by the National

Bureau of Standards in 1977. Using an encryption system that conforms to the DES standard generally is considered sufficient protection against unauthorised access. That is, most criminals and vandals would not be able to break into a communication system and steal or alter data which has been encrypted according to the DES standard. With the largest and fastest computers available today, however, DES encryption schemes probably are breakable.

A number of schemes for encryption have been proposed. In this section, we describe two techniques that are good candidates for local network use.

A. CONVENTIONAL ENCRYPTION

Figure 12.5a illustrates the conventional encryption process. The original intelligible message, referred to as plaintext, is converted into apparently random nonsense, referred to as ciphertext. The encryption process consists of an algorithm and a key. The key is a relatively short bit string that controls the algorithm. The algorithm will produce a different output depending on the specific key being used at the time. Changing the key radically changes the output of the algorithm.

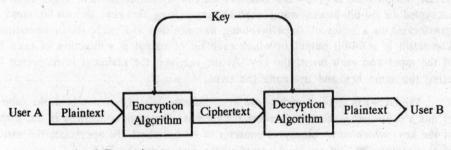

(a) Conventional Encryption

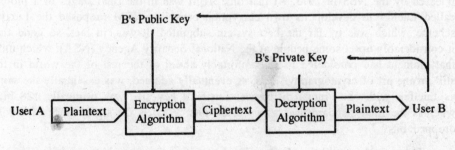

(b) Public-Key Encryption

Fig. 12.5 : Encryption

Once the ciphertext is produced, it is transmitted. Upon reception, the ciphertext can be transformed back to the original plaintext by using a decryption algorithm and the same key that was used for encryption.

The security of conventional encryption depends on several factors. First, the encryption algorithm must be powerful enough to make itimpractical to decrypt a message on the basis of the ciphertext alone. Beyond that, the security of conventional encryption depends on the secrecy of the key, not the secrecy of the algorithm. That is, it is assumed that it is impractical to decrypt a message on the basis of the ciphertext plus knowledge of the encryption/decryption algorithm. In other words, we do not need to keep the algorithm secret; we only need to keep the key secret.

This feature of conventional encryption is what makes it feasible for widespread use. The fact that the algorithm need not be kept secret means that manufacturers can, and have, developed low-cost chip implementations of data encryption algorithm. These chips are widely available and incorporated into a number of products. With the use of conventional encryption, the principal security problem is maintaining the secrecy of the key. This issue is addressed here.

THE DATA ENCRYPTION STANDARD

The most widely used encryption scheme is based on the data encryption standard (DES), adopted in 1977 by the National Bureau of Standards. For DES, data are encrypted in 64-bit blocks using a 56-bit key. Using the key, the 64-bit input is transformed in a series of steps involving transposition and exclusive-or operations. The result is a 64-bit output in which each bit of output is a function of each bit of the input and each bit of the key. At the receiver, the plaintext is recovered by using the same key and reversing the steps.

The DES has enjoyed widespread use. Unfortunately, it has also been the subject of much controversy as to how secure the DES is. The main concern is in the length of the key, which some observers consider to be too short. To appreciate the nature of the controversy, let us quickly review the history of the DES.

The DES is the result of a request for proposals for a national cipher standard released by the NBS in 1973. At that time, IBM was in the final stages of a project called Lucifer to develop its own encryption capability. IBM proposed the Lucifer scheme, which was by far the best system submitted. It was, in fact, so good that it considerably upset some people at the National Security Agency (NSA), which until that moment had considered itself comfortably ahead of the rest of the world in the still arcane art of cryptography. DES, as eventually adopted, was essentially the same as Lucifer, with one crucial difference: Lucifer's key size was originally 128 bits, whereas the final standard uses a key of 56 bits. What is the significance of the 72 dropped bits?

There are basically two ways to break a cipher. One way is to exploit properties of whatever mathematical functions form the basis of the encryption algorithm to make a "cryptoanalytic" attack on it. It is generally assumed that DES is immune to such attacks, although the role of NSA in shaping the final DES stantlard leaves lingering doubts. The other way is a brute force attack in which you try all possible keys in an "exhaustive search". That is, you attempt to decrypt ciphertext with every possible 56-bit key until something intelligible pops out. With only 56 bits in the DES key, there are 2x56 different keys - a number that is uncomfortably small, and becoming smaller as computers get faster.

Whatever the merits of the case, DES has flourished in recent years and is widely used, especially in financial applications. Except in areas of extreme sensit:vity, the use of DES in commercial applications should not be a cause for concern by the responsible managers.

COMMERCIAL COMMUNICATIONS SECURITY ENDORSEMENT PROGRAMME

Although DES still has a reasonably useful life ahead of it, it is likely that non-government organisations will begin to look for replacements for what is seen as an increasingly vulnerable algorithm. The most likely replacement is a family of algorithms developed under the NSA commercial COMSEC (communications security) Endorsement Program (CCEP). CCEP is a joint NSA-industry effort to produce a new generation of encryption devices that are more secure than DES, that are low-cost, and that are capable of operating at high data rates. Features of the new CCEP algorithms:

1. The CCEP algorithms are developed by NSA and are classified. Thus the algorithms themselves remain secret and are subject to change from time to time.

2. Industry participants will produce chip implementation of the algorithms, but the NSA maintains control over the design, fabrication and dissemination of chips.

Two types of algorithms come under the CCEP heading. Type I algorithms are designed to protect classified government information. Equipment using Type I CCEP will be available only to government agencies and their designated contractors. Type II algorithms are designed to protect sensitive but unclassified information. Type II gear is intended to replace DES gear. Unlike the Type I modules, which will handle classified information, the Type II equipment is controlled only to the point of sale. Presumably, after a Type II module is built into a computer or communication device and sold by a vendor, the customer can do with it as he or she pleases - short of exporting it overseas.

Although the purpose of developing the Type II equipment, as with the Type I equipment, was to provide a means of protecting government information, the Type II modules are available for use in non-government, private sector applications. As this equipment becomes more widely available, it is likely to become more widely used, at the expense of DES.

KEY DISTRIBUTION

For conventional encryption to work, the two parties to an exchange must have the same key, and that key must be protected from access by others. Furthermore, frequent key changes are usually desirable to limit the amount of data compromised if an attacker learns the key. Therefore, the strength of any cryptographic system rests with the key distribution technique, a term that refers to the means of delivering a key to two parties that wish to exchange data, without allowing others to see the key. Key distribution can be achieved in a number of ways. For two parties A and B:

1. A key could be selected by A and physically delivered to B.

2. A third party could select the key and physically deliver it to A and B.

3. If A and B have previously and recently used a key, one party could transmit the new key to the other, encrypted using the old key.

4. If A and B each have an encrypted connection to a third party C, C could deliver a key on the encrypted links to A and B.

Options 1 and 2 call for manual delivery of a key, which is awkward. In a distributed system, any given host or terminal may need to engage in exchanges with many other hosts and terminals over time. Thus, each device needs a number of keys, supplied dynamically. The difficulty with Option 3 is that if an attacker ever succeeds in gaining access to one key, then all subsequent keys are revealed.

Option 4 is the most attractive and could be handled from a host facility or network control centre. Figure 12.6 illustrates a possible implementation. For this scheme, two kinds of keys are identified.

-   **Session Key:** When two end-systems (hosts, terminals, etc) wish to communicate, they establish a logical connection (e.g. LLC connection or transport connection). For the duration of that logical connection, all user data are encrypted with a one-time session key. At the conclusion of the session or connection, the session key is destroyed.

-   **Permanent Key:** A permanent key is one used between entities for the purpose of distributing session keys.

The configuration consists of the following elements:

-   **Access control centre:** The access control centre determines which systems are allowed to communicate with each other.

-   **Key distribution centre:** When permission is granted by the access control centre for two systems to establish a connection, the key distribution centre provides a one-time session key for that connection.

-   **Network interface unit:** The NIU performs end-to-end encryption and obtains session keys on behalf of its host or terminal.

The steps involved in establishing a connection are shown in Figure 12.6. When one host wishes to set up a connection to another host, it transmits a connection-request packet (1). The NIU saves that packet and applies to the access control centre for permission to establish the connection (2). The communication between the NIU and the access control centre is encrypted using a permanent key shared only by the access control centre and the NIU. The access control centrehas one such unique key for each NIU and for the key distribution centre. If the access control centre approves

he connection request, it sends a message to the key distribution centre, asking for
session key to be generated (3). The key distribution centre generates the session
ey and delivers it to the two appropriate NIUs, using a unique permanent key for
ach NIU (4). The requesting NIU can now release the connection request packet,
nd a connection is set up between the two end systems (5). All user data exchanged
etween the two end systems are encrypted by their respective NIUs using the one-
ime session key.

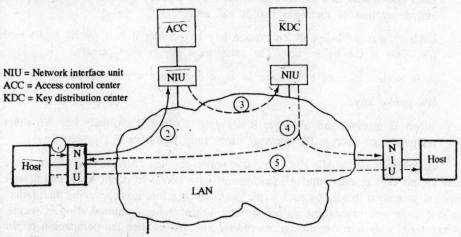

NIU = Network interface unit
ACC = Access control center
KDC = Key distribution center

1.   Host sends packet requesting connection.
2.   NIU buffers packet, asks ACC for session key.
3.   ACC approves request, commands KDC.
4.   KDC distributes session key to both NIUs.
5.   Buffered packet transmitted.

Figure 12.6. Key Distribution Across a LAN

Several variations on this scheme are possible. The functions of access control
d key distribution could be combined into a single-system. The separation makes
e two functions clear and may provide a slightly enhanced level of security. If we
sh to let any two devices communicate at will, then the access control function
not needed at all. When two devices wish to establish a connection, one of them
plies to the key distribution centre for a session key.

The automated key distribution approach provides the flexibility and dynamic
aracteristics needed to allow a number of terminal users to access a number of hosts
d for the hosts to exchange data with each other. A number of LAN vendors offer
me version of the scheme shown in Figure 12.6. It is a powerful and reasonably
xpensive means of enhancing network security.

. PUBLIC KEY ENCRYPTION

As we have seen, one of the major difficulties with conventional encryption
emes is the need to distribute the keys in a secure manner. A clever way around
s requirement is an encryption scheme that, surprisingly, does not require key
tribution. This scheme, known as public-key encryption and first proposed in 1976,
illustrated in Figure 12.5b.

For conventional encryption schemes, the keys used for encryption and decryption are the same. This is not a necessary condition. Instead, it is possible to develop an algorithm that uses one key for encryption and a companion but different key for decryption. Furthermore, it is possible to develop algorithms such that knowledge of the encryption algorithm plus the encryption key is not sufficient to determine the decryption key. Thus the following technique will work.

1. Each end-system in a network generates a pair of keys to be used for encryption and decryption of messages that it will receive.

2. Each system publishes its encryption key by placing it in a public register or file. This is the public key. The companion key is kept private.

3. If A wishes to send a message to B, it encrypts the message using

    B's public key.

4. When B receives the message, it decrypts it using B's private key No other recipient can decrypt the message since only B knows B's private key.

As you can see, public-key encryption solves the key distribution problem, since there are no keys to distribute! All participants have access to public keys, and private keys are generated locally by each participant and therefore need never be distributed. As long as a system controls its private key, its incoming communication is secure. At any time, a system can change its private key and publish the companion public key to replace its old public key.

A further refinement is needed. Since anyone can transmit a message to A using A's public key, a means is needed to prevent impostors. To develop this scheme, you need to know that public key encryption algorithms are such that the two keys can be used in either order. That is, one can encrypt with the public key and decrypt with the matching private key, or encrypt with the private key and decrypt with the matching public key. Now consider the following scenario: B prepares a message and encrypts it with its own private key, and then encrypts the result with A's public key. On the other end, A first uses its private key and then uses B's public key in a double decryption. Since the message was encrypted with B's private key, it could only come from B. Since it was also encrypted with A's public key, it can only be read by A. With this technique, any two stations can at any time set up a secure connection without a prior secret distribution of keys.

A main disadvantage of public-key encryption compared to conventional encryption is that algorithm for the former are much more complex. Thus, for comparable size and cost of hardware, the public-key scheme will provide much lower throughput. One possible application of public-key encryption is to use it for the permanent key portion of Figure 12.6, with conventional keys used for sessions keys. Since there are few control messages relative to the amount of user data traffic, the reduced throughput should not be a handicap.

Table 12.3 summarises some of the important aspects of conventional and public-key encryption.

TABLE 12.3 : Conventional and Public-Key Encryption

Conventional Encryption	Public-key Encryption
Needed to Work :	**Needed to Work :**
1. The same algorithm with the same key can be used for encryption and decryption.	1. One algorithm is used for encryption and decryption with a pair of keys, one for encryption andone for description
2. The sender and receiver must share the algorithm and the key.	2. The sender and receiver must each have one of the matched pair of keys.
Needed for Security :	**Needed for Security :**
1. The key must be kept secret	1. One of the two keyss must be kept secret.
2. It must be impossible or at least imparactical to decipher a message if no other information is available.	2. It must be impossible or at least impractical to decipher a message if no other information is available.
3. Knowledge of the algorithm plus samples of ciphertext must be insufficient to determine the key	3. Knowledge of the algorithm plus of the keys plus samples of ciphertext must be insufficient to determine the key.

ON-LINE CODERS

The easiest measure to take for LAN security is to attach an encryption device at either end of a communicationlink. Several companies make such devices and will modify them for specific applications. After the devices are installed, the system is fully transparent to the user. With each person using an encryption box, the message sent between parties will be encrypted while it is on the line.

Another way to set up a system is to place an encryption box between each PC and the network. Then all the data that goes out on the network and all data stored on the hard disk will be encrypted. Ideally, the device can be modified and tuned to provide the speed and security needed. If necessary, a public key system can also be built in.

To show how such a security system might work, let us suppose that we have three groups on a network: administration (admin), accounting and sales. All the data on the network can be encrypted. The administrator can read everything, but accounting and sales can read only their respective files. Each user encrypts the data on an optional basis. With each transmission the encryption device will ask the user whether to transmit in the clear or with encryption. The administrator's device will also ask of the administrator, "Which key do you want: admin, accounting or sales?

5. THE DISKLESS PC

The power of the PC itself is a potential security threat that should be considered. One of the advantages that the personal computer has over dumb terminals is its local storage capability. Information can be locally manipulated and stored on a PC's floppy diskettes, then transferred to the central storage. From central storage the information can be made available to other users and maintained and backed up properly.

With local storage devices, users can maintain their own back-up system, independent of the central system. The degree of autonomy associated with a personal set of data diskettes is appealing to many users. At the same time, such autonomy creates two threats to data security.

One threat is unintentional. Because two copies of data exist, one on the central disk and one locally, the copies may be updated independently. Eventually, unique data on one version may be lost when the two "copies" are merged.

The other threat is that a local disk drive permits data theft. A person with access to the network and with a local disk drive can copy large amounts of data onto floppy disks in just minutes. The data, then, can be easily hidden and removed from even reasonably secure buildings.

Most network vendors now provide the capability of booting a local PC workstation from a central server so that diskless PCs can be used on the network. Such machines require full-time networking and permit no local storage. A common reason for using diskless PCs is cost. Because diskless PCs require no local floppy controller or disk drive, the cost of a workstation is reduced. But equally important is the increased security offered by a diskless PC.

Take away the disk drive and you take away the means for stealing the 'data. But you also reduce the power of the PC. In many instances local storage is desirable so that the PC can be used as a stand-alone workstation in the event of a network failure. One answer is to exchange a local floppy for a local hard disk. Then not only would the user have all the benefits of local storage, but local speed and efficiency would improve also. No ready way, however, would be available to copy or remove data.

Diskless PCs have been hampered by software problems. Many applicationprogrammes are designed to run only from a local floppy disk drive. Diagnostics and the operating system itself have usually required at least one local drive.

Increasingly, however, software vendors are providing some mechanism for their application packages to be stored on a hard disk and used in a multiuser environment. A company can then make its own decisions about how to configure PCs. Probably the answer will be a variety of configurations to fit particular circumstances.

6. PROTECTION AGAINST CABLE RADIATION

Any time information is transmitted, even through cable, that information can potentially be intercepted by unauthorised persons. The possibility also exists that a vandal can tamper with data or destroy data files.

Several methods may be used for protecting data while it is on the cable. The first thing to do is to put the cable out of sight. This step should be taken anyway, to prevent damage to the cable and to meet building codes. Security is a secondary benefit. Install cables in protective raceways in areas where penetration is less likely.

A radio signal that is broadcast onto the air waves can easily be intercepted and the information stolen. Such emissions, however, are not limited to broadcasted radio signals. A data cable also radiates intelligible signals, just as a transmitting antenna does. Simple intercept equipment located near the cable can pick up and record these transmissions. More sophisticated devices can intercept the signals a considerable distance from the cable.

The likelihood of signal interception can be eliminated by using a shielded cable, which is a cylinder of braided copper wire that encases the intelligence-carrying wires. If one shield does not reduce emissions to satisfactory levels, more shields can be added. Frequently, cable with the necessary electrical characteristics is available in only one version. If additional shielding is needed, special shielding conduit is available that meets security standards.

Another way to eliminate the cable radiation problem entirely is by using fibre-optic cable. Fibre optics technology uses a glass fibre to carry a beam of light. Information is passed when the light is modulated. With fibre optics no signal is emitted outside the cable; therefore, data cannot be intercepted. Because fibre-optic cable is also extremely difficult to tap into physically, it is ideal for security purposes.

7. CALL-BACK SECURITY

Remote access to networks is a significant threat to data security. Remote workstations are part of many LAN environments, enabling a user to access networks remotely, log into the network, and use the system as if the user were local. Securing this type of access requires special measures.

Call-back security and user management are part of dial-up systems and can be used with remote PC-to-network traffic (see Figure 12.7). With call-back security, when you want to access a computer, you can call into a different number instead of calling in directly. You indicate that you want to access the network, and the security device arranges for a call-back to your location. In other words, the system has embedded within battery-supported memory a complete listing for every allowed user. Included in this file is a ID number that you must punch in when you want to access the file, a telephone number at which you can be reached, and the host systems to which you are allowed access.

This security device also keeps track of user priorities. If all available lines are busy, the device sets up a queue based on the priority of the user. The device will inform the caller regarding queue position. When a line becomes available, the device contacts the user. Therefore, the user never has to get busy signals. The device also keeps accounting information for traffic statistics and call-backs.

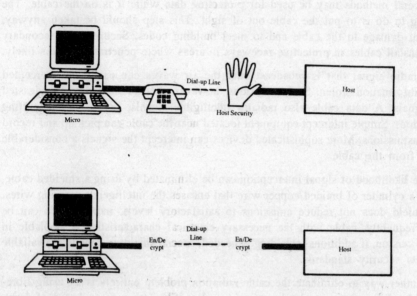

Fig. 12.7 : When a computer system can be accessed through telephone lines, security measures must be taken to protect against unauthorized access. Two ways to protect the system are call-back mechanisms and data encryption.

MANAGEMENT-LEVEL CONCERNS

Managers have a sensitive role in network security (see Figure 12.8). They must help users implement and execute measures like those discussed here and integrate these into network-wide policies that are followed rigorously. These policies also must go beyond the measures that users can implement, but without interfering with users' work.

Managers of sensitive LANs need to address the possibility of their LANs being tapped like telephone lines. With relatively simple electrical devices and a little time, an interloper can tap a LAN cable with little or no immediate evidence. Some LANs can even be tapped from a distance, with devices that monitor the radio-frequency emissions that almost all LANs produce. LANs that permit dial-up connections are particularly susceptible to such taps. LANs based on fibre-optic cable are the most tap resistant.

Call-back modems are a security measure used by many managers of dial-up LAN connections. These modems and their software accept user's calls and then instruct users to enter identifying information and to hang up. The modem then checks the user's access information and calls the user back only after the information is verified. Users who enter information that the system cannot verify are refused network access.

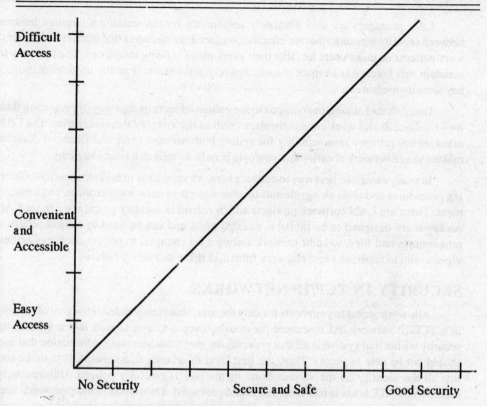

Fig. 12.8 : Good security usually reduces case of access to the computer.
Managers must weigh the trade offs between convenience and security
when implementing a specific system

Managers must also monitor connections between their LANs and other networks and computers. Managers must periodically audit access to and from network bridges, routers and other links, and they must regularly update the passwords and other security measures associated with these links. Managers may also have to help users implement more complex personal security measures as their LANs gain access to other networks and systems, and security risks increase.

Managers' must also implement measures that provide as much information as possible about network security and about attempted and successful breaches. Ideally, some combination of hardware, software, and physical procedures should be used to provide a near-constant audit of network access and use. This audit will not only help trace the paths of any breaches, but will aid in recovery from any problems these breaches may cause.

Software and procedures that increase accountability can be of great value to a LAN manager and to that manager's organisation. Sufficient information about accountability can limit the liability of an individual, a work group or an organisation, should an accidental or malicious breach of network security result in a loss of tangible assets or in a law-suit for some other reason.

LAN managers are also ultimately responsible for maintaining a constant balance between security measures that are effective, and security measures that interfere with users' work patterns or make users feel that their every move is being monitored. The best way to maintain this balance is to involve users actively and positively in the implementation of any security measures.

Users should also be encouraged to see enhanced security as a way of protecting their own livelihoods and work environments, as well as the assets of their enterprise. The LAN manager has primary responsibility for getting both network users and financial decision makers to see network security as a strategic benefit as well as a basic necessity.

In many cases, the best way to enhance network security is to include security-bolstering procedures and tools alongside aids to other aspects of network operations and management. There are LAN software products which enhances security gracefully. These LAN packages are designed to be invisible to LAN users and can be used to control access to programmes and files, to audit network software for changes, to protect networks against viruses, and to facilitate rapid recovery from disk drive and server failures.

SECURITY IN TCP/IP NETWORKS

Allowing access to your hosts for only the users that you intended is the goal of security in a TCP/IP network. As discussed previously, once a user is logged into a system, the security within that system is all that prevents the user from accessing information that user should not be able to access. Thus, the first level of security in a network is to make sure that all the security on the various hosts themselves is carefully policed. Unfortunately, security in UNIX hosts is based on userid and password. Thus, userids and passwords need to be very difficult to guess. The most effective method used to create a truly secure system is to have userids that are not personal names or initials but computer-generated in some reasonable random style and to have passwords that are likewise computer-generated. User will not like having userids and passwords that are not easy to remember. But, if someone trespassed into your system, that person will be able to work out userids if it appears that some form of a person's name is being used as a userid. If you find using computer-generated userids too difficult, you should at least force people to change their passwords regularly. Further, you should regularly use password scanning software to make sure people aren't using simple, easy-to-guess passwords like their name or car type.

A second level of security is to ensure that only users who you want are even accessing your network. If your network is completely disconnected from the outside world, you only need to concentrate on the security of your individual hosts. But if you are part of the Internet community and have linked up to the outside world, you need to consider measures to isolate your network from the rest of the Internet. One method is to place a "wall" between your network and the outside networks. This mechanism is often called a firewall because a "fire" in the outside network will not be allowed to enter your network. Routers can be programmed to analyze the network address of a user attempting to access your network and exclude those addresses that are allowed. Thus, routers can be used as firewalls to filter out the network addresses of users who you do not want to access your system.

Other issue is security: The **rlogin** command is sometimes used in place of the **telnet** command because system administrators can set up user validation so that no password is needed for a user to log in on another host. The **telnet** command always requires a password to be entered. Unfortunately, this approach while convenient for users, opens a security hole on the remote system when you use it. With access to the outside world via the Internet a reality for many networks, you should not have any passwordless userids. If you need to provide a *guest* password for a short period of time, you should create a special account for this purpose and then only assign a password when you want to provide access to that guest. By the way, userids on most UNIX systems can be set up not to allow login on that userid at all. These userids are normally present in the system for allowing ownership of system files.

Another issues of security involves permitting the use of anonymous file transfers. You can set up your system so that a file can be transferred between you system so that a file can be transferred between your system and another system without the user having a userid registered on your system. This is accomplished by setting up the FTP user with a special home directory for that user. Then a user can log in using the user anonymous and any password will be accepted for that user. Once logged in, the anonymous user will have access to those files that are in the home directory of the anonymous user. With careful attention to the permissions on other directories, only this one directory can be made available to outside users.

FIREWALL -FRIENDLY FTP

The FTP protocol uses a secondary TCP connection for actual transmission of files. By default, this connection is set up by an active open from the FTP server to the FTP client. However, this scheme does not work well with packet filter-based firewalls, which in general cannot permit incoming calls to random port numbers.

If, on the other hand, clients use the PASV command, the data channel will be an outgoing call through the **firewall**. Such calls are more easily handled, and present fewer problems.

An active open is done by the server, from its port 20 to the same port on the client machine as was used for the control connection. The client does a passive open.

For better or worse,, most current FTP clients do not behave that way. A new connection is used for each transfer; to avoid running afoul of TCP's TIMEWAIT state, the client picks a new port number each time and sends a PORT command announcing that to the server.

If a packet filter is used (as, for example, provided by most modern routers), the data channel requests appear as incoming calls to unknown ports. Most firewalls are constructed to allow incoming calls only to certain believed-to-be-safe ports, such as SMTP. The usual compromise is to block only the "server" area, i.e., port numbers below 1024. But that strategy is risky; dangerous services such as X Windows live at higher-numbered ports. Outgoing calls, on the other hand, present fewer problems, either for the firewall administrator or for the packet filter. Any TCP packet with the ACK bit set cannot be the packet used to initiate a TCP connection; filters can be configured to pass such packets in the outbound direction only. We thus want to change the behavior of FTP so that the data channel is implemented as a call from the client to the server.

Fortunately, the necessary mechanisms already exist in the protocol. If the client sends a PASV command, the server will do a passive TCP open on some random port, and inform the client of the port number. The client can then do an active open to establish the connection.

Recommendation

It is recommended that vendors convert their FTP client programs (including FTP proxy agents such as Gopher) to use PASV instead of PORT. There is no reason not to use it even for non-firewall transfers, and adopting it as standard behavior will make the client more useful in a firewall environment.

SECURITY CONSIDERATIONS

Few people feel that packet filters are dangerous, since they are very hard to configure properly. But they are quite popular. Another common complaint is that permitting arbitrary outgoing calls is dangerous, since it allows free export of sensitive data through a firewall. Some firewalls impose artificial bandwidth limits to discourage this. While a discussion of the merits of this approach is beyond the scope of this memo, we note that the sort of application-level gateway necessary to implement a bandwidth limiter could be implemented just as easily using PASV as with PORT.

Using PASV does enhances the security of gateway machines, since they no longer need to create ports that an outsider might connect to before the real FTP client. More importantly, the protocol between the client host and the firewall can be simplified, if there is no need to specify a "create" operation.

Concerns have been expressed that this use of PASV just trades one problem for another. With it, the FTP server must accept calls to random ports, which could pose an equal problem for its firewall, believe that this is not a serious issue, for several reasons.

First, there are many fewer FTP servers than there are clients. It is possible to secure a small number of special-purpose machines, such as gateways and organizational FTP servers. The firewall's filters can be configured to allow access to just these machines. Further precautions can be taken by modifying the FTP server so that it only uses very high-numbered ports for the data channel. It is comparatively easy to ensure that no dangerous services live in a given port range. Again, this is feasible because of the small number of servers.

CIRCUIT GATEWAYS

Just as the packet-filtering gateways operate at the network- layer level of a TCP/IP network, a circuit-gateway firewall operates at the transport-layer level--specifically for TCP connections. As discussed, packet-filtering gateways establish an electronic barrier that examines every network packet as the packet passes through the firewall. A circuit gateway, on the other hand, only creates an electronic barrier when two Internet hosts initially establish a TCP connection. When a client program tries to connect to a server on a host that a circuit gateway protects, the circuit-gateway firewall (rather than the server) actually accepts the connection using a special type of relay software. In other words, a circuit-gateway firewall sits as a barrier between both ends of a TCP connection; the gateway's relay software transfers data between the client and server programs on either side of the gateway. As you might suspect, only client programs that know how to talk to the circuit gateway can reach the server on the other side of the firewall. In other words, circuit-gateways require the use of special client programs.

Clients that want access to the server must negotiate a connection with the circuit-gateway relay that let the data transfer occur. The relay software intercepts connection requests that occur at all protocol ports the network security manager defines. After a client successfully negotiates a connection with the relay software, the circuit-gateway becomes essentially invisible. In other words, the circuit-gateway firewall establishes a security barrier only during connection negotiations. After the relay software validates the connection request, data transfer proceeds as though the relay software did not exist--the relay does not examine the content of the packets that pass through the firewall. After the security negotiations complete, the relay software acts much like a wire. In other words, the relay software becomes another part of the transmission medium. Remember, the relay software on the circuit gateway handles the security negotiations which initially occur and then essentially makes itself invisible. In other words, after the connection negotiations complete, the circuit gateway becomes invisible. Obviously, since its *your* circuit gateway, you will have the special client software necessary to negotiate the connection. The custom client software makes the security negotiations relatively transparent.

CONCLUSIONS

Every expert in home, automobile or business security is quick to point our that there is no lock that cannot be picked, given sufficient time and inclination. The incentive behind sophisticated locks, and policies that encourage and enforce their use, is therefore to make a given facility as difficult and daunting as possible to a potential thief.

Sound network security schemes must accomplish similar goals: They must deter potentially malicious users. In addition, they must encourage users to "lock" their LANs like they lock their cars and buildings. LAN security strategies must also protect networks from non-malicious accidental incursions, especially by those inexperienced with LANs.

Technology alone is inadequate to ensure security. True network security is a human issue, with responsibility divided between users and managers, just as network processing is increasingly divided between clients and servers. If viewed as a type of client-server risk management, security naturally becomes part of a larger network strategy to ensure total network reliability and to encourage users to participate actively in the protection of their vital network assets.

13

CLIENT/SERVER COMPUTING

INTRODUCTION

A server is a network device that provides services to intelligent client workstations, such as DOS- and OS/2-based PCs (personal computers). Macintoshes, and Unix-based technical workstations. In a client/server environment, some or all application processing is done on the client machine, while the servers provide access to network resources.

There are many types of servers and services, and they can provide controlled access to files (file service), access to network printers (print service), and access to electronic mail systems (mail service), to name a few. Computers on a network can be dedicated to providing one or more services, or services can be provided by computers that are also being used for application processing (someone's desktop personal computer, for example).

The heart of a server-oriented LAN system is the file server operating system, also called the LAN operating system or the network operating system. Examples of LAN operating systems include Novell's NetWare, Banyan's VINES. Microsoft's LAN Manager, Sitka's TOPS, and Artisoft's LANtastic. These operating systems include or make provision for other services, such as print service.

A LAN operating system can be a native operating system, interacting directly with the CPU (central processing unit) of the file server computer (Novell's NetWare, for example), or it can be a task or application running on top of a general purpose operating system such as MS-DOS (Microsoft's MS-Net, Artisoft's LANtastic, Webcorp's WEB), OS/2 (Microsoft's LAN Manager), or Unix (Banyan's VINES, Microsoft's LAN Manager, Novell's Portable NetWare). Generally, a native LAN operating system will provide a higher level of performance than a LAN OS operating as a sub-task of another host operating system.

FILE SERVERS

Computers that act as shared repositories for files are called file servers. File servers provide controlled access to files, and usually have some method of determining which users have access to which files and other system resources.

What makes a computer function as a file server is software. The particular machine that is used for a file server might be a standard PC or AT-type machine, a minicomputer, or a specialized proprietary computer designed specifically as a file server. In any case, it is the software running in that machine that defines it as a file server.

The primary purpose of file server software is to synchronize access to shared resources. This means the server software, in cooperation with applications programs, makes sure that users have simultaneous file access where appropriate, while preventing simultaneous access where it is inappropriate.

File servers can also provide various levels of security and access control, allowing a system manager to designate who has access to what resources. In this area there are vast differences in capabilities among various file server systems.

The efficiency and sophistication of a file server's data management and retrieval vary widely from one network operating system to another. High-speed disk access techniques, use of disk caching (keeping recently requested data blocks in server memory), and use of proprietary disk file structures are among the methods used to increase data retrieval speed.

File servers fall into several (sometimes overlapping) categories:

Proprietary Servers are machines designed specifically to be used as network servers for a particular vendor's LAN system. They often provide higher performance than generic servers because of features tailored to a server's needs. To their disadvantage, they usually operate only with a specific vendor's LAN hardware and operating system and are usually more expensive than their generic counterparts. Novell, Banyan, and 3Com have provided proprietary servers in the past, but have moved toward generic platforms.

Generic servers are usually industry standard mini- or microcomputers. For PC LANs, 80386- and 80486-based personal computers are commonly used as file servers. Generic servers often offer greater flexibility than proprietary servers.

Super Servers are computers designed specifically to be network servers, but which are not specific to one vendor's LAN operating system. Super servers usually provide certain enhancements, such as multiple processors, fault-tolerant or high-performance disk systems. Compaq, NetFrame, Dell, Tricord, and Everex, among others, all provide machines that fall into this category.

Dedicated Servers function strictly as servers, and are not available as user workstations. Dedicated servers generally provide better performance and system integrity than non-dedicated servers.

Non-Dedicated Servers function as user workstations as well as file servers. Although most manufacturers provide for non-dedicated servers, performance and system integrity issues can make this a risky approach. Users and applications can easily lock up a non-dedicated server. Non-dedicated servers can sometimes provide hardware cost savings, but these savings are often quickly offset by the increased time required to resolve problems. Non-dedicated servers almost always compromise system reliability.

File Service can be provided as a task running under another operating system. Microsoft takes this approach with LAN Manager, which runs as a task under OS/2, and Novell takes this approach with NetWare VMS for DEC VAXes and Portable NetWare for Unix computers. With this approach, performance is generally sacrificed to obtain the benefits of connectivity between dissimilar systems.

Central-file-server Systems

Most high-end LAN systems use a central file server approach. One or more computers on the LAN are specifically designated as file servers and generally run operating systems specially designed for file service tasks. Although hardware costs for central-server systems are usually higher than for peer-to-peer systems (described below), the added performance, security, system integrity, and ease of maintenance more than make up for the increased cost, especially in larger systems.

Peer-to-peer Lans

An alternative to the central server approach is the peer-to-peer approach. In a peer-to-peer LAN each user can offer his or her disks, printers, and other resources for use by others. This means that any workstation can become a server. Because a special server machine is not required, peer-to-peer LANs can be more cost-effective, but central-server LANs provide for easier manageability, easier backup, and greater security. In addition, peer-to-peer LANs usually rely on the workstation operating system to provide network services, and this usually means lower performance than central-server LANs.

PRINT-SERVERS

Print servers provide shared access to printers. Most LAN operating systems provide print service. Print service can run on a file server or on one or more separate print server machines. Non- file server print servers can be dedicated to the task of print service. or they can be non-dedicated workstations.

The disadvantages of using workstations as print servers are similar to the disadvantages of using file servers as workstations: The workstation may run a little slower when print services are being used, a user could shut down the server without warning, or an application could lock up the server. The consequences of a lock-up or shut-down on a print server, however, are usually less severe than the consequences of locking up a file server. The time involved in dealing with these problems, however, can be costly.

DATABASE SERVERS

Database management systems (DBMS) can be divided into three primary components: development tools, user interface, and database engine. The database engine does all the selecting, sorting, and updating. Currently, most DBMS combine the interface and engine on each user's computer. Database servers split these two functions, allowing the user interface software to run on each user's PC (the client), and running the database engine in a separate machine (the database server) shared by all users. This approach can increase database performance as well as overall LAN performance because only selected records are transmitted to the user's PC, not large blocks of files. However, because the database engine must handle multiple requests, the database server itself can become a bottleneck when a large number of requests are pending.

Database servers offer real potential for remote database access and distributed databases. Because the database server only returns selected database record(s) to the client machine (instead of large blocks of data), remote access over relatively slow telephone lines can provide acceptable performance. In addition, a client computer can make requests of multiple servers regardless of physical location.

FACSIMILE SERVERS

Facsimile (FAX) servers (or gateways) give multiple LAN workstations the ability to send and receive FAXes through a single network connection. The FAX server can be a workstation with an installed FAX board and special software or a specialized device designed for FAX service.

BATCH-PROCESSING SERVERS

Batch-processing servers allow time-consuming tasks, such as reports, to be off-loaded from a user's machine to an idle LAN workstation, allowing the user to continue working while the batch processor handles the off-loaded tasks. Third-party products, such as Campbell Software's Bobware Job Server, provide this capability.

COMMUNICATIONS SERVERS

Communications servers provide connections between client computers on a LAN and off-LAN services, or provide access to LAN resources from off-LAN systems. For example, communications servers can provide LAN users with terminal emulation and access to time- sharing computers, connections to remote systems, or dial-in access from remote PCs. Like file and print servers, communications servers can be dedicated or non-dedicated, depending on the particular communications server product. Communications service can also be a task running on a network file server (again, depending on the particular product).

Although communications services can be integrated into the file server operating system (Banyan VINES uses this approach), usually they are not. Communications servers include the following:

Host Gateways allow multiple LAN clients to access a time-sharing computer via a single connection to the LAN.

Asynchronous Communications Servers allow multiple LAN users to share a pool of dial-out modems or asynchronous connections to a host computer.

Remote Access Servers allow remote PCs or terminals to access LAN resources via dial-up phone lines or leased lines.

WHICH SERVICES GO WHERE?

You have a lot of flexibility in determining where server functions reside. File service, for example, can be handled by a dedicated machine, by a non-dedicated workstation, or be a task running under an operating system such as Unix or DEC's VMS. Print services, database services, and other services can all be handled in similar fashion.

How do you determine which service goes where? Here are some factors to consider:

CPU Load Factor and Resource Requirements. Consider the CPU usage, RAM (random access memory) requirements, etc. that services require. Putting multiple services on one machine may have adverse performance consequences. Also, even with single services, you must make sure that the server machine is adequate to the task. An old AT-286 might be fine as a print server, for example, but it will probably be inadequate as a mainframe gateway or a communications server.

Reliability. Consider the reliability of a service (and related hardware) if you are planning to add that service to an existing server. An unreliable service can cause another service to crash, or require the server to be shut down so a problem can be fixed. If a communications service needs to be shut down for resetting, for example, it would affect any other services running in the same machine. It is, at the very least, inconvenient to have to power down a file server that everyone relies on to reset a service used by a few.

Connectivity. Using a Unix-based computer or a DEC VAX as a NetWare file server is not going to provide the highest performance, but can provide PC users with easy, transparent access to minicomputer resources.

Cost. When making cost decisions consider the cost of lower performance, downtime, and troubleshooting should problems occur with multiple services that are installed on a single server.

14

LAN DATABASES

WHAT TO LOOK FOR IN A LAN DATABASE

Not too many years ago, the only Database Management Systems (DBMSs) that existed ran on large mainframe computers. In that environment, needs were usually thoroughly assessed before any software was purchased or code was written.

In today's PC environment, however, users often do the bulk of database design and programming themselves. This approach, while perhaps workable on a stand-alone PC, can be a problem in the LAN environment, where different levels of users may need access to the same data. LANs have extended the usefulness of database software by allowing a whole department or company to have access to the same data concurrently. However, a DBMS designed to be used by an occasional user for simple list management would probably be completely unusable for someone trying to create a complex inventory and invoicing application. Similarly, a DBMS optimized for free-form query of data stored in table form may not be the best program for some data entry and transaction processing systems.

Before deciding what database system will fit your needs, you need to examine what your needs really are and in what direction they are likely to go. You should realize that the system you design includes the computer system, but must be designed in the context of the larger system that constitutes the office. System design identifies the work that an office as a whole must accomplish, the people who will participate and what each will do, and the tools they will use and the precise steps to be taken by whom, when, where, and with what.

The system you design will change the work flow in your department or company, so the stakes can be high.

For example, you will be choosing the degree of centralization for your system. Some advantages of a more centralized system are that it can be easier for all users to access all data (the "big picture") and it can be easier for you to enforce data standards and security, and the hardware costs can be less.

On the other hand, a more distributed system encourages people to manage the information relevant to their jobs themselves. This helps avoid keeping information for its own sake. Distributed systems give remote users more immediate access to the computer as a dynamic tool of use to them in accomplishing work, rather than as a system for reporting work that is already done.

A system approach that fails miserably in one office might work perfectly well in another. Factors that influence the success of the approach include the fit of the software to the users' needs, the degree of training and support, and the fit between the company's management style and the system's style. For example, a system that enables salespeople in the field to use the computer for managing their contact schedules, writing orders, and communicating with customers directly will work well only if management supports that degree of independence. If communication with customers (mail contact, invoicing, and the like) is mainly conducted by the central office, the salesperson "ownership" and maintenance of customer names and addresses can impede customer communications. If sales are tightly controlled by the central company, this software system will frustrate salespeople and management alike, and will eventually go unused.

The system implementor rarely gets to start from scratch, nor design in a vacuum. Usually a system is being designed in reaction to the failures of the current set up. System designers often fail to take into account user attitudes shaped by previous systems, but the strength of strong negative assessments of certain programs or styles may preclude otherwise acceptable solutions.

The section, which follows, reviews the kinds of database software from which you can choose, and issues surrounding their implementation and use.

WHAT IS A DATABASE MANAGEMENT SYSTEM (DBMS)?

The label DBMS is applied to a wide range of software products, from simple filing systems to complete application development environments. A DBMS is basically composed of two parts:

A file management system

A user and/or programmer interface to the filing system, often including complete application development tools.

Both functions of the DBMS are important, and one or both may help determine the suitability of a DBMS for a particular situation or need.

WHAT ARE YOU USING THE DBMS FOR?

To help determine what DBMS is appropriate, you need to ask some questions:

1. Who is designing the database files and applications? If all or many users in an organization are creating databases and applications for their own use, you may want to place your emphasis on design tools that require little, if any programming. If a group of database programmers or developers are creating applications to be used by others for data entry and retrieval, flexibility and programmability may be primary concerns. Although many products claim to fill both needs, few, if any, really do.

2. Who is using the database? Are the users knowledgeable about PCs and software? Can they handle queries and ad hoc reports, or do they need well-defined, easy-to-use, pre- programmed applications? Generally the latter preprogrammed and easy-to-use systems are relatively inflexible. Can users live with a limited selection of preprogrammed reports? The more choices the user has, the more flexibility there is, but more choices make a system harder to use.

3. What is the orientation of the DBMS? Some DBMS systems are oriented towards the data structure, while others are oriented towards the user interface. For example, the table orientation of Borland's Paradox's data structure is very apparent to the user, while the data structure is transparent to a user of an application written in Data Access Corp.'s DataFlex. The table orientation of Paradox is usually better in situations where data will often be retrieved in an ad hoc, nonstructured way, while the screen orientation of DataFlex is often better for creating highly structured data entry and retrieval applications.

4. How is data retrieved? Sorting is fine for small files, but indexed retrieval and reporting is a must for efficient use of large databases. Although many database systems provide for indexing, they do not all do it the same way. Some, like DataFlex, DataEase International's DataEase, and Ashton-Tate's dBASE, allow virtually unlimited multifield indexes. Others, like Paradox, are more limited. The method of index updating can be important for performance as well. Some programs update indexes immediately on-line, which can slow performance but which makes fully updated data available to users sooner. Some programs allow batch keying and update, which is much faster for the data entry person, but which delays data availability for others. Batch data entry of some sort allows for off-site keying.

5. Can data be entered into multiple files (tables) through the same screen? While most sophisticated DBMS systems allow data to be entered into multiple files through the same screen, many require that each file have its own separate data window. This makes design more complex.

6. How much control does the applications designer have over the appearance of screen and output? Can the programmer completely control the screen design? Is this control available through the application's generation tools? Can the programmer design custom report formats?

7. Are users locked out of records in use by others, or is there some method to provide concurrent access? This is not important in all environments, but it can be critical in others.

8. Can reporting and updating be performed concurrently by different users? If the database has to be "locked" to run a report, valuable time may be lost.

9. What about access to and from other applications and files? Does the database have file import and export capabilities? Are there interfaces for programming languages?

10. Are applications and files easily transportable? Is it difficult to move a specific set of files and/or applications from one database to another?

11. What does it really cost? The cost per user on a LAN database varies greatly from product to product. Vendors have different pricing and licensing schemes. Some systems are priced by the user and some are priced by the file server. Within these schemes there are variations. With Revelation Technologies, Advanced Revelation, for example, you buy a single-user package at a retail of $950, then add users with "bump disks", which allow four additional users for a retail price of $495. With Microrim, Inc.'s R:BASE you have a three-user license initially ($725), then you may add six users at a time for $695 retail, or you can buy a single-server license (unlimited number of users) for $2,695.

Many DBMSs provide run-time systems that allow you to distribute applications at a nominal fee. Others allow you to distribute compiled code at little or no charge. The costs vary: The DataFlex multiuser run-time for DOS LANs retails at $300 per server, and provides the full DataFlex Query system. For a mere $9.95 you can buy a license to distribute an unlimited number of your Paradox applications. For $200 you can buy an Advanced Revelation run-time version for one user. Additional users are added using the Revelation bump disks at $495 for four users.

12. What about performance? Performance and response (data retrieval, saves/updates and reports) of LAN databases can vary from relatively fast (DataFlex) to relatively slow (Advanced Revelation). In general, several factors can affect performance of all DBMSs, including LAN speed, work-station processor type and speed, file server type and speed, etc. With some DBMSs, performance can be affected by available workstation RAM and/or the size of the database. DBMSs that use sort routines will generally slow down as the database gets larger, while DBMSs that use indexed retrieval will generally offer fairly flat performance regardless of the database size.

3. What about security? Depending on your particular LAN environment, a DBMS that has its own security system may be important, or the security may just be redundant and get in the way. With NetWare LANs, the latter is often true. If it is important, make sure that the implementation works in your own environment. Different vendors have different ideas of what security should be, and those ideas may not necessarily coincide with yours.

14.   What operating environments are supported? With the advent of OS/2 and the increasing interest in UNIX and XENIX, this question becomes more important. If you are planning to move to another operating environment, it would be nice to move your DBMS -- lock, stock and data file -- with you. If the vendor supports multiple environments, you might want to find out if the applications that you have written are transportable.

15.   Can applications interoperate over multiple operating systems? This is a question that would not have been asked a few years ago, but LANs are increasingly connecting systems that use different operating systems. For example, the same DataFlex files can be concurrently accessed by LAN users using MS-DOS, OS/2, UNIX, XENIX, AIX, and VAX VMS. In addition, they say applications written in DataFlex can be transported within the same processor family (8086, 286, 386, 486, and the VAX as one family; 68000-based systems as another) without recompiling. Fox Software's FOXBASE allows Macintosh users on NetWare to concurrently share database files transparently with PC users on the same network.

16.   What about support? Support plans vary as much as DBMSs do. Some examples: users of WordPerfect's DataPerfect receive unlimited installation and configuration assistance (no design, support, however) and a toll-free number to call; R-BASE users receive thirty days free support, then can buy a one-year contract that can cost $175 to $600 for a single user, depending on the products being supported; DataFlex users receive unlimited support on a toll line, a monthly newsletter, and monthly bulletins on known bugs, patches, and work-arounds. Many vendors offer different kinds of extended support programs for groups such as software developers, major accounts, etc.

DATABASE SERVICE AND SERVER-BASED APPLICATIONS

Software for DBMSs is undergoing rapid evolution in the industry. Database service and server-based applications are currently hot topics of discussion. Many writers and industry analysts assume that database service is inherently better and faster for shared database access than file service, and that file server-based servers are better than other approaches.

Currently, the standard approach to retrieving data from a networked database is file service. With file service, a database program running on a workstation PC requests blocks of files from the file server. With most database files, for example, only the file blocks that contain the requested data records and associated indexes, if any, are downloaded. In most cases that portion of the database is then locked to other users. The workstation PC can modify and/or update the specific locked records, then upload the file blocks containing them back to the server, at which time they will be unlocked to other users. With file service, database processing takes place at the workstation.

Database server systems split up the job of database processing: each user's workstation PC runs the "front end" or user interface software, while another machine on a network processes the database requests. This "back end" processor is called a database engine or database server. With this approach, only individual records are transmitted from the database server to a workstation. Because individual records are being sent to and from the workstation, traffic on the network may be lessened.

On the face of it, it sounds as if database service should be faster and more efficient for database processing than file service; yet this may not always be the case.

A database server can be implemented in several ways:

1.   It can be a separate, secondary process on a network file server

2.   It can be a Value-Added Process (VAP) on a file server, working as part of the LAN operating system

3.   It can employ a coprocessor in a LAN file server

4.   It can use a dedicated PC on the LAN

5.   It can be a separate background process on a designated LAN workstation

6.   It can employ a coprocessor in a LAN workstation.

All of these approaches can be considered server-based applications, and each has its own advantages and disadvantages. Remember, server-based does not necessarily mean file server-based, although that is still the current prevalent usage of the term.

1.   Database Service as a Second Task on a File Server

This is the approach that is currently receiving the most attention by the press. The CPU of the server divides its attention between its file server function and its database server function.

For example, Microsoft's network operating system LAN Manager runs the database service as a secondary, separate process on the network file server (that should be using the OS/2 PC operating system). The basic idea is that the file server machine is the "logical" place for database service to take place. What is not often considered sufficiently in this implementation is the degradation on overall performance that can result. With a slow network, a fast server, and little traffic, this approach may not worsen performance at all. But on a fast, busy network, sharing the server CPU between the file service and database service can create a performance bottleneck at the server, while workstation processors lie idle.

2.   Database Service as a Value-Added Server Process

A Value Added Process (VAP) is an extension to the file server software. A VAP performs tasks whose results are then integrated with the file server work. Although tighter integration of tasks could result in less overheads, this approach can have the same potential bottleneck performance problems described above when the database service is performed directly by the file server resources.

3. Application Coprocessor in the File Server

With this approach, a separate processor board is installed in the file server. Workstation database requests are routed to the coprocessor. This eases the load on the main processor while eliminating the LAN traffic that would ensue if database requests had to be sent across the cable to individual workstations for processing.

All other things being equal, using an application coprocessor in a file server probably provides the best performance of the database server designs available. It does not use file server CPU time for database processing, it does not add to traffic on the LAN cable, and it minimizes the time files or records are locked by workstation requests.

4. Dedicated Database Server

By using a dedicated database server (that is, a second PC separate from the file server and used only for database processing), you can reduce traffic on the LAN cable and free workstations from lengthy database processing.

You can store database files on the hard disk of the database server PC or on the file server. (For security and backup reasons, it can be desirable to store the files on the file server. In that case, the database server has to update the files on the file server, which increases LAN traffic that was supposed to be avoided).

5. Background Database Server on a Workstation

Under OS/2, you can use a workstation PC as a database server, where the server functions are performed as background tasks. This would have most of the attributes of a dedicated database server, but would provide lower performance due to the sharing of the workstation CPU, bus, and network interface.

6. Application Coprocessor in a Workstation

A coprocessor in a workstation PC would probably have about the same overall effect on performance as a separate database server. Because the expansion bus and network interface are being shared, performance of the host workstation could be affected in a heavy-traffic situation.

One additional performance factor to consider is the database server itself. Multiple requests and updates must be queued by the database server, while update processing with file service is provided by the workstation PC. With a busy system, the database server itself can become a bottleneck, while DBMSs that do not employ a database server distribute the workload to each user's workstation.

A serious potential problem with distributed database processing is that each of the workstations has the power to corrupt the entire database. With database service, since all database processing is being handled by a single dedicated CPU, there is less chance of file corruption.

System integrity is another factor to consider, especially with applications and/or coprocessors running in the file server. What if a server-based application "hangs up" the server? Applications have been known to hang single PCs, and they could also hang a file server running a server-based application.

One primary advantage of the database server approach is that a "client" workstation can access multiple database servers, so that physically separate databases can be treated by the user as one logical distributed database. A user can request data without necessarily knowing or caring where the data is physically located; the database software locates and delivers the requested data.

With this distributed database approach, available databases could include a PC database server on the local LAN, a mini- or mainframe computer on the local LAN or accessed through a gateway or bridge, or a remote database accessed through a remote gateway or bridge.

Because you are generally not moving vast amounts of data across a LAN when accessing a database server, low-speed remote LAN bridges (say, 19.2 Kb/sec. or lower) may become more viable. With database servers, you are only sending requests and retrieving records, not messaging large blocks of data at the client PC.

Distributed databases enable you to retain central control and empower remote users and offices.

While many database server systems have been announced, few are actually available for PC LANs, and very few benchmark tests have been published.

Most of the forthcoming database server systems are based on Structured Query Language (SQL). SQL is an ANSI standard for data retrieval based on IBM's design and specifications. Most announced SQL servers are based on the ANSI standard.

Even after the SQL database servers reach the market, it will take time to create or modify applications to make use of them.

In the long run, standardization on SQL servers will probably mean interchangeability of various vendor's DBMS front ends and applications generators with various database servers.

The big advantage of this approach is that users can get many different views of the same data, using familiar front-end DBMS interfaces, like Lotus 1-2-3, Paradox, DataFlex, DataEase, and dBASE.

Initially, however, DBMS vendors may have to choose sides, as each database engine developer attempts to lock front end developers into their "enhanced" standard SQL servers. This would in turn force users to choose the SQL server that runs their favourite interface, and that SQL server might not run other interfaces that they need. Eventually, however, front-end developers will provide their interfaces for all the SQL servers that survive the initial market struggle. They will have to in order to survive themselves.

Some DBMS vendors have already announced alliances with particular SQL database server vendors. For example, Borland's Paradox, Micro Database Systems' MDBS III, and Ashton-Tate's (taken over by Borland) dBASE IV will front-end the Ashton Tate/Sybase/ Microsoft SQL Server for LAN Manager. Paradox and WordTech's dBXL will work with Oracle's database server, while dBXL and Gupta Technology's SQL Windows and Oracle's front end will work with Novell's NetWare SQL.

On the downside, expect the first generation of SQL database servers to be slow performers. There will inevitably be problems to solve, incompatibilities and unexpected bottlenecks. As SQL database servers are optimized, performance will improve. Like the database machines used in mainframe and minicomputer environments, later generations of database servers may well use specialized operating software (and possibly even specialized hardware) optimized for database service.

As the technology matures, however, SQL (or whatever it may evolve into) and database servers will come into their own. Faster hardware, including machines optimized for database service, more sophisticated server software, and optimized applications, could all contribute to the process.

Much of the commentary about SQL database servers by the press and by vendors is speculative. It is too early to tell which products will prevail and what their practical shortcomings will be, since so few have actually been released.

SQL DBMS SERVERS

Novell NetWare SQL

Novell is offering NetWare SQL as their back-end database "engine" for NetWare 2.1 and above. NetWare SQL runs on a file server or NetWare External Bridge as a VAP. The workstation runs only the front-end application and the NetWare SQL Requestor, which takes the front-end application requests translates them into SQL requests, and transmits the SQL requests to the database server for processing. NetWare SQL relies on NetWare's System Fault Tolerance (SFT) for error recovery, but it continues transaction recovery and record locking within itself.

NetWare SQL uses the NetWare Btrieve record manager to access the database files. The NetWare Btrieve server program consists of two VAPs: BSERVER, which directly accesses database files on the server, and BROUTER, which routes requests to other servers. When there are multiple database servers on the network, BROUTER determines which server the data is on and routes the request there. BSERVER uses NetWare's Transaction Tracking System (TTS) to provide file roll-back and recovery.

NetWare XQL is Novell's application program interface to SQL. XQL provides access to the SQL database through ANSI-standard SQL statements and other lower-level function calls. Using XQL, a C, BASIC, Pascal, or COBOL application can pass requests to the NetWare SQL database.

Third-party front-end programs for NetWare SQL include WordTech's dBXL and Quicksilver, Gupta Technologies' SQL Windows, Revelation Technologies' Revelation, Borland's Paradox, and others. Novell itself provides a "blueprint" driver for Lotus 1-2-3 users.

Fox Software FoxServer

Fox Software, has a Microsoft company, provides a version of Novell's NetWare SQL called FoxServer. It incorporates dBASE language functions into NetWare SQL. This means that front-end applications can use SQL, XQL, Btrieve, and/or dBASE commands to directly access the database server.

Ashton-Tate/Microsoft SQL Server

Another example of SQL server software is Borland/Microsoft SQL Server, developed jointly by Microsoft, Borland and Sybase as their database engine for OS/2 servers. SQL server can run as a task in an OS/2-based file server, or on a separate machine running OS/2. Network operating systems supported by SQL Server include Novell NetWare, IBM LAN Server, and networks based on Microsoft LAN Manager. SQL Server is compatible with Sybase's minicomputer-based SQL server.

SQL Server provides on-line, write-ahead transaction logging. This means that transactions are written to a log file before the database is updated. In the event of a system failure, database changes can be recovered from the transaction log.

SQL Server incorporates a set of extensions (nearly all SQL databases have their own nonstandard extensions) called TRANSACT-SQL that can store commonly used group of commands at the database server and execute them with a procedure call. This means that a "client" workstation can send a single command to the server to execute complex transactions.

Among others, products that will "front-end" SQL Server include Borland's Paradox, Revelation Technologies' Revelation, Borland dBASE IV, and WordTech's dBXL and Quicksilver.

Gupta SQLBase

Gupta Technologies is a pioneer in SQL database servers. Gupta shipped the first SQL database server for PC LANs. Its SQL back-end engine offerings are SQLBase and SQLBase for OS/2, both of which work on any NetBIOS compatible LAN.

Gupta produces a powerful, event-oriented application program developer called SQLWindows. SQLWindows is a Microsoft Windows-based application generator that supports graphics, menus, dialogue boxes, and mice. Although SQLWindows only works with SQLBase now, Gupta plans to allow it to interface with other SQL DBMSs including ORACLE, Novell's NetWare SQL, Lotus's forthcoming DBMS product (based on Gupta's software), and Microsoft's SQL Server.

SQLWindows currently runs under DOS Windows and will eventually run under the OS/2 Presentation Manager. Since SQLWindows does not (yet) have a built-in report writer, Gupta has licensed SQR, a report writer produced by SQ Software originally intended to enhance the report writing capabilities of the ORACLE DBMS.

Gupta also supplies versions of WordTech's DBXL and Quicksilver dBASE-like products that will access the SQL-Base server.

SQLNetwork is a series of products that provides connectivity between Gupta's SQL products and IBM's mainframe-based DB2. SQL- Network uses IBM's Application Program-to-Program Communications (APPC) to provide this connectivity.

Oracle

Oracle Corporation, one of the largest independent vendors of DBMS software, currently provides a XENIX-based SQL database server for use with PC LANs. This means that PCs on NetWare LANs and others, must use network interface cards that support NetWare and the TCP/IP protocol concurrently, or a TCP/IP gateway to access the database server. Users on MS-Net and LAN Manager-based LANs and others must use similar methods.

A primary advantage of ORACLE is the fact that it currently runs in a wide range of operating environments on microcomputers, minicomputers and mainframes. Like Gupta Technologies, ORACLE supplies versions of WordTech's DBXL and Quicksilver dBASE-like products that will access its SQL database server.

15

AN OVERVIEW OF A NOVELL NETWORK

COMPONENTS

A Novell local area network (LAN) consists of a hardware and software combination which allows the sharing of information and resources. While the size, layout and application of the Novell LAN vary widely, the basic components are as follows:

- Software Selection
- Network Interface Cards
- One or more Fileservers
- One or more Workstations
- A Cabling System
- Application Software
- Peripheral Devices

Novell publishes several versions of NetWare. They differ in the maximum number of fileservers and users allowed, speed of data transmission, ability to prevent data loss or corruption, and of course, price. While it is possible to upgrade from one version to another, it is usually best to select one that will handle today's and tomorrow's requirements.

Each computer on the network (including fileservers) must contain a network interface card (NIC). This is the connection through which each computer shares information (via the cabling system) with the others. Novell markets NICs, but so do over a dozen other companies.

The fileservers and workstations can be any of a variety of IBM or compatible personal computers, or computers designed especially for the purpose of being network components. In some Novell configurations, the fileserver doubles as a workstation. The fileserver contains one or more fixed drives; workstations do not require fixed drives, and in some cases even floppy drives are optional.

Most DOS application software will run on a Novell network, but may not take full advantage of the network features. An application designed for network use will usually allow several users to access the same program and data at once, as well as interfacing with shared printers and other peripherals.

SOFTWARE

Novell NetWare software includes an operating system that runs on network fileservers, software "shells" that run on workstations, and a number of command files and utilities that reside on the fileserver(s). NetWare also comes with installation and configuration programs and diagnostic routines.

The Novell NetWare package contains many diskettes, as well as a number of manuals. With newer types and versions of NetWare, 1.4MB (3.5 inch) diskettes are also provided. They include a set of PUBLIC diskettes, a SYSTEM diskette, a LOGIN diskette, and others (depending on type and version).

Working Copies

As with any software, you should make duplicates as working copies, and keep the originals safely stored. This is especially important because certain information during the configuration of the software may make permanent changes to files on these diskettes. For years Novell used a copy-protection scheme that required the presence of a serialized "key device" in the fileserver. This has been removed from all versions of NetWare currently being published.

Use the DOS DISKCOPY utility to create a working copy of all NetWare diskettes. Refer to your DOS manual for proper use of DISKCOPY. Simply copying the files on each diskette to pre-formatted blanks will not work, as some of the NetWare programs depend on the volume labels assigned to each diskette.

Software Options

A number of versions of NetWare have been published. Today there are several available. While NetWare has a version for fileservers based on the 68000 microprocessor (NetWare 68) and a version for the 8088 or "XT-compatible" (NetWare 86), the vast majority of Novell networks being installed today are Advanced NetWare 386. This runs only on 80486-based computers, such as the IBM AT/486. It is considerably faster than NetWare 86. Workstations on Advanced NetWare 386 networks may be AT/286 or 386 based.

Today, most versions of NetWare being sold are to some degree "system fault tolerant" (SFT). SFT allows a network to continue functioning in the event of partial failure. This is accomplished through several software features. Duplicate copies of the dis directory and file allocation tables (FATs) are maintained, so that if one should become corrupt, there is a backup. This is a very valuable safety feature -- on normal hard disks, a corrupted FAT usually means a complete loss of data. Read-after-write verification detects immediately if the fileserver is attempting to use a section of the hard disk which has gone bad. With a feature called Hot Fix, this section is permanently marked as bad and the data is redirected to an area of the disk reserved for this purpose. These features are built into Advanced NetWare 2.1 and above, as well as ELS (Entry Level Solution) NetWare. With versions below Advanced NetWare 2.1, they are only found in systems specified by Novell as SFT Level 1.

An even greater degree of fault tolerance is found in SFT NetWare 2.1, or in the older version -- SFT NetWare 2 version 2.0. This includes the ability to have mirrored disks. Two identical hard disks are maintained by the system with all data written to both simultaneously. If one disk fails, a complete backup is still on line. Transaction Tracking System (TTS) is also provided. This tracks multiple updates to data files by your application program, and will cancel the last set of updates if your program is unexpectedly interrupted. As an example, if you are running an accounting package, the entry of an invoice can affect several data files. If the process is interrupted (by a power outage, for instance), the data files will no longer be properly integrated. TTS keeps up with file transactions, and if all updates are not completed, then they are all cancelled.

NetWare is available in both dedicated and nondedicated fileserver versions. A nondedicated fileserver is one that is used simultaneously as a workstation. This can slow the fileserver considerably and, therefore, lower overall network performance. It is best to only use nondedicated fileservers on small networks with relatively light work loads. There is also a risk that a user could accidently lock up, reset, or turn off a fileserver that is being used as a workstation.

The other factor to consider in selecting NetWare is the number of users supported. There is a type of NetWare 86 that only supports a maximum of eight workstations. It is usually marketed by the manufacturers of network interface cards (NICs), who bundle it with their products. ELS NetWare, while loaded with most of the features of the full-blown NetWare 286, is limited to less workstations. ELS NetWare Level I supports four users, and is similar to Advanced NetWare 286 version 2.0. ELS Level II is essentially an eight-user version of Advanced NetWare 286 version 2.15. Most other versions, including NetWare 86, support up to 100 workstations per fileserver.

Select a version of NetWare that will provide you with your current needs and allow for growth. Novell does make available certain upgrades so that if you need the features of a newer NetWare version, you do not have to purchase an entire new system.

ILE SERVERS

The fileserver is a mass storage device that is the heart of the Novell network. It contains one or more fixed drives and shares the programs and data they contain with the attached workstations. Various output devices, including printers and plotters, may be attached to a fileserver. These devices are also shared with the workstations. Depending on the type of Novell NetWare in use, a network may contain one or more fileservers.

Computer Type

While a wide variety of DOS computers are available that may be used as fileservers, you must consider the type of NetWare in use before selecting one. Computers using 8088, 8086, 80286 or 80386 microprocessors are the slowest and ideally are not used as fileservers. These would include the IBM PC XT, AT/286, AT/386, IBM PS/2 models 25 and 30. 80486-based machines provide the speed required for the best fileserver operation. These include the IBM AT/486 and compatibles, IBM PS/2 models 50 and above. Novell also markets a line of fileserver computers.

NetWare 86 is designed for use on an 8088/8086-based machine, though it is more typically used with an 80286- or even 80386-based machine for increased speed. NetWare 286 runs only on 80286- or 80386-based machines. It is designed to take full advantage of the 80286 and therefore is considerably faster than NetWare 86. ELS NetWare will run only on certain makes of machines. This is because it requires a very high degree of IBM BIOS compatibility. There are several machines which may be used, but be sure to check with the manufacturer or your dealer to verify compatibility.

Each fileserver must contain a network interface card (NIC). This communicates through the cable system to the NICs in each workstation. With some types of NetWare the fileserver must also contain a keycard, which is included in the NetWare package. As the fileserver will not function without the keycard, this prevents the unauthorized use of the NetWare software on more than one network.

Hard Drives

The fileserver must contain at least one hard drive. This contains the NetWare system files and utilities as well as the applications software and data. You prepare the hard drive with Novell's own format routine (as opposed to DOS) as part of the installation.

Most brands of hard drives that are compatible with your fileserver will work. If you are using an 80386- or 80486-based machine, it is important to select drives that are of a "standard type" for the brand of computer you have chosen. The drive type is determined by its number of read/write heads, the number of cylinders, and other technical specifications. Different manufacturers of computers consider various drive types standard. Non-standard drives are often used by formatting them with special utilities. Because Novell uses its own format, these utilities may not work. There are also a number of disk subsystems (hard drives mounted in a chassis outside of the fileserver) that are compatible with NetWare. The speed of the drive should also be considered. With a number of users relying on information from a drive at once, a slow drive can lower the overall system performance.

File Server RAM

The minimum amount of memory (or RAM) depends on both the type of NetWare in use and the size of your hard drives(s). Netware 86 fileservers should have 640K RAM. Netware 286 and ELS NetWare 286 can access extended memory. Nondedicated fileservers require memory for both fileserver and workstation applications, thus 640K base memory with 1 megabyte or more extended memory is recommended. Dedicated NetWare 286 may get by with as little as 640K. Novell uses a portion of RAM for hashing and (if configured to) caching of hard drives. Put simply, this means that commonly used information from the drives is kept in RAM for quick access and greatly improved system speed. The larger the drive(s), the more RAM that is needed for this task. An 80-megabyte total hard drive storage can be accommodated with the preceding configurations. Larger drives may need more.

UPS

An uninterruptible power supply (UPS) is strongly recommended for fileservers. This provides continuous power to the system in the event of a power outage. Because of the hashing and caching process described above, the system should be properly shut down to prevent loss or corruption of data. The UPS allows the operator time to do this. SFT NetWare provides a feature called "UPS monitoring". When used with a UPS that is designed to support this feature, the fileserver is alerted if the battery is almost drained (during prolonged power outages). The fileserver then proceeds to bring down the network in a safe manner.

WORKSTATIONS

Workstations are the individual computers through which you access the network. Each workstation is assigned a unique address (via settings on its network interface card). To the user, however, NetWare seems to make no distinction between workstations. In other words, the ability to access various resources on the network is determined by who is using the system, not which workstation they are using.

Computer Types

Workstations can be almost any IBM, COMPAQ, AT&T, or compatible DOS computer. They must have one expansion slot available for the NIC. There are a few machines that may not function properly on a Novell network. This is especially true of some of the very early compatibles. Check with the manufacturer or your dealer to be sure.

Hard Drives

The drives of the fileserver are made available to each workstation in a fairly transparent way. This means that accessing them is very similar to accessing drives on a stand-alone computer. A "local" hard drive can be used in a workstation, but is not needed. At least one floppy drive is needed to allow DOS and the NetWare shell (software that communicates with the network) to be loaded. This need is eliminated with the use of certain NICs that contain a "Boot ROM" which allows this software to be loaded directly off the fileserver.

Workstation RAM

The NetWare shell stays in memory and may require up to 64K of workstation RAM. Therefore, each workstation should have at least 64K in addition to the memory needed for DOS and user applications. Generally, it is ideal to provide each workstation with 1 MB or more total RAM.

NETWORK INTERFACE CARDS

Network fileservers and workstations communicate with each other through network interface cards (NICs). Each computer on the network must contain a NIC. The NIC occupies one expansion slot in the computer and provides an external connection to which the network cable is attached. There are several cabling schemes available, but the network cable in some way connects all the computers on the network.

Over a dozen manufacturers provide NICs that are Novell compatible. At the time of installation, you specify which NIC you will be using; NetWare configures itself to communicate through the particular card you select. Within one network, all NICs must be of the same type, but not necessarily the same manufacturer. There are several standards that have been established, and for each standard there may be multiple companies that make their own version. Two or more networks using different types or standards of NICs may be interconnected via a process called bridging. A bridge is essentially one fileserver (or in some cases workstation) that has two or more NICs, each cabled to a different network.

There are a number of specifications that differentiate the various NICs available for Novell networking. The main ones to consider are discussed in the following sections.

Type of Cabling

Cabling is often the first consideration in selecting the type of network hardware you will use. Each type of NIC has particular cable requirements. Different cable types include broad and base band (coaxial), twisted pair (same as telephone wiring), multi-conductor (usually 9 wire), and even fiber optic. Some NICs may allow the use of more than one type of cable; however, the cable you choose to use must be the same throughout the network.

Speed of Transmission

The speed at which data is transmitted over the network is determined by the NIC. It is measured in bits per second. A bit is the smallest unit of data, represented by a 1 or 0. Cards are rated in kilobits (thousand bits) or megabits (million bits) per second. Depending on the NIC you select, your network may communicate at anywhere from 500 kilobits/second (or .5 megabits) to 20 megabits/second, and above!

Method of Collision Control

In a network environment workstations and fileservers communicate with each other over a system of cabling. Because several computers may need to access the network simultaneously, there must be some way to control traffic.

One such method is called token passing. A token is a special string of data that is sent over the network, from one computer to the next. Whichever computer has the token may "broadcast" data or data requests over the network. Each computer must wait its turn to broadcast, thus collisions of data cannot occur. This whole process happens very quickly, so to the user it appears that all computers are communicating at once. ARCnet and Token-Ring are two NIC standards that use this method.

Another popular method is to allow computers to broadcast as needed. The network monitors this process and is able to detect data collisions. When one occurs, all NICs back up a step and begin transmitting their last data over again. This method is very fast in most networks; however, in very large networks the number of collisions can increase exponentially and erode overall performance. An example of this method, known as "multiple carrier collision detection and avoidance", is the Ethernet NIC.

Network Distance

In choosing a NIC and cabling scheme, bear in mind total area which the network will cover. Each manufacturer publishes distance specifications for their products. With some NICs, you may have the option of using different types of cables, and/or signal boosters, to attain maximum distances. There are also products available to allow networks to be bridged across considerable distances, using fiber optics, microwave, or dedicated phone lines.

Buffer Size

NICs have memory on them to serve as a buffer between the card and the network. This allows the NIC to transmit or receive data while the computer attends to other tasks. The larger the buffer a NIC has, the faster the overall operation can be.

Data Base Size

Most NICs are designed to fit in the 8-bit data bus slot of IBM, PC XTs and compatibles. These cards will also work in 286/386 level machines, but only as 8-bit cards. This means the NIC communicates with the computer 8 bits at a time. Some manufactuers have 16-bit versions of their cards available. These work only in 286/386/486 computers but speed overall network access considerably. Even if you do not use 16-bit NICs in workstations, you should consider them in fileservers.

OVERALL SPEED

The performance of a NIC depends upon the speed of transmission, the way it handles collisions, the amount of buffer memory on board, and the size of the data bus. The speed of the network can depend upon a number of factors, including speed of fileserver(s), speed of workstation(s), speed of shared hard disk(s), number of users, and speed of NICs. Therefore, it is not always advisable to buy very expensive, state-of-the-art NICs if the rest of the network is not fast enough to take full advantage of them. At the same time, do not negate the power of high-speed workstations by using excessively slow NICs.

16

ETHERNET

INTRODUCTION

One of the hottest topics of information technology is the local area network (LAN). LAN bears an indispensible role of service to information community. LAN provides basically a shared data access of an organisation which has several systems, split geographically, logically and physically. The three main physical attributes -- limited geographic scope (in the range of 0.1 - 10 KM), low delay or very high data rate (over 1 MBPS), and user's ownership, make LANs substantially different from conventional computer networks. Moreover, while wide area network (WAN) and metropolitan area network (MAN) allow users in network to access the shared databases, LANs go a step ahead and allow users to have shared access to many common hardware and software resources such as storage, input/output peripherals and communication devices. For example, a costly high resolution laser printer is usually shared by users in a LAN, and all users in a LAN use an inexpensive single transmission medium in a multidrop environment, as well as they use, whenever required, a single bridge or gateway to communicate with other homogeneous or heterogeneous network respectively.

LAN is hence a resource sharing data communication network that is usually used to connect computers, printers, terminal controllers (servers), terminals (key board/VDU), plotters, mass storage units (hard disk) and any other piece of equipment (e.g., word processing machine) that has some form of computer connectivity. LAN solves communication problems in a cost-effective way in an office, factory, university and such relevant environments. However, PABX (Private Automatic Branch Exchange) differs from LAN in that unlike LAN, PABX uses a separate pair of wires (transmission medium) to connect each device (or extension), low bandwidth (limited to that of telephone line) and rugged hardware switching for interconnection. Communication in LANs is peer to peer and not via intermediaries as with WANs and MANs. MAN's coverage is from a few miles to 100 miles and WAN's coverage is from 100 miles to 1000 miles. All these three networks follow layered architectural standard protocol like 7 layer ISO-OSI protocol or SNA protocol etc. for interconnection strategies.

LANs continue to be the driving force to implement the future white hope of digital wall socket which will act like today's electricity socket and telephone socket. The digital wall socket is to be used in handling explicit low or high data rate devices like copying machines, word processing machines, facimile displays, VDU, keyboards, microcomputers/PC, large computers etc. This may ultimately lead to 100 percent paper less "Office-of-the-future" and 100 percent automated "factory-of-the-future" with "deskless" managers, administrators and engineers etc.

One of the most successful LANs is Ethernet. Ethernet was the most popular LAN in 1987. As per Forrester Research Inc. in USA Ethernet covers 33 percent of LAN market with IBM token ring lagging behind at 22 percent. Dataquest estimated that Ethernet had covered 52 percent of installed LANs in USA. Is Ethernet hottest now? Whatever may be the answer to this question, it is a fact that Ethernet is still today very popular and will continue to be so at least for some time to come.

EVOLUTION

Historically, Ethernet was developed by the Xerox Corporation on an experimental basis around 1972. Based on this experimental experience, the second generation system was soon developed by the Xerox Corporation in late 1970's. Around 1980-81, under a joint effort of DEC (Digital Equipment Corporation), Intel and Xerox, an updated version of Ethernet specifications (Table 16.1) was designed. This historically lead to development of IEEE (Institute of Electrical and Electronics Engineers Inc) 802 standards (Table 16.2) of LAN. In reference to 7-layer OSI-ISO (Open System Interconnection of International Standards Organisation), the LLC (logical link control) is covered by IEEE 802.2 standard in Ethernet. LLC standard actually specifies the types of data transfer services. Ethernet covers IEEE 802.3 standard at MAC (medium access control) and physical level. While MAC actually specifies the accessing mechanism, physical level covers the electromechanical connectivity at network medium, LLC and MAC of LAN jointly form the data link of OSI-ISO protocol standard. Now-a-days Ethernet is available from many vendors. Such Ethernet is as per IEEE 802.3 standard. These are actually "Ethernet-like" networks. However, all LANs covering IEEE 802.3 standard are not Ethernet. But all Ethernets cover IEEE 802.3 standard.

Table 16.1 : Specification of Ethernets

	Parameters	Experiment Ethernet	Industrial/Commercial Ethernet
1.	Data rate	2.94 MBPS	10 MBPS
2.	Maximum end-to-end length coverage using repeaters/bridges	1 KM	2.5 KM

3.	Maximum segment length	1 KM	500 M
4.	Data encoding technique	Manchester	Manchester
5.	Co-axial cable impedence	75	50
6.	Co-axial cable signal level	0 to + 3 volt	0 to -2 volts
7.	Transceiver cable connectors' size	25 and 15 pin D series	Only 15 pin D series
8.	Preamble	1 byte of a pattern of 10101010	1 byte of a pattern of 10101010
9.	Size of CRC (cycle redundancy check)	2 byte	4 bytes
10.	Size of address field	1 byte	6 bytes

Table 16.2 : IEEE 802 Standards

Standard for MAC & Physical layer	Access Technique and topology	Transmission medium with allowed data	Basic application area
802.3	CSMA/CD with BUS topology	Broadband: Co-axial cable with 1MBPS/ 5MBPS/ 10 MBPS /20 MBPS Base band: Co-axial cable with 1MBPS	Office automation (OA)
802.4	Token passing with BUS topology	Broad band: Co-axial cable with 1.5444 MBPS/ 5MBPS 10 MBPS/ 20 MBPS Base band: Co-axial cable with 1MBPS/ 5 MBPS / 10 MBPS	Manufacturing automation (MA)
802.5	Token passing with RING topology	Base band: Shielded twisted wire pair with 1.4 MBPS. Co-axial cable with 4 MBPS/20 MBPS/ 40 MBPS	Process control real time application
802.6	Yet to be finalized	Yet to be finalized	MAN
802.7	–do–	–do–	Broadband LAN
802.8	–do–	–do–	LAN with fibre optics

| 802.9 | –do– | –do– | LAN in ON
(Integral services
digital network) |

*802.2 standard is for LIC of LAN
802.10 is for Network security

Ethernet, which was originally developed and patented in 1975, began an a research project to link personal workstations at the Xerox Palo Alto Research Centre. In 1980 Digital Equipment Corporation, Intel, and Xerox adopted a joint development policy and published a revised specification for a faster (10 Mbit/s) CSMA/CD bus, under the trademark 'Ethernet', referred to as Ethernet 1.0. The Institute of Electrical and Electronic Engineers (IEEE) Project 802 took Ethernet as the starting point for its CSMA/CD LAN standard, and Ethernet 2.0 was introduced in 1982 to come more into line with the IEEE's project 802.3 proposals. Unfortunately, Ethernet 2.0 and IEEE 802.3 are not identical, although they are able to co-exist on the same cable. As time passes it is likely that all manufacturers will produce products conforming to the IEEE specification, which is now an International Standard (ISO DIS 8802/3), and so incompatibility will cease to be a problem.

Since the first IEEE specification was announced for a 10 Mbit/s CSMA/CD network over coaxial cable, IEEE have continued to develop other CSMA/CD variations, notably CSMA/CD on broadband, over 'thin' coaxial cable and over twisted pair.

FEATURES OF ETHERNET

Why Ethernet is so popular? This is due to some of its important features. The most appealing features of the Ethernet are its protocol simplicity, and the relative low-cost and elegant implementation of LAN system which meets the following desirable characteristics of a local networking facility:

- high flexibility i.e. easy adaptability when devices and system to be added or removed. This is due to the bus topology and the cable tapping facility of Ethernet.

- the transmission medium and access control is easily extensible with minimum service disruption.

- high reliability which assures the continuation of the operation of the network in failure of one or more active element (node) like PC, terminal or workstation etc. This is due to the passive feature of Ethernet cable. Moreover, there is no centralized control but distributed control in Ethernet.

- the traffic will be bursty in nature. In office and engineering environment, nature of data is frequently bursty, and ironically Ethernet was specially made for office automation, although not in general.

MEDIUM ACCESS CONTROL FRAME FORMATS

The medium access control (MAC) frame is the envelope within which the station's data message is sent: its format is shown in Figure 16.1.

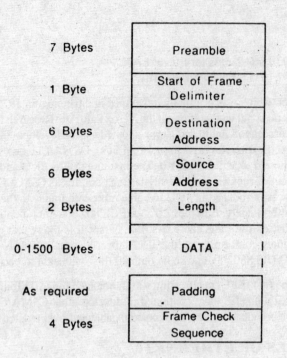

7 Bytes	Preamble
1 Byte	Start of Frame Delimiter
6 Bytes	Destination Address
6 Bytes	Source Address
2 Bytes	Length
0-1500 Bytes	DATA
As required	Padding
4 Bytes	Frame Check Sequence

Fig. 16.1 : Format of IEEE 802.3 CSMA/CD frame.

The frame is transmitted from top to bottom, and within each byte from left to
(least to most significant bit). The elements are as follows:

Preamble field. This field is a seven byte sequence of alternating 'one' and 'ze
values. The system uses Manchester encoding and this field enables each receiver to
a steady state synchronisation with the transmitter.

Start frame delimiter field. This is a one byte field with the bit sequence '1010
It indicates the start of the frame.

Address fields. Each frame contains the address of the intended recipie
destination address), and of the transmitting station (the source address). Althou
specification allows for either 2 byte or 6 byte addresses, the normal practice is to use
(48 bits). These addresses are normally allocated centrally, by IEEE, with manufa
being allocated blocks of addresses. Thus all equipment from one manufactur
normally have the same top few bytes of address.

The first two bits of the address have special significance. The first bit
destination address indicates whether this is the address of an individual station ('C
group of stations ('1'). This enables one message to be sent to a group of stations wi
one transmission, since all the stations on the LAN receive every packet. Such addres
termed multicast addresses. The second bit indicates whether the address is global

or locally ('1') administered. This avoids any possible duplication of addresses between IEEE-specified stations and any 'home grown' stations.

There is one special multicast address, called the broadcast address, which has the value "all ones". This is a message intended for all stations.

Length field. This is the value of the number of bytes in the data field of the packet. It is in the interpretation of this field that the IEEE specification differs from the Ethernet 2.0 specification. Ethernet uses this field as an indicator of the type of higher level protocol carried in the data field, and the length of the data is found within the data field. The values used for this field in Ethernet are, however, defined to be greater than any valid length for an IEEE frame, the maximum frame length being 1518 bytes. It is therefore possible for a station to operate to both standards simultaneously, as it can distinguish the standard in use within each frame from the value of this field.

Data and pad fields. The data field can contain any number of bytes of any value, up to the maximum frame limit of 1518 bytes. If the number of data bytes is such that the minimum packet size required for CSMA/CD will not be met, then the required number of extra bytes is added to the end of the data field, in the padfield. For the 10 Mbit/s LAN the minimum frame size is 64 bytes, but this will vary for the other versions of CSMA/CD.

Frame check sequence field. This is a cyclic redundancy check, designed to detect bit errors within the frame. It covers all of the bytes, starting at the destination address and is four bytes long. Any error in the FCS will cause the frame to be ignored, as will a frame which is too short or too long.

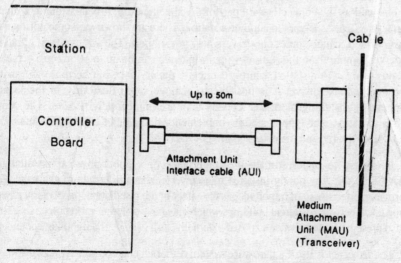

Fig. 16.2 : Typical CSMA/CD station connection.

COMPONENTS OF ETHERNET

Physically, a typical connection of a station to the cable is shown in Figure 16.2 comprises the transmission medium, a Medium Attachment Unit (MAU), and Attachm Unit Interface (AUI) cable and a controller board within the station.

The cable itself is a very stiff form of 50 ohm coaxial cable, the material of the outer jac depending on the degree of physical protection required. The normal cable for use with building has a PVC jacket, which is coloured yellow for ease of identification. The cabl marked at 2.5 m intervals with dark rings to indicate the optimum points for placing a M. more commonly known as a transceiver. Transceivers should only be placed on the cable a marked points in order to reduce the signal reflections inevitably introduced by each transcei

The transceiver performs the task of transmitting the frames onto the cable receiving them from it. It also monitors the signal levels on the medium, acts as an electr isolator between the station and the medium, and detects collisions and other error co tions; these it signals to the controller board in the station. There are two types of transcei The first can be clamped onto the cable, a pin making contact with the central co: conductor, and is known as a bee-sting or vampire. The second, which makes a 'butt- j connection using barrel connectors, requires the cable to be cut. The fact that a bee-s type of tap can be added or removed to the cable without disrupting the network i advantage, although in practice it can be difficult to make a good contact with the i conductor of the cable.

The transceiver communicates with, and is powered from, the station via an AUI c which is normally coloured blue and attaches to the controller board in the station. A signals which are passed along this cable (commonly called the transceiver cable or cable) as well as the connectors are part of the specification, it is possible to connec manufacturer's transceivers to another's station. There are, however, some optional te signals defined, which some transceivers may not support. The arrangement of havin transceiver remote from the station -- the drop cable can be up to 50 m long -- mean: the main cable can be installed securely in ducts or under floors. Furthermore, as transce are relatively inexpensive, it is possible to achieve some flexibility in the locatic equipment by installing more transceivers than are immediately needed. The contr which is specific to the type of station, implements all the other CSMA/CD functions the random back-off and the encapsulation of data.

It is easy to underestimate the importance of a good physical installation CSMA/CD LAN. Any poorly installed transceiver or damaged medium can have a se performance effect. Also of importance is the safety of the installation, particularly when is being taken between different buildings which may have different earth potentials. The can also present problems when exposed externally, as it can act as a lightning conductor

The Ethernet is itself a hardware system. Ethernet can connect typically a maxi number of nodes of 100 per segment and 1024 per total Ethernet. A Ethernet LAN have Ethernet cable, transceiver, interface unit, control unit, the user system and tern (Figure 16.3). Two types of 'co-axial' cable popularly known as "thick Ethernet" and

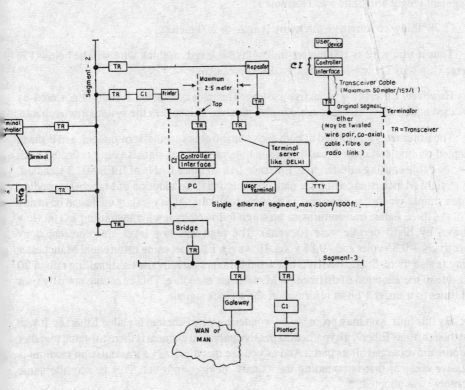

Fig. 16.3 :

net" is used, mainly as backbone (main, cable respectively in baseband and broadband
net. On this backbone cable, the communicating systems and peripherals are attached
ed). Taps may be intrusive where the cable is cut for tapping or may be non-intrusive
e the cable is drilled and a tap added without hampering the operation of the network.
nost common Ethernet, the baseband Ethernet is tapped non intrusively, whereas the
lband Ethernets used intrusive tapping using T junctions scheme. Baseband Ethernet
implementation where the entire bandwidth of backbone cable is used only for Ethernet
nunications. Signals in cable are not modulated signal. Thick Ethernet cable resembles
king every 2.4 meters usually by black ring around cable to show where the taps go.
ver, thickwire co-axial cable has maximum length limitation of 500 meters and thin
coaxial has limitation in the range from 189 meters to 1 km depending upon the vendors
sceivers and controllers. Ethernet may also run on twisted pair under certain restriction
n fibre. The length of twisted pair may range from 20 meters to 100 meters. Ethernets
pre optic medium have length restriction in the range of 30 meters to 5 km. In some

cases, thin wire Ethernet may be required to be connected to a thick wire Ethernet. Thin wire cable may be connected to thickwire through a barrel connector. In such a case, the restriction on segment length will follow the formula:

(3.28*thinwire length) + thickwire length <= 500 meters.

Thus if thin wire is 100 meters in length, the length of thick wire will be below 172 meters. Thin wire cable has higher signal loss problem.

However, Ethernet is a passive system. This means that the system is powered by connected nodes only. Ethernet cable is also passive. This makes the system more reliable.

The Ethernet is terminated at both ends with 50 ohms special terminators, and is made grounded on one end only to earth. Terminators prevent the signals being reflected back down the cable causing interference. Ethernet, like all other LANs of IEEE 802.3 standard, uses straight Manchester coding for data transmission. The adoption of Manchester coding ensures simple synchronisation and a DC value to 0 volts. At any instant cable can be in any one of the three states: transmitting a 1 bit (high followed by low), transmitting a O bit (low followed by high) or idle state (0 volts). The high and low level are represented by respectively + 0.85 volts and - 0.85 volts. However, Ethernet using differential Manchester coding is also there. Such 10 MBPS baseband Ethernet actually uses a signalling rate of 20 MHz due to the adoption of differential Manchester encoding. This encoding actually uses 2 bit times to transfer 1 bit of information and a clock signal.

By this time, you may probably be wondering why Ethernet is called Ethernet. It was once thought that "Ether", a hypothetical passive universal element is there to bound together the entire universe and all its parts. And as you see that this LAN's transmission medium is a passive element that is bounding the "smart" devices in a net. This is why the name "Ethernet" was adopted.

The Ethernet is a broadcast LAN. All nodes can listen each and every message transmitted on the net.

Transceiver is another important component of any LAN. It is clamped securely onto the Ethernet cable so that its tap makes contact with inner core. Transceivers are available in many different shapes, sizes and price-ranges, but they all provide users' devices to communicate with the cable. They also contain electronics circuit that handle carrier detection and collision detection too. A transceiver is so named because it allows simultaneous transmission and reception. A transceiver is fairly a dumb system. It transmits data, receives data and detects collision and notifies the same, if occured, to the controller.

Transceiver cable (maximum length is 50 meters) contains usually five numbers of individual shielded twisted pairs. Two of these pairs are used for data in and data out. Two more are similarly used for control signals in and out. The fifth pair is not always used, and it is used to allow the node to power the transceiver. Some transceivers allows upto eight nearby computers/workstations/users' terminals to be attached to them to reduce the number of transceivers needed. For example DEC has developed special box (DELNI Digital Ethernet Local Network Interconnect), that allows upto eight systems to connect to the box,

a single Ethernet transceiver taps the eight systems onto the main cable. DELNI has the
cy to work standalone and emulate an eight node Ethernet cable. When the systems are
ore than 50 meters away from DELNI or there are no more than eight co-located systems
equire to be on an Ethernet, DELNI is cost-effective than eight transceivers and cable.
lisadvantage is that DELNI is self powered. So failure of DELNI will fail eight nodes
cess network.

The interfacing unit detects data and accepts the data if it is meant for this address. It
creates and checks the CRC for error correction and recovery.

The controller unit (is a firmware or software device) transmits data frames to, and
ves data frames from transceiver via interfacing unit. It also buffers the data and
smits it when collision occurs, and determines the retransmission interval (which
s with load etc) and other aspects of network management.

For a complete network, one has to procure the components of LAN, network software
ardware and communication software (e.g. Netware 3.10).

Now, the basic components of Ethernet are discussed. Next we will discuss how does
hernet works.

THOD OF OPERATION

The basis of operation of Ethernet is the accessing technique known as CSMA/CD
er Sense Multiple Access/Collision Detection). All the stations on the LAN share a
on bus transmission medium. To transmit, a station waits for a quiet period (a period
no-one else is transmitting), and then sends the message in bit serial form, i.e. one bit
ing another serially along the cable. If the message collides with that of another station
ach transmitting station will detect the collision and will send a few extra jamming
o ensure that all stations also see it. The two stations will then remain silent for random
ls (backoff), before trying to transmit again.

To ensure that a collision will be detected, each packet must be large enough to occupy
ole length of the bus. The packet size is a function of the speed of transmission:
ly the higher the speed the larger the minimum packet, or the shorter the bus. The
pecification attempts to compromise to give a reasonable bus length at a reasonable
vithout too large a packet size.

here are many different types of CSMA technique, the technique adopted in Ethernet
sistent CSMA/CD. The problem of the non-persistent strategy is that after the current
ission and line detection, there may be good chance that the line is idle. The alternative
echnique is "1-persistent" where the nodes continuously sense the line and transmit
soon as it is free.

he CSMA/CD is a simple and straightforward way of providing every user a chance
mit whenever it has something to do. The concept behind CSMA/CD may appear to
ved from a technique used when people are talking in a mass gathering or meeting.
e is talking, one person may start talking. If two or more people start talking at the

same time, collision occurs, and both stop and wait for some random time before again starting to talk. In Ethernet if any node wishes to send data to another node on the network, the source listens to see if the line is free (quiet/idle). This is called **carrier sensing**. If the cable is idle, source node starts transmission. Some times it may so happen that two or more stations accidently may start transmission at the same time. The collision is also possible in some other cases. For example, if two nodes separated by a distance of propagation time t, both start transmission at an interval of time t, there will be collision. When collision will occur, transmitted data will be corrupted. A mechanism to detect collision is used by adopting the technique of "listen-while- transmitting". In this scheme at the source node, the transceiver's transmitting unit while sending the data, the receiving unit is listening to the data that is being sent. If the transceiver detects that the data received by receiving circuitry do not match with that transmitted by transmitting circuitry, it senses the occurrence of collision and accordingly sends a message to the controller of node. If there is match, the transmission process is allowed to go on. On receiving a collision-detection signal, controller stops sending data, and sends a burst of noise on the line (jamming) to assure that the other nodes sending data listen a collision. All collision detecting stations back off on detection of collision. The controller than waits for a random time before attempting for retransmission. For this a random generator is used. However, the mean wait is initially equivalent to an end-to-end round trip delay on the cable (which is about 2 sec for 500 meter co-axial cable). However, in case of second time collision, the controller doubles the previously generated random number thereby ensuring double of the mean delay of first collision, and so on (doubling operation) on repeated collision. Usually random generated is counted from assigned number to zero for measure of delay. The doubling operation is allowed for a prescribed number of times which is usually 16. After that the controller sends an error message to the host (system manager) notifying the occurrence of multiple-collision. Due to this collission and retransmission scheme, 100 percent channel utilization is not achieved. Ethernet, however, come close to 100 percent due to CSMA/CD technique, which polling and other techniques cannot achieve. The minimum Ethernet packet size (64 bytes) and maximum Ethernet cable segment length and propagation time, used together, guarantees that by the time the last bit of information is transmitted, the source node can accurately detect a collision if any other node attempt transmission at the same time.

However, if the utilization rate of the cable is low (i.e. load on the network is low), collision is rare, and the mean delay time rarely exceeds its minimum value of one end-to-end round-trip delay. When utilization is high (i.e. traffic load becomes heavy), collision becomes more common. Due to this feature, controller dynamically changes the re-transmission interval. This is why doubling operation is there in use.

When data is being transmitted, all node "hear" the data. On examining the first (after preamble) 6 bytes (address field) of the data packet, nodes may determine whether the data is destined for itself or not. If the message is for itself, it passes the message to the users' device through controller. Otherwise it ignores the message usually.

But why is CSMA for Ethernet? Because of distributed nature of the random accessing technique, they are well suited to LANs where simplicity of operation and flexibility are most important. Besides, since a large bandwidth is available in LAN, LAN under such accessing technique can be operated at a relatively low loadings avoiding unstable conditions. However, the performance of CSMA/CD is inversely proportional to the end-to-end propagation delay. Thus, Ethernet for office automation can use CSMA/CD most appropriately.

ETHERNET IC (INTEGRATED CIRCUIT) CHIPS

The following is a brief Ethernet IC chips that may be used to design a Ethernet:

Vendor	Controller/Interface Chip
Intel	82586 (controller)
	82501 (interface)
National	DP8390
Semi conductor	DP8790
	DP8341
	DP8342
Advanced	7996
	7990
Seeg	8003
Tech	8023
AMD/Mostek/	LANCE
Motorola	

APPLICATIONS OF ETHERNET

Ethernet historically and traditionally is used in office automation. Today, some organisations are experimenting with video on Ethernets as well as high resolution graphic access technique by which disk-less workstation may access shared disk structure. Ethernet are also used in laboratories and industries, robotics applications, factory automation, process control and many other non-office applications but in rare cases. Only consideration for adoption of Ethernet in non-office applications is its tolerance of interference from electrical motors, electro-magnetic radiation and other sources of distortions. But its use of CSMA/CD accessing technique (which is probablistic in nature), a node in the network may have to wait for arbitarily long period to send a message. Moreover, IEEE 802.3 standard does not have priorities in accessing scheme. This makes it unsuitable in which important message should not be delayed for unimportant frames to pass. These two factors reserve the application of Ethernet in manufacturing factory automation (MA) and in real time process control system. However, while in office the typical required response time is 2 to 10 second, in factory and process control the same is respectively in the ranges of 0.5 to 2 sec. and 0.1 to 0.5 sec. Ethernet can meet a response time of 2 to 10 sec. Ethernet is hence best for office automation. For manufacturing factory automation, LANs covering IEEE 802.4 standards are suitable.

SYSTEM LIMITATIONS

The limitation of the Ethernet from application point of view due to non-deterministic (probablistic) accessing has already been discussed. Next is that Ethernet does not perform well under heavy load condition. Due to randomness both in data arrival and service, tests have shown that Ethernets can utilize only 90 to 95 percent of available resources, under a full load condition. Maximum throughput of 10 MBPS, 500 meter Ethernet with a propagation speed of $2x10**8$ m/sec is only 9.96 MBPS. Ethernet does not guarantee of delivery of messages, as there is no scheme of sequence number checking, missing messages re-transmission requests and other such facilities.

As noted previously, all the frames transmitted on the CSMA/CD cable must be long enough to reach the end of the cable before the sender stops sending, otherwise two complete frames could be in transit and collide without being detected. The length of the cable is determined by setting a maximum end-to-end transmission time, and is thus related to the speed of transmission and the rate of attenuation along the medium.

The first IEEE CSMA/CD standard based on the Ethernet specification runs at 10 Mbit/s, and the maximum length of a trunk coaxial segment is set at 500 m. The IEEE have adopted a naming convention under which this LAN is now referred to as 10base5, (10 Mbit/s, base-band, (5x100)m segments), to distinguish it from the other variants, described

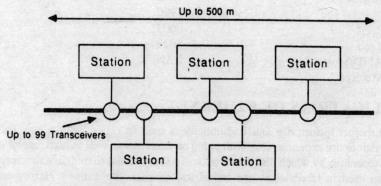

Fig. 16.4 : Single segment IEEE 802.3 LAN.

in this chapter. All the comments on the physical aspects of the LAN apply to 10base5 only.

Segment Configurations

The simplest 10base5 LAN comprises a single segment of up to 500 m (Figure 16.4), with stations attached at points at least 2.5 m apart. There is a limit of 100 transceivers on a segment, however, even though there are 200 marked attachment points. The minimum single segment arrangement can be extended by the use of repeater sets (a repeater plus two MAUs, normally simply referred to as a repeater), which regenerate the signal.

A repeater (Figure 16.5) can couple together two 500 m segments of coaxial cable. The repeater occupies one transceiver position on each segment and must pass all the signals from one cable to the other, including collision jamming, thus giving the illusion that the two segments are one. Another type of medium extension is the link segment, where two repeater sets link type of medium extension is the link segment, where two repeater sets link one coaxial segment to a remote coaxial segment via a fibre optic point-to-point link segment

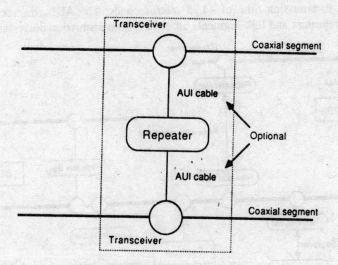

Fig. 16.5 : A coaxial to coaxial repeater.

between the repeaters. The fibre link can be up to 1 km long, but it is not possible to place a MAU on a link segment. Thus they are only useful for reaching distant corners of a site, or for traversing difficult environments where fibre optic cable is desired.

The critical limitation on extending 10base5 LANs in this way is the overall propagation time between the two furthest apart stations. The specification permits a maximum

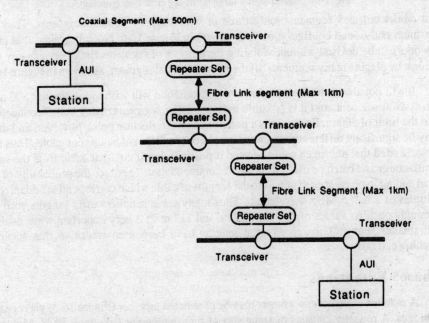

Fig. 16.6 : Example of a maximum segment configuration.

end-to-end transmission time of 44.95 microseconds. The AUIs, transceivers, coaxial segments, repeaters and link segments all contribute transmission delays and the overall

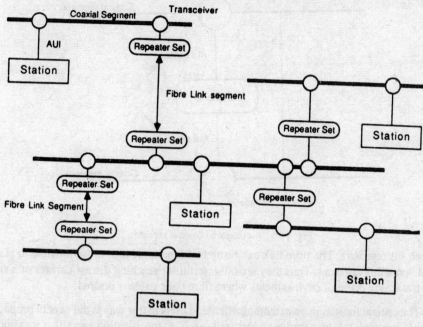

Fig. 16.7 : Example of a large multi-segment configuration.

limit works out to 5 segments, only three of which can be coaxial segments. Thus the maximum end-to-end configuration is as shown in Figure 16.6. Note, however, that large networks can be devised without violating the number of segments limit between any two stations, by placing many segments off the middle coaxial segment, as shown in Figure 16.7.

It will not always be the case that every installation will wish to use the full 500 m of each coaxial segment, and it is possible to link smaller segments, using barrel connectors, up to the limit of 500 m. Each join is a potential signal reflection point, however, and there many be significant differences in impedance between different batches of cable. Thus it is recommended that unbroken cable be used if possible, but if not, that cable from the same manufacturer and batch be used. A further recommendation, to reduce the probability of the signal adding in phase at each join, is to use lengths of cable which correspond to odd integral multiples of a half 5 MHz wavelength. Thus many cable suppliers offer lengths with the seemingly peculiar values of 23.4 m, 70.2 m, and 117 m. It is very important when dealing with smaller segments to record what lengths have been used where so that accurate matching can take place.

10base5 Extensions

A number of Ethernet segments may be connected together (Figure 16.3) via repeater or bridges. A repeater consists of some sort of microprocessor (like Intel 8088, Motorola MC 68000) and memory etc. They are standalone units. They repeat everything what is received from any segment to other segment and vice-versa. They connect two Ethernet segments via transceiver. Bridge, on the otherhand, store and forward the intended data only from a source segment to a destination segment. Bridge is made of some sort of processor, storage, buffers and a set of software.

Although 10base5 has been available for some time, the basic components are still relatively expensive. A controller board, transceiver and drop cable may cost more than

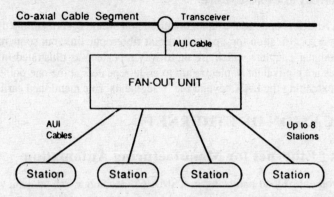

Fig. 16.8 : Typical FAN-OUT unit arrangement.

many PCs, and are even expensive relative to minicomputers. For that reason, several manufacturers market products which help to reduce costs, notably the transceiver fan-out box, or multi-port transceiver (Figure 16.8). This device enables up to eight stations to be

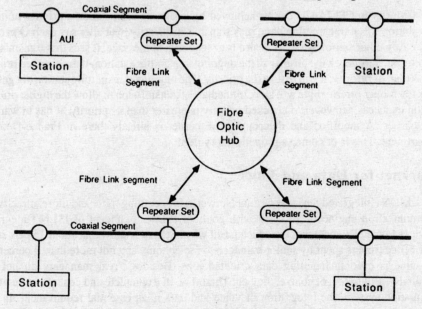

Fig. 16.8 : **Example of a fibre optic hub arrangement**.

connected, and can either be used as an 8 station LAN by itself or can be attached to a normal transceiver, thus giving eight transceivers at one point. This is a useful solution where there is a high density of stations (as 2.5 m of 10base5 cable can be difficult to hide between stations), and costs less than half the cost of 8 transceivers. It is also possible, by attaching eight multi-port boxes into one box in a tree structure, to create a 64 station LAN with no actual coaxial cable in the system. It is not, however, then possible to connect such a two tier system directly to a 10base5 cable.

Finally, the fibre optic star-coupler or hub should be noted. As mentioned earlier, IEEE has drawn up a specification for a point-to- point fibre-optic link, but some manufacturers have produced star couplers which are multi-way repeaters, as illustrated in Figure 16.9. These devices are equivalent to placing up to eight repeaters at the one point, but they do not assist in extending the LAN beyond the '5 segments' rule mentioned earlier.

MODIFICATION OF ETHERNET

Improving Ethernet for Manufacturing Automation

The problem of load balancing in CSMA/CD technique can be achieved to a large extent if each station on getting a transmission access is restricted to transmit only a fixed pre-assigned number (say P) of packets (non-exhaustive mode). After transmitting P packets, the station has to back off, for a time which must not be less than the time required for a bit to end-to-end of round of the bus. After passing off this time, the station can check the carrier further, and the process repeats.

Priority in CSMA/CD can be achieved by assigning each station a priority number. Any station when transmitting data, may transmit its priority byte after say each Q packets (Q P). Any other station which is desirous to send urgent message, if sees that transmission is going on, may check the priority of the ongoing transmitting station. If the checked priority is less than its priority, it will distort the priority. The ongoing transmitting station not getting back the proper priority byte will stop, immediately transmission to allow the higher priority station to access. However, if checked priority is greater than its priority, it has to wait for free carrier. A modified and deterministic Ethernet is already there in France-Defence Department. This is of course a properioratory item.

Ethernet for Data and Voice

ISDN (Integrated Services Digital Network) is becoming more and more attractive to communication engineers. In spirit with goals of ISDN, a concept of ISLN (Integrated Services Local Network) was introduced. But why? Statistics show that about 15 percent of their office time is spent by senior managers on telephone, and not more than 3 percent of the same is used in handling data oriented jobs. Besides, "real managers do not use terminals". But today, of course, they do. Therefore, in a complete and cost effective office automation system, the integration of voice and data is an essential requirement. In any organisation, why shall be there one PABX (for telephone) and one LAN (for data). However, early problem of LAN designs was to communicate data, but the real problem is to provide users' requirements of both data and voice communication. The pioneer vendors of Ethernet can examine whether Ethernet can be extended to cover ISLN requirement in either of two techniques: (i) conventional voice + data upto fascimile or (ii) upto full moving video.

THIN WIRE CSMA/CD (CHEAPERNET)

Thus far, this chapter has described the original IEEE 802.3 standard, but recently there have been several related CSMA/CD developments. The first is known as 10base2, or more commonly as thin wire CSMA/CD. As can be seen from the name, this version operates at 10 Mbit/s as before, and uses the same baseband transmission, but the medium is a thinner, more flexible cable. The cable is an industry standard known as RG58, and is much cheaper than 10base5 cable. The main limitation is that the length of a segment is limited to 185 m. Because of the different cable characteristics, only 30 stations can be placed on a 10base2 segment, but the inter-station gap is reduced to 0.5 m.

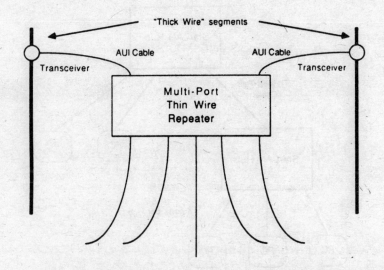

Fig. 16.10 : A typical thin wire multi-port repeater configuration.

The main advantage of 10base2 is that its greater flexibility means that the cable can be taken directly to the controller board within the station. Connection to the cable is via a simple T-piece, eliminating the need for the costly transceiver and drop cable, although stations can also be attached via a transceiver if required. The T-piece method has made it the most popular method of attaching the cheaper PCs to CSMA/CD networks, and has also gained the system the name of cheapernet. Although many users install CSMA/CD networks constructed entirely of 10base2 cable, it is possible to install a backbone LAN of 10base5 cable, with 10base2 segments running from it, attached via repeaters as normal. In practice, in order to make the cost even more attractive, 10base2 segments are often linked to a 10base5 cable using a multi-port repeater, as shown in Figure 16.10, it is also possible to mix thin and thick cable on the same segment, but this is not recommended.

BROADBAND CSMA/CD

A second variant, 10broad36, and also received IEEE approval. As the name implies, this is a broadband version, in which a few sets of frequencies are reserved for 10 Mbit/s CSMA/CD channels. The modems required for broadband, called broadband transceivers, present the normal transceiver interface to the station, and the big advantage of this technique is the 3.6 km segment limit.

Broadband transceivers operate in a different way from their baseband counterparts. Because the same controller boards are used, which send a Manchester encoded 10 Mbit/s signal to the transceiver, the signal must be narrowed or it would occupy some 80 MHz on the broadband cable. This is achieved by filtering the signal and changing the method of encoding the data. To improve the reliability further, the frame is scrambled, apart from the preamble part, which is still required for synchronisation.

On a baseband CSMA/CD network, the end of the frame is indicated by a total lack

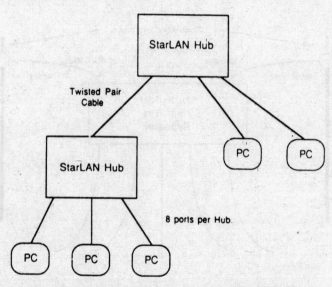

Fig. 16.11 : IEEE 802.3 1base 5 (Start LAN) configuration.

of signal on the medium. For broadband, as the carrier signal is always present, it is necessary to add a 23 bit sequence (a postamble) to the end of the frame. The final difference is that the baseband collision detection techniques are not applicable. Broadband transceivers can detect collisions only by seeing errors in the station's own address, i.e. the station listens to its own address on the receive channel, or the station's modem detects an incoming transmission just as the station tries to transmit, or the end of the unscrambled part of the packet fails to be detected at the correct time. The packets are so constructed that at least one of the colliding stations will detect one of the above conditions. When it does so it transmits a jamming signal in a reserved 4 MHz wide band immediately adjacent to the 14 MHz band used for the data itself. Thus any transmission in this band indicates a collision.

TWISTED PAIR CSMA/CD (STARLAN)

The most recent addition to the IEEE CSMA/CD stable of LANs is 1base5, which uses a tree topology and operates at 1 Mbit/s. In this system the medium used is twisted pair cable, and the repeaters are called STARLAN hubs (Figure 16.11). Like the 10base2 system it is intended for linking a moderate number of PCs together at low cost. Unlike the 10base2 system, it cannot be connected directly to any of the other IEEE CSMA/CD LANs because of the transmission speed differences. Up to 64 stations can be connected in a StarLAN system, with a station being up to 250 m from its hub. Two tiers of hub are permitted, and thus a station can be up to 500 m from the base hub.

1base5 is generating a great deal of interest in North America because unused telephone cable pairs can be used as the medium. The situation in Europe is not encouraging as the telephone cable within a user's building usually remains the property of the PTT, and non- approved equipment cannot be attached to it.

CONCLUSION

A number of important consideration of Ethernet have been highlighted. Ethernet is seen to be very effective for office automation. If the next generation of Ethernets are to be developed, they must be done in a direction to extend the application to manufacturing automation.

Of all the general purpose LANs, CSMA/CD, particularly the 10base5 version, has been on the market for longest and has a very large installation base. The 10base5 standard has been adopted by the International Standards Organisation as an international standard, and the number of manufacturers offering products continues to grow. It can be expected that at least some of the other variants will also become international standards.

IEEE continue to refine their work, and manufacturers continue to produce improved products. One can expect, for example, that the segment limitations outlined above will be relaxed as repeater technology improves, and that the cost of transceivers and controllers will fall as the standard is now stable, and thus more manufacturers are prepared to produce equipment conforming to it.

17

DIGITAL NETWORK ARCHITECTURE

INTRODUCTION

There are a lot of network architectures in the networking world, but few have the features and capabilities of the Digital Network Architecture (DNA) from Digital Equipment Corporation (DEC). In this chapter, we will discover some of the basic features of this architecture and of the most popular implementation of this architecture, the DECnet network product.

HISTORICAL DEVELOPMENT

In 1974, DEC decided to develop a communications and network architecture that could provide communication facilities between DEC systems to help leverage machine sales to current and potential customers. The product, later called DECnet, was based upon an architectural model called the Digital Network Architecture (DNA). Through the use of a common architecture, Digital hoped to offer communications capabilities and facilities between dissimilar processor architectures and dissimilar operating systems in a cohesive way.

DECnet is a set of programs and protocols produced by DEC for use on its computer systems. The architecture of DECnet is called DNA. Since it is sometimes difficult to separate the pure architecture aspects from the pure implementation aspects, we will use the term DECnet for convenience to mean DECnet and/or DNA.

The intention of DECnet is to allow any of DEC's customers to set up a private network. Thus there are many isolated DECNETs in the world, like SNA networks, in contrast to the ARPANET of which there is only one (although a number of other organizations have copied it). DECnet also differs from the ARPANET in another major respect: there is no distinction between hosts and IMPs (Interface Message Processors). A

DECnet is just a collection of machines (nodes), some of which may run user programs, some of which may do packet switching, and some of which may do both. The functions performed by any given machine may even change in time.

Like SNA, DECnet has evolved in time. In particular, early version of DECnet did not have the capability for machine A to communicate with machine B unless there was a physical connection between the two machines. If A and B both had connections to a third machine C, but no direct connection with each other, the software did not allow A and B to communicate via C. To retain compatibility between the early and later versions, a distinction is made between "small" nodes and "full" nodes, the former running the old software and the latter running the new software. Small nodes can communicate only with adjacent nodes, whereas full nodes do not have this restriction.

A further decision was to release the DECnet implementation in phases. It was recognised early on that keeping track of software version numbers on different systems was already a problem. Adding the complexity of making sure that the right versions of network software were on the right versions of the various operating systems would horribly compound the configuration problem. To solve some of the issues involved, Digital began the usage of "phases" of network software release with a certain level of functionality being imposed on each phase. Nodes (systems) on the network that contained the proper level of functionality described in the phase specification could easily converse with other nodes in the same phase of product release, regardless of operating system or hardware involved. Through this mechanism, the confusion as to what version of what needed to be configured was radically reduced.

Each phase of DECnet prescribes three distinct types of issues·

1.   The operating systems supported by the phase.

2.   The communications hardware supported by the phase.

3.   New features introduced in each phase.

Through this mechanism, dissimilar operating systems and computing hardware could be properly configured and activated once the proper DECnet product for that phase was available. Also, as products became obsolete, they could easily be identified for nonsupport and deleted from future phases.

Another benefit of the phase mechanism is the Digital decision to have a newer phase of the DECnet product support the immediately previous phase. This allows a period of time in which two different phases of the software would be totally compatible with each other and allow a migration period to the new phase.

DECnet is what is known as a peer-to-peer network product. This means that no one node is the "master" node. No one node controls or owns the network. All nodes may converse with all other DECnet nodes if they provide the proper access control information and other types of information necessary to support the communications link between the nodes. This type of architecture makes networking very flexible and easy to configure as major software and hardware changes and updates are not usually necessary to add nodes to the network or reconfigure the network topology. The down side is that it is difficult to manage a peer-to-peer network due to the lack of centralized authorization facilities and the need to poll nodes on the network for link, performance, and other pertinent pieces of information. This can cause not only a heavy burden for the system manager but, if network tools are introduced that issue the polls to other nodes, the overhead may increase markedly on the network.

To understand properly why DECnet and the DNA have evolved to where they are today, it is useful to understand the evolution to date.

PHASE I

Originally offered in 1976, DECnet Phase I was intended to supply basic file transfer needs and, hopefully, task-to-task communications. Phase I left much to be desired and did not conform to the standards that it does today for the simple fact that the standards did not exist. Most of the standards that DECnet conforms today were started around 1978, and those standards were incorporated in the Phase II DECnet product and subsequent releases. But, just like most "new" ideas, DECnet was growing in a positive direction and has achieved stature because of it.

In addition to not conforming to network standards, Phase I of DECnet only supported the simplest of asynchronous communication hardware and only allowed few nodes on a Phase I network. Routing was not available, so all nodes wishing to converse had to be directly connected to each other, seriously stifling the network configuration possibilities. Few operating systems were supported (such as RSX-11D and IAS on the PDP-11 line of processors and the short-lived implementation of DECnet/8 on the PDP-8E) and little expertise at Digital and at customer sites compounded problems for all.

Many a time systems suffered bizarre system crashes and extreme degradation of the processor due to DECnet problems. Most of these problems were fixed in Phase II, but to say that Phase I had problems would be a large understatement.

PHASE II

Phase II introduced closer conformance to the International Standards Organisation (ISO) Open Systems Interconnection (OSI) Architecture standard. It also introduced numerous bug fixes and a bit more documentation to reduce the "magical" quality of DECnet. It was also the first release where all PDP-11 and DEC-20 operating systems actually communicated in a reasonable fashion. File transfers actually transferred, task-to-task communication was possible, and the concept of manual routing was introduced. Basically, to get from node (system) A to node C through node B, one had to enter explicitly the nodes through which the message was to travel. Considered a "poor- man's router", it did work, and thus basic routing capability was formed.

In addition to fixing most of the problems with Phase I, many more operating systems were added to be supported list. TOPS-10, TOPS-20, RSX-11M, RSTS/E, RT-11, and others could become members of a DECnet network. Towards the end of the Phase II product life, the VAX was introduced and support for Phase II was introduced as an add-on product for the VMS operating system.

PHASE III

Phase III DECnet provided full routing functionality, expanded task-to-task capability, expanded file support capabilities, closer adherence to standards, and, on RSX-11M (initially), a new feature -- alternate link mapping. Alternate link mapping is a technique used that allows DEC nodes on dissimilar types of networks (one, say, on an X.25 network and another at the end of a DMR-11) to communicate by letting the lower protocol layers figure out where the remote node was and change the message to the proper protocol or device to allow transparent communications. This began the era of usage of DECnet on "foreign" networking technology instead of the traditional DDCMP (Digital Data Communications Message Protocol) protocol-oriented nets. Now, customers could have nodes connected to public packet switched networks (PPSNs, e.g., X.25) and to traditional DDCMP-oriented networks and communicate between each other using the same user interface.

Phase III also gave customers the concept of remote (virtual) terminals. A remote terminal is one where a user "sets" himself to a remote node and logs in as if the remote node were the host. A communications package on a PC is very similar to a remote terminal. Basically, the user starts up a program on the host system and it initializes network communications with a remote program on the remote node. This program creates an "environment" that looks to the remote system as if the incoming network connection is just another terminal. This allows the user at the host to do anything at the remote he could if he was directly connected to the host via modems or cables. While some of the capabilities existed in previous phases of DECnet, this was the first phase where such work was accomplished in earnest.

Another important feature of Phase III DECnet was the introduction of transparent programming capabilities on VAX systems. Previously, to communicate across the network under program control, one had to use a special library of calls to DECnet to transfer data. A typical exchange should be to "open" the network, "connect" to the remote node, send and receive data, "disconnect" from the remote node, and "close" the network. This type of programming, while not overly hard, could get somewhat confusing and usually required a fairly detailed knowledge of network operations and architecture on the part of the programmer. With the advent of transparent programming capabilities (on VAX systems only), DECnet is a breeze to use when communicating task-to-task. The programmer simply "opens" a remote node's communicating program just as one would open a file. The remote program is then treated as a sequential file and simple read and write operations are used in the language preferred, thus precluding the need to have a detailed understanding of networks and their many idiosyncrasies. For instance, a FORTRAN program would open the program at the remote node with an OPEN statement, write to the program with a WRITE statement, and read data from the remote node with a READ statement. Another important feature of DECnet Phase III was the inclusion of DECnet in the VMS V3.0 executive. Now, instead of a layered product that "sat" on top of the executive, the DECnet "executive" was made integral with the VMS executive, thus improving throughput and increasing ease of use and functionality.

Probably the most important feature of the Phase III release was the implementation of full routing. Instead of having to figure out which node to go through to get to a remote node, the network routing database takes care of all routing duties. With the support of 255 nodes in the routing algorithms, flexible networks could now be configured and used.

PHASE IV

DECnet Phase IV appeared on doorsteps in the fall of 1984 and has some enhancements that make the DECnet architecture closer to the ISO OSI standard and more compatible than ever. Inclusion of Ethernet support and, for VAX customers, the computer interconnect (CI) in the lower layers of the architecture, Phase IV, like its predecessors, retained "backward" compatibility with previous Phase releases, ensuring that functioning networks will continue to do so.

Of significance, over and above the support for the Ethernet LAN, was the support for Phase IV DECnet on the Microsoft MS-DOS operating system for the PC as well as the DEC version of UNIX, Ultrix. While the support for the PC was expected, it is interesting that it was supported due to the fact that the operating system is not a DEC-provided and supported operating system. This marked a change for Digital, providing a DEC product on a non-DEC computer and non-DEC operating system.

Third-party vendors began to offer DECnet Phase IV compatible systems for non-DEC supported systems and operating systems. TCI introduced DECnet for MS-DOS and various versions of UNIX (through their CommUnity product series); Thursby Software Systems (TSS) introduced TSSNet, a DECnet implementation for the Apple Macintosh; and other companies began to offer products for other non-DEC environments. At the end of March 1988, there were an estimated 16 different operating systems supported through a DEC-provided DECnet product or a compatible third-party product.

PHASE V

In December 1987, Digital announced support for DECnet Phase V. Phase V is a new evolution in the DNA realm, as it fully supports the OSI model, including usage of OSI protocols at all layers, where reasonable and supportable. The intent of Phase V is simple: provide the look and feel of DECnet, but do so using all OSI protocols and capabilities, thereby making DECnet a true OSI implementation and able to converse with other OSI-based systems.

While it seems that Phase V is just another phase of network architecture for DNA, it is much more. To implement Phase V and retain compatibility of user interface and "feel" is very difficult. Further, the need to support completely dissimilar communications protocols and routing algorithms from any previous implementation requires a massive recode of the architecture on selected operating systems. Another issue is which operating systems to support with Phase V capability and which will be summarily "dropped".

Phase V DECnet provides additional functions besides OSI capabilities. It supports a distributed naming service, distributed file service, distributed queueing service, File Transfer Access and Management (FTAM), Virtual Terminal Protocol (VTP), domain networks (with subareas), generic management protocols, and other capabilities. Support for domains also requires a recode of the addressing scheme to support the expanded addressing need. In DECnet Phase IV, node addresses consisted of a 16-bit address that contained the network node address and node area. In the OSI addressing scheme, a 20-octet address is used with six of the octets being used for a specific node (48-bits). Through this method, extremely large networks can be supported.

Now that we have seen a little of DECnet's growth and functionality, let us look at what makes DECnet tick.

HOW DOES DECNET WORK?

DECnet is implemented on DEC machines as a Layered Product (with the exception of VAX/VMS). This means that to get DECnet on your processor, you have to have a license to operate DECnet on your system and a distribution (media) kit if you so desire. Frequently, in a multinode site of similar machines, only selected machines will get a fully-supported license and all remaining networked machines will get a license to operate. This reduces the implementation cost of networks substantially and also the number of distribution kits floating around the shop. It is not usually a good idea to get one distribution kit for a large, multinode network that is located in different locations. This leads to network update delays, support problems, and other intangibles that have to be seen to be believed. Remember also

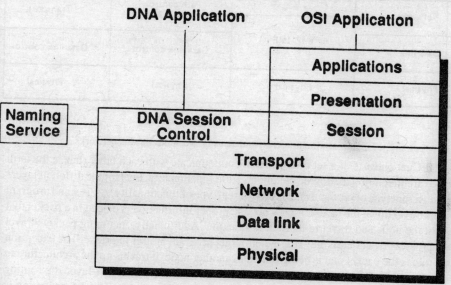

Fig. 17.1 : DECnet Phase V Architecture

that a RSX-11M DECnet distribution kit will NOT work on a RSTS/E system. Get the right kit for the right operating system. If you are a VAX user, you will get a DECnet "key" from Digital to unlock the transport layer (described below) and allow node-to-node communications.

DECnet has five layers (see Figure 17.1). The physical layer, data link control layer, transport layer, and network services layer correspond almost exactly to the lowest four ISO layers. However, the agreement breaks down at layer 5, since DECnet has no session layer, and the remaining layer, the application layer, is a mixture of the ISO presentation and application layers. The relation between DECnet and the ISO model is shown in Figure 17.2. Be sure you notice that DEC has chosen to call layer 3 the transport layer, whereas the ISO transport layer is layer 4.

Layer	ISO	ARPANET	SNA	DECNET
7	Application	User	End user	Application
6	Presentation	Telnet, FTP	NAU services	
5	Session	(None)	Data flow control	(None)
			Transmission control	
4	Transport	Host-host		Network services
		Source to destination IMP	Path control	
3	Network			Transport
2	Data link	IMP-IMP	Data link control	Data link control
1	Physical	Physical	Physical	Physical

Fig. 17.2 : Approximate correspondences between the various networks.

DECnet consists of a set of layers that communicate with each other (hence the term "layered architecture") to provide communication functionality. Each of the different layers uses a different type of protocol and has a different type of functionality. As user and program requests travel down the layers of DECnet, the proper information is placed in a packet that will exit the node and travel to its final destination. Additionally, incoming packets travel up the protocol layers until they reach their target program or user interface. The exception to this rule is the packet that is being routed to another node. It travels up the architecture to the session control layer. In the session control layer and the transport layer the routing databases are kept and in turn determine where the packet is to go. The determination is made and the packet is sent on its way to the next node whether it is the final destination or another routing node that will help the packet reach the final destination.

The bottom three layers of the DNA are the ones that get the real workout. At the lowest level are the DECnet hardware interfaces. These interfaces hook up to local area network cables (Ethernet and CI), modems (DDCMP devices such as DMR-11s and X.25 devices such as the KMS-11/BD), or local wire/coax connections (DZ11s, DL11s, DMR-11s, etc.). On some hardware, such as the DEUNA/DEQNA interfaces for Ethernet, the actual network protocol is built and stripped at the hardware level. Therefore, little information about the actual communications protocol is necessary in the layers of the DECnet product. In some situations, however, this is not entirely true. In the usage of serial, asynchronous communications (such as DZ11 to DZ11 on PDP-11 systems), the protocol may be implemented in software to ensure error-free delivery of communications packets. The transport layer works to get the data out of the correct interface and the session control layer gets the data to the correct node. Even if users on a given node are not sending or receiving anything, if the node is a routing node (not all nodes are; this is dependent upon the network configuration), it may very well be doing a great deal of work that is unseen by the user community. It is felt, however. To do processing, a program requires access to the CPU; this means that a very active routing node can degrade overall processing capabilities at the node to a great degree, depending on the volume of routing traffic, processor power and capability and tuning of the system.

DECnet has two databases that are critical to its functionality; the **permanent database** and the **volatile database**. The permanent database is used to store static information concerning the node and its interfaces as well as network program states when the node is "turned on". This can be interpreted as "this is who I am and what I can do and access" type of information. The permanent database is read by the network loader upon initialization of DECnet at the node and loaded into memory tables. The volatile database is the memory-resident table(s) that is created after DECnet is initialized and is used for all information until the system shuts down or until the network is stopped at the node. The volatile database keeps track of interface status, the routing matrix, adjacent node status, and counters. Both databases are easily modified by the system manager of the node in question through network utilities.

When DECnet is "turned on", this starts an endless chain of HELLO and TEST messages that are passed around the network when things are idle to ensure network integrity. If an adjacent node does not answer the messages within a predetermined time frame, it is considered unreachable and the database is updated to reflect same. When the node is activated again, it will answer the messages and the status will change to reachable. This continually happens throughout the life of DECnet on the node.

Just like anything else that is built by humans, DECnet and its components (hardware and software) occasionally break. When this happens, the system manager/user has a few tools at his disposal to help resolve the problem. Loopback testing is the technique that is used to test faulty components. A program is initiated on the node that tries to talk to a receiver task either on the same node or on other nodes. Think of it as a flashlight trying to find a mirror to reflect in. At each level, there is a mirror that can be activated to reflect the "light" until the reflection does not happen. When this occurs, the faulty component has been isolated and repairs can take place.

Installation of the DECnet product is not terribly difficult, but care must be taken to ensure that all nodes on the network are configured properly to get the best possible performance. On PDP-11 and DEC-20 systems, DECnet can be installed in about an hour by a person experienced with layered product installations and some communications background. On VAX, it takes about 30 minutes to get everything configured correctly. It is important to note that things like network data packet sizes should be the same on all nodes to prevent needless processing and potential problems. Little things such as this can cause performance problems, but to bring up DECnet, provided the hardware is installed correctly, not much has to be done.

At the user level, DECnet communicates with remote nodes through DEC-supplied utilities. VAX people have it pretty easy -- most of the DCL commands have DECnet functionality embedded in them. PDP-11 people are not so lucky. Utilities such as NFT (Network File Transfer) are supplied to allow DECnet user functions. Do not let things like NFT frighten you. The utilities have the same functionality and syntax as already established utilities such as PIP. They require little training and are fairly straightforward in their use.

As can be seen, DECnet can help expedite information transfer and increase system flexibility. But, it does have its problems.

With any processing environment, security is an issue that most system users and managers are plagued with and assaulted with from all sides. Implementation of a network, ANY network, will not help solve these problems. If anything, it will compound them. DECnet assumes that it is operating in a nonhostile environment; hence, it has little in the way of security features. Granted, not many folks would be so industrious as to place a protocol analyzer on a phone to get information as it passes from site to site, but this can happen. Additionally, the network is only as secure as the least secure system. If a single system has poor security and audit control, that system is a potential target for network exploitation. Users of DECnet are cautioned to tighten up system security on network nodes as exploitation over the network is difficult to trace and is possible.

Probably the most aggravating problem with networks is that they break. As discussed before, it is possible to repair a network, but it is also necessary to know how it works. This means that trained network specialists are frequently needed to fix broken networks and, needless to say, they can be difficult to find. Expertise in system and network architecture communications theory, protocol design and implementation, use of analyzers and other debugging tools, communications component design (modems, switching centers, etc.) programming, etc., are necessary qualities for the trained network analyst. Frequently, the network analyst will use most of these tools to fix the broken network and get it back up and running in a minimal amount of time.

DECnet is not for everybody, but neither is jogging or karate. Selection of the DECnet product for your environment needs to be from the result of many hours of traffic analysis, cost analysis, support staff identification, and needs analysis. But, for the flexibility, timeless, and functionality DECnet is tough to beat.

DECNET VS SNA

Since SNA and DECnet have similar goals -- to provide a general framework for networking and distributed processing -- it is interesting to compare and contrast them. On the whole, SNA offers more parameters, features, and options than DECnet does, and is correspondingly more complicated. For example, both SNA and DECnet have a message that is used to establish a connection between remote processes. The DECnet message, CONNECT INITIATE, has about 10 parameters. The corresponding SNA message, BIND, has three times as many parameters.

The physical layer is similar in both architectures; both can handle most of the types of lines available. Although the goals of the data link layer are the same in both architectures, the protocols differ in several ways. Frames in SNA are delimited by a special bit sequence, whereas frames in DECnet contain a character count in the header telling how long the frame is. SNA frames may be an arbitrary number of bits, whereas DECnet frames must be multiples of 8 bits. The network layers of the two architectures differ greatly. In SNA all packets belonging to a given connection follow the same route through the subnet, whereas in DECnet each packet is routed independently of all its predecessors. The transport layers provide the higher layers similar service -- error free, sequenced connections -- but their implementations are quite different due to the great difference in the underlying network layer. SNA has an elaborate session layer, whereas DECnet has none. Finally, the approach to the presentation layer is also different. In SNA it is possible for users to request various transformations on data passed from the application layer to the session layer, such as text compression and encryption. In DECnet these transformations are not possible, although there is a file access protocol that reads and writes remote files, providing transformations where needed.

18

SYSTEMS NETWORK ARCHITECTURE

INTRODUCTION

IBM has a networking product that they have invested a great deal of time and money into. It is somewhat expensive, difficult to configure, difficult to change, but it does work and has some interesting features that are useful to understand. Called Systems Network Architecture (SNA), it is a networking product and a philosophy of networking at the same time. In this chapter, we shall discover a bit more about it and what it means to networking.

EVOLUTION

SNA is a network architecture intended to allow IBM customers to construct their own private networks, both hosts and subnet. A bank, for example, might have one or more CPUs in its data processing department and numerous terminals in each of its branch offices. Using SNA, all these isolated components could be transformed into a coherent system.

Prior to SNA, IBM had several hundred communication products, using three dozen teleprocessing access methods, with more than a dozen data link protocols alone. The basic idea behind SNA was to eliminate this chaos and to provide a coherent framework for loosely coupled distributed processing. Given the desire of many of IBM's customers to maintain compatibility with all these (mutually incompatible) programs and protocols, the SNA architecture is more complicated in places than it might have been, had these constraints not been present. SNA also performs a large number of functions not found in other networks, which, although valuable for certain applications, tend to add to the overall complexity of the architecture.

SNA has evolved considerably over the years, and is still evolving. The original **release,** in 1974, permitted only centralized networks, that is, tree-shaped networks with only **a single** host and its terminals. From our point of view, that is no network at all. The 1976 release allowed multiple hosts with their respective trees, with intertree communication possible only between the roots of the trees. The 1979 release removed this restriction, allowing a more general intercommunication.

SNA started off in 1974 as a means of extending the host architecture of IBM mainframe systems. In 1978, it underwent a fairly drastic revamp to allow true networking capabilities and was again overhauled in 1984 to allow what IBM calls "a system of networks." A "system of networks" is basically the allowance of smaller, private networks (such as token ring LANs, terminal networks, etc.) based upon differing technologies, to be interconnected into a larger, more distributed network. IBM tends to view the overall network topology as a large distributed system, hence, the term a "system of networks".

SNA VS DECNET

As you are probably already aware, DEC likes to compare the DNA to the Open Systems Interconnect (OSI) Reference Model on a regular basis. As you are also aware, Digital supports multiple technologies at layers 1 and 2 of the model (such as Computer Interconnect (CI), Ethernet (NI), DDCMP (async and sync), X.25, and others), which utilize multiple base protocols. For instance, CI uses SCS protocol to communicate; Ethernet utilizes various protocols such as MOP, LAT, CTERM, and others. The issue at hand is that there is no one singular protocol at layer 2, specifically, that DEC claims to be "the" protocol for use on all processors. This is because DEC wants to support multiple protocols at all networking levels and wants to encourage networking of dissimilar machines and use the latest network technology, where reasonable.

IBM has a somewhat different view of the computing and network world. While SNA is implemented in layers, such as OSI, the layers do not represent the same meanings as the OSI labels except for layers 1 and 2. Regardless of the layer 1 hardware, at layer 2 the preferred protocol that is "the" protocol in the IBM world is SDLC (Synchronous Data Link Control) protocol. This means that if you want to talk to most SNA supported devices, you had better be able to speak SDLC. IBM views this as a feature as it provides a single, uniform line discipline that is predictable, stable, and implemented on a wide variety of processors. IBM can get away with it as well. When you own 70% of the computing marketplace, it is fairly straightforward to dictate how conformance will be handled. So, DNA looks at being able to support multiple lower-level technologies and protocols. SNA supports SDLC as the primary protocol and is starting to allow connection of other network technologies, such as the token ring, but still supporting SDLC as the main access protocol at layer 2.

At the host level, the DNA architecture differs from the SNA world in a radical way. In DNA, there is no "master" node -- all nodes are equal in the eyes of the network. If a node goes down, for whatever reason, it does not necessarily "kill" the network or cause a catastrophic condition on the network. Even in the Ethernet environment, if the only router on the segment (which would also happen to be the Designated Router) were to die a miserable death, the end-nodes would still continue to communicate without the use of the router. SNA is philosophically different. A central point of control (called a Systems Service Control Point -- SSCP) in a group of nodes (called a DOMAIN) controls all connection requests and network flow. SSCP services are typically provided by mainframe-resident access services. Upon establishing the SSCP in a domain, all control to nodes in the domain is then hierarchical -- every critical transaction to the communications process must be controlled by the SSCP. The most common mainframe-resident SNA access method is called VTAM (Virtual Telecommunications Access Method). An older access method called TCAM (Telecommunications Access Method) is still around on some nodes, but IBM does not push its sale and it requires an extremely technical and competent staff to manage it, as it is difficult to configure, maintain and use. VTAM provides a means for host-resident programs, queues, etc to gain access to remote facilities on an SNA network in a manner similar to the way that DECnet allows user programs and utilities to access other nodes and resources. The similarities stop there, however. VTAM controls the access from unit-to-unit in a domain. It has to know who is where, what services they provide, etc., through system generation and parameter tables that are located in various parts of VTAM and in 370x network controllers. The end result is that if the mainframe that has VTAM running on it dies, for any reason, new connections may not be able to be done and other networking functions will suffer. In the DECnet environment, connections to other nodes continue unabated (unless the node that dies is a routing node, but that will cause problems in both networking technologies). IBM, realizing the weakness of host-resident network control, came out with a niew version of Network Control Program (NCP) software for the 370x-series of network controllers called NCP/VS. NCP/VS's main purpose will be to provide mini-SSCP services for some connection requests and to offload some of the SSCP functions that a host typically has to make down to the network controller level. This will have the effect of reducing connection dependency on the host and also speeding up some of the connection access time between entities on the network that wish to connect with each other.

NETWORK SPACE

An SNA network consists of a collection of machines called nodes, of which there are four types, approximately characterized as follows. Type 1 nodes are terminals. Type 2 nodes are controllers, machines that supervise the behaviour of terminals and other peripherals. Type 4 nodes are front end processors, devices whose function is to relieve the main CPU of the work and interrupt handling associated with data communication. Type 5 nodes are the main hosts themselves, although with the advent of low-cost microprocessors, some controllers have acquired some host-like properties. There are no type 3 nodes.

Each nodes contains one or more Network Addressable Units or NAUs. A NAU is a piece of software that allows a process to use the network. An analogy may be helpful here. Consider a building with a telephone socket in every office. Each socket has a unique, hardwired address (extension number) permanently associated with it. To use the telephone system, a person plugs a telephone into a convenient socket, and thereafter can be called at the extension belonging to the socket. Similarly, each NAU has a network address. To use the network, a process must connect itself to a NAU, at which time it can be addressed and can address other NAUs. The NAUs are thus the entry points into the network for user processes.

There are three kinds of NAUs. A logical unit or LU is the usual variety to which user processes can be attached. A physical unit or PU is a special NAU associated with each node, which is used by the network to bring the node online, take it offline, test it, and perform similar administrative functions. The PU provides a way for the network to address a physical device, without reference to which processes are using it. The third kind of NAU is the System Services Control Point or SSCP, of which there is normally one per type 5 node and none in the other nodes. The SSCP has complete knowledge of, and control over, all the front ends, controllers, and terminals attached to the host. The collection of hardware and software managed by an SSCP is called a domain. Figure 18.1 depicts a simple two domain SNA network.

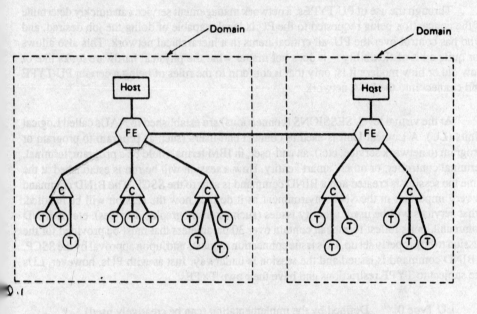

Fig. 18.1 : A two domain SNA network, FE = Front End, C = Controller, T = Terminal.

SNA views entities in the network space as being Network Addressable Units (NAUs). A NAU is nothing more than an IBM term that means that all items capable of working together in a networking environment, both at the physical and virtual levels, have a method of being selected for access. To do this, SNA assigns designators to functions that physical devices or programs provide. A Physical Unit (PU) provides physical connectivity between devices. Every node on an SNA network contains a PU and can be accessed by the SSCP for the domain in which the PU lives. Programs, as a rule, do not establish connections to PUs, as they provide level 1 and level 2 network capabilities that are of interest only to the networking system (i.e. SCP or another PU wishing to downline-load a PU). PUs (and all other NAUs) are characterized by "what" they are capable of doing through the use of PU TYPE designators, as follows:

PU Type 5	Physical unit in a subarea node with SSCP (VTAM or TCAM node)
PU Type 4	Contained in a subarea node without SSCP (37x5 controller)
PU Type 3	Not defined
PU Type 2	Peripheral node PU, such as a remote system, terminal, etc.
PU Type 2.1	Enhanced PU Type 2, which will supersede PU T1 and PU T2
PU Type 1	Support in a 37x% to support single terminals such as 3767. '

Through the use of PU TYPEs, a network management service can quickly determine if the connection being requested to the PU is legal, capable of doing the job desired, and who has control over the PU, all critical items in a hierarchical network. This also allows for quite a bit of flexibility -- it does not matter what the physical hardware looks like or how old or how modern it is, only that it conform to the rules of being a certain PU TYPE and connect into the SNA network.

At the virtual level, SESSIONS (connections) are established to NAUs called Logical Units (LU). A Logical Unit is used to connect end-users (such as program to program or program to network service, etc.); an end-user, in IBM terms, could be a program, terminal, terminal controller, or other "smart" entity. How a session will be run is established at the time the session is created and a BIND command is sent to the SSCP. The BIND command is very important in the SNA environment as it defines how the session will be handled, what services will be used, security issues (such as cryptographic services), etc. A BIND command, in its fullest form, can contain over 30 parameters that must be provided for the session to be properly set up. LUs issue connection requests and, upon approval by the SSCP, a BIND command is issued and the session is underway. Just as with PUs, however, LUs are subject to TYPE restrictions and have their own TYPEs:

LU Type 0	Defined by the implementation (can be creatively used).
LU Type 1	Application programs-to-device communications to access nondisplay types of devices such as printers, hard-copy terminals, SNA character streams, etc.
LU Type 2	Application program communications to 3270 display terminals.
LU Type 3	Application program communications to printers utilizing a subset of the 3270 data stream.
LU Type 4	Application program communications similar to the services provided by LU T1.
LU Type 6	Interprogram (program to program) & 6.1 communication that is SNA defined and part of the new distributed operating system function
LU Type 6.2	Usually called "Advanced Program-to-Program Communication" (APPC). This is basically a generalized task-to-task interface for general purpose data transfer and communication.
LU Type 7	Application program communications to 5250 display terminals.

In the areas of LUs, there are three types of LUs: non-SNA specified (LU0), terminal access LUs (LU types 1, 2, 3, 4 and 7), and program-to-program LUs (types 6, 6.1, and 6.2). To complicate things even more, LUs have "qualifiers" that are imposed at the BIND command that determine how data is represented to the destination LU, what kind of presentation services will be provided, and what kind of transmission subsystem profile may be used. When programming in the SNA environment, these features can be very useful when moving applications from one display class to another as it will allow porting of applications from one LU type to another with minimal modifications if the application is coded carefully to start with. As a result, the use of the data stream "qualifiers" to LU connectivity can be a real help in the high-transaction, large-terminal environments that mainframe systems are usually involved with 2000+ terminals on-line simultaneously).

SNA LAYERS

SNA is a vendor-developed network architecture in wide-spread use. SNA is a mainframe-oriented network architecture that also uses a layered approach. The layers defined as part of SNA are shown in Figure 18.2. See also Figure 18.3. Generally, the services included as part of the SNA architecture are similar to those defined in the OSI model. However, there are some differences in the way that the services are organized and grouped into layers, so there is not an exact one-to-one correspondence between the layers in the two architectures.

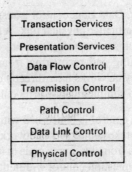

Fig. 18.2 : SNA Layers.

One possible mapping of the SNA protocol hierarchy onto the ISO hierarchy is shown in Figure 17.2. The two models do not correspond especially well, especially in layers 3, 4 and 5, so other authors may choose to map them slightly differently.

The SNA layers are further discussed below:

Physical Control Layer. The lowest layer takes care of physically transporting bits from one machine to another. Physical Control handles the transmission of bits over a physical circuit. Although the physical control layer is addressed in the architecture. SNA does not actually define specific protocols for this layer. Rather, the SNA architecture assumes the use of various existing international standards at this level.

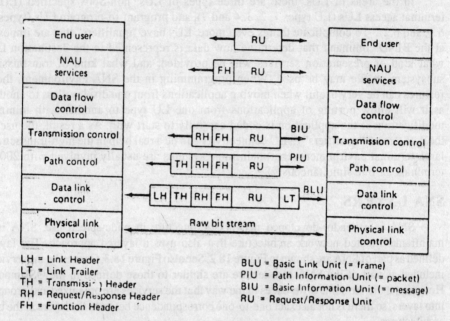

LH = Link Header
LT = Link Trailer
TH = Transmission Header
RH = Request/Response Header
FH = Function Header

BLU = Basic Link Unit (= frame)
PIU = Path Information Unit (= packet)
BIU = Basic Information Unit (= message)
RU = Request/Response Unit

Fig. 18.3 : Protocol hierarchy and units exchanged in SNA.

Data Link Control Layer. Data Link control is responsible for the transmission of data between two nodes over a particular physical link. A primary function of this layer is to detect and recover from transmission errors. Data link control layer constructs frames from the raw bit stream, detecting and recovering from transmission errors in a way transparent to higher layers. Many networks have directly or indirectly copied their layer 2 protocol from SNA's layer 2 data communication protocol, SDLC.

Path Control Layer. Path control is concerned with routing data from one node to the next in the path that a message takes through the network. This path often crosses through several nodes as a message moves from the source node to its destination. Path control layer is concerned with routing and congestion control within the subnet. It can block unrelated packets together into frames to enhance transmission efficiency and can deal with the hierarchical addressing used in SNA.

Transmission Control Layer. Transmission control keeps track of the status of connections, or sessions, between network users, controls the pacing of data flow within a session, and sees that the units of data that make up a message are sent and received in the proper sequence. This layer also provides an optional data encryption/decryption facility.

Transmission control layer's job is to create, manage and delete transport connections, called sessions in SNA. In effect, it provides a uniform interface to higher layers, independent of the properties of the subnet. Once a session has been established, it regulates the rate of flow between processes, controls buffer allocation, manages the different message priorities, handles multiplexing and demultiplexing of data and control messages for the benefit of higher layers, and performs encryption and decryption when requested to do so.

Data Flow Control Layer. Data flow control is concerned with the overall integrity of the flow of data during a session between two network users. This can involve determining the mode of sending and receiving, managing groups of related messages, or determining the type of response mode to use.

Data flow control has nothing at all to do with controlling the flow of data in the usual sense. Instead, it has to do with keeping track of which end of a session is supposed to talk next, assuming that the processes want such a service. This layer is also heavily involved in error recovery. A somewhat unusual feature of the data flow control layer is the absence of a header used to communicate with the corresponding software on the other end. Instead, the information that would normally be communicated in a header is passed to transmission control as parameters and included in the transmission header.

Presentation Services Layer. Presentation services is responsible for formatting data for different presentation media used in a session. This can involve converting messages from one character code to another and formatting data for display on various types of devices.

Transaction Services Layer. Transaction services provides application services to end users of the network. These application services include operator control over sessions, document distribution and interchange, and distributed data access.

NAU services provides two classes of services to user processes. First, there are presentation services, such as text compression. Second, there are session services, for setting up connections. In addition, there are network services, which have to do with the operation of the network as a whole.

No local area networks conform completely to the SNA architecture. However, SNA is important to LAN technology because in many situations, a LAN must connect to, and be made a logical part of, an SNA mainframe network.

NETWORK TOPOLOGIES

Topologically, an SNA network does not look much different than a DNA network, but traffic-wise there are substantial differences. IBM is a company that utilizes the "divide and conquer" mentality quite well and provides "smart" clusters of terminals or network concentrators as cooperating entities in the SNA environment. This means that terminals that are smart can be directly connected to; terminals that are dumb can have a terminal concentrator hooked up to them and the concentrator can be connected to SNA. For optimization of line usage and traffic flow, network controllers can be used to connect multiple terminal clusters or other network controllers together, providing flexible networking configurations that can be changed as growth requires without necessarily replacing existing hardware. Also, since all nodes on the network can be addressed by "names" the reconfiguration of a network, properly done, does not affect application programs that have been written for the SNA environment. Application programs still call the service by "name" and it magically happens as long as the proper VTAM tables and NCP tables have been updated to reflect whatever changes have taken place.

SNA networks are not limited to a single domain, either. SSCPs can provide session connections across domain boundaries ("cross- domain" session) to requesting LUs, effectively providing large network connectivity with segmented network management facilities. To do this requires flow control, path control, and many other network features. SNA provides these and much more, making it a very sophisticated technology with the capability of providing additional functionality at incremental expansions.

Probably the two most glaring differences between DEC networking products and IBM SNA products is one DEC strength and one IBM strength. The DEC strength is that Digital provides connectivity to a wide variety of technologies and to a wide variety of processor architectures; SNA is fairly limited in scope and capabilities and requires much manual intervention. The IBM strength is that the SNA product set provides very powerful network management tools (such as Network Communications Control Facility (NCCF), Network Problem Determination Application (NPDA), etc.) performance analyzers (VTAM Performance Analysis and Reporting System - VTAMPARS), cryptographic facilities, processing management, change management, and other features; DEC has few and they are marginally useful in many situations.

SNA DIRECTIONS

What will IBM do with SNA and why do you care? Well, the general consensus in the networking world is that after the dust settles, there will be two main networking architectures: OSI and SNA. SNA is currently undergoing changes and IBM is also heavily involved in the OSI space as well (mostly to satisfy European customers who require OSI in their networks), so expect to see IBM continue to push SNA and, when available on IBM systems, OSI. Also, since IBM has to provide services to its customers, such as banks, and those customers will want to provide services on the Integrated Services Digital Network (ISDN) such as bank at home, shop at home, etc., for IBM to maintain market leverage in the mainframe area, it will have to provide ISDN connectivity, and ISDN connectivity means OSI communications capability.

Another main reason to watch SNA is IBM's push into the office automation space. IBM issues things called "Statements of Direction" that are essential to pay heed to if you are planning on keeping up with developments at IBM. In the area of office automation, the statement was made that "All IBM Office Systems, Will Be Integrated". This is a fairly strong statement that has communications implications galore. With IBM's Distributed Office Support System (DISOSS) product set, the use of communications between systems is critical and getting more attention. When consideration is also given to two document standards on the market -- DIA (Document Interchange Architecture: a method by which document formats, protocols, etc., are defined to communicate between end-users) and DCA (Document Content Architecture: a document representation methodology) -- the fact that PU2.1 was created with the need of connecting items such as the Displaywriter and the Scanmaster 1 to an SNA network and the fact that IBM firmly recognizes the need to provide multifunction support in the office means that SNA will have to expand in scope and usage and will eventually become a favoured method to connect office environments of IBM customers.

Another major reason for SNA watching is the IBM Systems Network Interconnect program (SNI). SNI provides for interconnection, protocol conversion, and gateways to other architectures and systems. While SNI is still somewhat new, it bears watching.

SUMMARY

SNA is basically a hierarchical network with the ability to interconnect different types of actual hardware technologies, similar to other types of network architectures. Where SNA differs is in the wealth of connectivity offerings as well as the ability to support a great many integrated network management and connectivity tools. As such, it is a powerful and flexible architecture that provides configured networks with a plethora of network solutions to various business and scientific problems.

19

TRANSMISSION CONTROL PROTOCOL/INTERNET PROTOCOL

INTRODUCTION

One of the problems with networks that is prevalent today is that there are many different protocols and network types. The hardware choices are confusing enough, but software protocol suites that run over the various types of network hardware solutions can absolutely boggle the mind. Ethernet, for instance, boasts a vast number of protocol suites such as DDCMP, LAT, MOP, XNS, SCS, TCP/IP, VRP, NRP, and a slew of other three-letter acronyms for various protocols that will solve all the problems a customer could possibly have.

Within the scheme of protocols, however, some still seem to rear their ugly heads, no matter how hard the industry tries to put them down or get rid of them. One suite, **Transmission Control Protocol/Internet Protocol (TCP/IP)**, is such an occurrence. Every other vendor of networks will claim that their protocol is better and that TCP/IP is going away. Some will point to the decisions made by the US Department of Defense (DOD) to eventually migrate to internationally recognized and standardized communications hardware and protocols, obviating the need for TCP/IP and eventually replacing it. Some view TCP/IP as a workhorse whose time has come to be put out to pasture.

Then there are the zealots -- those that think that the ONLY communications protocol suite for use in the world is TCP/IP and all others are fluff.

Somewhere in the middle of the two camps are those who do not know what to do with TCP/IP or, worse, do not even really understand its significance to networks. Unfortunately, these individuals are usually the managers of such diverse camps of attitudes and must make decisions on whether to use TCP/IP on a project or not.

Although it is the ISO open systems protocols which have received most recent publicity, there are other well established protocol sets, particularly on Ethernet, which have a large share of the current LAN market. Some argue that these protocols offer a better alternative to the largely untried and potentially cumbersome ISO set, but most manufacturers indicate a willingness to adopt ISO protocols at some point of time in future.

The non-ISO protocol described in this chapter illustrate different approach from the ISO protocol set to Open Systems working. TCP/IP, is a vendor-independent wide area network protocol set, which has been widely used on LANs for peer-to-peer communications. Here, we will examine the TCP and IP networking protocols and some implementations that have become de-facto standards in the military area as well as academic and UNIX areas.

In recent years, knowledge of the capabilities of Transmission Control Protocol/Internet Protocol (TCP/IP) has spread far in the globe. IT managers in all types of organizations have begun to research its suitability as an internetworking. TCP/IP seems to be a ready-made solution to the commercial information systems requirements of intercommunication and interoperation.

In US, government officials and research communities and many UNIX aficionados are already well versed in the vocabulary and configuration issues of this set of protocols. But for the newcomer to TCP/IP, the existing sources of information are, in many cases, written by developers apparently for developers. Most information is primarily technical with detailed descriptions of the bits, flags and fields of the protocols. But less information is given about the practical problems of implementing TCP/IP from scratch, in, for example, a commercial rather than a technical or research environment; here the skills and constraints may be very different. The information needed does exist, but one has to read a considerable quantity of material before finding what one needs.

ORIGIN OF TCP/IP

A comprehensive set of 'ready-made' communications protocols called TCP/IP became widely available and well-known only when Berkeley Software Distribution released Berkeley UNIX 4.2BSD in September 1983. This was not a coincidence; its inclusion in this release was funded by the US government. TCP/IP protocols are based on standards originally developed for the US government and US research community. With the release of UNIX 4.2BSD, these communications standards emerged from the confines of the US Department of Defense and the US university and research networks; TCP/IP became *the way* to interconnect UNIX systems. Berkeley UNIX 4.2BSD and subsequent releases spread quickly throughout the US university and commercial communities. With UNIX achieving wide popularity as an 'open system', the fame of TCP/IP has continued to spread. But TCP/IP is not, and never has been, narrowly confined to UNIX. It was developed to allow free interchange of data among all machines, independent of type, manufacturer, hardware or operating system.

In the late 1980s, TCP/IP received a further boost to its fortunes when Sun Microsystems published the specification for Open Network Computing (ONC), often called the **Network File System (NFS)**. NFS adds important functions to TCP/IP and is now very widely available and regarded as an integral part of the TCP/IP protocol suite. It is particularly valuable for the commercial implementor because of the simple user interfaces that it provides.

TCP/IP was developed to satisfy the need to interconnect various projects that included computer networks and also allow for the addition of dissimilar machines to the networks in a systematic and standardized manner. While it is quite true that smaller defense projects may not have warranted the use of TCP/IP for project aspects, edicts from various DOD concerns such, as the Undersecretary of Defense for Research and Development forced many government contractors and in-house developed projects to use the suite to conform with DOD requirements.

The suite of protocols commonly referred to as TCP/IP (US Military Standards 1778 and 1777) was developed by the United States Department of Defense for its A.R.P.A. (Advanced Research Project Agency) network. This is a very large scale, wide area, network linking many major commercial, university and military establishments. The relevance of TCP/IP to LANs is two-fold. First, as it is a datagram based protocol, it is well suited to LAN access methods, particularly, Ethernet. Secondly, it is particularly popular within the UNIX community, giving it a large user base, many of whom wish to use LANs.

Cost-effective implementations of TCP/IP are now available for all types and sizes of machines from the largest mainframe to personal computers and workstations. This has brought TCP/IP and its capabilities to the attention of a very wide audience. Computer managers and users in commercial organizations throughout the world have begun to implement TCP/IP as a way of solving the problems of interworking between machines of different manufacture.

TCP/IP provides all the facilities for two computer systems to exchange information (intercommunication), interpret it properly, and present it in a format which can be understood by the local machine and its users (interoperation). NFS gives a simple and locally-familiar representation of a set of remote and possibly unfamiliar computer filing systems; like the original components of the TCP/IP suite, NFS is now available for many different computers.

TCP/IP COMMUNICATIONS ARCHITECTURE

In 1977, ISO began to develop a communications architecture which would become an international standard, a set of communications protocols known as **Open Systems Interconnection** (OSI). This initiative had the same general aim as TCP/IP — intercommunication and interoperation across different manufacturers' computing architectures. But unlike TCP/IP, in a way that met a published set of 'open' international standards. Now

OSI comprises many hundreds of standards, each of which has taken years to develop, agree and publish in its final ISO form. Regrettably, the best known aspect of OSI is still the OSI reference model and its seven layers, Figure 19.1 as the model itself is only a development aid to allow standard developers to produce the detailed communications standards within a consistent architectural framework.

In the standard which describes the reference model, OSI standards developers state that they will exclude any details which would be implementation dependent. The result is that while the standards have been kept 'pure', many details which would aid development of viable OSI products are excluded from the standards themselves. While some would argue that OSI is more rigorous in its standardization than TCP/IP, the OSI development process seems to have become enmeshed in procedures weighed down by the difficulties of obtaining consensus in large committees and dogged by supplier politics. By confining OSI standards to abstract definitions in a complex vocabulary, defined just for the purpose, and then charging considerable sums for copies of those standards, ISO committees have, undoubtedly, if unintentionally, slowed the OSI development process and the delivery of useful conforming products.

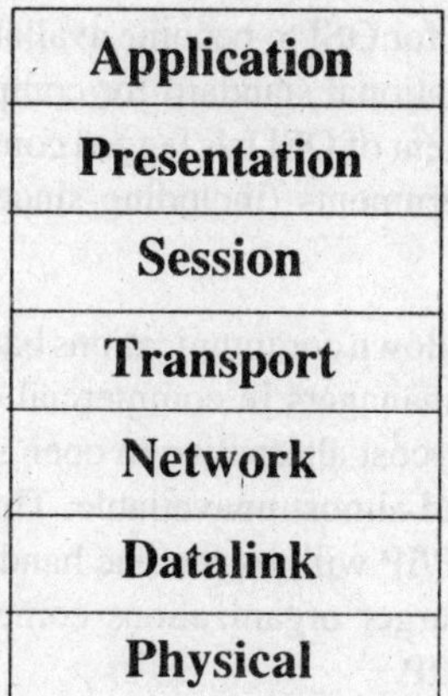

| Application |
| Presentation |
| Session |
| Transport |
| Network |
| Datalink |
| Physical |

Fig. 19.1 : ISO OSI reference model

With a more restricted geographic and technical scope, TCP/IP developers adopted a pragmatic approach. TCP/IP standardization was based on the Request For Comments (RFC), a flexible and fast standardizatiion process using electronic mail to publish and exchange comments and ideas, and to update drafts. Developers often outlined parts of a standard in a familiar computer language, usually 'C' which, while not intended to be implemented directly, gave a very good starting point for an initial implementation.

TCP/IP standards are freely available on-line from a number of computer systems, originally without full drawings or graphics, but today with all the quality of a laser-printed, desktop-published document as PostScript files. For manufacturers of communications and computing products, the contrast with OSI could not be more stark; it is just so much easier to obtain TCP/IP information than OSI. Standards were produced more quickly and they are written in a readable and comprehensible form by developers for developers.

Ths US government demanded TCP/IP for all systems, thereby ensuring every US government computer supplier provided it. They also funded universities to implement the standards. In the USA, such publicly funded work enters the public domain, and, if not of a military nature, is freely available to all citizens. While it may not be used directly for commercial purposes, having a working example in 'C' source code certainly assists future developments by commercial suppliers!

Neither OSI nor TCP/IP has been developed in isolation. There has been a considerable interchange of ideas and techniques, particularly evident in the changes in OSI since the mid-1980s with the development of the connectionless OSI suite. Nor have the OSI standards been ignored by suppliers. As with TCP/IP in the USA, universities have been busy developing OSI implementations and governments have, since the mid-1980s, required OSI-conforming products . But this activity has not as yet created a general market demand and the same level of fully developed OSI computing products, except perhaps with the notable exception of X.25 network equipment.

The 'pump priming' of TCP/IP has been more successful and has ensured, thereby, that it has moved ahead much faster than OSI. Governments and commercial organizations worldwide have waited patiently for OSI to become available and to reap the benefits of the promised flexibility of an international standard for computer communications and inter-operation. In short, the development of OSI has lagged considerably behind TCP/IP, despite support from a number of governments (including since 1985, the US government and Department of Defense).

When it comes to breaking down communications barriers between different computer suppliers, information systems managers in commercial companies now see TCP/IP as a fully functional, proven and low-cost alternative to open systems interconnection. OSI, by comparison, is still immature and almost unavailable. This may change in the mid-1990s, but the explosive interest in TCP/IP will, on the one hand, delay OSI implementation and, on the other, encourage it, as larger organizations come up against some of the known fundamental limitations of TCP/IP.

As with much of the specialist vocabulary which surrounds computers and telecom-munications networks, the term TCP/IP will conjure up different concepts to different readers. TCP/IP is used as shorthand for a large set of standards with many different features and functions. The letters 'TCP/IP' stand for two communications protocols, **Transmission Control Protocol (TCP)** and **Internet Protocol (IP)**. These were developed during the late 1970s and early 1980s as the key communications protocols for the US 'Internet', the collected set of interconnected communications networks (originally comprising ARPAnet, but now including NSFnet, and NYSERnet, and the Department of Defense Network among many others). Today these support the US government, Department of Defense, US military, and the university, education and commercial organizations conduct research on behalf of those bodies. (Use of the US Internet for commercial traffic between commercial organiza-tions is not allowed.)

The two protocols, TCP and IP, are but two of the building blocks required for a complete communications 'architecture', but the term 'TCP/IP' is most often used as a

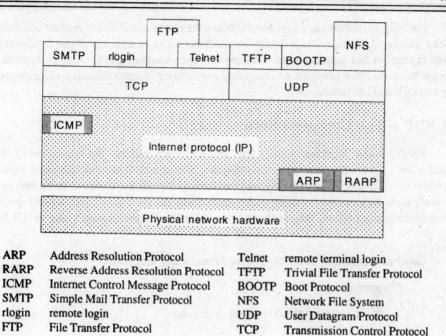

ARP	Address Resolution Protocol	Telnet	remote terminal login
RARP	Reverse Address Resolution Protocol	TFTP	Trivial File Transfer Protocol
ICMP	Internet Control Message Protocol	BOOTP	Boot Protocol
SMTP	Simple Mail Transfer Protocol	NFS	Network File System
rlogin	remote login	UDP	User Datagram Protocol
FTP	File Transfer Protocol	TCP	Transmission Control Protocol

Fig. 19.2 : TCP/IP architecture

shorthand term of the whole communications 'architecture' specified originally by the US Department of Defense. This architecture is a much bigger set of standards than just TCP and IP. We shall also use 'TCP/IP' to mean the complete architecture, except where this will cause confusion.

Communications architectures have been developed by computer manufacturers since the mid-1970s. An architecture describes three facets of communications in an abstract way which is independent of particular hardware or technology. The three aspects are:

(1) Data exchange (intercommunications)

(2) Data interpretation (interoperation)

(3) System management

Like the OSI reference model, communications architectures are described in layers; each layer providing its own functions but using the functions of the layer below. This layering decouples the functions of one layer from another making layered architectures flexible; their designers can respond to changes in technology and in application software without a major upheaval for existing users. The implementation and existing installations can be extended, as new, often faster techniques and technologies become available. It is important to realize that the standards do not specify the interfaces seen by computer users. Though suppliers often base their implementations on a competitor's successful product, one must expect that user interfaces will differ, in major or minor ways, from supplier to supplier.

For TCP/IP, the architectural standards and the operational US Internet are controlled by the Internet Activities Board (IAB). The IAB devolves its responsibilities for development, operations and management to a number of subcommittees and working groups which it controls and to other commercial companies specializing in communications and computing research and consultancy.

TCP/IP – The Complete Suite

The TCP and IP, describe only the communication aspects, the movement of data across a set of interconnected physical networks. The complete architecture must include standard mechanisms for interpreting and converting data for the common tasks that users of computers have come to expect. As these tasks sit on top of and depend on the communications protocols, they are sometimes called the **Upper Layer Protocols (ULPs)**.

Generally, computer users have needed three major functions:

– File transfer

– Terminal access (vertual terminal protocols)

– Mail preparation and transfer

Now, in commercial environments other tasks have become equally important:

– Resource sharing (files, printers, plotters)

– Diskless workstations

– Transaction processing

– Management

– Directory services

– Security

Those familiar with the resource-sharing Local Area Network (LAN) (such as Microsoft LAN Manager and Novell NetWare) will have seen the power of remote or distributed file and disk sharing and of peripheral sharing; for some companies, diskless workstations have a number of advantages.

In a complete, modern architecture, standard protocols are needed for all these new distributed systems as well as for the proven minicomputer and mainframe-based architectures.

The TCP/IP protocol suite addresses these issues comprehensively. The standards are not static but are being added to at a steady rate. Current activities relate to new facilities in directory services at the application layer and improvements in routing and addressing mechanisms at the lower layers.

Upper Layer Protocols

Beginning with the well-known application layer protocols, File Transfer Protocol (FTP), Telnet (TCP/IPs virtual terminal protocol), and Simple Mail Transfer Protocol (SMTP), NFS adds a disk/file system resource-sharing capability, LPR deals with printing, the BOOT Protocol, (BOOTP) provides the basis for diskless workstation operation, and Simple Network Management Protocol (SNMP) is the Internet standard for management. As Figure 19.2 shows, TCP is complemented by the User Datagram Protocol (UDP).

Lower Layer Protocols

IP is not the lowest level of the layered architecture. TCP/IP does not explain new standards for low-level communications but TCP/IP standards include descriptions of how IP operates over the commonly available long-distance and local physical communications networks. These descriptions include many proprietary networks as well as CCITT and other international standard transmission mechanisms.

For long-distance operation over public telecommunications circuits, the standards include point-to-point leased and dial up, synchronous and asynchronous links, and X.25 connections. For local communications, Ethernet Version 2 (as specified by DEC, Intel and Xerox) is by far the most widely used. ISO/IEEE networks (ISO 8802.3, 8802.4 8802.5) and FDDI (ISO 9314) are also specified as are proprietary networks such as ARCNET.

TCP/IP PROTOCOL SET STRUCTURE

The TCP/IP suite is not a single protocol. Rather, it is four- layer communication architecture that provides some reasonable network features, such as end-to-end communications, unreliable communications line fault handling, packet sequencing, internetwork routing, and specialized functions unique to DOD communications needs such as standardized message priorities. The bottom layer, network services, provides for communication to network hardware. Network hardware used in the various networks throughout the DOD typically reflects the usage of FIPS (Federal Information Processing Standard) compliant network hardware (such as IEEE 802 series of LANs and other technologies such as X.25). The layer above the network services layer is referred to as the internet protocol (IP) layer. The IP layer is responsible for providing a datagram service that routes data packets between dissimilar network architectures (such as between Ethernet, and, say, X.25). IP has a few interesting qualities, one of which is the issue of data reliability. As a datagram service, IP does not guarantee delivery of data. Basically, if the data gets there, great. If not, that's OK too. Data concurrency, sequencing, and delivery guarantee is the job of the TCP protocol. TCP provides for error control, retransmission, packet sequencing and many other capabilities. It is very complex and provides most of the features of the connection to other applications on other systems.

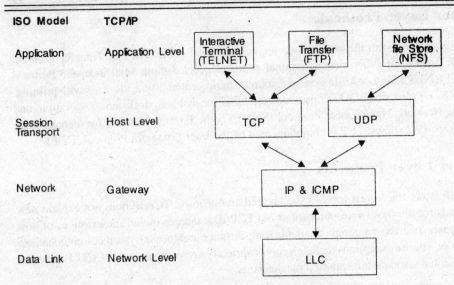

Fig. 19.3 : TCP/IP protocol relationships

To understand properly what TCP/IP is all about, it is important to understand that: a) it is not OSI in implementation (although some argue that there are substantial similarities) and b) it is a unique network architecture that provides what are considered traditional network services in a manner that can be overhead intensive in some implementations.

The structure of the TCP/IP protocol set is shown in Figure 19.3, alongwith the approximately equivalent ISO model layers. It can be seen that this is essentially a four layer model, although the layers are not as clear cut as in the ISO model, and the model has been drawn from analysis of what is used, rather than being defined first and then the protocols specified. The TCP/IP philosophy is the antithesis of the ISO philosophy. In ISO protocols, everything appears to be put into the protocol, but parts are made optional. In TCP/IP, the protocols are kept very simple. If more functionality is required, then another protocol is added to deal with the situation. The main protocols are as follows:

IP   The Internet Protocol, which provides a connectionless datagram 'network' layer.

ICMP   The Internet Control Message Protocol, is an example of the bolt-on approach mentioned above. It adds functionality to the IP protocol and can be considered as an extension to that protocol.

UDP   The User Datagram Protocol provides the rough equivalent of the ISO connectionless transport service.

TCP   The Transmission Control Protocol is a connection oriented, reliable end-to-end transport protocol.

The protocols which run above TCP include TELNET, a terminal access protocol, and a file transfer protocol FTP. The four main protocols are now examined further as a contrast to the ISO approach.

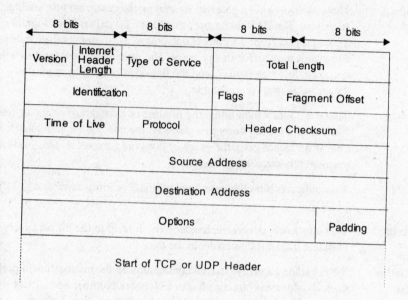

Fig. 19.4 : Format of an internal datagram header

INTERNET PROTOCOL

There is a second difference in philosophy between ISO and the TCP/IP approach, which revolves around the word 'network'. In the TCP/IP model, a network is an individual packet switched network which may be a LAN or a WAN, but is generally under the control of one organisation. These networks connect to each other by gateways, and the resulting collection of such networks is called a catenet (from concatenation). The internet protocol provides for the transmission of datagrams between systems over the whole catenet. It specifically allows for the fragmentation and reassembly of the datagrams at the gateways, as the underlying networks may demand different packet sizes.

The Internet Protocol (US Military Standard 1771) is a very simple protocol, with no mechanism for end-to-end data reliability, flow control or sequencing. The header, however, shown in Figure 19.4, is quite complex, the fields being as follows:

Version	The version number of IP. There have been several new releases, which (given the size of ARPANET) must co-exist for some time.
IHL	The IP header length. Because of the options field, the header is not a fixed length. This field shows where the data starts.
Type of service	This field allows for a priority system to be imposed, plus an indication of the desired, but not guaranteed, reliability required.

Length	The total length of the IP packet. Although there is a theoretical maximum of 64 Kbytes, most networks operate with much smaller packets, though all must accept at least 576 bytes.
ID/flags/ offset	These fields enable a gateway to split up the datagram into smaller segments. The ID field ensures that the receiver can piece together the fragments from the correct datagrams, as fragments from many datagrams may arrive in any order. The offset tells how far down the datagram this fragment is, and the flags can be used to mark the datagram as non-fragmentable.
Time to live	This is a count which limits the lifetime of a datagram on the catenet Each time it passes through a gateway, the count is decremented by one. If it reaches zero, the gateway does not forward it. This prevents permanently circulating datagrams.
Protocol	This indicates which higher level protocol is being carried, e.g. TCP or UDP.
Checksum	This checksum covers the header only. It is up to the higher layers to detect transmission errors in the data.
Source/dest address	To assist the gateways to route datagrams by the most efficient path each IP address is structured into a Network Number and a local address. There are three classes of network providing different numbers of locally administered addresses.
Options	The final part of the header is a variable number of optional fields, which are used to enforce security or network management.
Padding	This field is used to align the header to the next 32-bit boundary.

Because there is no facility for error reporting in IP, for example, the sender of a datagram is not informed if the intended recipient is available, an extra protocol is used particularly to help gateways between networks. This is called the Internet Control Message Protocol (ICMP) which, although it is carried over IP, is considered to be an integral part of it. It does not help in making IP reliable, however, it merely reports errors without trying to recover from them.

Examples of ICMP messages include TIME EXCEEDED when the lifetime of a datagram expires, and DESTINATION UNREACHABLE when a gateway or network has failed. The gateways also exchange routing information using another extra protocol, called the gateway-to-gateway protocol. This enables the gateways to have up-to-date information on the loading on certain routes, so that bottlenecks can be avoided.

USER DATAGRAM PROTOCOL

The User Datagram Protocol (UDP) provides a connectionless transport service to applications. Unlike the ISO protocols, which are layer independent, it assumes that IP is running below, and implementations must have access to incoming IP headers.

The UDP header, shown in Figure 19.5 is very simple, and can be considered as an extension of the IP header to permit multiple services to be addressed within the same IP network address.

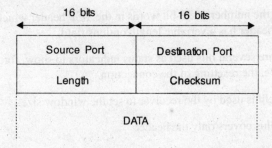

Fig. 19.5 : Format of user datagram protocol header

TRANSMISSION CONTROL PROTOCOL

TCP (US Military Standard 1781) provides a highly reliable, connection oriented, end-to-end transport service between processes in end systems connected to the catenet. TCP only assumes that the layer below offers an unreliable datagram service, and thus could run over any such protocols. In practice, however, it is invariably linked to IP. TCP provides the types of facility associated with the ISO Class 4 transport service, including error recovery, sequencing of packets, flow control by the windowing method, and the support of multiplexed connections from the layer above. The format of the TCP header is shown in Figure 19.6. The operational procedures are similar to the ISO connection oriented protocols, such as LLC Type 2. The fields in the header are as follows:

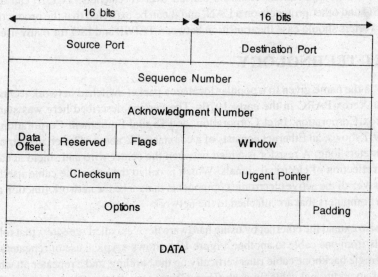

Fig. 19.6 : Format of TCP header

Source/dest ports	These fields identify multiple streams to the layer above.
Sequence/ack number	These are used for the windowing acknowledgement technique.
Data Offset	This is the number of 32-bit words in the TCP header which, like the IP header has a variable length options field.
Flag bits	There are several bits used as status indicators to show, for example, the resetting of the connection.
Window	This field is used by the receiver to set the window size.
Checksum	Again this covers only the header.
Urgent pointer	The sender can indicate that an urgent datagram is coming and urges the receiver to handle it as quickly as possible.
Options	This variable-sized field contains some negotiation parameters, to set the size of the TCP packets for example.
Padding	To align to the next 32-bit boundary.

The procedures used by the TCP protocol are too complex to describe here. It can be seen, however, that the catenet style of networking has benefits for linking LANs -- hence the widespread use of TCP/IP on LANs. It should not be assumed, however, that TCP/IP networks are immune from the compatibility problems discussed earlier for ISO networks. Differences in interpretation of the protocols can drastically reduce interoperability and there are reports of deficiencies in many of the protocols. One interesting recent development, however, is an experimental implementation of the ISO transport service on top of TCP, which means that ISO applications could be carried over IP catenets. TCP/IP can also co-exist with ISO and other protocols on a LAN, and it can be expected that the production of protocol converters should ease the transition between TCP/IP and ISO for many users.

ETHERNET TECHNOLOGY

Ethernet is the name given to a popular local area packet-switched network technology invented at Xerox PARC in the early 1970s. The version described here was standardized by Xerox Corporation, Intel Corporation, and Digital Equipment Corporation in 1978. Figure 19.7 shows, an Ethernet consists of a coaxial cable about 1/2 inch in diameter and up to 500 meters long. A resistor is added between the center wire and shield at each end to prevent reflection of electrical signals. Which is called the *ether*, the cable itself is completely passive; all the active electronic components that make the network function are associated with computers that are attached to the network.

You can also extend the ethernet by using hardware devices called *repeaters* that relay electrical signals from one cable to another. Figure 19.8 shows a typical use of repeaters in an building. A single backbone cable runs vertically up the building, and a repeater attaches the backbone of an additional cable on each floor. Computers attach to the cables in each floor. Only two repeaters can be placed between any two machines, so the total length of a single Ethernet is still rather short (1500 meters).

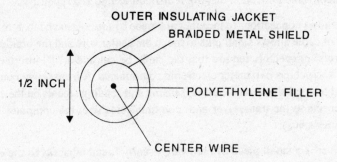

Figure 19.7 : Coaxial cable used in an Ethernet

Repeaters are less expensive than other types of interconnection hardware, making them the least costly way to extend an Ethernet. However repeaters have two disadvantages.

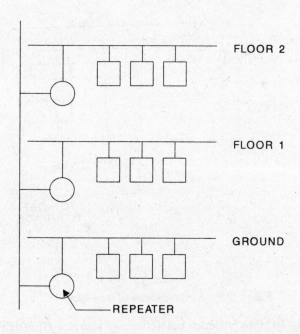

Figure 19.8 : Repeaters used to join Ethernet cables in a building

First, because repeaters repeat and amplify all electrical signals, they also copy electrical disturbance or errors that occur on one wire to the other. Second, because they contain active electronic components and require power, they can fail. In an office environment, the failure may occur in an inconvenient location making it difficult to find and repair.

Figure 19.9 shows connections to the ether are made by *taps*. At each tap, a small hole in the outer layers of cable allows small pins to touch the center wire and the braided shield (some manufacturers' connectors require that the cable be cut and a "T" inserted). Each connection to an Ethernet has two major electronic components. A *transceiver* connects to the center wire and braided shield on the ether, sensing and sending signals on the either. A *host interface* connects to the transceiver and communicates with the computer (usually through the computer's bus).

The transceiver is a small piece of hardware usually found adjacent to the ether. In addition to the analog hardware that senses and controls the ether, a transceiver contains digital circuitry that allows it to communicate with a digital computer. The transceiver can sense when the ether is in use and can translate analog electrical signals on the ether to and from digital form. The transceiver cable that runs between the transceiver and host interface carries power to operate the transceiver as well as signals to controls its operation.

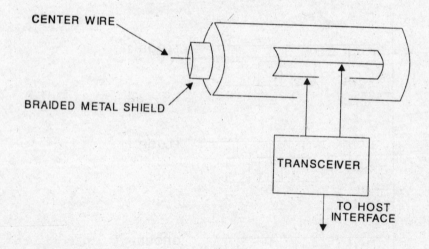

Figure 19.9 : A cutaway view of the cable

The Ethernet is a 10 Mbps broadcast bus technology with best-effort delivery semantics and distributed access control. It is a *bus* because all stations share a single communication channel; it is *broadcast* because all transceivers receive every transmission. It is enough to understand that transceivers do not filter transmissions — they pass all packets onto the host interface, which chooses packets the host should receive and filters out all others. Ethernet is called a *best-effort delivery* mechanism because it provides no information to the sender about whether the packet was delivered. For example, if the destination machine happens to be powered down, the packet will be lost but the sender will not be notified.

Ethernet access control is distributed because, unlike some network hardware, there is no central authority granting access. The Ethernet access scheme is called *Carrier Sense Multiple Access* with *Collision Detect (CSMA/CD)*. It is *CSMA* because multiple machines can access the Ethernet simultaneously and each machine determines whether the ether is idle by sensing whether a carrier wave is present. When a host interface has a packet to transmit, it listens to the ether to see if a message is being transmitted. When no transmission is sensed, the host interface starts transmitting. Each transmission is limited in duration because that there is a maximum packet size. However, the hardware must observe a minimum idle time between transmission, which means that no single pair of communicating machines can use the network without giving other machines an opportunity for access.

The standard Ethernet is rated at 10 Mbps, which means the data can be transmitted onto the cable at 10 Mbps.Although many recent computer scan generate data at Ethernet speed, raw network speed should not be thought of as the rate at which two computers can exchange data. Instead, network speed should be thought of as a measure of network total traffic capacity. Think of a network as a highway connecting multiple cities. High speeds make it possible to carry high traffic loads, while low speed means the highway cannot carry as much traffic. For example, a 10 Mbps Ethernet, can handle a few computers that generate heavy loads, or many computers that generate light loads.

Recent advances in technology have made it possible to build Ethernets that do not need the electrical isolation of coaxial cable. Which is known as *twisted pair Ethernet*, the technology allows a conventional 10 Mbps Ethernet to pass across a pair of copper wires much like the we used to interconnect telephones. The advantage of using twisted pair is that it reduces cost and makes it possible for many groups to use existing wiring in place of adding new cable.

When high capacity is not needed, the networks can still use Ethernet-like technology, but operate at slightly lower speed. The advantages are primarily economic. Lower speed means less complicated hardware and lower cost. One reason lower speed networks coast less is that the interfaces need less buffer memory and can be built from inexpensive integrated circuits.

Costs can also be reduced if high-speed digital circuits can connect directly to the cable without using a transceiver. In this situation, an Ethernet can be implemented with standard coaxial cable such as that used for cable television. Which is called *thin-wire Ethernet*. The thin cable is inexpensive, but supports somewhat fewer connections and covers slightly shorter distances than standard Ethernet cable. Workstation manufacturers find thin wire Ethernet an attractive system because they can integrate Ethernet hardware into single board computers and mount BNC-style connectors directly on the back of the machine. Because they require no special tools, BNC connectors make it possible for users to connect workstations to Ethernets. Of course, allowing users to add their own machines to networks has disadvantages. Which means that the network is susceptible to disconnection, inconnect wiring, or intentional abuse. In most situations, the advantages outweigh the disadvantages.

The other method of reducing costs uses a single physical cable to carry multiple, independent Ethernets. Known as *broadband*, the technology works much like broadcast radio. The transmitter multiplexes multiple Ethernets onto a single cable by assigning each Ethernet a unique frequency. Receivers must be "tuned" to the correct frequency so that they receive only the desired signal. Although the equipment needed to connect to a broadband cable is somewhat more expensive than equipment needed to connect to a conventional baseband cable, *broadband* eliminates the cost of laying multiple cables.

An Ethernet host interface provides an *addressing mechanism* that keeps unwanted packets from being passed to the host computer. Recall that each interface receives a copy of every packet — even those addressed to other machines. The hardware filters packets, ignoring those are addressed to other machines and passing to the host only those packets that addressed to it. The addressing mechanism and filter are required to prevent a computer from being overwhelmed with incoming data.

To determine which packets are meant for a computer, each computer attached to an Ethernet, is assigned a 48-bit integer known as its *Ethernet address*. Ethernet hardware manufacturers purchase blocks of Ethernet addresses and assign them in sequence so that no two hardware interfaces have the same Ethernet address.

The Ethernet address is fixed in machine readable form on the host interface hardware. Because Ethernet addresses belong to hardware devices, they are sometimes called *hardware addresses* or *physical addresses*.

The 48-bit Ethernet address does more than specify a single hardware interface. It can be one of three types:

- The physical address of one network interface,
- The network *broadcast* address,
- A *multicast* address.

The broadcast address, all 1s, is reserved for sending to all stations simultaneously. Multicast addresses provide a limited form of broadcast in which a subset of the computers on a network agree to respond to a multicast address. Every computer in a multicast group can be reached simultaneously without affecting computers outside the multicast group.

To accommodate broadcast and multicast addressing, Ethernet interface hardware must recognize more than its physical address. A host interface usually accepts at least two kinds of transmissions: those addressed to the interface physical address and those addressed to the broadcast address. Some interfaces can be programmed to recognize multicast addresses or even alternate physical addresses. When the operating system starts, it initializes the Ethernet interface, giving it a set of addresses to recognize.

Figure 19.10 shows the Ethernet frame format that contains the physical source address as well as the physical destination address. In addition to identifying the source and destination, each frame transmitted across the Ethernet contains a *preamble, type field, data field,* and *Cyclic Redundancy Check (CRC).* The preamble consists of 64 bits of alternating *0*s and *1*s to help receiving nodes synchronize. The 32-bit CRC helps the interface detect transmission errors: the sender computers the CRC as a function of the data in the frame, and the receiver recomputes the CRC to variety that the packet has been received intact.

The frame type field contains a 16-bit integer that identified the type of the data being carried in the frame. From the Internet point of view, the frame type field is essential because it means Ethernet frames are *self-identifying.* When a frame arrives at a given machine, the operating system uses the frame type of determine which protocol software module should process the frame. The main advantages of self-identifying frames are that they allow multiple protocols to be used together on a single machine and they allow multiple protocols to be intermixed on the same physical network without interference. For example, one could have an application program using Internet protocols while another used a local experimental protocol. The operating system would decide where to send incoming packets based on their frame type. The TCP/IP protocols use self-identifying Ethernet frames to distinguish among several protocols.

Preamble	Destination Address	Source Address	Frame Type	Frame Data	CRC
64 bits	48 bits	48 bits	16 bits	368-1200 bits	32 bits

Figure 19.10 : The Externet Frame Format

The use of Ethernet repeaters as one technique for extending a physical Ethernet to multiple physical wire segments. Although repeaters were a popular extension many years ago, most sites now use *bridges* to interconnect segments. Unlike a repeater, which replicates electrical signals, a bridge replicates packets. In fact, a **bridge is a fast computer with two Ethernet interfaces and a fixed program**. The bridge operates both Ethernet interfaces in *promiscuous mode,* which means, that they capture all valid packets that appear on their respective Ethernets and deliver them to the processor in the bridge. If the bridge connects two Ethernets, E_1 and E_2, the software takes each packet arriving on E_1 and transmits it on E_2 and vice versa.

Bridges are superior than repeaters because they do not replicate noise, errors, or malformed frames; a completely valid frame must be received before it will be reproduced. However, bridge interfaces follow the Ethernet CSMA/CD rules, so collisions and propagation delays on one wire remain isolated from those on the other. As a result, an arbitrary number of Ethernets can be connected together with bridges. Bridges hide the details of interconnection: a set of bridged segments acts like a single Ethernet. A computer can communicate across a bridge using exactly the same hardware signals it uses to communicate on its own segment. Most bridges do much more than replicate frames from one wire to another, they make intelligent decisions about which frames to forward. Such bridges are called **adaptive**, or **learning** bridges. An adaptive bridge consists of a computer with two Ethernet interfaces. The software in an adaptive bridge keeps two address lists, one for each interface. When a frame arrives from Ethernet E_1, the adaptive bridge adds the 48-bit Ethernet *source* address to the list associated with E_1. Similarly, when a frame arrives from Ethernet E_2, the bridge adds the source address to the list associated with E_2. Thus, over time the adaptive bridge will learn which machines lie on E_1 and which lie on E_2

After recording the source address of a frame, the adaptive bridge uses the destination address to determine whether to forward the frame. If the address lists show that the destination lies on the Ethernet from which the frame arrived, the bridge does not forward the frame. If the destination is not in the address list, the bridge forwards the frame to the other Ethernet. In otherwords, an adaptive Ethernet bridge connects two Ethernet segments forwarding frames from one to the other. It uses source addresses to learn which machine lie on which Ethernet segment and it combines information learned with destination addresses to eliminate forwarding when unnecessary.

Most bridges are much more sophisticated and robust. When first powered up, they check for other bridges and learn the topology of the network. They use a distributed spanning-tree algorithm to decide how to forward frames. In particular, the bridges decide how to propagate broadcast packets so that only one copy of a broadcast frame is delivered to each wire. Without such an algorithm, Ethernets and bridges connected into a cycle would produce catastrophic results because they would forward broadcast packets in both directions simultaneously.

ProNET TOKEN RING TECHNOLOGY

ProNET-10 is a commercial local area network product that offers an interesting alternative to the Ethernet, based on networking research at universities, and manufactured by Proteon Incorporated, a ProNET-10 consists of a passive wiring system that interconnect computers. Like the Ethernet, the low-speed version operates at 10 Mbps, is limited to short geographic distances, and requires attached computer to have an active host interface.

Unlike the Ethernet or related bus technologies, proNET-10 requires hosts to be wired in a one-way ring and uses an access technology known as *token passing*. The primary distinguishing feature of token-passing systems is that they achieve fair access by having all machines take turns using the network. At any time, exactly one machine holds a *token* which grants that machine the right to send a packet. After sending its packet, the machine passes the token to the next machine in sequence, and so on. Thus, when none of the machine has anything to send, they continually pass the token around, when they all have packets send, they take turns sending them.

Token passing can also be used with Ethernet-like bus topologies, ring topologies like those used by proNET-10 make token passing especially simple because the physical connections determine the sequence through which the token passes. The key is that a given machine does not know the identify of the machine to which it passes the token.

To understand how a ring operates, we require to look at the hardware. The ring network is not a continuous wire — it consists of point-to-point connections among the host interfaces of computers on the net. At each host, one wire carries incoming signals, and another carries outgoing signals.

Conceptually, each host interface operates in one of three modes: *copy mode, transmit mode,* or *recovery mode.* As Figure 19.11 shows, the first two modes represent normal operation, with the choice depending on whether the machine currently holds the token. I_3 in transmit mode, holding the token and sending a packet to interface I_2. When not holding the token, an interface runs in copy mode, reading bits from the incoming wire and copying them to the outgoing wire. In copy mode, the interface also watches the data stream to find packets addressed to the local machine, placing a copy of such packets in the machine's memory. When holding the token, the interface operates in transmit mode, sending a packet on the outgoing wire and verifying correctness by reading it back from the incoming wire.

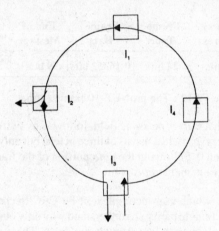

Figure 19.11 : A token ring network

To understand that ProNET-10 is a LAN technology that only has small propagation delays. When constructed from shielded copper cable, the ring can span at most a few adjacent buildings. When fiber optic cable is used, the ring can span longer distances. In any case, propagation delays are short. As a consequence, signals can propagate through the entire ring and return to the sender so quickly that the beginning of a packet completes its trip around the ring while the sender continues to transmit. The advantages of short propagation delay is that a station can determine quickly whether the ring is broken. It can also determine whether electrical interference or broken hardware along the path introduces any errors into the packet.

Unlike the Ethernet, ProNET-10 interface hardware does not have fixed addresses assigned by the manufacturer. Instead, each interface comes with a set of 8 switches that allows a system administrator to choose any of 255 possible addresses. However, a given ProNET-10 network is limited to 255 machines. The address must be selected and configured using physical switches on the board. It cannot be changed quickly or easily once the interface is installed, nor can it be changed by software. However, making an address configurable has two important advantages. First, it means that proNET-10 addresses can be much smaller than Ethernet addresses (8 bits instead of 48 bits). Second, customers can change ProNET-10 addresses when installing boards, the network hardware address of machine need not change when the host interface hardware is replaced.

An installer is required to ensure that each interface on a given ring is assigned a unique address between 0 and 254. An address of all *1*s (255) is reserved for broadcast traffic. Using proNET-10 with TCP/IP, installers should avoid assigning any host address zero.

Figure 19.12 shows the proNET-10 frame format. Fields are specified in bits because the network is bit-oriented and does not always align data on octet boundaries. The network hardware requires the data field to be an exact multiple of octets, making is easy to transfer data to the host computer's memory.

Start of Message	Destination Address	Source Address	Frame Type	Frame Data	End of Message	Parity	Refuse
10 bits	8 bits	8 bits	24 bits	0-16352 bits	9 bits	1 bit	1 bit

Figure 19.12 : The proNET-10 frame format

Each frame begins with a *start of message* field, followed by two octets of *destination* and *source* address. The *frame type* field consists of three octets, but only the first is currently used; the last two must contain 0. Following the *data* portion of the frame comes an *End of Message* field, a single *parity* bit, and a *refused* bit.

In contrast to Ethernet, which uses a complex 32-bit CRC to check for transmission errors, proNET-10 uses only a single parity. To understand why only one bit is needed, recall that proNET is a LAN technology with low propagation delay. The sending site receives a copy of the frame during transmission, and can easily compare bits in the copy to see if they have been changed. In fact, the parity bit is unnecessary except as a check on the *refused* bit.

Because a token passing ring relies on all hosts to forward the token when they finish transmitting, failures at one node can stop the ring. For example, a malfunction or electrical interference damaged the token. Unless the ring included a mechanism to recover, all transmission would cease. To recover from token loss, the proNET-10 has each station run two timers. One timer, called a *flag timer*, is reset whenever the station detects an activity and the other, called a *token timer,* is reset when a token arrives. If either timer has expired when the station has a packet to send, the station changes to recovery mode and eventually generates a new token for the ring. On an otherwise idle ring, the token circulates continually. Thus, the flag timer expires quickly (after 3 ms) if the ring is completely idle. The token timer must allow for large packet transmissions by up to 255 other stations, so that it has a much longer expiration time (400 ms). Ring technologies that allow more stations or larger packets use longer expiration times (e.g., proNET-80 uses 700ms).

The first station to enter recovery mode assumes it holds the token and transmits its packet. Following the packet, it transmits the token as if nothing had gone wrong. As it transmits, the station monitors the ring to check that the packet circulates completely. If so, the ring has recovered and everything proceeds as usual. In the improbable case that two stations simultaneously attempt to transmit after a token loss, they detect the problem because they do not receive back their own transmission. The two stations back off, wait a random time, and try again. To guarantee that they do not both wait exactly the same amount of time, each station computes a delay proportional to its hardware address. However, if two broads begin circulating packets simultaneously, only one survives. The recovery algorithm is both efficient and reliable. It guarantees that in only a few trips around the ring, one station will decide it holds the token and all other stations will agree.

In practice, most installations configure proNET-10 networks into star-shaped rings to improve reliability. The idea is to use a passive wire center as the hub of a physical star topology even though the network operates logically as a ring. Figure 19.13 shows such a connection.

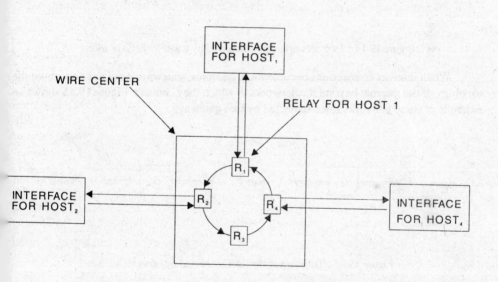

Figure 19.13 : The connection of three hosts through a passive wire center

Relay R_3 does not receive power because there is not host connection. R_3 closes the ring and connects R_2 to R_4. Because other relays receive power, they connect their respective hosts into the ring. Thus, an electrical signal sent from Host 4 passes through relay R_4, to relay R_1, up to the interface on Host 1, back to relay R_1, over to relay R_2, and so on.

INTERNET ARCHITECTURE

Two networks can only be connected by a computer that attaches to both of them. A physical attachment does not provide the interconnection we have in mind, because such a connection does not guarantee that the computer will cooperate with other machines that wish to communicate. To have a viable internet, we need computers that are willing to shuffle packets from one network to another. Computers which interconnect two networks and pass packets from one to the other are called *internet gateways* or *internet routers*.

Consider an example consisting of two physical networks shown in Figure 19.14. In the figure, machine *G* connects to both network 1 and network 2. For *G* to act as a gateway, it must capture packets on network *1* that are bound for machines on network 2 and transfer them. Similarly, *G* must capture packets on network 2 that are destined for machines on network *1* and transfer them.

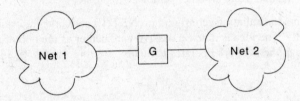

Figure 19.14 : Two networks interconnected by a gateway (G) or router

When internet connections become more complex, gateways need to know about the topology of the internet beyond the networks to which they connect. Figure 19.15 shows an example of three networks interconnected by two gateways.

Figure 19.15 : Three networks interconnected by two gateways

In this example, gateway *G₁* must move from network *1* to network 2 all packets destined for machines on either network 2 or networks 3. As the size of the internet expands, the gateway's take of making decisions about where to send packets becomes more complex.

The idea of a gateway seems simple, but it is important because it provides a way to interconnect networks, not just machines.

Note that in a TCP/IP internet, computers called gateways provide all interconnections among physical networks.

You might suspect that gateways, which must know how to route packets to their destination, are large machines, with enough primary or secondary memory to hold information about every machine in the internet to which they attach. However, gateways used with TCP/IP internets are usually minicomputers; they often have little or no disk storage and limited main memories. The concept of building a small internet gateway is gateways route packets based on destination network, not on distinction host.

If routing is based on networks, the amount of information that a gateway needs to keep is proportional to the number of networks in the internet, not be number of machines.

Note that TCP/IP is designed to provide a universal interconnection among machines independent of the particular networks to which they attach. Thus, we want the user to view an internet as a single, virtual network to which all machines connect despite their physical connections. In addition to gateways that interconnect physical networks, internet access software is needed on each host to allow application programs to use the internet as if it were a single, real physical network.

The advantage of providing interconnection at the network level now becomes clear. Because application programs that communicate over the internet do not know the details of underlying connections, they can be run without change on any machine. Because the details of each machine's physical network connections are hidden in the internet software, only that software needs to change when new physical connections appear or old ones disappear. It is possible to optimize routing by altering physical connections without event recompiling application programs.

A second advantage of having communication at the network level is more subtle: users do not have to understand or remember how network connect or what traffic they carry. Application programs can be written that operate independent of underlying physical connectivity. In fact, network managers are free to change interior parts of the underlying internet architecture without changing application software in most of the computers attached to the internet.

Figure 19.16 shows, gateways do not provide direct connections among all pairs of networks. It may be necessary for traffic traveling from one machine to another to pass across several intermediate networks. Thus, networks participating in the internet are analogous to highways in the U.S. interstate system: each net agrees to handle transit traffic in exchange for the right to send traffic throughout the internet. Typical users are unaffected and unaware of extra traffic on their local network.

It is important to understand a fundamental concept: from the internet point of view, any communication system capable of transferring packets counts as a single network, independent of its delay and throughput characteristics, maximum packet size, or geographic scale. Figure 19.16 uses the same small could to depict all physical networks because TCP/IP treats them equally despite their differences.

Note that the TCP/IP internet protocols treat all networks equally. A local area network like an Ethernet, a wide area network like the NSFNET backbone, or a point-to-point link between two machines each count as one network.

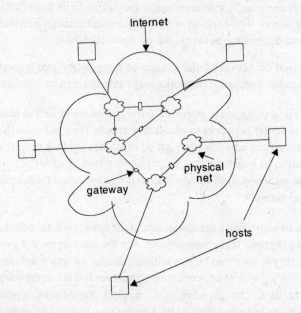

Figure 19.16 : The structure of physical networks and gateways that provide interconnection.

TCP/IP NETWORK PLANNING

The aim of TCP/IP network planning and design is to provide a communications infrastructure that meets the requirements of the organization with readily available equipment and skills. It must provide the correct level of performance for different functions within the organization, at different places, and at acceptable costs. In setting up a local and wide are structure for TCP/IP, the first task of the designer is to consider what each of these terms means for that situation. Each case is unique but the overall size of the organization and its network requirement will determine the complexity of the problems to be solved.

Size and Growth Rate

Whatever aspect of human communications you consider, it could be said that a measurement of success is often that the size and usage grows rapidly. As a result of experience in road network planning, this has become known as the 'motorway (or highway) effect'. If a system is useful, people change their travel habits and use the system in new ways that the planners never envisaged. Traffic grows to fill the space available. In an organization a successful network has been seen to grow at a rate which was totally unexpected and to expand rapidly to cover the company.

It is advisable to consider the initial size of the network while planning a TCP/IP installation and have some indication of maximum size and growth rate. This measure of size has two dimensions:

1.   The total number of attached ports, that is, computer and router connections to the network

2.   The geographic coverage

It is also important to consider in what ways the network could grow — by addition of devices on the same network or by connection to other TCP/IP installations. In the first case, all the issues are under the control of one organization; in the second, they may not be. The problems to be solved will be different in each case. Today's computer applications and systems are distributed on workstations and PCs throughout the sites and buildings where the computer users sit. Some types of change cannot be centrally managed and must be carried out at each machine. These changes are always difficult and labour-intensive, and hence costly. As far as possible, they must be predicted and eliminated.

These considerations can affect the detailed planning process the LAN and WAN links, the planning of the address space and of the bridges and routers which interconnect LANs and sites. Planners will wish to determine solutions to the following questions. How many cable systems will there be? How can they be interconnected successfully? Will bridges suffice or are routers required? How should the address plan for the network evolve? Is there a requirement for the Domain Name Service? Is responsibility split or with one person or body? If it is split, is the division by function, by location, or by technology? Is there a need to split application management from communications management? Is there a need to split communications management into more than one subfunction?

Existing Standards

To avoid duplication of effort and perhaps more importantly to avoid choosing incompatible solutions to the same TCP/IP options and problems, it is quite important to determine if there are any other existing TCP/IP implementations in the organization. Some systems may hide their use of TCP/IP; the Banyan VINES resource-sharing LAN or any communications management system which uses the simple network management protocol are current examples. If other examples do exist and will share the same cables or TCP/IP equipment at any time, the developments must be coordinated. In some situations there may already be a central authority for TCP/IP implementation which has set local standards for the use of TCP/IP. These standards should relate to:

   –   Addressing conventions

   –   Host-naming conventions

   –   Local area network

   –   Choice of equipment

   –   Choice of network software

   –   Configuration and managment of the network

   –   Configuration and management of the applications

It is easier if these standards can be used rather than starting from scratch.

Traffic Flows and Capacity

While planning the network layout and capacity it is important to know the volume of information which will be carried. At the simplest level, high-performance routes in the network must follow the high traffic flows in the organization. Faults on those major arterial routes will affect more users, so they, if any, may need to be protected against failure.

Judging future traffic flows is always one of the most difficult estimates in installing new TCP/IP systems. One of the great successes of modern software development techniques is to provide an effective barrier between the application developer and the underlying network. But it leaves the network planners with a major problem. Some people can relate the use of an application to the traffic it will generate.

Given the continued growth in workstation performance, existing LAN implementations already seem slow. For many commercial environments, a single physical LAN can support only 20 to 50 workstations and one or two file servers before the network must be partitioned with bridges or routers. The need for 100 Mbps Fiber Distributed Data Interface (FDDI) or even higher network speeds (1 Gbps — 10 Gbps) is evident, particularly for backbone networks and image systems, but the costs of such a system are not yet within the budgets of most network operators.

In the absence of such speeds, planners must ration the limited resource of normal speed LANs. They must understand how particular applications use the network and what the traffic flow between different user groups and applications processors are at different times of the day and business year. Key question are as follows:

– What will be the total volume of data on different parts of the network at the busiest time of the day? Is this traffic seasonal?

– How will the traffic grow with time, taking into account the changing and improving user perception of the network services and the increase in number of attached devices and a move towards more demanding applications?

– How is the traffic distributed among adjacent machines and to more remote machines?

The only way of obtaining such information is to measure the operation of real applications and extrapolate the results. Armed with the traffic information, and its growth, it is time to consider the network structure.

PARTITION THE NETWORK

Bridges and **routers** partition the network and improve performance for workstations on the same cable. The majority of network traffic should be local to the group of users and a small percentage (15-30%) should cross the bridges into a backbone network which interconnects different user groups. If this traffic split cannot be achieved, then the bridge is not used in the optimum way.

Splitting a network into small pools of users interconnected by routers and bridges is always a poor substitute for that single, reliable, large, high-speed network, for at any time a high proportion of the traffic is less than optimum. By adding bridges and routers to a network the cost per user, the administrative and the technical difficulties all increase and the reliability and performance between some remote portions of the network can fall to unacceptable levels. So why do it? In local area networks it is justified by the **containment of traffic** to physical networks which that traffic *must* traverse; this reduces the load on the local LAN segment and there is a dramatic improvement in performance for local traffic to local file servers. For long-distance wide-area interconnection, there must be a convertor between different link layer technologies. The prime purpose of a bridge in a LAN is to *prevent* traffic flowing where it does not need to, rather than to allow traffic to flow where it will. In many networks, it is only secondary function of the brdige to provide communications where none existed by translating to a different type of cable and extending the cable length limits of the basic LAN specification.

In network partitioning, routers have few advantages and few disadvantages over bridges. They have a more positive role to play. Routers relay only what they are specifically told to relay. They are part of the IP protocol and are designed to interconnect network technologies of different performance. Routers are particularly useful at matching the high speeds of LANs to the much lower speeds of intersite communications circuits that are now available. On the other hand they have a higher cost and lower performance and need more careful management than bridges.

USING BRIDGES

Bridges filter traffic by Media Access Control (MAC) Address. They must examine each frame received on each port and build a table of frame source addresses with the port on which the frame was received. When the bridge learns that a source and destination are on the same port, it will not pass traffic for that destination to any other cable.

The important performance factors of bridges are described as follows:

–   *Filtering rate* — the ability to examine frames for possible relaying.

–   *Forwarding rate* — the ability to relay frames which have to be relayed.

–   'Routing' algorithm that allows bridges to be connected redundantly in parallel and in loops but prevents frames circulating round the loops.

–   *Transit delay* — normally related to forwarding rate.

–   Filter table size.

–   Variations in performance with filter table occupancy.

Bridges Filtering Rate

Bridges can filter at the theoretical maximum rate for Ethernet of 14880 frames per second. Even in busy operational networks the offered traffic will not be this demanding, for this figure is based on all minimum-sized frames. The true demand depends on the type of TCP/IP services in use. Networks used mainly for character-by-character TCP/IP Telnet terminal server traffic have a much higher number of small frames that those used for file transfer and NFS. The importance of a bridge operating at this theoretical maximum figure is not that it can examine that number of frames per second but that there is no limitation to the number of successive short frames that can be captured by the bridge, since it can capture at the maximum possible rate.

The frame rates on Token Ring systems are theoretically much higher than on Ethernet (20 000 fps on 4 Mbps and 80 000 fps on 16 Mbps Token Ring) but the overheads of TCP/IP mean that the absolute maximum practical frame rates are approximately 7700 and 31 000 respectively. Bridges for TCP/IP traffic could be chosen accordingly.

For multi-port hub bridges, one must ensure that each bridge port can examine all frames on every port simultaneously and that the specification does not just give some aggregate figure.

Limited Horizon

A TCP/IP application working through a bridge has a limited horizon. A bridge isolates two cable segments so that systems have no knowledge of the traffic on the other cable, that is, on the other side of the bridge. A bridge is more likely to be unable to relay all traffic, not because it does not have the power, but because the output cable is continuously busy. Frames will queue in the bridge but bridges eventually throw away any frames that are older than about one second. Most low-level protocols — those which carry data over bridges — do not have any error correction or flow control. End stations may retransmit these lost frames from higher level software but, in an extreme case, this may just add to the network congestion that caused the problem in the first place.

It is up to the network manager to design the network so that traffic is distributed correctly and does not concentrate on one work area or in one bridge. Using a high-speed FDDI or Token Ring backbone or a hub bridge may complicate the design of the network. Traffic flows can become more critical, for they may arrive on the high-speed backbone successfully but focus on one work area where a number of key resources are located. High-performance resources, such as ONC (NFS) servers, should either be directly attached to the backbone or must be distributed on a number of feeder work area LANs.

Broadcasts, Broadcast Storms and Multi-Cast Frames

TCP/IP protocols use two techniques which impact on the performance of a bridged network. They use **broadcast** and **multicast frames** for discovering the locations of resources and for communicating between systems which cooperate to provide a common service.

Multicast frames take capacity on the cable but are not processed by every station. They become a problem only on slower wide area bridged links. 'Slow' is a relative term; for today's LANs, 'slow' could be 256 kbps, 128 kbps or less.

Broadcast frames are much more detrimental to performance. They are generated by ARP, RARP, BOOTP, and RIP. Every system on an Ethernet or Token Ring network must process *every* broadcast frame. If the number of broadcast frames increases, the performance of every system will degrade noticeably. A frame takes some time to process, independent of its size. Each broadcast frame can reduce the performance of a PC by almost one normal data frame of 1000 to 1450 bytes. PCs slow down noticeably with 10 to 15 broadcast packets per second.

Bridges relay broadcast frames everywhere. To try to filter broadcasts is to destroy the possibility of any-to-any communication. So networks which are interlinked only with bridges reach a size where the percentage of broadcast traffic from all the devices is unacceptable. Unless the broadcast traffic can be reduced, it becomes impossible to manage the network or to grow it further successfully.

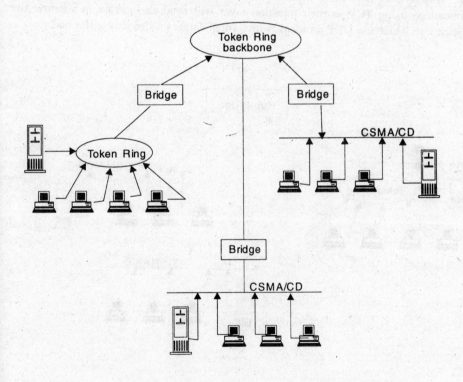

Fig. 19.17 : Bridging to a backbone

It has been known for in-house application programmers who do not appreciate the potential harmful effects to write applications using broadcasts. On more than one occasion, a complete LAN, including powerful minicomputers, has been brought to a standstill by a **broadcast storm** of about 100 packets per second. Broadcast storms are sometimes attributed to Ethernet design limitations; it is often not realized that the broadcast storm is usually caused by a combination of bad software design and a poor bridged network structure of any type of LAN.

Bridging to a Backbone

As an aid to structuring the distribution of data between work areas it is common practice to use a **backbone** LAN to carry the transit traffic. This backbone may be built with the same technology as the work area, though often on a more robust cable (Thick Ethernet, 10Base5, rather than Thin Ethernet, 10Base2, or Unshielded Twisted Pair, 10BaseT), or it may use a different technology (16 Mbps Token Ring or 100 Mbps FDDI).

Figure 19.17 shows, this topology places a minimum of two bridges in series between any two work areas. Unless application processors or file servers are directly attached to the backone, the performance for demanding file transfer applications is affected by this double hop. This is most noticeable if the backbone is no faster than the work areas. Those applications using TCP as their transport layer will need an increase in window size; applications which use UDP protocols with a small datagram size may suffer badly.

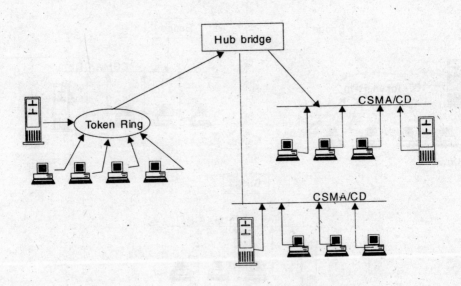

Fig. 19.18 : Hub bridge or multiport bridge

Hub Bridges

Hub and **multiport bridges** replace the backbone network with a single internal high-speed bus of greater speed than any LAN. This reduces the double hop effect but requires more extensive cabling and potentially reduces the backbone to a single point of failure (Figure 19.18).

IDENTIFYING A NETWORK CONNECTION

Connections to a TCP/IP network are often known to each other and to users in three different ways, all of which identify the same connection to the network but at different levels of TCP/IP:

− As names: in the **fully qualified host** and **domain** name

vax1.icds.com.in

Using the domain name scheme is often not considered early enough in the planning of commercial networks; users of larger networks will find it invaluable.

− As a group of four numbers separated by full stops. This is the **IP** or **network address** used by the IP layer of TCP/IP

164.120.9.61

− On a shared LAN by its network interface card address the 48-bit **MAC address** (Medium Access Control address often called the physical address)

02 60 8C 12 34 56

The three levels of address is required, since they all refer to the same connection to the TCP/IP Internet The reason is that while at any one time these addresses identify the same location, over a period of time a each may change for different reasons. The three types of address allow a degree of flexibility where none would exist if the functions were not separated:

- The host and domain name should remain unchanged for the longest time, for it is completely determined by the system designers and managers, though it will often change if there is a major change in machine location.

- The IP address may change due to network growth and reconfiguration, for instance, if a machine is moved from one location in a building to another.

- The MAC address may change for similar growth or performance reasons, or because the network card is replaced following a card failure. The shortest lived address is likely to be the MAC address.

The fully qualified domain name is for 'human consumption' and consists of a set of identifiers, separated by full stops, which describe a computer in a hierarchical relationship to all others. For example:

machine.department.site.organization.org_type.country

Introducing flexibility brings with it the possibility of error and communications failure if the flexible functions are not managed and controlled correctly.

PLANNING THE IP ADDRESS SCHEME

To plan an IP addressing scheme you must have the following information:

(i)   The maximum number of host ports that your organization could ever wish to interconnect. The whole of your organization is not just your particular department, but the whole organizational structure, if necessary, worldwide, which may at any time be interconnected.

(ii)   An understanding of the numbers of devices at each location and in each building on each site. Assume one address per member of staff in those buildings and leave some 25% spare.

(iii)   An understanding of the different departments, their geographic locations, and the likelihood that they will need to communicate. An estimate of the amount of information that is exchanged is useful but it has a very short-lived value.

(iv)   A knowledge of any other current users of TCP/IP and any standardization decisions that have been taken already.

In a small organization of a few hundred people, getting this information is straightforward in comparison to a large corporation; but it is the large corporation that must have accurate figures and which must derive centralized standards that are adhered to everywhere.

Internet Protocol

The Internet Protocol (IP) may be described as the network layer protocol of TCP/IP. IP is operated and interpreted by each intermediate relay in an interconnected set of LANs and WANs which is using the TCP/IP protocol suite to communicate. Such a collection is often called an **internetwork** and the intermediate relays are routers. IP provides a best efforts delivery service based on a technique called **datagram transmission**; 'best efforts' and 'datagram' because no attempt is made by IP to recover any errors which may occur in transmission. IP supports routing and relaying of information between communicating hosts or end devices according to the Type or quality Of Service (TOS) they require. IP allows routing errors to be trapped and reported and their effects on system performance to be minimized. IP does not make assumptions about the underlying network of physical cables, LAN hardware (Ethernet, Token Ring or FDDI) or the point-to-point wide area links (PTT circuits).

IP Addressing

The IP address is one component in the Internet protocol. The IP address is a number that uniquely identifies the *connection* of a host computer or end system as OSI would call it, to a physical network as it communicates with other computers or end systems. Hosts with more than one connection have a different IP address for each one. IP routers also have their own IP addresses for they can be the source and destination of IP datagrams.

The purpose of the IP address is twofold: to identify each connection to the internetwork in a way that is independent of the underlying physical network (LAN or WAN) technology, and to collect a group of connections together to simplify routing. Internetwork routers use IP addresses to make routing decisions.

IP addresses must be unique in the communicating internetwork. If not, communications will fail erratically. Since TCP/IP protocols do not directly provide any technical means by which IP addresses can be automatically made unique, it is up to network managers to configure and manage them correctly by traditional manual methods aided by database and network management technology.

MAC Addresses

Where TCP/IP systems are connected to a shared cable such as an Ethernet or Token Ring LAN, communication between stations must take place using MAC addresses, normally built into the network adapter card. Since the IP address is configured independently of the MAC address, it remains unchanged even if the network card fails and is replaced.

Every Ethernet or Token Ring card comes with a preconfigured 48-bit MAC address, its universally managed address. LAN standards also allow locally managed addresses; network cards can be loaded with a 48-bit address chosen by the network manager. Locally managed addresses are not normally used in TCP/IP systems. AS IP addresses in TCP/IP must be controlled and managed, there is little value is adding a second layer of management by also configuring and controlling MAC addresses. But the issue of MAC address management does not disappear completely from the TCP/IP story; some of the facilities of TCP/IP such as the Boot Protocol, BOOTP, use the MAC address as a fixed reference point for obtaining other information. If you wish to use these features, you must at least have a record of the MAC address of each computer for which the facility will be used. These addresses appear as a reference point in look-up tables in information servers. But, as discuss above, the MAC address can change if the network card is replaced. In a large network, keeping an up-to-date record of MAC addresses and ensuring that all servers have the correct record can be time-consuming.

Few advanced star wiring systems have management facilities that can record the MAC address attached to each user drop cable. Such systems make it easier to record the location of particular MAC addresses.

CHARACTERISTICS OF THE IP ADDRESS

The IP address is a 32-bit number which must be unique in internetwork. Devices which must have an IP address include every connection of each application processor and of each network router. As mentioned previously, computers with more than one network connection have a different IP address for each connection. In TCP/IP literature, such computers are referred to as **multihomed**. These connections are usually on different networks. This is the reason for sizing the network-by-network connections rather than the number of computers, though these numbers will often be very similar.

Unlike some other network addressing schemes, the IP address does not necessarily convey any information about geographic location. Given an IP address you can only deduce a management authority; that authority could manage one corporate network which in itself has global coverage and meshes with many other global networks. This has interesting implications for routing between two worldwide networks. In other way, the IP addressing scheme is *not hierarchical* unlike the telephone or telex network or for that matter the CCITT X.121 addressing scheme for the X.25 interface to public packet switched networks.

The 32-bit IP address has two components a **network number** or network identifier and a **host number** or host identifier. Some 'class bits' can be extracted from the network number, but trying to examine these on their own can lead to confusion. It is safer always to think of the network number as containing the class bits.

It is the network number which identifies the controlling organization and the port number which identifies the particular connection within the authority of that organization. The term 'host number' is historic and this name could cause confusion for, as we have seen, a multihomed host has more than one IP address and hence more than one host number. For reasons that will become apparent later, it would be unusual for two ports on the same machine to have the same network number.

Class bits + Network number	**Host number**

Fig. 19.19 : Format of the Ip address

The terms **net id** and **host id** are in common usage for network number and host number. IP addresses are divided into five address classes (A to E). It is important to understand that these divisions were conceived to ease the management of addresses by the Internet Activities Board (IAB); they have less immediate significance for the network manager.

The first three classes, A, B, C, are available for normal allocation and for host-to-host communications. Class D and class E addresses are not for general use; class D is reserved for special use by IAB designated protocols and class E is reserved for future use. One use of class D addresses is by routers, so network managers may encounter them while monitoring router protocols.

There are no practical distinctions in the way in which computer systems with class A, class B or class C addresses use those addresses. With some noted exceptions, which are discussed further below, any address from any class is equivalent for communications purposes. In principle, any host can communicate equally well using an address from any of these three classes. The distinguishing feature of each class of address is the number of network numbers and the number of host connections which each network number can support. The limitations of each class are described as follows:

Network class	Max. number of network numbers	Max. number of hosts on each network number
A	126	16 777 214
B	16 382	65 53~
C	2 097 150	254
D	Not applicable — reserved for multicast systems	
E	Reserved for IAB use	

NETWORK NUMBERS AND HOST NUMBERS

The choice of network numbers is most important. Network connections with the same network number should communicate directly on the same physical LAN. Network connections with different network numbers do not communicate directly; they must use the services of a router. This router either is directly connected between the two LANs to which the hosts connect or it in turn knows of a router which can relay the message towards its ultimate destination as shown in Figure 19.20.

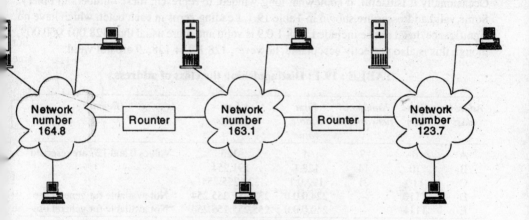

Fig. 19.20 : Choosing network numbers

These factors determine the basic rules for choosing network numbers and host numbers. They may alternatively be stated as:

- Computers separated only by bridges or repeaters will have the same network number.

- Computers or workstations separated by routers have different network numbers.

For the the network implementor, the most important factor is the choice of IP address for a particular host is affected by the presence of routers. The positioning of routers is determined by the exact geography of the underlying physical networks which connect computers, floors, buildings, sites and countries into a complete internetwork. It is also heavily influenced by organizational needs, traffic flows and traffic volume. The layout will change as the network grows and matures. If a bridge is replaced by a router, the network number on one side of the new router must change.

A TCP/IP addressing scheme evolves as the needs of users are better understood during the design process. Adding a TCP/IP addressing scheme to a LAN must take into account the existing layout of that LAN.

One factor is key. Network planners must attempt to design an addressing scheme that can remain substantially unchanged in a changing environment. This can be achieved using subnetwork addressing.

The convention is the address is written down, or described to software, in **dotted decimal notation**. Each eight bits of the address (each **octet**) is converted to a decimal number in the range 0 to 255, and separated by a dot (.). While the US standards initially specified 'dotted decimal notation' some computer staff are more at home with hexadecimal notation. **Dotted hexadecimal** (and UNIX or C-style hexadecimal) and **octal** notations are sometimes used and will be accepted by some (though by no means all) implementations. Occasionally it is useful, if somewhat long-winded, to represent these numbers in binary. Some valid addresses are shown in Table 19.1. Leading zeros in each octet, which have no significance, need not be included. 128.1.0.9 is valid and more usual than 128.001.000.009, though this is also perfectly acceptable; however, 128.1.9 or 128...9 are not valid.

TABLE : 19.1 : Distinguishing the class of address.

Address class	Class bits	Number of network bits	First usable value	Last usable	Remark
A	0	7	1	126	Values 0 and 127 are reserved
B	10	14	128.1	191.254	
C	110	21	192.0.1	223.255.254	
D	1110	–	224.0.0.0	239.255.255.254	Not available for general use
E	1111	–	240.0.0.0	255.255.255.254	Not available for general use

Distinguishing the class of address

The five classes of address have already been mentioned. The class of address is determined by certain bits in the first eight bits, that is, in the first decimal number of the four as shown in Table 19.1. The magnitude of the first number that defines the class of the address is given in the table.

There are two important features of this system:

(1)   The division between one class and the next is always at an octet boundary. This simplifies finding the boundaries between the classes of address, since each decimal number represents one octet.

(2)   When the network number is written down the 'class bits' are always included in the first octet, to ensure that the class of address and hence the true network number are unambiguous.

It is important that users of TCP/IP, planners and implementors should be fully familiar with the different classes of address and the limitations that they place on network growth. Many people new to the subject at first find the technique of dotted decimal notation a little eccentric. But it should become second nature to recognize the class of address, the network number, and the host id. As compared to other network addressing schemes, the TCP/IP addressing range is quite limited. Current work in the IAB is investigating the options for extending the address range.

IAB AND NETWORK NUMBER REGISTRATION

The addresses in an internetwork must be unique, there has to be a registry which ensures that such a policy can be enforced. TCP/IP was developed for use on the US Internet. This collection of networks is managed by many different authorities, with the IAB as overall design authority. In this environment of devolved management, the network number has two functions. First, since each IP address on the whole set of interconnected networks must be unique, the network number is used to identify one addressing authority, often called an autonomous system, responsible for issuing unique connection ids in that part of the address space. The second function is to support routing.

The IAB ensures that IP addresses on the Internet are unique, by registering and issuing network numbers to organizations that have reasons to connect to the Internet. Such organizations *do not choose* their own network number, it is issued to them. They agree to undertake certain network management responsibilities when they request an official IAB address allocation. They must then issue host Ids so that they are unique within their own network number address space. If they fail to issue unique host numbers, only the services of that organization will be affected.

The IAB has devolved the clerical task of registering and issuing IP network numbers to the Internet Retistry, part of the Internet Assigned Numbers Authority (IANA) which controls all numbers in the TCP/IP protocol suite, which must be managed if correct operation is to be guaranteed. The Internet Registry is operated by the Department of Defense Network Network Information Center (DDN NIC), now located in Chantilly, Virginia.

CONFIGURING THE IP ADDRESS

Every computer, workstation, personal computer, network router and network management station which 'speaks IP' must have a different IP address for each of its connections. The IP address is entered through the normal configuration management processes. IP addresses are usually represented and entered in dotted decimal notation; occasionally dotted hexadecimal notation is accepted. The address is usually stored in non-volatile memory, either RAM or on a disk file when available. Diskless workstations often have no nonvolatile storage. They obtain their IP address across the network at start-up time using BOOTP or RARP. Visiting each device to change the IP address is time-consuming, particularly in dispersed networks. BOOTP provides a mechanism for centralizing the distribution of IP addresses and other useful TCP/IP parameters, even for machines which do have storage. The key to distributing the correct IP address and other information via

BOOTP is the MAC address of the interface card. It is then *essential* to record accurately the MAC address used by each machine on the network that uses the BOOTP service. This is excellent policy for fault diagnosis and security in any case, though it is often neglected.

In an operational network, IP addresses become recorded in distributed tables and in software in machines. While this is bad practice, it is unavoidable. Frequent wholesale changes to IP addresses must not occur, so preplanning is essential. Such changes are labour-intensive because of the widespread distribution of addresses; the change introduces errors and has unpredictable consequences for the integrity of operational applications and for the time taken to restore any-to-any communications.

RESERVED IP ADDRESSES

Certain IP network numbers and host numbers are reserved for the use of particular aspects of TCP/IP communication. Not all these protocols are regularly used. Once you configure a connection with a reserved IP address, the faults caused are likely to be obscure, apparently intermittent and difficult to isolate. Not all host software checks that the IP address it is requested to use in invalid.

The following addresses are reserved:

- Network number 127.X.X.X, where X.X.X is any set of numbers. This is used for a local software loopback test.

- A network numbr of all 0s is classless and means 'my current network which I do not know the number of' — sometimes referred to as 'this network'.

- A network number of all 1s.

- Host number 0 is reserved to refer to a particular network number. For example, 192.0.0.1 is the first class C network address which could be allocated.

- Host number 'all 1s' is reserved to broadcast to all hosts on a specific network; it can only be used as a destination address.

- The full address 0.0.0.0 is reserved. It is used in two ways: as a source address when the host does not know its genuine address, for example during bootstrapping of a diskless workstation, and by routers in a list of addresses to advertise the default route, the route to all networks which are not explicitly listed.

- The full address 255.255.255.255 is reserved as a destination address to mean 'broadcast to all hosts on my network'. 0.0.0.0 as a destination is an obsolete form of 255.255.255.255.

IP Addresses with routers and dial-up devices

Few older router implementations need a point-to-point wide-area PTT or dial-up link between two LANs should be identified with its own unique IP network number with only two connections attached. In the larger network this is wasteful of the limited resource of IP network numbers. Check with your router manufacturer that the most modern techniques, which conserve network and subnetwork numbers, are used in their implementation.

HOW TCP/IP WORKS?

Most networks provide some sort of connection mechanism to get from point A to point B. Other networks worry about how to get from node A on network X to node B on network Y. If a program wishes to send information from itself on node A to another node on the same network, TCP will provide the packet sequencing, error control, and other services that are required to allow reliable end-to-end communications. This does not mean that IP is required. In fact, some implementations of TCP connect directly to the network services layer and bypass IP altogether. If, however, a program on node A on an Ethernet wished to connect to a destination program on node B on an X.25 network, an internet routing function would be necessary to get data packets sent properly between the two dissimilar network services. IP would take the packet from TCP, pass it through a gateway that would provide conversion services, and then send the packet to the IP layer at the remote node for delivery to the remote TCP layer and, subsequently, the destination program. A good comparison would be as follows:

a)   Program A on node ALPHA wishes to connect to program B on node BETA on the same network. Program A would send a data packet to TCP with the proper destination address. TCP would then encapsulate the data with the proper header and checksums in accordance with whatever services the program requested and pass the TCP packet to the IP layer. IP would then determine, from network directory information, that the remote node is on the same network as itself and simply pass the packet through to the network services layer for local network routing and delivery.

b)   Program A on node ALPHA on network X wishes to connect to program B on node BETA on network Y. In this situation, data would be handled as in case a) above, but IP would determine that the destination is not on the local network. As a result, the IP layer in node ALPHA would determine the best route to get to the remote node and send the TCP packet to the next IP node in the path to get to the remote. IP does not care which program the source wants to connect to; all it cares about is which node to send the packets to.

IP nodes in the path from node ALPHA to node BETA will examine the packet to determine the destination and will forward the packet to the proper IP until it reaches the destination network IP. That IP determines that the node is on its local network and the packet is handed to the network services layer for the network on which BETA resides for delivery to node BETA.

Once the packet is received at the final destination IP, it is passed up to the TCP layer, which breaks out the packet header to figure out which program on the destination node is to receive the data. First, however, the packet header is examined carefully to insure that it has arrived in the proper sequence and that there are no special handling issues that need to be serviced. Once TCP is satisfied that everything is reasonable, the data is delivered to the destination program.

While all of this seems pretty straightforward, there are some implementation issues that make all of this complex. Since TCP and IP allow many service options such as message priority, security classification, data segmentation at the TCP level, packet segmentation at the IP level, and other issues that some network architectures, such as DECnet, need not concern themselves with, there can be some considerable overhead associated with packet processing. As a result, TCP/IP performance varies significantly from network hardware to network hardware as well as from machine implementation to machine implementation.

Now that we have examined the generalized delivery model, let us look at some of the specifics.

WHAT TCP WAS BUILT TO DO?

One of the base problems that TCP was built to address is the issue of connection from a particular program on a particular node on a particular network to a remote program destination that may or may not be on the same network as the originator. As such, a method of addressing nodes needed to be developed that identified a particular program on a particular node in a particular network. A possible solution is to develop hard addresses for all entities on a particular network. While this solves the problem, it is inflexible and usually does not provide an upwardly-flexible network architecture. Another problem is that some networks have their own proprietary (and sometimes bizarre) addressing scheme that must be considered as TCP/IP are above the local network addressing scheme mechanisms in the network architecture and will need to use the local mechanism on packet delivery. To solve the problem, TCP/IP uses a three-layer addressing mechanism that allows for delivery of packets across dissimilar network architectures.

To begin with, each program (called a PROCESS in TCP) has a unique one-up address on each machine. That unique local program address is combined with a particular node address to form something called a port. The port address is further combined with the local network address, forming a new entity called a socket. There can be many, many sockets on a TCP/IP network but each socket identifies, exactly, one specific application on a specific node on a specific network. Through this mechanism, IP will get the packets to the proper node and TCP will deliver the packet to the proper program on that node. Some nodes provide a standard process type (such as type 23 for remote log-ins) that are "known" to other network entities and that provide certain standard services. Through this mechanism, TCP provides a multiplexing capability that is essential in the efficient use of the network resource.

From One Socket to Another

As with any network, two sockets that wish to connect to each other must have a mechanism by which this happens. TCP provides this in various ways. One of the more common ways connections are established is via an ACTIVE/PASSIVE network OPEN. A PASSIVE OPEN is when a receptive socket declares itself to be open and available for incoming connections (this would typically be the mode used by something like a database server). A PASSIVE OPEN, however, may be set up in various ways. First, the PASSIVE

OPEN may be set up to be FULLY SPECIFIED, which means that the socket issuing the PASSIVE OPEN tells the network exactly which socket may connect to it, including security levels allowed and other related details. Another type of PASSIVE OPEN is the UN-SPECIFIED PASSIVE OPEN in which the socket will accept any connection request from any remote socket provided that the remote system requesting connection meets prescribed security and other criteria. In both types of network OPENS, it is pertinent to point out that the socket OPENing the network may also declare timeout values for all data received from the originator of the connection. This allows for the expeditious handling of data as well as providing a means by which "old" messages are handled in a reasonable fashion and messages requiring special handling (in terms of time) are processed correctly.

Another type of OPEN is the ACTIVE OPEN. Unlike the PASSIVE OPEN, the ACTIVE OPEN aggressively seeks a connection to a particular socket. An ACTIVE OPEN will only be successful if there is a cooperating and corresponding PASSIVE OPEN or other ACTIVE OPEN from the destination socket.

Once a connection has been established between two sockets, data may be transferred between the sockets. TCP provides several mechanisms for data transfer, but the two most popular are segmented data transfer and PUSH mode. Segmented data transfer allows TCP to send user data in chunks across the network. As such, TCP may send the data in such a manner that allows for the best efficiency for the network being used. This means that even if the user has transferred 25 blocks of user data to TCP, TCP may not send it all at once, opting to segment the data in such a manner as to provide optimal flow of data on the network. While this technique is great for data flow issues and network congestion issues, it can be troublesome for transfers in which the data needs to get to the remote system NOW! In such cases, the user may specify the PUSH flag. A PUSH request forces TCP to send whatever has been passed from the user to TCP right away with no consideration for optimal flow control. In addition to the PUSH flag, the user may specify the urgency of the data being transferred to keep the remote system on its toes.

How much data is allowed to be sent from one socket to another is a function of the network and programs involved. Since TCP was developed with multiple network architectures in mind, it allows some level of link negotiation on connection and data transfer that provides for maximum buffer sizes (somewhat dynamically) and maximum buffer allocation.

TCP Sequencing

To insure that everything gets to where it is going and in the proper order, TCP provides packet sequencing services as well as error detection functions utilizing a 16-bit checksum in the TCP header area. It is also interesting to note that TCP presumes the IP layer to be unreliable and, therefore, includes a 96-bit pseudoheader in front of the actual TCP packet header that includes the source address, destination address, protocol being used, and segment size. Through the use of the pseudoheader, TCP protects itself from IP delivering the packet to the wrong place (or not at all) by misinterpreting TCP header fields. The checksum in the TCP header also includes the pseudoheader bits to insure that everything is clean when it hits the remote side.

After the connection is established and all data has been transferred, the link may be shut down via user request. This is the clean way. It is very possible that the link may also be abruptly aborted due to link drop or some catastrophic failure of the network or socket-to-socket linkage. TCP provides mechanisms to handle both situations. A CLOSE primitive issuance tells TCP that the user is finished with the network link and to close down the link gracefully by sending all remaining data in local buffers and notifying the remote socket that the sending user wishes to CLOSE the link. The remote TCP socket notifies the user that a CLOSE has been issued. The user may then send any remaining data and issue a CLOSE to the sender. When the sender receives the CLOSE acknowledgement from the receiver, it sends a TERMINATE to the user and notifies the remote TCP that a TERMINATE has been issued. The remote TCP socket sends a TERMINATE to the remote user and the link is closed completely.

If a network link abort occurs, for whatever reason, the ABORT primitive is sent to the remote TCP, which tells the remote user that a TERMINATE has occurred. No more data of any kind is transmitted on the link and the link is closed immediately on both sides. Obviously, a link termination of the ABORT kind is not desirable, as data may be lost and other integrity issues may be involved.

TCP Needs Not an IP

It is important to understand that TCP need not be connected to an IP, although that is frequently the case. TCP provides the essential network connection and data transfer features a user would require to connect with a particular program on a remote system. Some companies use TCP as the protocol of choice when setting up simple direct-connect network connections (where the remote node is hard- wired to the originating node) or when performing tasks such as downline system loading. In any case, TCP is a powerful and full-featured protocol that provides reasonable network services for user data.

Many times, however, just getting the data from one socket to another may involve the connection to various types of network technologies. A TCP packet coming in from an asynchronous link may need to be routed on to an Ethernet to reach its ultimate destination. Because of the need to connect and properly route data through to its proper network and destination socket, the IP layer was developed.

WHAT IS AN IP?

IP is a datagram service. It basically provides rudimentary internetwork routing services without any regard to the destination program, TCP formats, error control, packet sequencing, etc. Its function in life is to get the packet to the right network and eventually, to the right node. Further, IP allows for expedited routing of packets that need to get to a destination quicker than other, routine packets. In many respects, with the exception of routing priority, IP functionality is similar to Ethernet packet handling. If a packet arrives that is damaged (there is an IP checksum), the packet is discarded. What is in the data field of the packet is of no interest to IP. IP could be sending a TCP packet or some other protocol for all it cares. As long as the proper SEND (user sending to the network) primitive fields have been filled in, IP will send the packet on its merry way. When the packet reaches the remote node and the checksum figures out OK, IP sends the packet to TCP (or whatever the receptor protocol is) via a DELIVER directive and all is well with the universe. If the packet gets trashed in the process of being delivered, so be it. If the packets arrive out of sequence, that is not IP's problem. If a packet is missing, again, IP does not care. IP gets the data packet (usually a TCP packet) from point A on network X to point B on network Y. That is all, nothing more.

Gateways and IP

To provide the internetwork routing function, IP makes use of special nodes called gateways. A gateway, in IP terms, is a machine that allows two dissimilar networks to be connected to each other. The two networks may or may not be the same type (Ethernet, X.25, token ring, etc.), as IP operates above the hardware itself and is only interested in the virtual connection function, not the physical path or hardware used. As such, there may be a need to segment large messages from the upper software layers into sizes that are applicable to the remote network's allowances. To do this, IP will segment large messages into proper-sized chunks (such as when going from 1500 byte Ethernet packets to 128 byte X.25 packets) for the destination network and reassemble them at the remote destination IP layer before delivery to the user. If a packet gets destroyed in the segmented message and the remote IP detects the packet loss, the entire segment is killed off by the remote IP. Obviously, TCP would detect that a segment is missing and request a retransmission from the remote TCP for any missing packets. TCP has the option of forcing IP NOT to segment packets, but this is usually not implemented as it can cause routing problems where differing network technologies are concerned.

IP also provides for proper security classification of packets being sent to a remote site. If an intermediary gateway or network is not at least the same security level as the transmitted packet, the packet will not be sent through that network. As a result, some strange routing of data may occur sometimes as IP must contend with the problem of expeditious routing but also the problem of security- oriented routing.

Finally, IP has some different terminology than that typically used in a network. In many networks, the concept of a "hop" is the routing of a data packet through a node on its way to its final destination point. In IP, a hop is when a data packet goes through a gateway to another network. Therefore, it is quite possible that a packet may wander through various nodes in a local network before it actually gets to the remote network gateway, depending, of course, upon previously discussed variables. If the packet does not incur a route through a gateway, it, in IP terms, has not incurred a hop. If it transverses through two gateways, it would be considered to have incurred two hops on its path to the final destination. Hops, therefore, are not referred to in the same manner as many other popular communications architectures.

As can be seen, TCP and IP are not the same and may actually be implemented totally independent of each other for separate uses. More often than not, however, they are both included in many offerings from various vendors.

TCP/IP APPLICATIONS

In any network architecture, the protocols and transmission methods are not enough. Users frequently want and need utilities that implement the protocols in the network architecture to allow file transfer, program communication, virtual terminal support, and electronic mail. Most TCP/IP implementations are the same and a few standard applications exist.

TELNET PROTOCOL

Telnet was designed to work between any host (i.e., any operating system) and any terminal. RFC 854 defines the lowest common denominator terminal, called the **network virtual terminal** (NVT). The NVT is an imaginary device from which both ends of the connection, the client and server, map their real terminal to and from. That is, the client operating system must map whatever type of terminal the user is on to the NVT. The server must then map the NVT into whatever terminal type the server supports.

The NVT is a character device with a keyboard and printer. Data typed by the user on the keyboard is sent to the server, and data received from the server is output to the printer. By default the client echoes what the user types to the printer, but we will see that options are normally supported to change this.

The term *NVT ASCII* refers to the 7-bit U.S. variant of the ASCII character set used throughout the Internet protocol suit. Each 7-bit character is sent as an 8-bit byte, with the high-order bit set to 0. An end-of-line is transmitted as the 2-character sequence CR (carriage return) followed by an LF (linefeed). We show this as \r\n. A carriage return is transmitted as the 2-character sequence CR followed by a NUL (byte of 0). We show this as \r\0.

Telnet is a terminal access application layer interface. It provides terminal access support for dumb terminals communicating with remote hosts. These terminals can connect in three ways:

(i)   real terminals connected to TCP/IP Telnet 'terminal servers'

(ii)   real terminals directly connected to hosts running TCP/IP

(iii)   PCs running both terminal emulation and TCP/IP software

The standard for the Telnet service does not provide terminal emulation in its own right. In practice, this is only apparent to programmers, as the command telnet for end users usually causes terminal emulation to be invoked on top of the standard client Telnet service.

The main functionality the Telnet aims to provide is compatibility between computer systems so that client-end applications can gain terminal access to a remote server-end host without having prior knowledge of how to support any particular terminal type. The specific use is to allow remote terminals to connect to an application sever host, maybe through an intermediate computer, and appear as if they are terminals directly connected to that host.

The service the user sees is the terminal service of the remote host. Once connected, they are validated by user and passwords and then are allowed access to authorized applications. The remote service is represented in the best possible fashion on their local terminal screen. They must know how to operate a terminal for the computer they access; no attempt is made to map two different computing command environments, only to translate the different keyboard and display mechanics to generate those commands and display the results. The Telnet server has to make a connecting Telnet client appear like any other terminal user to its host operating system by activating all the necessary validation programs and creating an environment for each logical connection made to it. Once a user logs out from the Telnet server's host computer, it is also responsible for terminating the logical connection that was in place across the network.

In Figure 19.21, all users are able to access host A with the same functionality as if they were directly connected to the host as, for example, is terminal A. For such a connection to appear to the host as if it is a directly attached terminal, a reliable transport layer is required, so Telnet normally operates over TCP.

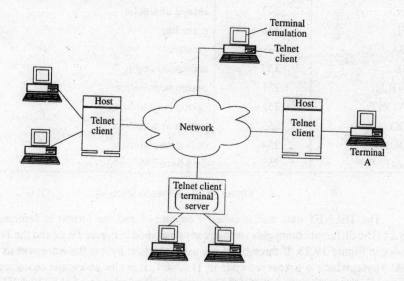

Figure 19.21 : Telnet model

Telnet Commands

Telnet uses in-band signaling in both directions. The byte 0xff (255 decimal) is called IAC, for "interpret as command." The next byte is the command byte. To send the data bytes 255, two consecutive bytes of 255 are sent. Figure 19.22 lists all the Telnet commands.

The Internet standards describe the TELNET options that can be negotiated. Figure 19.43 provides a list of TELNET option codes, along with their code and the relevant RFCs,

if available. Do not assume that all these options are provided in each **vendor** product; many
TELNET products do not support **all available** options.

Code Name	Code (decimal)	Purpose
EOF	236	end-of-file
SUSP	237	suspend current process
ABORT	238	abort process
EOR	239	end of record
SE	240	suboption end
NOP	241	no operation
DM	242	data mark
BRK	243	break
IP	244	interrupt process
AO	245	abort output
AYT	246	are you there
EC	247	escape character
EL	248	erase line
GA	249	go ahead
SB	250	suboption begin
WILL	251	option negotiation
WONT	252	option negotiation
DO	253	option negotiation
DONT	254	option negotiation
IAC	255	data byte 255

Figure 19.22 : Telnet commands

The TELNET data unit is called a *command*, and the format is depicted in Figure
19.24. The different commands were already described in Figure 19.22 and the Telnet option
codes in Figure 19.23. If three bytes are used, the first byte is the **interpret as command**
(*IAC*) byte, which is a reserved code in TELNET. It is also an escape character because it
is used by the receiver to detect if the incoming traffic is not data but a TELNET command.
The next byte is the **command code**, used in conjunction with the IAC byte to describe the
type of command. The third byte is called the **option negotiation** code. It is used to define
a number of options to be used during the session.

Telnet Negotiation

Telnet starts with both sides assuming an NVT, the first exchange that normally takes place
across a Telnet connection in option negotiation. The option negotiation is symmetric either
side can send a request to the other.

Telnet options	Code	Description	RFC
Transmit binary	0	Ignore control codes in data	856
Echo	1	Character echoing	857
RCP	2	Reconnect option	NIC 15391
Suppress-go-ahead	3	Suppress the half duplex go ahead function	858
NAMS	4	Negotiate Approximate Message Size	NIC 15393
STATUS	5	View status of Telnet options	859
Timing-mark	6	Used to help on problems with type ahead	860
RCTE	7	Used with long echo delay circuits	726
NAOL	8	Negotiate output line width	NIC 20196
NAOP	9	Negotiate page output size	NIC 20197
NAOCRD	10	Used with NAOL and NAOP	652
NAOHTS	11	Negotiate horizontal tabstops	653
NAOHTD	12	Horizontal tabstop definition	654
NAOFFD	13	Form feed disposition option	655
NAOVTS	14	Vertical tabstop option	656
NAOVTD	15	Vertical tabstop disposition	657
NAOLFD	16	Linefeed disposition	658
EXTEND-ASCII	17	Extended ASCII option	698
LOGOUT	18	Logout option	727
BM	19	Byte Macro option	735
DET	20	Telnet Data Entry Terminal	732
SUPDUP	21	SUPDUP display controls	736
SUPDUP-OUTPUT	22	Used with SUPDUP	749
SEND-LOCATION	23	Send location id to Telnet server	779
TERMINAL-TYPE	24	Terminal type option	930
END-OF-RECORD	25	To alter the end of record character	885
TUID	26	User identification	927
OUTMRK	27	Output mark	933
EXOPL	255	To allow for more options...	—

Figure 19.23 : Telnet options

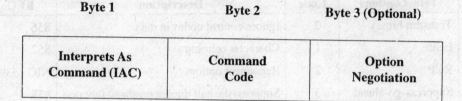

Byte 1	Byte 2	Byte 3 (Optional)
Interprets As Command (IAC)	**Command Code**	**Option Negotiation**

Figure 19.24 : Telnet command format.

Either side can send any one of the following four different requests option.

1. WILL: The sender wants to enable the option itself.

2. DO: The sender wants the receiver to enable the option.

3. WONT: The sender wants to disable the option itself.

4. DONT: The sender wants the receiver to disable the option.

Since the rules of Telnet allow a side to either accept or reject a request to enable an option (cases 1 and 2 above), but require a side to always honor a request to disable an option (cases 3 and 4 above), these four cases lead to the six scenarios are shown in Figure 19.25

	Sender		Receiver	Explanation
1.	WILL	→		**sender** wants to **enable** option receiver says OK
		←	DO	
2.	WILL	→		**sender** wants to **enable** option receiver says NO
		←	DONT	
3.	DO	→		sender wants **receiver** to **enable** option receiver says OK
		←	WILL	
4.	DO	→		sender wants **receiver** to **enable** option receiver says NO
		←	WONT	
5.	WONT	→		**sender** wants to **disable** option receiver must say OK
		←	DONT	
6.	DONT	→		sender wants **receiver** to **disable** option receiver must say OK
		←	WONT	

Figure 19.25 : Six scenarios for telnet option negotiation

Option negotiation requires 3 bytes: the IAC byte, followed by the byte for WILL, DO, WONT, or DONT, followed by an ID byte specifying the option to enable or disable.

The RFCs shown in Table 19.1 should be studied if you wish to gain an indepth understanding of the many functions of Telnet terminals. This part of chapter provides an example of one of these functions; the echo service.

Echoes are used in practically all workstation environments to allow the data entered on the keyboard to be placed (echoed) onto the screen. In some situations, the echo occurs only locally. In others, the echo is sent to the receiving machine and then echoed back to the transmitting machine. The particular implementation of the echo depends on the type of hardware and software that exists on the workstations.

The Telnet echo option allows two users to determine how echoing will occur during the session. The command format for the echo is as follows:

```
IAC WILL ECHO (255 251 1)
```

Note that the values in parentheses represent the IAC, command code, and option negotiation parameter explained in Figure 19.23 and Figure 19.24

This command allows a user to begin echoing the characters it receives over the connection back to the sender of the data characters. Conversely, the command:

```
IAC WON'T ECHO (255 252 1)
```

specifies that the sender of this command will not echo, or wishes to stop echoing, the data characters it receives back to the sender.

Another command is used to request that the receiver of the command begin echoing. This command takes the form:

```
IAC DON'T ECHO (255 253 1)
```

The last Telnet echo command is used by the sender to require the receiver of the command either to stop or not start echoing characters it receives over the connection. This is formatted as:

```
IAC DON'T ECHO (255 254 1)
```

The Telnet echo option defaults to won't echo and don't echo. That is, no echoing is done over the connection.

Another commonly used option is the transmit binary, in which the data stream is interpreted as 8-bit binary images. To request permission to use this service, the sender issues:

```
IAC WILL TRANSMIT-BINARY (255 251 0)
```

The sender of the next command, if it does not want the connection to be operated with the transmit binary option, issues:

```
IAC DON'T TRANSMIT-BINARY (255 254 0)
```

All The Telnet operations are conducted in a similar manner to these examples. So, the Telnet protocol is simple and easy to implement.

TELNET SECURITY

Telnet provides an important feature of level of security. A user connecting to a host using Telnet will be vetted in the same way as other interactive user. So logging in normally requires a user id and password.

An important feature of operating systems is that, by default, users connecting across a network, are prevented from logging in as a **privileged user**. Privileged use can be further restricted to a single directly attached console port. Often this means that somebody attempting to log in as a privileged user using Telnet will be disconnected immediately. This, of course, is a security feature to make it more difficult to gain illegal access to the operating system features of a host.

Telnet carries user information including login ids and passwords in TCP segments without encryption. Access to network cables and to monitoring equipment may be a security issue in some environments.

RLOGIN PROTOCOL

Rlogin is from Berkeley Unix and was developed to work between Unix systems only, but it has been ported to other operating systems also. Rlogin appeared with 4.2BSD and was intended for remote login only between Unix hosts. This makes it a simpler protocol than Telnet, since option negotiation is not required when the operating system on the client and server are known in advance. Over the past few years, Rlogin has also been ported to several non- Unix environments.

The 4BSD UNIX system includes a remote **login** service, rlogin, that supports trusted host. It allows system administrators to choose a set of machines over which login names and file access to their accounts by authorizing remote login based on remote host and remote user name. Thus, it is possible for a user to have login name X on one machine and Y on another, and still be able to remotely login from one of the machines to the other without typing a password each time. Because of automatic authorization, remote login makes facilities useful for general purpose programs as well as human interaction. One variant of the 4BSD **rlogin** command, **rsh**, invokes a command interpreter on the remote UNIX machine and passes the command line arguments to the command interpreter, skipping the login step completely. The format of a command invocation using **rsh** is:

rsh machine command

Typing

```
rsh vax ps
```

on any of the machines in the network executes the **ps** command on machine *vax* with UNIX's standard input and standard output connected across the network to the user's terminal. The user sees the output as if he were logged into machine *vax*. Because the user can arrange to have **rsh** invoke remote commands without prompting for a password, it can be used in programs as well as from the keyboard.

Protocols like **rlogin** understand both the local and remote computing environments, they communicate better than general purpose remote login protocols like Telnet. For example, *rlogin* understands the UNIX notions of *standard input, standard output*, and *standard error*, and uses TCP to connect the remote machine. Thus, it is possible to type

```
rsh vax ps >filename
```

and have output from the remote command redirected into file *filename*. *Rlogin* also understands terminal control functions like flow control characters (typically Control-S and Control-Q). It arranges to stop output immediately without waiting for the delay required to send them across the network to the remote host. Finally, rlogin exports part of the user's environment to the remote machine, including information like the user's terminal type (i.e., the *TERM* variable). As a result, remote login sessions appear to behave like local login sessions.

FILE TRANSFER PROTOCOL (FTP)

File transfer is among the most frequently used TCP/IP applications, and it accounts for much network traffic. Standard file transfer protocols existed for the ARPANET before TCP/IP became operational. These early versions of file transfer software evolved into a current standard known as the *File Transfer Protocol (FTP)*.

Like Telnet, FTP was designed from the start to work between different hosts, running different operating systems, using different file structures, and perhaps different character sets. Telnet, however, achieved heterogeneity by forcing both ends to deal with a single standard; the NVT using 7-bit ASCII. FTP handles all the differences between different systems using a different approach. FTP supports a limited number of file types (ASCII, binary, etc.) and file structures. RFC 959 is the official specification for FTP. This RFC contains a history of the evolution of file transfer over the years.

FTP differs from the other applications that we have described because it uses two TCP connections to transfer a file. First, the *control connection* is established in the normal client-server fashion. The server does passive open on the well-known port for FTP(21) and waits for a client connection. The client does an active open to TCP port 21 to establish the control connection. The control connection stays up for the entire time that the client communicates with this server. This connection is used for commands from the client to the server and for the server's replies.

The IP type-of-service for the control connection should be "minimize delay" since the commands are normally typed by a human user.

Secondly, *data connection* is created each time a file is transferred between the client and server.

The IP type-of-service for the data connection should be "maximize throughput" since this connection is for file transfer.

Figure 19.26 shows a typical configuration for FTP operations.

This figure shows that the interactive user normally doesn't deal with the commands and replies that are exchanged across the control connection. Those details are left to the two protocol interpreters. The box labeled "user interface" presents whatever type of

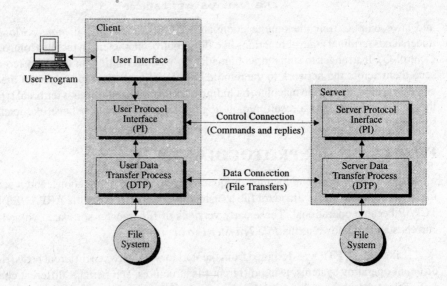

Figure 19.26 : A typical configuration for FTP operations.

interface is desired to the interactive user (full-screen menu selection, line-at-a-time commands, etc.) and converts these into FTP commands that are sent across the control connection. Similarly the replies returned by the server across the control connection can be converted to any format to present to the interactive user. This figure also shows that it is the two protocol interpreters that invoke the two data transfer functions, when necessary.

Data Representation

From the beginning, FTP protocol designers developed the protocol to work with different host computers using different operating systems, file structures, and character sets. As a result, FTP requires users to choose from a wide variety of options for file-transfer operations. FTP options fall into four categories; file types, file formats, file structures, and transmission modes. The following sections describe each of these options.

1.   **FTP File Types**: FTP can manage four different *file types*: local, image(or binary), EBCDIC, and ASCII. The local file-type supports file transfers between hosts that use different byte sizes. As you many aware that the early TCP/IP development occurred on computer systems that did not use 8-bit bytes. The local file-type is a holdover from those days. In other words, the local file-type lets a user transfer data from a host that uses eight-bits-per-bytes to a host that uses a different number of bits-per-byte (7 or 10, for example). For a system that uses 8- bit bytes, the local file-type is identical to the image file- type. Since most modern computers use 8-bit bytes, there is little use for a local file-type FTP transfer today.

The image (or binary) file-type transfer treats file data as a contiguous data stream. In other words, an image file transfer does not include (or identify) any type of boundaries in the internal data structure of a file (such as a carriage-return for the end of a line). Typically, FTP users transfer most files as image files. As you have learned, most computers use ASCII codes to represent textual data. However, some systems, such as IBM mainframes and minicomputers, use EBCDIC instead. EBCDIC (pronounced Eb-si-dick) stands for Extended Binary Coded Decimal Interchange Code. Although EBCDIC and ASCII both use eight bits to represent characters, their respective codes are very different. As such, a computer that understands EBCDIC will not understand ASCII (although many programs exist that will translate between the two schemes).

FTP'S EBCDIC file-type transfer is an alternative file transfer method for two computers that use EBCDIC encoding. In other words, if the hosts on each end of the FTP connection use EBCDIC, they can use FTP's EBCDIC file-type transfer to simplify the transfer of text-based files. ASCII file-type transfers are the default for FTP file transfers. To use the ASCII file-type transfer, the sending host must convert the local text file into NVT ASCII (7-bit ASCII). The receiving host must then translate NVT ASCII into the local convention for text storage.

The primary problem with ASCII file-type transfers are the end-of-line markers. As you have learned, the end-of-line market that various computers use differs from the NVT ASCII convention of a carriage-return line-feed (CRLF) character pair. As such, host receives that use end-of-line identifiers other than CRLF must scan each byte of incoming data to identify the end of each line of text. Obviously, such a requirement adds significant data-processing overhead to the receiver program. In other words, a receiver that uses CRLF end-of-line markers (the same as those FTP's ASCII file-type transfers use) can simply read data from the incoming data queue and write the data to a local file. On the other hand, a receiver that uses a different convention must examine every byte pair in the incoming data queue to determine when the program needs to substitute its own end-of-line marker (typically, a single line-feed character).

2.   **FTP File Formats:** FTP users can choose to transfer files as ASCII or EBCDIC. When a user specifies ASCII or EBCDIC as the file-type transfer, the user must also specify *a format control*. FTP defines three types of format controls; nonprint, Telnet format control, and FORTRAN carriage control. For text files, FTP's default format control is nonprint, which means the file contains no vertical format information, such as vertical tabs, that a printer might use to position text on paper. The Telnet format control, on the other hand, uses vertical format controls for printers. Telnet vertical format controls are embedded character sequences that tell a printer how to print the surrounding text. FORTRAN also uses specially embedded characters. FORTRAN carriage control means the first character of each line is a FORTRAN control character, which, in turn, specifies that line's formatting. The Telnet format control and FORTRAN carriage control are holdovers from the early days of the Internet. Today, most FTP implementations (especially on UNIX-based systems) restrict the format control to nonprint only.

3.   **FTP Transmission Mode:** This specifies how the file is transferred across the data connection.

    (a)   Stream mode.

        (Default) The file is transferred as a stream of bytes. For a file structure, the end-of-file is indicated by the sender closing the data connection. For a record structure, a special 2-byte sequence indicates the end-of-record and end-of-file.

    (b)   Block mode.

        The file is transferred as a series of blocks, each preceded by one or more header bytes.

    (c)   Compressed mode.

        A simple run-length encoding compresses consecutive appearances of the same byte. In a text file this would commonly compress strings of blanks, and in a binary file this would commonly compress strings of 0 bytes. This is rarely used or supported. There are better ways to compress files for FTP.

If we calculate the number of combinations of all these choices, there could be 72 different ways to transfer and store a file. Fortunately we can ignore many of the options, because they are either antiquated or not supported by most implementations.

Common Unix implementations of the FTP client and server restrict us to the following choices:

•   Type: ASCII or image.
•   Format control: nonprint only.
•   Structure: file structure only.
•   Transmission mode: stream mode only.

This limits us to one of two modes: ASCII or image (binary).

FTP Service Commands

The commands and replies sent across the control connection between the client and server are in NVT ASCII. This requires a CR, LF pair at the end of each line (i.e., each command or each reply).

The only Telnet commands (those that begin with IAC) that can be sent by the client to the server are interrupt process (<IAC,IP>) and the Telnet synch signal (<IAC,DM>) in urgent mode). We'll see that these two Telnet commands are used to abort a file transfer that is in progress, or to query the server while a transfer is in progress. Additionally, if the server receives a Telnet option command from the client (WILL, WONT, DO, or DONT) it responds with either DONT or WONT.

Command	Description
USER (userid)<cr,If>	User ID to be logged in
PASS (password)<cr,If>	The user's password
ACCT<cr,If>	Account information
CWD (directory)<cr,If>	Change working directory
CDUP <cr,If>	Change to parent directory
QUIT<cr,If>	Logout
PORT (socket)<cr,If>	Define the socket to be used
TYPE type<cr,If>	Type definition
RETR(filename)<cr,If>	Retrieve a file
STOR(filename)<cr,If>	Send a file
DELE(filename)<cr,If>	Delete the file
RMD(directory name)<cr,If>	Delete the directory
MKD(directory name)<cr,If>	Create the directory
LIST(directory name)<cr,If>	A directory listing for users
NLST(directory name)<cr,If>	A directory listing for programs
STAT<cr,If>	Status
HELP<cr,If>	List of these commands available on server

Figure 19.27 : FTP client/server commands.

The commands are 3 or 4 bytes of uppercase ASCII characters, some with optional arguments. More than 30 different FTP commands can be sent by the client to the server. Figure 19.27 shows some of the commonly used commands.

Code	Description
1yz	Positive Preliminary reply: The server initiated the requested action; expect another reply before proceeding with a new command.
2yz	Positive Completion reply: The server successfully completed the requested action. The client can initiate a new request.
3yz	Positive Intermediate reply: The server accepted the command but the requested action requires more information.
4yz	Transient (temporary) Negative Completion reply: The server did not accept the command, and the requested action did not occur.
5yz	Permanent Negative Completion reply: The server did not accept the command and the requested action did not occur.

Figure 19.28 : The significance of the first digit in FTP reply codes.

FTP REPLIES

The replies are 3-digit numbers in ASCII, with an optional message following the number. The intent is that the software needs to look only at the number to determine how to process the reply, and the optional string is for human consumption. Since the clients normally output both the numeric reply and the message string, an interactive user can determine what the reply says by just reading the string and not have to memorize what all the numeric reply codes means.

The FTP protocol uses a reply-code scheme that is practically identical to the SMTP. In other words, each digit in the reply code has special significance. Figure 19.28 briefly describes the significance of the first digit in an FTP reply code.

Likewise, the second digit in the FTP reply codes refines the message slightly more, as shown in Figure 19.29

Code	Description
x0z	Syntax: These replies refer to syntax errors, syntactically correct commands that don't fit any functional category.
x1z	Information: These are replies to requests for information, such as status or help.
x2z	Connections: These replies refer to the control and data connections.
x3z	Authentication and accounting: These replies are for the login process and accounting procedures.
x4z	Unspecified as yet.
x5z	File system: These replies indicate the status of the Server file system vis-a-vis the requested transfer or other file system action.

Figure 19.29 : The significance of the second digit in FTP reply codes.

Figure 19.30 lists the control codes the FTP specification currently defines.

Connection - Management

There are three uses for the data connection.

1. Sending a file from the client to the server.

2. Sending a file from the server to the client.

3. Sending a listing of files or directories from the server to the client.

FTP servers use the FTP data connection to send file listings to the FTP client. Although the server could use a multiline response to a file-list query, the data connection offers a couple of advantages. First, an FTP implementation may limit the number of lines that a multiline response can include Second, sending file listings through the data connec-

Code	Description
110	Restart marker reply. In this case, the text is exact and not left to the particular implementation.
120	Service ready in nnn minutes.
125	Data connection already open; transfer starting.
150	File status okay; about to open data connection.
200	Command okay.
202	Command not implemented, superfluous at this site.
211	System status, or system help reply.
212	Directory status.
213	File status.
214	Help message.
215	NAME system type.
220	Service ready for new user.
221	Service closing control connection. Logged out if appropriate.
225	Data connection open; no transfer in progress.
226	Closing data connection. Requested file action successful.
227	Entering Passive Mode
230	User logged in, proceed.
250	Requested file action okay, completed.
257	"PATHNAME" created.
331	User name okay, need password.
332	Need account for login.
350	Requested file action pending further information.
421	Service not available, closing control connection.
425	Can't open data connection.
426	Connection closed; transfer aborted.
450	Requested file action not taken. File unavailable.
451	Requested action aborted: local error in processing.
452	Requested action not taken. Insufficient storage space in system.
500	Syntax error, command unrecognised.
501	Syntax error in parameters or arguments.
502	Command not implemented.
503	Bad sequence of commands.
504	Command not implemented for that parameter.

(continued on the next page)

Code	Description
530	Not logged in.
532	Need account for storing files.
550	Requested action not taken. File unavailable.
551	Requested action aborted: page type unknown.
552	Requested file action aborted. Exceeded storage allocation.
553	Requested action not taken. File name not allowed.

Figure 19.30 : Currently defined FTP reply code.

tion makes it easier for a terminal-based FTP user to capture and save file listings in a file. When either the client or server uses the data connection to transfer files (or other information, such as a file listing), they usually follow the procedure described next. First, the client creates the data connection. Because the client initiates all commands that require use of the data connection, the client must also create the connection to receive the requested data. However, also remember that the client transmits its requests across the control connection not the data connection itself.

The client also created the connection. The client performed an active open on the connection. That is, the client created a socket and then actively connected it to the remote host. In effect, the client and server exchanged messages across a socket connected to the server's well-known protocol port. The FTP control connection remains open during the entire FTP session with the server. However, the FTP client creates and maintains the data connection only, as long as a transfer operation is in progress. After a transfer operation completes, the client closes the data connection. In other words, the FTP client maintains the data connection only for the duration of a particular transfer operation. Each time the client needs to exchange data with the server (across the data connection), the client creates a new data connection. The key point to note here is that the FTP data transfers do not occur at a well-known port they occur on a port that the client's host selects.

As such, an FTP client must perform a passive open on the data- connection socket and then tell the server which port on the client's host to contact. Otherwise, the FTP server has no idea where to send the data the client requested through the control connection. After the client tells the FTP server which protocol port to use, the server performs an active open, and the client's host uses the socket and protocol port the FTP client specified. In other words, for the data connection, the FTP client acts like a server. The client creates a socket, binds the socket to a local address, tells the server which address to contact, and then listens for an incoming connection. However, the difference between an FTP client and a real server is that an FTP client only a accepts a connection from the FTP server on the other end of the control connection. As you may recall from the concurrent and iterative server discussions in previous chapters, a server socket typically stores a wildcard for the remote host address. In other words, the server socket accepts connections from any remote host. An FTP client stores the address of the FTP server in the socket created for the data connection. As such, the socket will accept only connections from the FTP server. The same process to create the data connection occurs regardless of whether the client wants to send or receive a file. In both cases, the client creates the socket, binds it to a local address, tells the FTP server which port to contact, and then listens for a connection from the FTP server. In other words, in both cases (for sending and receiving files), the FTP client performs a passive open and the FTP server performs the active open.

TRIVIAL FILE TRANSFER PROTOCOL (TFTP)

TFTP is the Trivial File Transfer Protocol. It is intended to be used when boot strapping diskless systems. It is not as complex as FTP, nor does it have as many functions. It does not consist of much code, nor does it consume much memory; consequently, it can be used on small machines.

TFTP has no provision for a username or password. This is a feature (i.e., "Security hole") of TFTP. Since TFTP was designed for use during the bootstrap process it could be impossible to provide a username and password.

The feature of TFTP was used by many crackers to obtain copies of a Unix Password file and then try to guess passwords. To prevent this type of access, most TFTP servers nowadays provide an option whereby only files in a specific directory (often /tftpboot on Unix systems) can be accessed. This directory then contains only the bootstrap files required by the diskless systems.

For additional security, the TFTP server on a Unix system normally sets its user ID and group ID to values that should not be assigned to any real user. This allows access only to files that have world-read or world-write permissions.

Each exchange between a client and server starts with the client asking the server to either read a file for the client or write a file for the client. In the normal case of boot-strapping a diskless system, the first request is a read request (RRQ). Figure 19.31 shows the format of the five TFTP messages. (Opcodes 1 and 2 share the same format.)

The first 2 bytes of the TFTP message are an *opcode*. For a read request (RRQ) and write request (WRQ) the *filename* specifies the file on the server that the client wants to read from or write to. We specifically show that this filename is terminated by a byte of 0 in Figure 19.31. The *mode* is one of the ASCII strings netascii or octet (in any combination of uppercase or lowercase), again terminated by a byte of 0. netascii means the data are lines of ASCII text with each line terminated by the 2-character sequence of a carriage return followed by a linefeed (called CR/LF). Both ends must convert between this format and whatever the local host uses as a line delimiter. An octet transfer treats the data as 8-bit bytes with no interpretation.

Each data packet contains a *block number* that is later used in an acknowledgment packet. As an example, when reading a file the client sends a read request (RRQ) specifying the filename and mode. If the file can be read by the client, the server responds with a data packet with a block number of 1. The client sends an ACK of block number 1. The server responds with the next data packet, with a block number of 2. The client sends an ACK of block number 2. This continues until the file is transferred. Each data packet contains 512

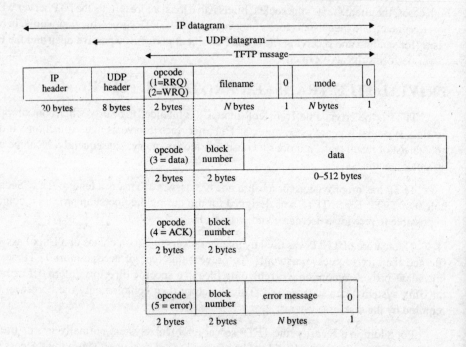

Figure 19.31 : Format of the five TFTP messages.

bytes of data, except for the final packet, which contains 0-511 bytes of data. When the client receives a data packet with less than 512 bytes of data, it knows it has received the final packet.

In the case of a write request (WRQ), the client sends the WRQ specifying the filename and mode. If the file can be written by the client, the server responds with an ACK of block number 0. The client then sends the first 512 bytes of file with a block number of 1. The server responds with an ACK of block number 1.

This type of data transmission is called a *stop-and-wait* protocol. It is found only in simple protocols such as TFTP. TFTP is designed for simplicity of implementation, not high throughput.

The final TFTP message type is the error message, with an *opcode* of 5. This is what the server responds with if a read request or write request can't be processed. Read and write errors during file transmission also cause this message to be sent, and transmission is then terminated. The *error number* gives a numeric error code, followed by an ASCII error message that might contain additional, operation system specific information.

Since TFTP uses the unreliable UDP, it is up to TFTP to handle lost and duplicated packets. Lost packets are detected with a timeout and retransmission implemented by the sender. As with most UDP applications, there is no checksum in the TFTP messages, which assumes any corruption of the data will be caught by the UDP checksum.

BOOTSTRAP PROTOCOL: BOOTP

We learned that the Reverse Address Resolution Protocol (RARP) is used to obtain an IP address from a physical address. Although widely used, RARP has some disadvantages. Because it is intended to operate at the hardware level, it is cumbersome to obtain and manage the routine from an applications program. It also contains limited information. Its purpose is to obtain an IP address, but not much other information is provided. It would be useful for the message reply to contain information about other protocols supported by the machine, such as the gateway address, server host names, etc. Because of these problems with RARP, the Internet now supports the bootstrap protocol, also known as BOOTP.

BOOTP uses an IP datagram to obtain an IP address. This approach seems somewhat circuitous at first glance, but the destination address in the IP datagram is a limited broadcast value (all ones, yielding 255.255.255.255). A machine that chooses to use BOOTP sends out an IP limited broadcast. A designated server on the network receives the BOOTP message and sends a proper answer back to the inquirer in the form of yet another broadcast.

BOOTP utilizes UDP at the transport layer. Consequently, the operation is connectionless. The UDP uses a checksum to check for data corruption. BOOTP performs some transport layer functions by sending a request to the server. Then a timer is started, and, if no reply is received within a defined period, BOOTP attempts a retransmission.

BOOTP requests and replies are encapsulated in UDP datagrams, as shown in Figure 19.32

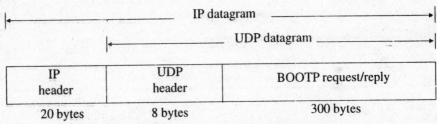

Figure 19.32 : Encapsulation of BOOTP requests/replies within a UDP datagram

Figure: 19.33 shows the format of the 30-byte BOOTP request and reply.

Opcode is 1 for a request and 2 for a reply. The *hardware type* field is 1 for a 10 Mbits/sec Ethernet, the same value that is in the field of the same name in an ARP request or reply. Similarly, the *hardware address length* is 6 bytes for an Ethernet.

The *hop count* is set to 0 by the client, but can be used by a proxy server.

The *transaction* ID is a 32-bit integer set by the client and returned by the server. This lets the client match a response with a request. The client should set this to a random number for each request.

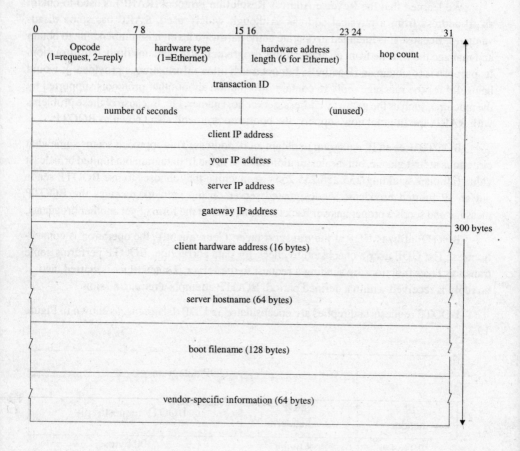

Figure 19.33 : Format of BOOTP request and reply.

Number of seconds can be set by the client to the time since it started trying to bootstrap. The servers can look at this value, and perhaps a secondary server for a client won't respond until the number of seconds has exceeded some value, implying that the client's primary server is down.

If the client already knows its IP address, it fills in the *client IP address*. Otherwise, the client sets this to 0. In the latter case the server fills in *your IP address* with the client's IP address. The server IP address is filled in by the server. If a proxy server is used that proxy server fills in its *gateway IP address*.

The client must set its *client hardware address*. Although this is the same value as in the Ethernet header, by placing the field in the VDP datagram also, it is easily available to any user process (e.g., a BOOTP server) that receives the datagram. It is normally much harder (or impossible) for a process reading UDP datagrams to determine the fields in the Ethernet header that carried the UDP datagram.

The *server hostname* is a null terminated string that is optionally filled in by the server. The server can also fill in the *boot filename* with the fully qualified, null terminated pathname of a file to bootstrap from.

The *vendor-specific area* is used for various extensions to BOOTP.

When a client is bootstrapping using BOOTP (an opcode of 1) the request is normally a link-layer broadcast and the destination IP address in the IP header is normally 255.255.255.255. The source IP address is often 0.0.0.0 since the client does not know its own IP address yet. 0.0.0.0 is a valid source IP address when a system is bootstrapping itself.

Now-a-days, BOOTP is not used just for diskless workstations, but also for providing centralized control of IP addresses. It allows IP addresses to be managed from a single database and standard software configurations to be used even though the workstation may have disks.

System managers can define a standard software configuration that can be implemented on all systems without even having to configure and IP address on each workstaion. The one key fact to obtain during installation is the physical (MAC) address of the LAN card for each installed system. This is the key to correct distribution of all other information. By this method, workstations can learn everything from their IP address to their default router, additional routers, domain name, host name, location of domain name servers and time servers.

Of course, the other use of BOOTP is for diskless workstations. In this case BOOTP is significant because it can allocate not just IP addresses for a node, but also the IP address of common hosts, routers and the name of program files to be downloaded. BOOTP does not download files; it will supply just the server IP address and the name of a file to be down-loaded. TFTP is often used to download files indicated by BOOTP.

SIMPLE MAIL TRANSFER PROTOCOL: SMTP

The mail application layer in TCP/IP has undoubtedly helped in the development of the TCP/IP system itself by allowing information and ideas to be transferred freely throughout the Internet as draft RFCs.

SMTP is a service to allow mail packages to communicate with one another between different computers. As the name implies, it is a simple protocol.

Mail systems can be augmented to provide friendly services such as sending mail to groups of users, allowing word processors to transmit their files automatically, sending documents with the mail as attachments or handling registered mail so it is possible to know if and when the recipient has read an item.

SMTP is found in two RFCs. RFC 822 describes the structure for the message, which includes the envelope as well. RFC 821 specifies the protocol that controls the exchange of mail between two machines.

Figure 19.34 shows an outline of e-mail exchange using TCP/IP.

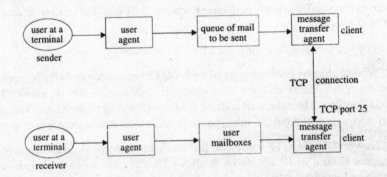

Figure 19.34 : Outline of Internet electronic mail

Note the use of the terms *user agent (UA)* and *message transfer agent (MTA)*. As you can see, the user agent replaces the e-mail program and the message transfer agent replaces the client and server processes.

Internet documentation frequently uses the term *agent* to refer to special purpose software the performs a task for a person or another program. Most Internet e-mail specifications refer to an e-mail program as a *user agent (UA)*. Likewise, a *message transfer agent(MTA)* is a client or server program that performs e-mail- related services, such as sending or receiving mail for a host computer.

You interact with a user-agent program, which, in turn, interacts with an e-mail container (or possibly an MTA program) on your behalf. At the same time, the MTA program acts as an agent on behalf of a host computer. The user agent shields you from interacting with a wide variety of different e-mail hosts. Likewise, the MTA shields the host from a wide variety of user agents of other MTAs.

The user agent (user-interface) to an e-mail system is separate from the message transfer agent. Although you can implement both the user agent (UA) and the message transfer agent (MTA) in a single program, you should isolate the design of each agent in separate modules. Although closely related, the two agents perform very different functions. Many long-time Internet users (UNIX-based) are familiar with Internet e-mail programs, such as MH, Berkeley Mail, Elm, Mush, and Pine. However, Windows-based Internet users may be more familiar with products such as the PC Eudora e-mail program. Each of these programs is a user agent. Each provides an Internet user with an interface to the Internet e-mail system. The purpose of an e-mail program (user agent) is to put a friendly front-end on a network's e-mail system.

On the Internet, the message transfer agent (client and server programs) represent the Internet's e-mail system. Before you can understand the user-agent interface into the Internet e-mail system, you need to understand a little more about message transfer agents. As explained in the following section, Internet MTAs that establish TCP connections to communicate with other MTAs typically use the Simple Mail Transfer Protocol (SMTP).

The core of the Internet's e-mail system is the message transfer agent. As previously mentioned, the message transfer agent represents the e-mail system to a host computer. Although Internet e- mail users rarely work with a message transfer agent (message transfer agents are not exactly user-friendly), MTAs play a crucial role in all e-mail transmissions. For example, after the user-agent software sends an e-mail message to a message queue (which you can view as a container file), the message transfer agent retrieves the message and transmits it to another MTA. This process of passing the message from one MTA to another continues until the message reaches its destination address. To communicate with another MTA across a TCP connection, most Internet message transfer agents use the Simple Mail Transfer Protocol (SMTP). Normally, such MTA communication on the Internet uses Network Virtual Terminal (NVT) ASCII. NVT is similar to a network virtual protocol, which hides computer differences related to line-feeds, form-feeds, carriage-returns, end-of-line markers, and other terminal characteristics. NVT uses standard, 7-bit ASCII encoding for all data, including letters, digits, and punctuation marks. Internet professionals commonly refer to NVT's use of 7-bit ASCII as NVT ASCII.

SMTP COMMANDS

The Simple Mail Transfer Protocol provides for a two-way communication between the client (local) and server (remote) MTAs. The client MTA sends commands to the server MTA, which, in turn, sends replies back to the client MTA. In other words, SMTP commands require replies from the SMTP receiver-module. SMTP refers to the exchange of SMTP commands and replies between two hosts (MTAs) as a *mail transaction*. As discussed, SMTP uses NVT ASCII for data. However, the Simple Mail Transfer Protocol also uses NVT ASCII for SMTP commands. SMTP defines keywords as commands to perform its mail transfer operations. Figure. 19.35 provides a brief description of the SMTP commands (keywords) that the SMTP specification (RFC 821) defines.

According to the specification, a minimal SMTP implementation must include the commands marked required (X) in Figure. 19.35. The other SMTP commands are optional. Each SMTP command either ends with a space (if arguments follow) or a carriage-return line-feed (CRLF). Notice that the descriptions in Figure: 19.35 use the term *mail data* rather than mail message. As you will learn, SMTP extensions permit MTAs to transfer image, audio, and video files using SMTP. In other words, the SMTP protocol and associated commands can transfer more than just text-based e-mail messages. As such, when you read SMTP-related articles, do not restrict the term *message* to text-based data.

Command	Required	Explanation
HELO	X	Identifies the sender-SMTP to the receiver-SMTP--a *hello* command.
MAIL	X	Initiates a *mail* transaction that eventually transfers mail data to one or more mailboxes.
RCPT	X	Identifies an individual *recipient* of mail data.
DATA	X	The receiver-SMTP treats lines that follow the DATA command as mail *data*. For SMTP, the CRLF period CRLF character string identifies the end of mail data.
RSET	X	Aborts *(rests)* the current mail transaction.
NOOP	X	Requires the receiver-SMTP to perform no action *(no operation)* other than return an OK reply. (Used for client/server testing purposes.)
QUIT	X	Requires the receiver-SMTP to return an OK reply and close the transmission channel.
VRFY	*	Asks the receiver-SMTP to confirm or verify that the argument identifies a user. *RFC 821 does not require the VRFY command as a minimal implementation. However, RFC 1123, Requirements for Internet Host--Application and Support, Braden, 1989, lists the VRFY command as mandatory for SMTP implementations on the Internet.*
SEND		Initiates a mail transaction that delivers data to one or more terminals. (Note that SEND delivers data to a terminal rather than a mailbox)
SOML		Initiates a SEND or MAIL transaction that delivers mail data to one or more terminals or mailboxes.
SAML		Initiates a SEND and MAIL transaction that delivers mail data to one or more terminals and mailboxes.
EXPN		Asks the receiver-SMTP to confirm that the argument identifies a mailing list and, if so, to return *(expand)* the membership of the list.
HELP		Asks the receiver-SMTP to send helpful information to the sender-SMTP.
TURN		Requires the receiver-SMTP either to send an OK reply and take on the role of sender-SMTP or return a refusal reply and retain the role of receiver-SMTP.

Figure 19.35 : Commands included in the Simple Mail Transfer Protocol (SMTP)

SMTP REPLIES

SMTP requires server MTAs to acknowledge every command that they receive from a client MTA. As discussed, server MTAs respond to each SMTP command with a three-digit reply code followed by helpful text information. Each SMTP command can result in only one reply code. However, a single reply code may include several lines of text.

Note: Normally, only the EXPN and HELP commands will result in multiline replies. However, SMTP permits multiline replies for any SMTP command.

Each digit in the SMTP reply codes has special significance. The first digit indicates whether the command result was good (2), bad (5), or incomplete (3). An unsophisticated (SMTP-based) client MTA can simply examine the first digit of the reply code to determine its next action. The second and third digits of the reply code continue to refine the reply code explanation. If you model a custom protocol after SMTP, be sure to study the design of SMTP reply codes. SMTP's technique of assigning special significance to specific reply code digits is an excellent example to follow. Figure 19.36 lists the SMTP reply codes that RFC 821 defines.

Reply Code	Description
211	System status or system help reply
214	Help message
220	<domain> Service ready
221	<domain> Service closing transmission channel
250	Requested mail action okay, completed
251	user not local; will forward to <forward-path>
354	Start mail input; end with <CRLF>.<CRLF>
421	<domain> Service not available, closing transmission channel
450	Requested mail action not taken: mailbox unavailable
451	Requested action aborted: local error in processing
452	Requested action not taken: insufficient system storage
500	Syntax error, command unrecognized
501	Syntax error in parameters or arguments
502	Command not implemented
503	Bad sequence of commands
504	Command parameter not implemented
550	Requested action not taken: mailbox unavailable
551	User not local; please try <forward-path>
552	Requested mail action aborted; exceeded storage allocation
553	Requested action not taken: mailbox name not allowed
554	Transaction failed

Figure 19.36 : The SMTP reply codes with descriptions

SMTP Size Limitations

SMTP states that implementations should not impose length limits on objects (perhaps, for future expandability). However, SMTP currently defines the size limits listed in Figure 19.37.

SMTP Object	Size Limitation
User	The maximum length of a username is 64 characters.
Domain	The maximum length of a domain name or number is 64 characters.
Path	The maximum length of a reverse-path or forward-path, including the punctuation and element separators, is 256 Characters.
Command line	The maximum length of a command line, including the command word and the <CRLF>, is 512 characters.
Reply line	The maximum length of a reply line, including the reply code and the <CRLF>, is 512 characters.
Text line	The maximum length of a text line, including the <CRLF>, is, 1,000 characters.
Recipients buffer	The maximum number of buffered recipients is 100.

Figure 19.37 : Object size limitations currently imposed by SMTP.

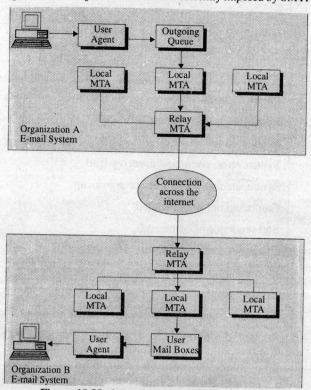

Figure 19.38 : Internet e-mail with relay agents.

Relay Agents

The first line of informational output by our local MTA in our example is "Connecting to mailhost via either." This is because the author's system has been configured to send all nonlocal outgoing mail to a relay machine for delivery.

This is done for two reasons. First, it simplifies the configuration of all MTAs other than the relay system's MTA. Second, it allows one system at an organization to act as the mail hub, possibly hiding all the individual systems.

Today, most network e-mail systems on the Internet use relay agents. Figure 19.38 shows a typical Internet e-mail configuration that uses relay agents.

In this scenario there are four MTAs between the sender and receiver. The local MTA on the sender's host just delivers the mail to its relay MTA. This relay MTA could have a hostname of mailhost in the organization's domain. This communication uses SMTP across the organization's local internet. The relay MTA in the sender's organization then sends the mail to the receiving organization's relay MTA across the Internet. This other relay MTA then delivers the mail to the receiver's host, by communication with the local MTA on the receiver's host. All the MTAs in this example use SMTP, although the possibility exists for other protocols to be used.

E-MAIL PIECES: ENVELOPES, HEADERS AND BODY

Electronic mail is composed of three pieces.

1.   The *envelope* is used by the MTAs for delivery. In our example the envelope was specified by the two SMTP commands:

```
MAIL From: <krish@sun.tuc.mit.edu>
RCPT To: <krish@mit.edu>
```

RFC 821 specifies the contents and interpretation of the envelope, and the protocol used to exchange mail across a TCP connection.

2.   *Headers* are used by the user agents. We saw nine header fields in our example: Received, Message-Id, From, Date, Reply-To, X-Phone, X-Mailer, To, and Subject. Each header field contains a name, followed by a colon, followed by the field value. RFC 822 specifies the format and interpretation of the header fields. (Headers beginning with an X-are user- defined fields. The others are defined by RFC 822.) Long header fields, such as Received in the example, are folded onto multiple lines, with the additional lines starting with white space.

3.   The *body* is the content of the message from the sending user to the receiving user. RFC 822 specifies the body as lines of NVT ASCII text. When transferred using the DATA command, the headers are sent first, followed by a blank line, followed by the body. Each line transferred using the DATA command must be less than 1000 bytes.

The user agent takes what we specify as the body, adds some headers, and passes the result to the MTA. The MTA adds a few headers, adds the envelope, and sends the result to another MTA.

The term *content* is often used to describe the combination of headers and the body. The content is sent by the client with the DATA command.

NetBIOS

Before describing the relationship between NetBIOS and TCP.IP, we will first review how NetBIOS was developed and what it means for networks today. To assist with this explanation, we will consider the normal BIOS (Basic Input/Output System) that is used in IBM PCs and compatibles.

The BIOS in a PC is intended to provide a standard interface to hardware, such that the type of hardware supplied in the machine becomes irrelevant. The BIOS handles commands to send and receive information from the disks, keyboard, communication ports and screens. It provides a level of independence from their specific physical attributes and establishes a standard set of commands for programs and programmers (Figure 19.39).

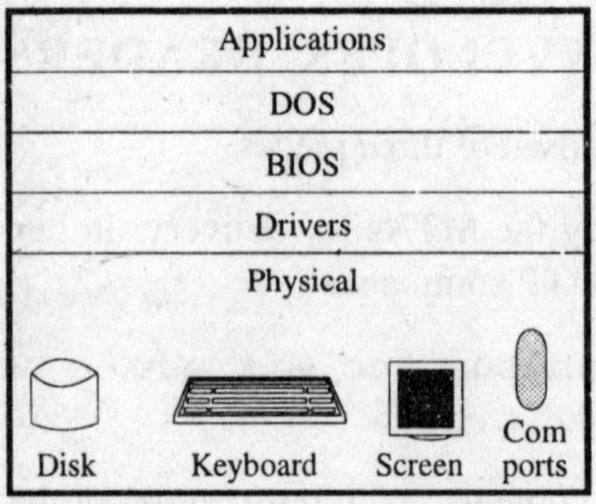

Figure 19.39 : PC architecture

The BIOS has no concept of files — that is the function of the operating system that uses it — it just sends information to the relevant devices. This isolates programmers from the detail of the hardware — the screen, keyboard layout, and disk formats — of a particular machine implementation. It allows simple transportation of programs to different hardware platforms, compatibles and clones, without the need for exactly the same make and format of hardware. Applications become independent of hardware; they become BIOS dependent, but this has proved to be far more stable.

NetBIOS is an interface developed by IBM and Sytek Inc. for the original IBM PC Network. It allows application programs to communicate with the underlying network protocols and hardware. NetBIOS is best thought of as an interface for naming and accessing resources in a LAN structure. It is equivalent to the BIOS in IBM's computer architecture.

NetBIOS provided an interface to the Sytek network hardware and pro: :cols, irrespective of their details. A major difference between the functions of BIOS and of NetBIOS is that before you can read and write information from network devices, you .nust connect to them first. NetBIOS supports the ability to open connections, read and write data, and close connections.

Above NetBIOS was a layer called the session layer. This equates to a Network Operating System (NOS), and manages access to resources on the network just as the local operating system, DOS for example, manages local resources.

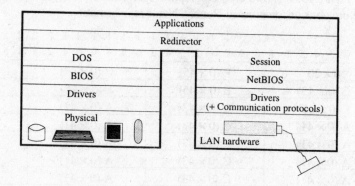

Figure 19.40 : Architecture of a PC showing BIOS and NetBIOS

The RFC 1002 defines a proposed standard protocol to support NetBIOS services in a TCP/IP environment. Both local network and internet operation are supported.

This RFC 1002 contains the detailed packet formats and protocol specifications for NetBIOS-over-TCP. RFC 1002 is a companion to RFC 1001.

Name Format:-

The NetBIOS name representation in all NetBIOS packets (for NAME, SESSION, and DATAGRAM services) is defined in the Domain Name Service RFC 883 as "compressed" name messages. This format is called "second-level encoding" in the section entitled "Representation of NetBIOS Names" in the Concepts and Methods document.

Domain names messages are expressed in terms of a sequence of labels. Each label is represented as a one octet length field followed by that number of octets. Since every domain name ends with the null label of the root, a compressed domain name is terminated by a length byte of zero. The high order two bits of the length field must be zero, and the remaining six bits of the length field limit the label to 63 octets or less.

To simplify implementations, the total length of label octets and label length octets that make up a domain name is restricted to 255 octets or less.

The following is the uncompressed representation of the NetBIOS name "FRED ", which is the 4 ASCII characters, F, R, E, D, followed by 12 space characters (0x20). This name has the SCOPE_ID: "NETBIOS.COM"

EGFCEFEECACACACACACACACACACACACA.NETBIOS.COM

This uncompressed representation of names is called "first-level encoding" in the section entitled "Representation of NetBIOS Names" in the Concepts and Methods document.

Figure 19.41 shows the pictographic representation of the compressed representation of the previous uncompressed Domain Name representation.

```
                  1 1 1 1 1 1 1 1 1 1 2 2 2 2 2 2 2 2 2 2 3 3
0 1 2 3 4 5 6 7 8 9 0 1 2 3 4 5 6 7 8 9 0 1 2 3 4 5 6 7 8 9 0 1
```

0 × 20	E (0 × 45)	G (0 × 47)	F (0 × 46)
C (0 × 43)	E (0 × 45)	F (0 × 46)	E (0 × 45)
E (0 × 45)	C (0 × 43)	A (0 × 41)	C (0 × 43)
A (0 × 41)	C (0 × 43)	A (0 × 41)	C (0 × 43)
A (0 × 41)	C (0 × 43)	A (0 × 41)	C (0 × 43)
A (0 × 41)	C (0 × 43)	A (0 × 41)	C (0 × 43)
A (0 × 41)	C (0 × 43)	A (0 × 41)	C (0 × 43)
A (0 × 41)	C (0 × 43)	A (0 × 41)	C (0 × 43)
A (0 × 41)	0 × 07	N (0 × 4E)	E (0 × 45)
T (0 × 54)	B (0 × 42)	I (0 × 49)	O (0 × 4F)
S (0 × 53)	0 × 03	C (0 × 43)	O (0 × 4F)
M (0 × 40)	0 × 00		

Figure 19.41 : Pictographic representation of the compressed representation of the previous uncompressed domain name representation

Each section of a domain name is called a label. A label can be a maximum of 63 bytes. The first byte of a label in compressed representation is the number of bytes in the label. For the above example, the first 0x20 is the number of bytes in the left-most label, EGFCEFEECACACACACACACACACACACACA, of the domain name. The bytes following the label length count are the characters of the label. The following labels are in sequence after the first label, which is the encoded NetBIOS name, until a zero (0x00) length count. The zero length count represents the root label, which is always null.

A label length count is actually a 6-bit field in the label length field. The most significant 2 bits of the field, bits 7 and 6, are flags allowing an escape from the above compressed representation. If bits 7 and 6 are both set (11), the following 14 bits are an offset pointer into the full message to the actual label string from another domain name that belongs in this name. This label pointer allows for a further compression of a domain name in a packet.

NetBIOS implementations can only use label string pointers in Name Service packets They cannot be used in Session or Datagram Service packets.

Note that the first octet of a compressed name must contain one of the following bit patterns. (An "x" indicates a bit whose value may be either 0 or 1.):

    00100000 - Netbios name, length must be 32 (decimal)
    11xxxxxx - Label string pointer
    10xxxxxx - Reserved
    01xxxxxx - Reserved

General Format of Name Service Packets

The NetBIOS Name Service packets follow the packet structure defined in the Domain Name Service (DNS). The structures are compatible with the existing DNS packet formats, however, additional types and codes have been added to work with NetBIOS.

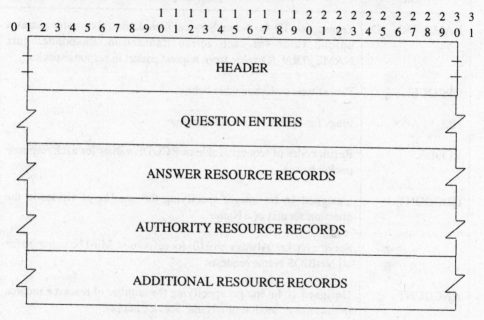

Figure 19.42 : Format of name service packets.

If Name Service packets are sent over a TCP connection they are preceded by a 16 bit unsigned integer representing the length of the Name Service packet.

Header:-

Figure 19.43 shows, the header format of name service packets.

The Field used in Header Format are described as follows:

The OPCODE field is defined as:


```
                1 1 1 1 1 1 1 1 1 1 2 2 2 2 2 2 2 2 2 2 3 3
0 1 2 3 4 5 6 7 8 9 0 1 2 3 4 5 6 7 8 9 0 1 2 3 4 5 6 7 8 9 0 1
```

NAME_TRN_ID	OPCODE	NM_FLAGS	RCODE
QDCOUNT		ANCOUNT	
NSCOUNT		ARCOUNT	

Figure 19.43 : Header format of name service packets.

Field	Description
NAME_TRN_ID	Transaction ID for Name Service Transaction. Requestor places a unique value for each active transaction. Responder puts NAME_TRN_ID value from request packet in response packet.
OPCODE	Packet type code, see table below.
NM_FLAGS	Flags for operation, see table below.
RCODE	Result codes of request. Table of RCODE values for each response packet below.
QDCOUNT	Unsigned 16 bit integer specifying the number of entries in the question section of a Name Service packet. Always zero (0) for responses. Must be non-zero for all NetBIOS Name requests.
ANCOUNT	Unsigned 16 bit integer specifying the number of resource records in the answer section of a Name Service packet.
NSCOUNT	Unsigned 16 bit integer specifying the number of resource records in the authority section of a Name Service packet.
ARCOUNT	Unsigned 16 bit integer specifying the number of resource records in the additional records section of a Name Service packet.

0	1	2	3	4
R		OPCODE		

The OPCODE includes a 5-bit parameter field, each bit of which is used as a flag described below:

Symbol	Bit(s)	Description
OPCODE	1-4	Operation specifier: 0 = query 5 = registration 6 = release 7 = WACK 8 = refresh
R	0	RESPONSE flag: if bit == 0 then request packet if bit == 1 then response packet.

The NM_FLAGS field is defined as:

0	1	2	3	4	5	6
AA	TC	RD	RA	O	O	B

The NM_FLAGS include 7-bit parameter field, each bit of which is used as a flag described below:

Symbol	Bit(s)	Description
B	6	Broadcast Flag. = 1: packet was broadcast or multicast = 0: unicast
RA	3	Recursion Available Flag. Only valid in responses from a NetBIOS Name Server -- must be zero in all other responses. If one (1) then the NBNS supports recursive query, registration, and release. If zero (0) then the end-node must iterate for query and challenge for registration.
RD	2	Recursion Desired Flag. May only be set on a request to a NetBIOS Name Server. The NBNS will copy its state into the response packet. If one (1) the NBNS will iterate on the query, registration, or release.
TC	1	Truncation Flag. Set if this message was truncated because the datagram carrying it would be greater than 576 bytes in length. Use TCP to get the information from the NetBIOS Name Server.
AA	0	Authoritative Answer flag. Must be zero (0) if R flag of OPCODE is zero (0). If R flag is one (1) then if AA is one (1) then the node responding is an authority for the domain name. End nodes responding to queries always set this bit in responses.

Question Section:-

Figure 19.44 shows the Question Entries Format of Name Server Packets.

The Field used in Question Format are described below:

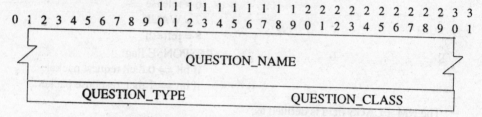

Figure 19.44 : Question format of name service packets.

Field	Description
QUESTION_NAME	The compressed name representation of the NetBIOS name for the request.
QUESTION_TYPE	The type of request. The values for this field are specified for each request.
QUESTION_CLASS	The class of the request. The values for this field are specified for each request.

QUESTION_TYPE is defined as:

Symbol	Value	Description
NB	0x0020	NetBIOS general Name Service Resource Record
NBSTAT	0x0021	NetBIOS NODE STATUS Resource Record

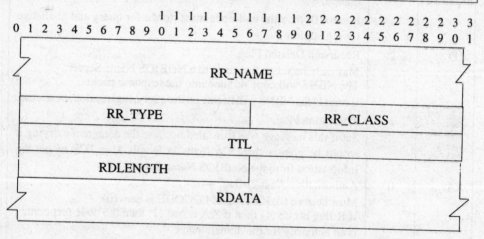

Figure 19.45 : Resource record (RR) format of name server packets.

QUESTION_CLASS is defined as:

Symbol	Value	Description
IN	0x0001	Internet class

Resource Record (RR):

Figure 19.45 shows the Answer Resource Records of Name Server Packets:

The Field used in Resource Record are described as follows:

Field	Description
RR_NAME	The compressed name representation of the NetBIOS name corresponding to this resource record.
RR_TYPE	Resource record type code
RR_CLASS	Resource record class code
TTL	The Time To Live of a the resource record's name.
RDLENGTH	Unsigned 16 bit integer that specifies the number of bytes in the RDATA field.
RDATA	RR_CLASS and RR_TYPE dependent field. Contains the resource information for the NetBIOS name.

RESOURCE RECORD RR_TYPE field definitions:

Symbol	Value	Description
A	0x0001	IP address Resou
NS	0x0002	Name Server Resource Record
NULL	0x000A	NULL Resource Record
NB	0x0020	NetBIOS general Name Service Resource Record
NBSTAT	0x0021	NetBIOS NODE STATUS Resource Record

RESOURCE RECORD RR_CLASS field definitions:

Symbol	Value	Description
IN	0x0001	Internet class

NB_FLAGS field of the RESOURCE RECORD RDATA field for RR_TYPE of "NB":

0	1	2	3	4	5	6	7	8	9	1 0	1 1	1 2	1 3	1 4	1 5
G	ONT			RESERVED											

Symbol	Bit(s)	Description:
RESERVED	3-15	Reserved for future use. Must be zero (0).
ONT	1,2	Owner Node Type:
		00 = B node
		01 = P node
		10 = M node
		11 = Reserved for future use
		For registration requests this is the claimant's type.
		For responses this is the actual owner's type.
G	0	Group Name Flag.
		If one (1) then the RR_NAME is a GROUP NetBIOS name.
		If zero (0) then the RR_NAME is a UNIQUE NetBIOS name.

The NB_ADDRESS field of the RESOURCE RECORD RDATA field for RR_TYPE of "NB" is the IP address of the name's owner.

NetBIOS provides a standard interface to LAN cards, allowing peer-to-peer connections to be established between machines. Although this interface was developed for the IBM PC, NetBIOS can now be found on mini and mainframe computers as well. This allows mini and mainframes to participate as file and print servers in what was originally a DOS PC domain. The term 'PC Network' has become obsolete. It is now a generic term for sharing data among any type of machine including PCs; it is more appropriate to talk today about Network Operating Systems (NOSs).

The NetBIOS interface is available with most NOSs. Microsoft LAN Manager and Microsoft Networks systems (MSNET) use NetBIOS. It is also available for Novell NetWare. NetBIOS can run over many networks XNS, TCP/IP, IPX and X.25, so it has become a powerful tool for system integration. NetBIOS provides the 'interoperation' aspects of the internetworking equation.

FINGER PROTOCOL

The Finger protocol returns information on one or more than users on a specified host. It's most commonly used to see if someone is currently logged on, or to figure out someone's login name, to send them mail.

Many sites do not run a Finger server for two reasons:

(i)   a programming error in a earlier version of the server was one of the entry points used by the infamous Internet worm of 1988.

(ii)   the Finger protocol can reveal detailed information on users (login names, phone numbers, when they last logged in, etc.) that many administrators consider private.

The Finger server has a well-known port of 79. The client does an active open to this port and sends a one-line query The server processes the query, sends back the output, and closes the connection.

Before you can communicate with another user, you must know the user's Internet address. One of the commands you can use to determine the address of user is the **finger** command. The **finger** command tells you two things:

*   Who is logged in at the current time
*   Information about a specific user account

For example, let's say you need to get in touch with someone at a particular host system. You think you know their user ID, but you're not quite sure. You can use the **finger** command to see if they are on line, and if so, you can figure out what their ID might be.

The simplest way to use the **finger** command is to discover who is on your local computer system. To use the command in this way, simple type the following:

Finger   <ENTER>

If the **finger** program is available on your system, you should see a list of users currently logged into your system.

finger   dci   <ENTER>
                    User id

You can find more detailed information about an individual by following the **finger** command with their ID.

The ID you use does not need to belong to a currently connected individual (someone who is logged in); it can be any user ID recognized by your system. Using **finger** in this way lists the full name of the individual, how long they have been on, and other information about the user.

You can also use the **finger** command to find out who is logged onto other computer systems. This is done is one of two general ways. First, you can discover who is logged onto another system by including the system name in the command, as follows:

```
Finger @niit.columbia.edu      <ENTER>
```

This command tries to connect with the remote site (**@niit. columbia.edu**) and if successful, lists the users logged into that system. The information you get back depends on a couple of things. Primarily how the **finger** command functions at the remote site and whether that site supports the **finger** command being used from remote locations. Not all sites support remote **finger**ing; if they do not, you might see a message indicating that there are no users connected or that there was an error in connecting. If remote fingering is supported, however, you will see a display similar to the one shown when you used **finger** on your local system.

Another way to use **finger** remotely is to display specific information about a user at a remote site by providing a full Internet address. For instance, the following command displays specifics about a user connected to a computer at Columbia University:

```
ABC> finger smith@niit.columbia.edu   <ENTER>
```

WHOIS PROTOCOL

The **Whois** protocol is another information service. Any site can provide a Whois server, the one at the InterNIC, rs.internic.net, is most commonly used. This server maintains information about all registered DNS domains and many system administrators responsible for systems connected to the Internet. Another server is provided at **nic.ddn.mil**, but contains information only about the MILNET. Unfortunately the information can be out of data or incomplete. RFC 954 lists in detail Whois service.

The **Whois** server has a well-known TCP port of 43. It accepts connection requests from clients, and the client sends a one-line query to the server. The server responds with whatever information is available and then closes the connection. The requests and replies are transmitted using NVT ASCII. This is almost identical to the Finger server, although the requests and replies contain different information.

For example, if you want to connect to a computer at Arizona State University, but you don't remember the computer's Internet address, you can quickly look up that address using **whois**. To use the **whois** command, you simply use the following syntax:

```
whois [-h host] text
```

where *host* is the optional name of a particular host who's server you want to search, and *text* is the name, domain, or host you want to find.

As an example, let's assume you wanted to search for hosts related to Brigham Young University, in Provo, Utah. The common acronym for the school is BYU, so you figure that is a good place to start. Using this information, you can enter the following command:

```
whois byu <ENTER>
```

You can take you **whois** search even one step further, if you wish. For instance, let's say that the VAX system at BYU (**yvax.byu.edu**) caught your interest. You could get information on this particular host in the following manner:

```
whois yvax.byu.edu <ENTER>
```

Since you entered a host name (not a domain name), **whois** will provide you with information about the host. This information lets you know what sort of system it is, as well as who runs the system.

GOPHER

Gopher is a menu-driven front end to other Internet resource services, such as Archie, and anonymous FTP. Gopher is one of the easiest to use, since its user interface is the same, regardless of which resource service it's using.

The use Gopher, Telnet into **is.internic.net** and login as gopher.

VERONICA

veronica is a tool used in conjunction with **gopher,** developed by the folks at the University of Nevada. It is basically an extension to **gopher,** providing a major feature (an index) that many people felt was lacking in the original product. As the number of **gopher** servers in the world grew, there was no comprehensive index to the information in each of the **gopher** servers. Basically this means that there is no easy way to quickly search all the **gopher** databases and extract only the information that matches your particular needs. This is where **veronica** comes in. **veronica** does nothing more than search indexes of all the titles of documents in **gopher** servers around the world. Through a **gopher** menu choice that accesses **veronica,** you can then perform a keyword search on this index. The results are returned in a form that **gopher** can display in its normal format.

ARCHIE

Most of the resources used in this text were obtained using anonymous FTP. The problem is finding which FTP site has the program we want. Sometimes we don't even know the exact filename, but we know some keywords that probably appear in the filename.

Archie provides a directory of thousands of FTP servers across the Internet. We can access this directory by logging into an Archie server and searching for files whose name contains a specified regular expression. The output is a list of servers with matching filenames. We then use anonymous FTP to that site to fetch the file.

There are many Archie servers across the world. One starting point is to use Telnet to **ds.internic.net**, login as **archie**, and execute the command servers. This provides a list of all the Archie servers, and their location.

WAIS: WIDE AREA INFORMATION SERVERS

You are already familiar with the more common searching tools available on the Internet, such as **gopher** and **archie.** But what happens when you can't find a specific database for your research? When you have a well-defined topic on which to search, you can get your work done in minimal time and effort using the tools previously presented. On the other hand, you may have some esoteric subject that just can't be defined in one simple word or phrase.

In a more personal sense, WAIS behaves much like a reference librarian at your public library, in that it looks for the information you request. If you provide a topic or a few descriptive keywords, any good librarian knows exactly where a certain book is located. From the vast indexes maintained in a WAIS server, WAIS also knows just where to find information based on the parameters you provide.

WAIS keeps you from the concern of *where* to find the data you need. Specifically, the database that WAIS can access are not all located at the same site. It would be impractical and a waste of resources to keep and maintain all the databases in one place. This would require a vast amount of storage space and computer processing, not to mention make it difficult for contributors to keep database items current.

That is where WAIS comes in. There are WAIS databases in many locations across the Internet. Each of these databases is indexed, and WAIS consults the index to satisfy your search requests. This index points to the database items (the source documents) the contain that word.

PING

PING is a very simple protocol that uses the user datagram protocol (UDP) segment. Its principal operation is to send a message and simple wait for it to come back.

PING is so named because it is an echo protocol and uses the ICMP echo and echo-reply messages. Each machine is operating with a PING server whenever IP is active on the machine. PING is used principally by systems programmers for diagnostic and debugging purposes. It is very useful because it provides the following functions:

- The *loopback ping* is used to verify the operation of the TCP/IP software.
- The *ping address* determines if a physical network device can be addressed.
- The *ping remote IP address* verifies whether the network can be addressed.
- The *ping remote host name verifies* the operation of a server on a host.

WWW: WORLD WIDE WEB

World Wide Web lets us browse a large, worldwide set of services and documents using a tool called *hypertext*. As information is displayed, certain keywords are highlighted, and we can select more information on those keywords.

To access WWW, Telnet to **info.cern.ch.**

X WINDOW SYSTEM

The **X Window System** was developed by Massachusetts Institute of Technology (MIT). It is a method of controlling an advance graphical 'windowed' interface. From the perspective of TCP/IP, the X Window System is a message protocol between an X server and an X client as shown in Figure 19.46.

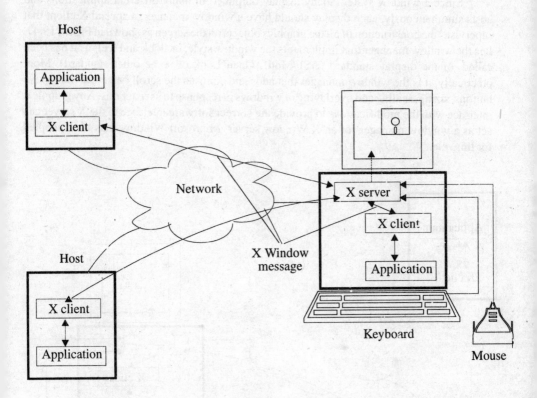

Figure 19.46 : X Window protocl

With the X Window System, the boundary between user interface, which is not normally defined, and the communications protocol may seem to been breached, but in fact it is intact. RFC1013 only describes the protocol between server and client. The style of the display is determined by other standards, typically the OSF/Motif display standard promoted by the Open Software Foundation Inc.

This protocol is explained in RFC1013. Copyright remains with MIT, though permission is given to distribute the RFC document as long as the copyright is acknowledged. Other aspects of the X Window System, although not published as RFCs, are described in standards available from the X Consortium at MIT.

Unlike every other reference to client and server in TCP/IP, with X Window the server is normally at the user's workstation and the client, which generates the new drawing instructions, is at the application host. The X server operates the display terminal, drawing graphics objects and text in response to messages from the X client. The server must also report user actions such as keystrokes and mouse movements to any X clients that will be affected by them.

Since a window system many display output from many different applications and hosts simultaneously, each display should have a window manager, a special X client that supervises the construction of all the graphics objects on the screen as shown in Figure 19.47. It is the window manager that implements the window style, or 'look and feel' as it has been called, of the display standard (ASF/Motif, Open Look or some other standard). More practically, it is the window manager that adds and controls the scroll bars, title line, move buttons, sizing, scaling and overlaying of windows in response to user actions. Any graphical interface with the modifications to provide the correct software interface to the X server can act as a window manager for an X Window server. Microsoft Windows has been adapted for this role.

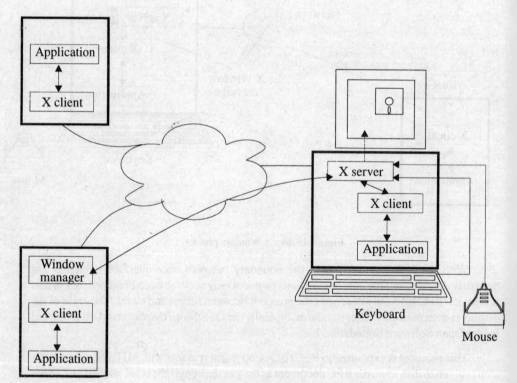

Figure 19.47 : The X Window manager

The X terminal

The X terminal is an X Window display station that implements the X server, which it runs no user applications (X clients) locally. All display requests are received on the network connection. Extensions to the X user interface can provide for colour, image support and Display PostScript among others.

Some X terminals have been adapted to operate over dial-up modem links. Since modem links are limited to 9600 bps or 144000 bps before compression, many suppliers offer some form of data compression for this type of connection. The result is a usable, if somewhat sluggish, display system provided that the dial-up link is carrying data for a single X terminal user. Where possible, higher speed lines should be used for X terminals. The increasing availability worldwide of ISDN 64 kbps 'dial-up' circuits will alleviate these restrictions.

The X Window System

Graphics applications, particularly when bit-mapped graphics is involved, are demanding both of processing power and of communications capacity. The communications requirements will increase if the X server and window manager are not on the same workstation. The earliest X Window terminals operated with a remote, host-based window manager; the standards specifically provided for it. In this case, every user action, from a key press to a pointer (mouse) movement generates network traffic, with a large movement of the pointer potentially generating a stream of X protocol messages.

The X Window protocol uses TCP reliable connections between a server and its client. Each TCP data segment sent may be individually acknowledged, almost doubling the expected traffic. If the protocol is confined to a LAN segment reserved for the purpose, this traffic is unlikely to be an issue. Where X systems cross bridges or routers between LANs or more particularly cross wide area lines, the traffic generated by particularly actions should be measured for every X implementation being considered. The network capacity and layout should then be planned carefully to carry the expected traffic. Some of the more recent X terminal implementations use a local window manager, which removes a high proportion of the traffic from the network.

Tuning TCP may not improve the performance of an interactive protocol like X Windows as much as a bulk transfer protocol like FTP.

THE NETWORK FILE SYSTEM

The Network File System (NFS) was also developed by Sun Microsystems Incorporated, to allow computers to share files across a network or networks. NFS is computer-independent and is also independent of lower layers, such as the transport layer, because it rests above the RPC (Remote Procedure Calls).

NFS consists of two other protocols called the *mount protocol* and the NFS *protocol*. The purpose of the mount protocol is to identify file system and the remote host to be accessed. The NFS protocol is responsible for performing the file transfer operations.

A number of manufacturers have produced versions of NFS which operate on their systems, so it is now available on most computers, from PCs to large mainframes, in some form. NFS provides an excellent way of transparently connecting PCs, mini-and mainframe computer systems together; it allows files to be stored centrally, shared among communities of mixed computers and supports remote printing.

Sun Microsystems Inc. extended this UNIX service to allow PCs to access their computers using NFS through a product called PC-NFS, since when NFS and PC-NFS have become available on most computing platforms. Unlike other TCP/IP applications, NFS users need no specific training in using this system. When NFS is properly configured, users merely believe they have acquired additional disk capacity and printers. So NFS provides a resource-sharing network system with similar features to Novell NetWare or LAN Manager from Microsoft.

NFS ARCHITECTURE

Figure 19.48 shows an architecture of NFS, which is usually implemented over TCP/IP protocol suite but is not exclusive to it.

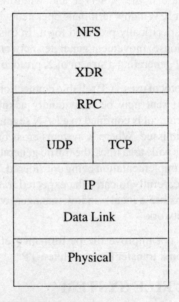

Figure 19.48 : NFS architecture

There are three layers:-

S.No.	Layer	Description
(i)	RPC	Defines the format of messages used by remote procedure calls.
(ii)	XDR	The external Data Representation is a consistent representation of data between different machine architectures
(iii)	NFS	The Network File System, is an application layer interface for file transfer, access and management.

The RPC, XDR, and NFS adds another three layers to the transport layer of the TCP/IP model, making a seven layer model, which is similar to the OSI model in terms of functionality of the layers.

NFS provides transparent *file access* for clients to files and filesystems on a server. This differs from FTP which provides *file transfer*. With FTP a complete copy of the file is made. NFS accesses only the portions of a file that a process references, and a goal of NFS is to make this access transparent. This means that any client application that works with a local file should work with an NFS file, without any program changes whatsoever.

NFS is a client-server application built using Sun RPC. NFS clients access files on an NFS server by sending RPC requests to the server. While this could be done using normal user processes--that is, the NFS client could be a user process that makes explicit RPC calls to the server, and the server could also be a user process--NFS is normally not implemented this way for two reasons. First, accessing an NFS file must be transparent to the client. Therefore the NFS client calls are performed by the client operating system, on behalf of client user processes. Second, NFS servers are implemented within the operating system on the server for efficiency. If the NFS server were a user process, every client request and server reply (including the data being read or written) would have to cross the boundary between the kernel and the user process, which is expensive.

Figure 19.49 illustrates the typical arrangement of an NFS client and an NFS server. It is transparent to the client whether it's accessing a local file or an NFS file.The kernel determines this when the file is opened. After the file is opened, the kernel passes all references to local files to the box labeled "local file access," and all references to an NFS

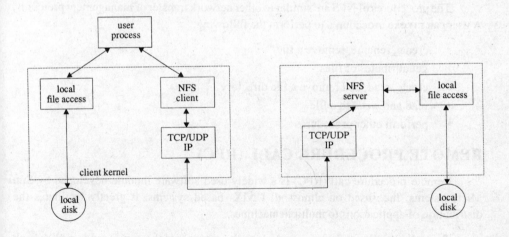

Figure 19.49 : Typical arrangement of NFS client and NFS server

file are passed to the "NFS client" box. The NFS client sends RPC requests to the NFS server through its TCP/IP module. NFS is used predominantly with UDP, but newer implementations can also use TCP. The NFS server receives client requests as UDP datagrams. Although NFS could be made to use the port mapper, allowing the server to use an ephemeral port, UDP port is hardcoded into most implementations.

When the NFS server receives a client request, the requests are passed to its local file access routines, which access a local disk on the server. It can take the NFS server a while to handle a client's request. The local filesystem is normally accessed, which can take some time. During this time, the server does not want to block other client requests from being serviced. To handle this, most NFS servers are multithreaded--that is, there are really multiple NFS servers running inside the server kernel. How this is handle depends on the operating system. Since most Unix kernels are not multithreaded, a common technique is to start multiple instances of a user process that performs a single system call and remains inside the kernel as a kernel process. Similarly, it can take the NFS client a while to handle a request from a user process on the client host.

An NFS server performs its operations through several procedures. These procedures are *stateless,* in that no state tables are maintained to track the progress of the procedures' operations. This approach might seem a bit strange. After all, file reading, and especially writing, is inherently state oriented (sometimes called "stateful") because these operations must be tracked. NFS solves the problem by assuming that any required state-oriented services are implemented in other protocols. A user application could therefore contain the state- oriented logic (file locks, write positions, etc.) and call NFS for the use of its procedures.

The procedures of NFS are similar to other network transfer or management protocols. A user can invoke procedures to perform the following:

- create, rename, remove a file
- get attributes of files
- create, read, and remove a file directory
- read and write to a file
- perform other procedures

REMOTE PROCEDURE CALL (RPC)

Remote procedure call (RPC) is a widely used software module developed by Sun Microsystems, Inc., used on almost all UNIX- based systems. It greatly facilitates the distribution of applications to multiple machines.

Typically the client sends commands to the server, and the server sends replies back to the client. All the applications we've looked at so far DNS, TFTP, BOOTP, SNMP, Telnet, FTP, an SMTP are built this way.

RPC, *remote Procedure Call*, is a different way of doing network programming. A client program is written that just calls functions in the server program.

When the client calls the remote procedure, it's really calling a function on the local host that's generated by the RPC package. This function is called the *client stub*. The client stub packages the procedure arguments into a network message, and sends this message to the server. A *server stub* on the server host receives the network message. It takes the arguments from the network message, and calls the server procedure that the application programmer wrote.

When the server function returns, it returns to the server stub, which takes the return values, packages them into a network message, and sends the message back to the client stub. The client stub takes the return values from the network message and return to the client application.

An RPC package provides numerous benefits.

(i)   The programming is easier since there is little or not network programming involved. The application programmer just writes a client program and the server procedures that the client calls.

(ii)   If an unreliable protocol such as UDP is used, details like timeout and retransmission are handled by the RPC package. This simplifies the user application.

(iii)   The RPC library handles any required data translation for the arguments and return values. For example, if the arguments consist of integers and floating point numbers, the RPC package handles any differences in the way integers and floating point numbers are stored on the client and server. This simplifies coding clients and severs that can operate in heterogeneous environments.

Figure 19.50 illustrate the format of an RPC procedure call message, when UDP is used.

The *transaction* ID (XID) is set by the client and returned by the server. When the client receives a reply it compares the XID returned by the server with the XID of the request it sent. If they don't match, the client discards the message and waits for the next one from the server. Each times the client issues a new RPC, it changes the XID. But if the client retransmits a previously sent RPC the XID does not change.

Call/response: This field indicates whether the header is a call, value 0, or a response, value 1.

RPC protocol version number: This allows multiple versions of RPC programs to be supported on a network. A server is able to respond to a request based upon the version of the request. For the NFS program, version 2 should currently be used.

Program number: This number identifies the particular RPC program to be accessed on a server. For example:

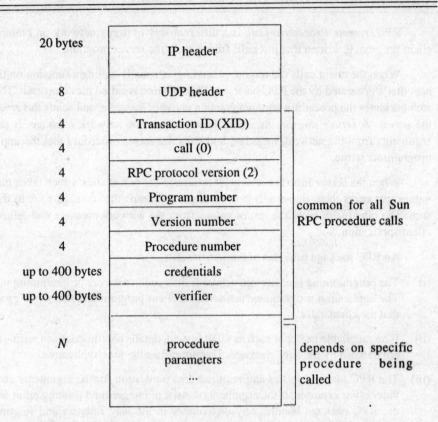

Figure 19.50 : Format of RPC procedure call message as a UDP datagram.

Application	Programme Number
Portmapper	100000
NFS	100003
NIS	100004
mountd	100005
lockd	100021
Status monitor	100024

Program version: This number allows multiple versions of RPC programs to be supported on a network. A server is able to deal with a request based upon the version of the request. This simplifies upgrades and maintaining backwards compatibility.

Procedure number: Programs are normally composed of a number of different procedures. The procedure number defines which procedure within the program is required.

The NFS procedures shown below are all accessed through program number 100003 and the procedure numbers used in the RPC header identify the specific procedure required of NFS.

NFS procedure	Procedure number	Description
null	0	Do no work, just return a response
getattr	1	Get file attributes
setattr	2	Set file attributes
getroot	3	Obsolete
lookup	4	Get file handle and attributes
readlink	5	Read from symbolic link
read	6	Read a defined number of bytes from a named file
cache	7	Write to cache
write	8	Write a defined number of bytes from a named file
create	9	Create a file
delete	10	Delete a file
rename	11	Rename a file
link	12	Link to a file
symlink	13	Create a symbolic link to a file
mkdir	14	Make a directory
rmdir	15	Remove a directory
readdir	16	Get a directory listing
statfsres	17	Get file system attributes

The *Credentials* identify the client. In some instances nothing is sent here, and in other instances the numeric user ID and group IDs of the client are sent. The server can look at the credentials and determine if it will perform the request or not. The *verifier* is used with Secure RPC, which uses DES encryption. Although the credentials and verifier are variable-length fields, their length is encoded as part of the field.

The format of procedure parameters depends on the definition of the remote procedure by the application. How does the receiver know the size of the parameters? Since UDP is being used, the size of the UDP datagram, minus the length of all the fields up through the verifier, is the size of the parameters. When TCP is used instead of UDP, there is no inherent length, since TCP is a byte stream protocol, without record boundaries. To handle this, a 4-byte length field appears between the TCP header and the XID, telling the receiver how many bytes comprise the RPC call. This allows the RPC call message to be sent in multiple TCP segments, if necessary.

Figure 19.51 shows the format of an RPC reply.

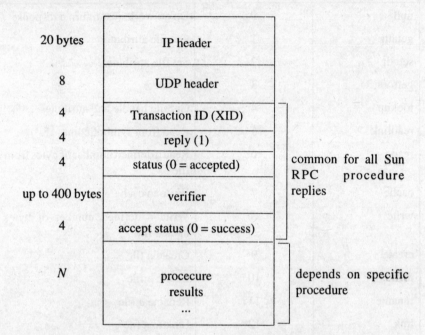

20 bytes	IP header	
8	UDP header	
4	Transaction ID (XID)	
4	reply (1)	
4	status (0 = accepted)	common for all Sun RPC procedure replies
up to 400 bytes	verifier	
4	accept status (0 = success)	
N	procecure results ...	depends on specific procedure

Figure 19.51 : Format of RPC procedure reply message as a UDP datagram. This is sent by the server stub to the client stub, when the remote procedure returns.

The XID in the reply is just copied from the XID in the call. The *reply* is 1, which we said differentiates this message from a call. The status is 0 if the call message was accepted. The message can be rejected if the RPC version number isn't 2, or if the server cannot authenticate the client. The *verifier* is used with secure RPC to identify the server.

The *accept status* is 0 on success. A nonzero value can indicate an invalid version number or an invalid procedure number, for example. As with the RPC all message, if TCP is used instead of UDP, a 4-byte length field is sent between the TCP header and the XID.

eXternal Data Representation (XDR)

XDR, used to encode the values in the RPC call and reply messages--the RPC header fields (XID, program number, accept status, etc.), the procedure parameters, and the procedure results. Having a standard way of encoding all these values is what lets a client on one system call a procedure on a system call a procedure on a system with a different architecture.

XDR defines numerous data types and exactly how they are transmitted in an RPC message (bit order, byte order, etc.). The sender must boiled an RPC message in XDR format, then the receiver converts the XDR format into its native representation. Figures 9.3 and

9.4, illustrates that all the integer values we show (XID, call, program, number, etc.) are 4-byte integers. Indeed, all integers occupy 4 bytes in XDR. Other data types supported by XDR include unsigned integers, booleans, floating point numbers, fixed-length arrays, variable-length arrays, and structures.

PORT MAPPER

As with TCP/IP, the term 'NFS" refers to a complete family of products, although Sun Microsystems Inc., the developers of NFS, prefer to call it Open Network Computing (ONC). Every program on a server needs to have a different UDP (or TCP) port number. ONC is comprised of a number of separate programs and requires several different ports. To reserve flexed well- known ports for the whole ONC family would be difficult to manage. Some of the numbers selected might already be used by other applications in some environments. This would complicate management as manual changes would have to be made for some machines at installation time and a consistent set of port numbers would not be available across all machines.

ONC programs use a process known as the **portmapper**. When an RPC process starts up, it obtains a free port number by some local means and then it registers itself and its port number with the portmapper process. When a program wishes to access a procedure on another computer, it uses the portmapper procedure on that machine. Portmapper is an RPC process that is always on well- known port 111. Using the portmapper procedure call, an application can find the port on which a particular program number has registered itself. The portmapper replies to the originator, giving the port number, so the originator is then able to send direct to the relevant port.

We can summarize as follows:

The RPC server programs containing the remote procedures use ephemeral ports, not well-known ports. This requires a "registrar" of some form that keeps track of which RPC programs are using which ephemeral ports. In Sun RPC this registrar is called the port mapper.

MOUNT PROTOCOL

Same as other UNIX programs ending in 'd', **mountd** is the mount daemon in UNIX systems, although other operating systems will tend to use the same name. mount is the command used on UNIX systems to make a file system available, very much like taping a: or c: under DOS. mountd is the server program for remote mount requests. As NFS is supposed to provide a transparent service to the user, the same mount command is used to establish connections with a remote system. The mount command is modified slightly to cater for NFS; there is a command line option for this.

One of the features of NFS is that the NFS server is stateless. The server does not keep track of which clients are accessing which files.

The client must use the NFS mount protocol to mount a server's filesystem, before the client can access files on that filesystem. This is normally done when the client is boot-strapped. The end result is for the client to obtain a file handle for the server's file system.

To make remote files available on a host requires that the file systems themselves on the rem ate host be made available on the local host. Executing the **mount** command creates a local directory that is a place-holder for the remote directory on the remote host. The **mount** command will make even local file systems available. The **mount** command does not require that the user know whether the file system is local or remote, if an appropriate entry for the file system is found in the /etc/filesystems file. The mount command does not require that the user start a user session on the remote host. The command

```
mount/smith/large
```

will request that the file system **/smith/large** be made available to users on this host. The entry in the /etc/filesystems file informs the **mount** command that this file system is located on the host **smith** and the file system on that remote system is called **/large**. Once the **mount** command finishes, a user can examine any file in the **/smith/large** file system in much the same way they examine or use a file in a local file system.

Part of the entry in the /etc/filesystems file provides information to the **mount** command on which host this file system is located. Once the **mount** command is successful, the distinction between local files systems and remote file systems will not be visible.

For file systems that are not registered in the /etc/filesystems file, the **mount** command must contain the information about where the file system is physically located. Thus, the **mount** command

```
mount ranch:/stuff /ranch/stuff
```

is a request to mount a directory on **ranch** called **/stuff** as **/ranch/stuff**. Usually, remote file systems are mounted on a local system using the name of the host and the name of the remote file system. A remote file system can be mounted on a local system under a name different from its name on the remote system, but users can be confused by this approach. Once a file system is successfully mounted, changing to the **/ranch/stuff** directory on the local system will make available to the local user the same files that a user on that remote system sees.

THE FUTURE OF TCP/IP

TCP/IP's future is bound inexorably to the future of the Internet. Researchers created the first TCP/IP protocols expressly for the original Internet, and they continue to expand and improve the protocols as the Internet evolves. The subject of this text represents, perhaps, the greatest testament to this support. Without IPng, it is doubtful that the Internet can continue to survive and grow.

The relationship is not one-sided, either. Just as developments on the Internet drive protocol designs, new TCP/IP protocols can have a profound effect on the Internet. In March 1989, scientists at the European Laboratory for Particle Physics proposed a new protocol for accessing various types of linked information. Their efforts spawned the World Wide Web, and its HTTP protocol is now the fastest-growing source of Internet traffic.

As TCP/IP and the Internet meet the twenty-first century, they will encounter both opportunities and challenges. By some estimates, the possibilities are tremendous--continued growth of the existing network, deployment of exciting new applications, and still more innovative uses of networking technology. Skeptics, however, pose several valid questions for TCP/IP and the Internet. Can IP (Ing internet Protocol new generation) achieve successful deployment before time runs out on classic IP (IP version 4)? Can the Internet adjust to a larger and more diverse set of users? Indeed, how will the Internet deal with its own effects on society as a whole?

FUTURE GROWTH AND TECHNOLOGY

Both the TCP/IP technology and the internet continue to evolve. New protocols are being proposed; old ones are being revised. National Science Foundation (NSF) has added considerable complexity to the system by introducing its backbone network, several regional networks, and hundreds of campus networks. Other groups continue to connect to the Internet as well. The most significant change comes not from added network connections, however, but from additional traffic. Physicists, chemists, and space scientists manipulate and exchange much larger-volumes of data than computer science researchers who accounted for much of the early Internet traffic. These other scientists introduced substantial load when they began using the Internet, and the load has increased steadily as they continue to find new uses.

Growth in demands for networking should not be unexpected. The computer industry has enjoyed a continual demand for increased processing power and larger data storage for many years. Users have only begun to understand how to use networks. In the future we can expect continual increases in the demand for communication. Thus, higher-capacity communication technologies will be needed to accommodate the growth.

Many factors have contributed to the Internet's recent growth, and, in July 1995, few offer any hint of abating. Of the 100 largest U.S. corporations, only 60 have a presence on the Internet's World Wide Web. Several of the major on-line services began providing direct Internet access only recently. Microsoft's service, the Microsoft network, is not even available yet. That service alone may add 500,000 to 1,000,000 new users by the end of the year.

The Internet is also reaching users in new places; in fact, it is rapidly approaching the point where it can reach users anywhere, Cellular phones, two-way pagers, and personal digital assistants offer communication without geographic limitations. The technology that will truly enable growth of these networks--personal communication services--is still under development, but that has not deterred deployment. Already, cellular digital packet data (CDPD) networks operate in six U.S. metropolitan areas; that number will triple by year's end. CDPD, which builds on existing mobile phone technology, uses TCP/IP to transport its users' data. Future networks, those built to carry data from their inception, will rely on TCP/IP as well.

FUTURE OF INTERNET ARCHITECTURE

During 1991 and 1992, a number of RFCs have discussed the areas of concern in the current architecture, and possible changes to the Internet architecture and protocols which would overcome some of the known limitations. The following are of interest to the commercial user.

1. **Routing and Addressing**: This is the most urgent architectural problem, as it is directly involved in the ability of the Internet to continue to grow successfully.

2. **Multi-Protocol Architecture**: The Internet is moving towards widespread support of both the TCP/IP and the OSI protocol suites. Supporting both suites raises difficult technical issues, and a plan — i.e., an architecture — is required to increase the chances of success. This area was facetiously dubbed "making the problem harder for the good of mankind."

    Clark had observed that translation gateways (e.g., mail gateways) are very much a fact of life in Internet operation but are not part of the architecture or planning. The group discussed the possibility of building the architecture around the partial connectivity that such gateways imply.

3. **Security Architecture**: Although military security was considered when the Internet architecture was designed, the modern security issues are much broader, encompassing commercial requirements as well. Furthermore, experience has shown that it is difficult to add security to a protocol suite unless it is built into the architecture from the beginning.

4. **Traffic Control and State**: The Intenet should be extended to support "real-time" applications like voice and video. This will require new packet queueing mechanisms in gateways — "traffic control" — and additional gateway state.

5. **Advanced Applications**: As the underlying Internet communication mechanisms matures, there is an increasing need for innovation and standardization in building new kinds of applications.

NEW APPLICATIONS

Just as new users are joining the Internet, TCP/IP's designers are busy developing new things for them to do. Electronic commerce represents a particularly interesting application. As a communication media, the Internet provides a direct connection between sellers and possible buyers. Today, the network does not provide enough security to exploit this connection. Except through a few limited programs, sellers and buyers cannot authenticate each other's identity, nor can they adequately protect any confidential information they exchange. In recognition of this problem, and of the enormous potential of the application, TCP/IP's designers have adopted the security framework of IPng to fit the architecture of classic IP. Security has become so important that it cannot wait for IPng.

From a less commercial perspective, audio and video conferencing represent exciting new applications for the Internet. Indeed, a subset of the network already has considerable experience in this area, Since 1992, some users have a limited ability to send and receive multicast traffic across the Internet. Those users form the Virtual Internet Backbone for Multicast IP, or MBONE for short. With this network subset, and with early versions of the RTP and RTCP protocols, more than 10,000 users in 30 countries enjoy everything from TCP/IP engineering sessions to a rock concert by the Rolling Stones.

Still the MBONE remains experimental and limited mostly to scholarly, scientific, and engineering conferences. In the future, three factors will push multimedia conferencing into the mainstream of the Internet. First, new network technologies will provide the bandwidth that multimedia craves. These technologies include ATM for the network infrastructure and data delivery to the home user via the cable television industry's plant. Second, the MBONE will grow to encompass most of the Internet. Multicast services were a late addition to classicIP, and retrofitting existing networks has been difficult. IPng, on the other hand, defines multicast delivery as a core function. As the Internet migrates to IPng, multicast support will become pervasive. The third factor driving multimedia conferencing is the progress of protocols that support real time applications. RTP, RTCP, and RSVP will mature to the point that they become part of commercial products.

The convergence of fast network technology, multicast delivery, and commercial-quality applications poses some interesting questions. What happens when home and business users can buy shrink-wrapped software to run on their high-bandwidth networks with built-in support for multicast distribution? How well can schools supplement traditional classrooms with distance learning applications? How much do computer networks supplant television networks as the distribution method for multimedia entertainment? Answers to all these questions border on speculation, for now. Most assuredly, however, they will not remain unanswered much longer.

USES OF THE TECHNOLOGY

The implications of a pervasive network like the Internet extend beyond traditional computer communications, as engineers find new ways to exploit the technology. For example, all 14,000 residents of Glasgow, Kentucky rely on a network that may soon be a part of the Internet. Few of these residents, however, own a computer.

The electric power company in Glasgow has connected the whole town into a 2-Mbit/s network. Although the network can provide traditional communications services, its purpose is a lot more mundance--it reads electric power meters. This function may not seem particularly interesting, but the technology saves the city hundreds of thousands of dollars each year.

In fact, device control, like that promoted by the Glasgow Electric Plant Board, could represent a major market for TCP/IP networks. Potential gains in efficiency, economy, and functionality and available for many types of devices. Most modern automobiles now include a network that its components use to coordinate their operation. If those components could also communicate with a network that provided real time traffic and weather conditions, they may be able to further enhance the performance of the car and its driver. Airplanes, too, have succumbed to the lure of networking. The International Civil Aviation Organization has plans to integrate aircraft and ground control into a ubiquitous, global network.

Back on the ground, at least a dozen vending machines already own connections to the Internet. For now, this application remains confined to a few college experiments, although one vending service company plans to use wireless networks to continuously monitor all its vending machines. It will instantly know which items need restocking and which machines need repair.

CHALLENGES FOR THE FUTURE

To make even part of this vision reality, the internet must overcome significant challenges. The most pressing technical problem is one of the factors that led to the development of IPng--routing table explosion. The network has already grown so large that some parts experience intermittent connectivity. The routers simply cannot keep pace with changes to so large and diverse a topology. IPng introduces a new address format that lets protocols like IDRP shrink routing tables. But even as TCP/IP's designers race to complete the IPng definition and begin deployment, some question whether the effort can be finished in time.

The Internet's growth has strained the network in other ways as well. Most noticeable is the change in the very culture of the network. Developed initially for research and engineering experimentation, the Internet originally served users with very similar interests and backgrounds. This culture fostered cooperation to nurture and develop the network. The "tragedy of the commons" was not a cause for concern, as few users would even consider individual gain at the Internet's expense.

Since the early days, the network's appeal has broadened considerably. Now it is home to an incredibly diverse group of users, with a wide variety of talents and interests. Many new users are not experts in computer communications, and frequently misunderstand the ramifications of their actions. Some users may even act unscrupulously, and deliberately and knowingly attain personal profit at the network's expense. To continue its growth, the Internet must learn to accommodate these users. The network community must decide what limits to place on its users, and when and where those limits apply. It must devise ways to promote desirable behaviour and discourage undesirable actions. In effect, the Internet needs to develop a government for the networked community.

Just as the Internet must adapt to all of society, its users, indeed most of the world, face several challenges arising from the power of computer networks. With the advent of digital cash, central banks in powerful countries risk the loss of much of their economic power. What currency will develop on the Internet? How will traditional governments manage and tax it?

Another important issue is privacy. Imagine a world of the not very distant future. Users shop from home, selecting catalogs and ordering items from thousands of suppliers. For entertainment, they request interactive movies or play multimedia games over the network. When they do leave their homes, mobile communication devices in their vehicles track their progress, automatically paying tolls as necessary, and alerting them to traffic and weather conditions ahead.

What some find frightening is the fact that computers can store information as easily as they can transfer it. At what cost to their privacy will citizens accept these new conveniences? Who will tolerate technology that can monitor every purchase, communication, leisure activity, and journey? Can network technology evolve to provide its benefits while ensuring its users that they have not lost more than they have gained?

SUMMARY

TCP/IP is a serious protocol suite. It provides reasonable network services for most applications and is extensible, well documented, and fairly straightforward to implement. Best, it is capable of connecting dissimilar machines on dissimilar networks together into one big happy network. After all, that is all we really want anyway.

20

INTERNETWORKING AND CONNECTIVITY

INTRODUCTION

Information does not exist in a vacuum. Just as the need to share information between desktop computers in an office has forced the profileration of LANs, the need to share information beyond a single workgroup is forcing the adoption of LAN-to-LAN links, host gateways, asynchronous communications servers, and other methods of communicating with other systems.

This chapter provides a basic and somewhat simplistic overview of some of the options available for expanding communications horizons. This is by no means an in-depth discussion -- it is meant to be a starting point for building an understanding of available communications solutions.

LAN-TO-LAN CONNECTIONS

The three primary ways to connect LANs together are repeaters, bridges, and routers. See Figures 20.1 and 20.2 and Table 20.1.

REPEATERS

Repeaters are devices that amplify and reshape the signals on one LAN and pass them to another. All traffic is forwarded by a repeater from one LAN to the other. Repeaters are usually used to extend LAN cable distances or connect different media types.

Repeaters connect LANs together at the lowest layer, the Physical layer, of the OSI model (see Figures 20.3, 20.4 and 20.5). This means that repeaters can only connect identical

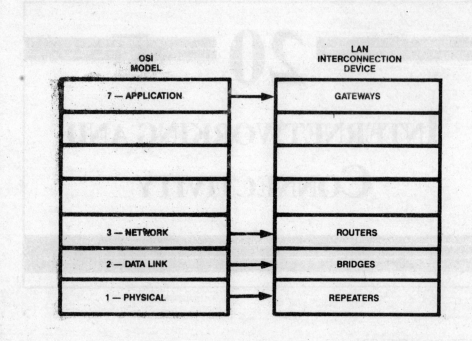

Fig. 20.1 : Repeaters, bridges, routers, and gateways mapped into the OSI 7 L

LANs, such as Ethernet/802.3 to Ethernet/802.3 or Token Ring to Token Ring. Two physical LANs connected by a repeater become one physical LAN. Because of this, the proper use and placement of repeaters is specified as part of a LAN architecture's cabling parameters.

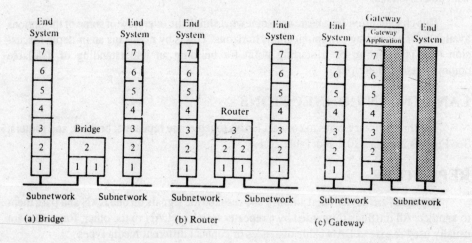

Fig. 20.2 : Repeaters Connect at the Physical Layer

Table 20.1 Internetworking Terms

Communication Network

A facility that provides a data transfer service among stations attached to the network.

Internet

A collection of communication networks interconnected by bridges, routers, and/or gateway.

Subnetwork

Refers to a consituent network of an intrenet. This avoids ambiguity since the entire internit, from a user's point of view, is a single network.

Bridge

A device used to interconnect two LANs that use identical LAN protocals. The bridge acts as an address filter, picking up packets fuom one LAN that are intended for a destination on another LAN and passing those packets on. The bridge operates at layer 3 of the OSI model.

Router

A device used to connect two networks that may or may not be similar. The router employs an internet protocol present in each router and each host of the network. The router operates ot layer 3 of the OSI model.

Gateway

A device used to connect two sets of computers that use two different communications architectures. The gateway maps from an applications on one computer to an application that is similar in function but differs in detail on another computer. The gateway operates at layer 7 of the OSI model.

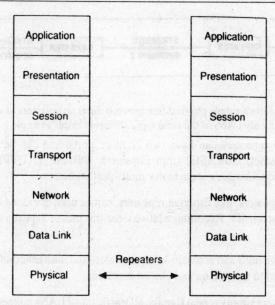

Fig. 20.3 : Repeaters Connect at the Physical Layer

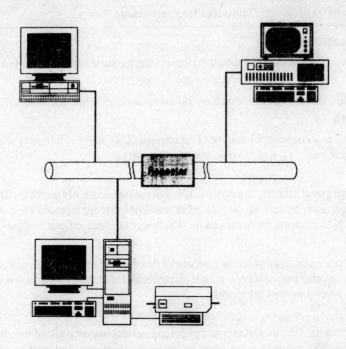

Fig. 20.4 : The use of repeaters **allows cable** lengths to be longer.

Fig. 20.5 : Repeaters form a simple physical link between different segments of a LAN. They can link only LANs of the same type—Ethernet in this example.

Ethernet/802.3 repeaters can have two or more ports, and can be used to connect 10Base5 (thick Ethernet), 10BASE2 (thin Ethernet), 10BASE-T (UTP), and fiberoptic cables. 10BASE-T concentrators are actually multi-port repeaters.

Token Ring repeaters, like Ethernet repeaters, can be used to extend distances as well as connect dissimilar media. Recommendations for the use of repeaters will vary from vendor to vendor.

ARCNET active hubs and active links are repeaters and, like Ethernet and Token Ring repeaters, can be used to mix media and extend distances.

Because repeaters simply repeat signals, all traffic on all LANs connected by repeaters is propagated to all others. As LANs grow and traffic increases, this can make performance drop.

BRIDGES

Bridges connect LANs together at the Data Link layer of the OSI model (see Figures 20.6, 20.7 and 20.8). Specifically bridges connect at the Media Access Control (MAC) sublayer of the Data Link layer, and are often referred to as MAC-layer bridges. In the past, Novell incorrectly referred to NetWare routers as bridges.

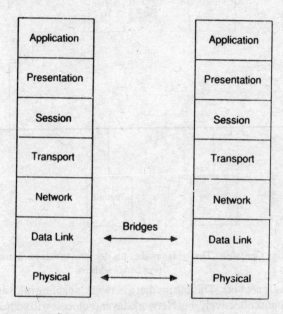

Fig. 20.6 : Bridges Connect at the Data Link Layer.

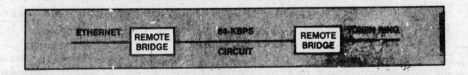

Fig. 20.7 : Bridges provide a protocol transparent connection. This diagram shows a typical multi-protocol remote bridge application.

Bridges connect similar or identical LANs. Bridges can be used to connect Ethernet/802.3 to Ethernet/802.3, 10-Mbps Ethernet/802.3 to 1-Mbps StarLAN, 4-Mbps Token Ring to 4-Mbps Token Ring, or 4-Mbps Token Ring to 16-Mbps Token Ring. Like repeaters, bridges can be used to connect LANs using different media (10BASE-T to 10BASE5, for example).

Bridges are transparent to the network-layer protocols (such as IPX and IP) being used on the network. Two networks connected via a bridge are physically separate networks, but

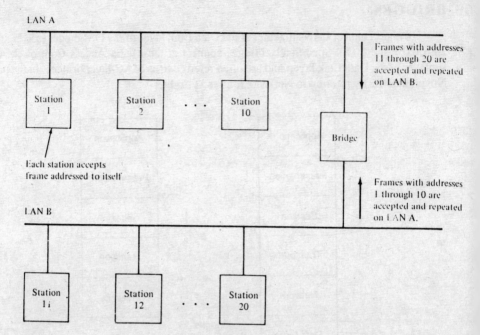

Fig. 20.8 : Bridge Operation. The bridge makes the decision to relay a frame on the basis of destination MAC address.

logically a single network. This means that a network's cabling rules apply to each individual network, not both collectively, but Network-layer protocols will address the bridged network as if they were one.

Bridges segment traffic by only forwarding traffic that is addressed to stations on the opposite side of the bridge. This means that bridges do not forward local traffic. This can considerably reduce overall traffic in a multi-LAN internetwork.

Many bridges can be configured to perform various types of logical filtering. Depending on the particular bridge, packets can be filtered based on source or destination addresses, frame type, or even the type of network-layer protocol being used. Filtering is used for security and performance optimization.

Bridges can be proprietary devices, or they can be software and hardware residing in a general purpose computer, such as a PC.

When used properly, bridges can increase overall network performance. By sectioning a large LAN into smaller LANs linked together with bridges, local transmissions can be kept in the local area, and only traffic addressed to another subnetwork will need to cross a bridge. In this way, overall LAN traffic can be reduced. If used improperly, however, such as multiple bridge in series, bridges can become bottlenecks impeding the flow of data.

Transparent Bridges

The type of bridges used for Ethernet/802.3 LANs is called a transparent bridge. This is because the existence of the bridge is transparent to workstations, file servers and other network devices. The bridge performs all the functions necessary to route traffic between bridged networks.

Transparent bridges keep routing tables of physical addresses of network devices and forward traffic based on the locations of the particular network device to which packets are being sent. Early bridges required the system administrator to manually build the routing tables. Current bridges automatically learn station addresses and build the routing tables, and are sometimes referred to as learning bridges.

Spanning Tree Algorithm

Transparent bridges do not allow redundant paths. By using a scheme called the Spanning Tree Algorithm, however, alternate paths are allowed. In simplest terms, the Spanning Tree Algorithm ensures that only one bridge path between any two networks is active at a time. If a bridge path fails, another bridge path (if it exists) will automatically be activated. Not all bridges support the Spanning Tree Algorithm, and although Spanning Tree Algorithm is now part of the IEEE 802 specifications, not all bridges that support the Spanning Tree Algorithm conform with the IEEE specifications.

Source Routing Bridges

Although transparent bridging can be used with Token Ring networks, IBM has promoted another bridging method called source routing. With source routing, the bridge does not keep track of the route by which packets are sent. Each network node that initiates communication with another node across one or more bridges must keep track of the route used. Unlike transparent bridges, source routing bridges allow redundant paths.

To establish a route, the station initiating communication broadcasts a discovery packet, which makes its way through the network's source routing bridges. The discovery packet keeps track of the bridges it crosses on the way to the destination. Depending on the configuration of the bridges and the method used to send the discovery packet (the description of which is beyond the scope of this book), the discovery packet will arrive at the destination via one or more routes, meaning one or more copies of the discovery packet will be received at the destination.

The destination returns its response(s) using reverse addressing, meaning it uses each discovery packet's list of crossed bridges, in reverse order, to return its response(s). If the initiating station receives responses via more than one route, the first response received establishes the route to be used.

When using source routing bridges with NetWare, there are several things to remember:

- There have been several implementations of source routing support in NetW shells, so make sure that all NetWare stations on Token Ring LANs connecte source routing bridges have recent versions of the NetWare shells. (The sh shipped with NetWare 2.2 and 3.x should be fine.)

- If a NetWare workstation is going to use source routing bridges, that station n run the ROUTE.COM program.

- All file servers that will be accessed via source routing bridges must h ROUTE.NLM (NetWare 3.x) or ROUTE.VP0 (NetWare 2.x) loaded.

ROUTERS

Routers connect LANs at the Network layer of the OSI model (see Figures 20.9 20.10). Routers connect LANs that use the same Network-layer protocol, such as IPX-to- and IP-to-IP. Because routers operate at the Network layer, they can be used to link dissin LANs, such as ARCNET, Ethernet, and Token Ring.

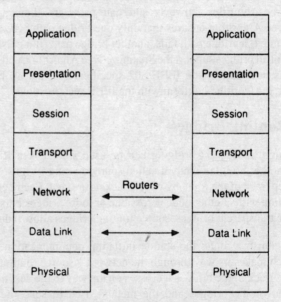

Fig. 20.9 : Routers Connect at the Network Layer

Two networks connected via a router are physically and logically separate netw Network-layer protocols have their own addressing scheme separate from the addressing sc of MAC-layer protocols. This addressing scheme may or not include the MAC- addresses of the network cards. Each network attached to a router must be assigned a lo identifier, or network address, to designate it as unique from other physical networks.

For example, NetWare's IPX routers (NetWare file servers or external Net routers using ROUTER.EXE) use each LAN card's MAC- layer address and a lo address for each network assigned by the router installer.

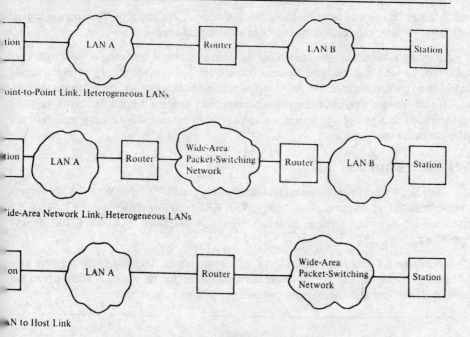

Fig. 20.10 : LAN Internetworking Requirements

A router can support single or multiple Network-layer protocols. NetWare 2.2 file ers and NetWare external routers, for example only support NetWare's IPX protocol. Ware 3.11 file servers, on the other hand, can route IPX, IP, and Apple Talk, if the proper ng software is loaded into the file server.

Dedicated routers from Proteon, Cisco, Wellfleet, and others can route a number of rent protocols.

Like bridges, routers only forward traffic addressed to the other side. This means that traffic on one LAN will not affect performance on another. Again, like bridges, routers e proprietary devices, or can be software and hardware residing in a general purpose uter, such as a PC.

Like transparent bridges, routers maintain routing tables. A router's routing table, ver, keeps track of network addresses and possible routes between networks, not idual node addresses. Using routers, redundant paths between networks can be estab- l, and traffic will be routed between networks based on some algorithm to determine st path. The simplest routers usually select the path with the fewest number of router as the best path. More intelligent routers consider other factors, such as the relative nse times of various possible routes, when selecting the best path.

Because routers operate at the network layer, they can connect dissimilar types of , such as ARCNET and Ethernet. LAN cards using different frame types, such as 802.3

and Ethernet II, can co- exist on the same LAN cable, but are actually separate logical networks. A router can connect two or more such logical networks.

Routing is more complex than bridging, and, all other things being equal, routers are somewhat slower than bridges. Routers usually do not provide the extensive filtering capabilities that some bridges do. Another downside to routers is that there are few standards, so different vendor's products may not interoperate. Routers do provide better network segmentation than bridges, however, so that things like broadcast packet storms will not affect an entire internetwork.

NetWare Routers

The NetWare operating system includes routing capabilities. NetWare 2.x file servers and NetWare external routers (running ROUTER.EXE) can route NetWare's IPX, NetWare 3.x, however, can route multiple protocols. Currently, NetWare 3.11 routes IPX, IP, and Apple Talk.

NetWare 2.x and NetWare external routers determine the best route between two LANs by counting the number of router hops. NetWare 3.x, however, considers both the number of hops and the response time when determining the best route.

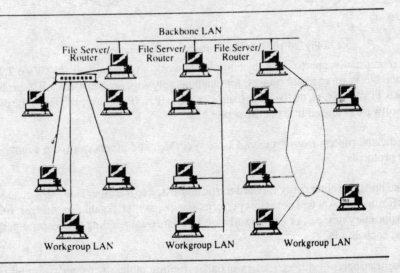

Fig. 20.11 : Backbone and Workgroup LANs with NetWare File Servers as Routers.

NetWare routers, especially file server internal routers, are very cost effective. To turn a NetWare file server into a router, you simply add one or more network cards, load the correct LAN driver(s) (NetWare 3.x) or re-install the operating system (NetWare 2.x), and the file server is a router (see Figure 20.11). Another advantage of NetWare internal routers is that they can cut down the number of router hops in a properly designed network.

On the downside, NetWare routers do not have the management features of more sophisticated dedicated routers.

BRIDGE/ROUTER HYBRIDS (BROUTERS)

Some sophisticated routers provide bridging capabilities for protocols they do not route. These hybrid bridge/routers have become known as brouters. Some protocols, such as DEC's Local Area Transport (LAT) protocol, cannot be routed. In addition, a router or brouter may not support all routable protocols. A particular brouter with IP and XNS support only, for example, would route those protocols, but use the bridge function for LAT, which can not be routed, and IPX, which its router function does not support.

REMOTE BRIDGES AND ROUTERS

Some bridges and routers can link LANs together remotely through a variety of links. To be effective, remote bridges and routers need to be very fast or must be used very efficiently.

A remote bridge or router consists of two units separated by a communications link of some sort. The communications link is most commonly a digital synchronous data link with transfer capabilities between 56 Kbps and 1.5 Mbps, but can be an analog asynchronous dial- up line with modems operating between 9.6 and 19.2 Kbps.

Like local bridges and routers, remote units can be proprietary boxes or hardware and software that installs in a PC or AT type computer.

Synchronous and Asynchronous Communication

With synchronous communication, data is sent in blocks, with synchronization characters transmitted before each block sent. After synchronization characters are sent, the receiving device accepts all bits transmitted until characters signaling the end of the transmission are sent. If another block is to be sent, new sync. characters are sent, and the process is repeated.

In general, synchronous protocols provide greater throughput and better error recovery than asynchronous protocols. In addition, some synchronous protocols, such as X.25 and Frame Relay (described below), provide for multi-point links. Bridges and routers using X.25 or Frame Relay protocols can be linked across public and private wide area data networks.

With asynchronous communication, or async., as it is usually called, data is transmitted as characters in a continuous bit stream. Before and after each character is sent, start bits and stop bits indicate the beginning and end of each character. When transmission errors occur, entire streams of data need to be retransmitted.

Async. communication can take place in either half duplex or full duplex mode. Half duplex means that only one side can send data at a time, while full duplex means that both sides can send data simultaneously. To be effective, LAN bridges and routers require full-duplex communication.

Async. is relatively inefficient, because it has a high operational overhead (including the start bits and stop bits) and error recovery generally prolongs response times. Async. does have the advantage, however, of easily operating over standard, voice-grade, dial-up telephone lines, but V.32 and V.42 modems can also easily operate over dial-up lines in synchronous mode.

Remote Communication Links

Common communication links include:

Digital Data Service (DDS). DDS provides dedicated lines running at speeds up to 56 Kbps. DDS is available through the major long- distance carriers and regional phone companies.

T-1 lines. T-1 lines are digital communications links operating at 1.544 Mbps in the United States and 2.048 Mbps in Europe, where it is known as E-1. T-1 carriers in the United States also offer Fractional T-1, which provides a portion of a T-1 line's bandwidth at proportionally reduced cost. T-1 is available through the major long- distance carriers and regional phone companies.

X.25 networks. Most public data networks, such as CompuServe, Tymenet, Accunet, and Sprintnet, and many private data networks use the CCITT X.25 packet-switching protocols for wide area communications. Like a LAN, an X.25 network is a packet-switched network that allows communications between multiple locations. X.25 networks usually provide digital access at speeds up to 56 Kbps.

Frame Relay networks. Frame Relay is very similar to X.25, except that it can offer access at up to T-1 speeds. While X.25 performs point-to-point error checking. Frame Relay performs end-to- end error checking. This means that X.25 packets that are routed through multiple communications links have error checking between every two links, while Frame Relay packets only have error checking between the starting link and the ending link. This can considerably speed overall throughput.

Frame Relay is relatively new and is just starting to be widely implemented.

Dial-up lines. Dial-up phone lines can provide synchronous or asynchronous communications at up to 9.6-19.2 Kbps (under ideal conditions, up to 38.4 Kbps). A dial-up line requires a modem, which, at higher speeds, is much more expensive than the data service unit/channel service unit (DSU/CSU) usually required for a digital line.

Not all remote bridges and routers support all communication links.

Remote Bridge and Router Performance

Remote bridges and routers are going to seem very slow for those used to LAN speeds. For example, a 56-Kbps line has slightly more than 1/200th the data transfer rate of Ethernet, while a 9.6-Kbps line has slightly less than 1/1000th of Ethernet's data transfer rate. In fact, for many applications, these speeds are unworkable.

Proper planning is essential when using remote bridges and routers. You must decide in advance what kind of traffic the remote link will support and select products and services accordingly. Here are some guidelines:

9.6 to 19.2 Kbps supports e-mail, file transfer, host access, and network management.

56 Kbps supports all of the above, plus database server access and limited data file access.

1.544 to 2.048 Mbps supports all of the above, plus extensive data file access and remote program access.

With higher-speed bridges and routers, the major cost is not the bridge hardware and software but the remote link itself. The monthly cost of a high-speed line may be hard to justify in many cases, especially compared to remote program or data file access, when weighed against the effective throughput of that line using a remote bridge or router.

Often, a properly designed system using a remote access server (see below) can be much more effective than a remote bridge or router for remote program or data file access.

NetWare Asynchronous Remote Router

The NetWare Asynchronous Remote Router software allows LAN-to-LAN connections over dial-up lines at up to 38.4 Kbps. The router software can be installed in a NetWare 2.1 through 2.2 file server. In this configuration, it requires a communications card that is supported by Novell's Asynchronous Input/Output (AIO) specification, such as Newport Systems' Asynchronous Communications Interface (ACI) or Gateway Communications' Wide Area Network Interface Module (WNIM), which must also be installed in the file server. The router software can also be installed in a NetWare external router with or without a AIO board. When used with Gateway's WNIM, the router can operate at up to 9.6 Kbps. When used with Newport's ACI, the router can operate at up to 38.4 Kbps. With standard COM ports the router is limited to 2.4 Kbps.

Because of the slow speeds available, use of the async router must be carefully planned and controlled.

Microtest LANMODEM and Shiva Netmodem/E

Microtest Corp.'s LANMODEM and Shiva Corp.'s Netmodem/E are network-attached modems that can function as remote async. routers or async communication servers at data rates as high as 57.6 Kbps (with data compression). LANMODEM is available for Ethernet, Token Ring, and ARCNET, and Netmodem/E is available for Ethernet.

NetWare Link/Newport LAN²LAN Routers

NetWare Link products are remote routers that operate at speeds up to 2.048 Mbps. Novell currently sells two Link products; Link 64, which operates up to 64 Kbps, and Link/T1, which operates up to 2.048 Mbps. These products are manufactured for Novell by Newport Systems Solutions, and are also available from them. Because Novell and Newport package the products differently, and because, Newport offers some enhancements not available from Novell, both companies offerings will be discussed.

NetWare Link/64 and Link/T1 route NetWare IPX communications, including Novell's NetBIOS and SPX protocols, over wide area networks. The NetWare router dynamically determines the shortest path for each packet based on current network topology, and it automatically bypasses inoperative links. Link/64 and Link/T1 can be installed in a NetWare 2.1 or above or 3.x file server, or in external NetWare router. To NetWare, the remote router appears to be another LAN.

The Link products connect with standard wide area communications equipment, including Data Service Units/Channel Service Units (DSU/CSUs), synchronous modems, multiplexers, and data switches.

Remote users can access other LAN-based communications service via the Link products, including asynchronous communications servers and host gateways.

Both Link/64 and Link/T1 require one of Novell's Synchronous/+ Adapters. Novell sells three configurations of the adapter: V.35, at speeds up to 2.048 Mbps; RS-422/X.21, at speeds up to 2.048 Mbps; and RS-232, at speeds up to 19.2 Kbps; Novell only supplies ISA adapters. Newport supplies both ISA and Micro channel versions (see below).

As stated earlier, Newport also supplies these products (like Novell, through the dealer/distributor channel), but packages them somewhat differently and provides some additional features and enhancements.

Unlike Novell, Newport bundles the software and hardware. All the Newport bundles support RS-232, RS-422, V.35, and X.21 interfaces and are available in both ISA and Micro Channel versions (except the compression router). The Newport products include: LAN^{2}LAN/768, which supports speeds up to 768 Kbps; LAN^{2}LAN/Compression Router, which supports speeds up to 768 Kbps and data compression at speeds up to 128 Kbps; LAN^{2}LAN/Mega, which supports speeds up to 2.048 Mbps; and LAN^{2}LAN X.25 Access, which provides routing over X.25 networks at speeds up to 384 Kbps. (Novell used to supply a Link/X.25 [not made by Newport] that is now supplied by Microdyne Corp. [formerly Federal Technology]).

Newport provides upgrades from one level to another, and will also provide upgrades to Novell-supplied products. Newport versions of these products support IP and AppleTalk routing concurrently with IPX routing.

Novell's Packet Burst Technology

Novell's packet burst technology is designed to alleviate problem that becomes apparent when using NetWare across wide area communications links. In normal mode, a NetWare client can only request data from (or send data to) a NetWare server in increments small enough to fit into single data packets.

For example, a client (receiver) makes requests of a file server (sender) for a block of data in increments small enough to fit in single IPX packets. The receiver makes a request, waits for the response, then makes another request. This is usually fine for on-LAN traffic, but it can create a severe bottleneck across considerably slower remote LAN connections.

Using packet burst technology, an entire message is sent as a single communications stream. In a packet burst transmission, the transmitter sends labeled fragments of the message in the form of IPX packets to the receiver. The receiver sorts them as they arrive; they need not arrive in sequence. At the end of the message, an End Of Message flag is sent to the receiver. When the receiver receives the End Of Message flag, or after a timeout (no data is received for a specific period of time), an acknowledgement is sent to the sender. This acknowledgement includes a list of the packets the receiver has not yet received, as well as any bad packets that have been received.

When the transmitter receives the acknowledgement, it retransmits any message fragments that the receiver says are missing. This process continues until the receiver acknowledges that the message has been completely received.

Beta testers have reported significant increases in throughput, as much as 400 to 700 percent in some cases, over remote LAN-to-LAN links.

Packet burst technology requires client and server software to operate. The client portion is in the BNETX.COM shell, and the server portion is in the PBURST.NLM NetWare Loadable Module (NLM). Packet burst works with NetWare 3.1 and higher.

ASYNCHRONOUS COMMUNICATION SERVERS

An asynchronous communication server (ACS) is designed to let LAN users share asynchronous communications modems (or other asynchronous links) across a LAN. An ACS can be a dedicated PC with one or more multi-port communication boards and several attached modems, or it can be a background task running as a TSR in a user's workstation. Async servers are designed to provide either dial-out services (modem pooling), dial-in services (remote LAN access), or both.

Dial-Out Services (Modem Pooling)

Dial-Out services allow users on a Lan to access remote services (such as bulletin boards and online databases) by using available modems attached to the ACS, rather than attached to their own computers. (See Table 20.2 for a summary of dial-out advantages and disadvantages).

Table 20.2 Dial out advantages and disadvantages

Dial-Out Option	Advantages	Disadvatages
Modem-sharing software in a user's PC (NMP^2. Modem Assist Plus, pc ANYWHERE IV/LAN, LAN+Modem CoSession ACS).	Low cost. Least amount of space used. Modemsharing software can often be run in a FAX server PC or other specialized server so that operation and performance of a user's PC is not affected.	TSR communications software can conflict with other applications in host PC. Modem-sharing can affect performance of host PC. User must leave the host running for others to have modem access. Application lockup at the host will stop communication session.
Dedicated PC with multi-port adapter(s) and ACS software (NACS, ACS).	ACS operation will not affect workstation operation. Multiple ports can be defined for multiple functions.	Dedicated ACS is more expensive than sharing modems attached to users' workstations. ACS uses more space.
Clustered CPU communications server (FlexCom. Chatterbox).	Supports multiple communications functions in one box. Often has additional management software.	Usually as expensive or more expensive than dedicated ACS. Uses more space than shared modems attached to user's PCs.
Network-attached modem-communications server (LANMODEM and Netmodem/E).	Plug-and-play operation. Uses very little space. Can be used for remote login.	Relatively new technology. Limited number of connection (one or two).

A major advantage of using async servers for this is the reduced number of modems and telephone lines required -- a large number of users can use a small pool of modems on an as-seeded basis.

There are a couple of possible disadvantages. In some cases, the cost of the ACS hardware and software can end up being greater than the cost of locally attached modems, and communications software choices are somewhat limited.

There are four basic approaches to async dial-out servers:

– Modem sharing software running as a TSR in a user's workstation, allowing a modem on that user's workstation to be shared by others on the LAN. This is the approach taken by Network Products Corp.'s NMP^2, Fresh Technology's Modem

Assist Plus, Symantec's pcANYWHERE IV/LAN, Cross Information's LAN+Modem, and Triton's CoSession ACS.

– A standard personal computer, with one or more multi-port adapters, used as a dedicated server. This is the approach used with Novell's NetWare Asynchronous Communications Server (NACS) and Network Products Corp.'s ACS[2]

– A clustered CPU communications server. This consists of a case, power supply, a passive back plane (an expansion board with slots for add-in-cards), a LAN card, and one or more PC-on-a-board processor cards. Evergreen Systems' FlexCom and J&L Information Systems' Chatterbox are examples of this approach. These products can provide dial-in/dial-out services, remote routing, FAX service, and other services in one box.

– Network-attached modem/communications server. This is the approach taken by Microtest's LANMODEM and Shiva's NetModem/E. (See "Microtest LAN-MODEM and Shiva Netmodem/E" above).

Asynchronous Acces Methods

There are two commonly used access methods for moving data between a user's workstation and an ACS: interrupt 14 and NASI/NCSI.

Interrupt 14 (also called Int14), is a special interrupt method of communicating with a PC's COM port via BIOS calls. This is the method supported by IBM for communications servers, and many applications provide Int14 support. To use Int14, the ACS must provide Int14 support, and an Int14 handler must be installed at the workstation that will be accessing the ACS. The Int14 handler is usually a TSR loaded prior to loading the workstation's communications software, but it can also be a function of the communications software itself.

Novell's NetWare Asynchronous Services Interface (NASI) and Network Products Corp.'s Network Communications Services Interface (NCSI) are applications interfaces that allow workstation communications software to access an ACS. NASI and NCSI are functionally identical. Like Int14, NASI/NCSI provides the application interface to allow asynchronous communications software running on a user's workstation to access a communications port on a NASI/NCSI-compatible communications server. NASI/NCSI-compatible communications servers include Novell's NACS and Network Product Corp.'s ACS2 and NMP. Unlike Int14, NASI/NCSI does not make BIOS calls, and it can provide more flexibility and somewhat better performance than Int14. NASI/NCSI software must be loaded as a TSR in the workstation prior to loading the communications software.

NASI/NCSI is usually the preferred access method for asynchronous services on a NetWare LAN, and is supported by over 20 communications and terminal emulation programs, including Crosstalk, Procomm, Mirror, Reflection, Smartcom, and Smart-Term.

Remote Login and Remote Access Services

Remote login and remote access services allow remote LAN users to dial in to a LAN via dial-up or dedicated leased lines.

Remote Login

Remote login means that the remote user logs in to a network device (usually a file server or host computer) via a remote connection to some device on the network.

For file server access, remote login can be handled via the type of ACS used for dial-out services, or via a modem connected directly to a file server. (A file server-attached modem, however, can impact file server performance, since every character received by the modem generates a processor interrupt). In addition, products such as Netmodem/E from Shiva Corp. or LANMODEM from Microtest can function as dial-in communications servers. (See Microtest LANMODEM and Shiva Netmodem/E above).

Remote login is usually not suitable for remote program load or data file access from a file server, due to the relatively slow speed of async connections. With file server access, data is moved between client and server in large blocks. Even with the best line conditions, loading a 200-Kbyte program or data file over a 9.6-Kbps link would take three-and-a-half to four minutes. For these purposes, remote control (see below) is usually more effective.

Remote login can be very effective for terminal/host communications, however. Using terminal emulation and communication software to access a Unix host through modems and a terminal server, for example, can be very effective, because only screen and keyboard characters are transmitted.

Remote Access Services

Remote access service means that a remote user establishes a connection with a network workstation and takes control of that workstation's resources. There are several ways that this can be approached: (For a quick summary of remote access service's advantages and disadvantages, see Table 20.3).

Table 20.3 : Remote Access Service's advantages and disadvantages

Remote Access Service Option	Advantages	Disadvantages
Remore control software loaded on user's workstation after hours.	No additional hardware required	Only available after hours. Requires local modem.

Dedicated workstation(s) with remote control software.	Available at any time. Reusable technology.	Requires PC and LAN card for every connection. Uses a lot of space.
Dedicated workstations accessed through ACS.	Available at any time. Reusable technology.	Requires PC and LAN card for every connection. Uses a lot of real estate. ACS adds to cost and complexity.
PC-on-a-board (one or more) installed in a NetWare file server.	Available at any time. Requires no extra real estate.	Communication server problem can affect the server operation. PC-on-a-board products often more expensive than standard PCs.
PC-on-a-board (one or more) installed in an external NetWare router.	Available at any time. Requires less real estate than multiple PCs. Uses single LAN connection for multiple sessions.	PC-on-a-board products often more expensive than standard PCs.
PC-on-a-board (one or more) installed in an Clustered CPU communication server.	Available at any time. Requires less real estate than multiple PCs. Uses single LAN connection for multiple sessions. Can provide other communication services, such as dial-out FAX. May provide additional management capabilities. Greater expansion capacity than standard PC.	PC-on-a-board products and communication server, often more expensive than standard PCs.
Single PC with multiple logins (NAS).	Available at any time. Requires less real estate than multiple PCs. Uses single Lan Connection for multiple sessions. Direct x.25 connection available, offering reduced long-distance line changes.	Multi-taking software can conflict with applications. Since multiple users share a single CPU, performance can be a problem.

- For after-hours access, users can load one of several remote control packages, such as pcANYWHERE (or pcANYWHERE IV/LAN), Carbon Copy, Co/Session, or Close Up, on their LAN workstations when they go home; then access them via modems attached to the workstations.

-   One or more dedicated workstations can be set up for dial-in access using attached modems and remote control software. Personal computers or diskless LAN workstations without screens or keyboards are often used for this purpose.

-   One or more PC-on-a-board processors can be installed in a NetWare file server or external NetWare router. PC-on-a-board products are supplied by several companies, including Cubix and Integrated Workstations.

These boards, which function as individual personal computers, can be installed in a NetWare file server or external router. External routers can be standard PCs or specialized clustered CPU communications servers. These consist of a case, power supply, a passive backplane (an expansion board with slots for add-in cards), a LAN card, and one or more PC-on-a-board processor cards. Evergreen Systems' FlexCom and J&L Information Systems' Chatterbox are examples of this approach. These products can provide dial-in/dial-out services, remote routing, FAX service, and other services in one box.

-   A single PC using multi-tasking software can provide multiple remote control sessions. Novell's NetWare Access Server (NAS) uses this approach. The NAS consists of a 386 or 486 PC, a LAN card, communications board(s), and NAS software. The NAS software uses modified versions of Quarterdeck's DesqView and Symantec's pcANYWHERE to provide up to 16 concurrent NetWare sessions. Supported communications boards include Gateway Communication' Wide Area Network Interface Module (WNIM), providing four async connections at up to 19.2 Kbps; Newport Systems' Asynchronous Communication Interface (ACI), providing eight async connections at up to 38.4 Kbps; and Newport's X.25 Communications Interface (XCI) for direct, synchronous connection to an X.25 data network at up to 384 Kbps. XCI supports up to 1 concurrent user connections.

Most X.25 public data networks (PDNs) in the U.S., such as SprintNet CompuServe Accunet, and Tymenet, provide asynchronous access from almost anywhere in the country via a local phone call. Reduced long-distance charges will usually more than offset the cost of PDN access.

LAN-TO-HOST GATEWAYS AND COMMUNICATIONS SERVICES

In many companies, terminals used to access minicomputers and mainframes (otherwise known as host computers) are being replaced by networked computers. Networked PC-to-host can be accomplished in a number of ways, depending on the type (and location) of the host computer.

-   A networked personal computer can connect to a host computer via a separate out-of-LAN connection.

-   A networked personal computer can connect to a host computer via a LAN-to-host gateway.

- A networked personal computer can connect to a host computer via a direct network connection to the host or some host-attached device (such as an IBM cluster controller or front-end processor).

- Some combination of the above.

Gateways connect at all seven layers of the OSI model (see Figures 20.12, 20.13 and 20.14).

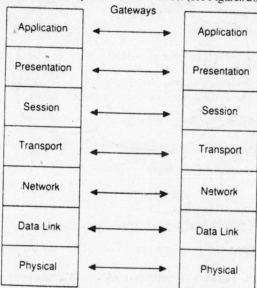

Fig. 20.12 : Gateway Connect at All Seven Layers

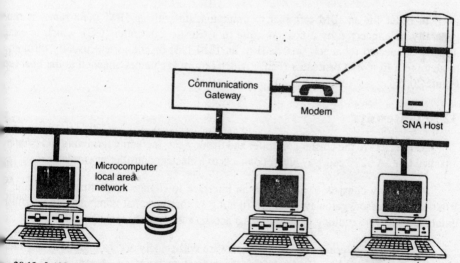

g. 20.13 : LAN users can access the mainframe through an intelligent device called a gateway. The gateway onverts mainframe and micro protocols so that information can pass between the two environments.

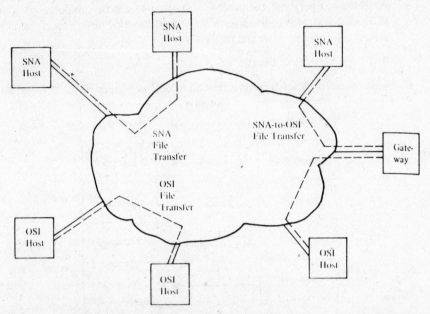

Fig. 20.14 : Gateway Operation

SNA and 3270

IBM's Systems Network Architecture (SNA) is a relatively complex, hierarchical system for connecting IBM terminals, printers, and other equipment to IBM mainframe computers.

In order for an IBM terminal to communicate with an IBM mainframe, it must generally be connected by a coaxial cable to a Cluster Controller (CC), which is either directly connected (channel- attached) to an IBM host or connected, usually through modem, to a front-end processor (FEP), which in turn is channel-attached to the host (see Figure 20.15).

3270 Gateways

3270 refers to the cluster controller and the devices, including terminals and printer attached to it. A 3270 gateway either connects to a cluster controller or emulates it.

A gateway consists of a PC with an interface to connect to a cluster controller of front-end processor, gateway software running in that personal computer, and terminal emulation software running in each PC that accesses the host through the gateway.

A PC running terminal emulation software will usually access a gateway PC using Novell's IPX protocol or IBM's NetBIOS application interface. According to a study conducted by Novell a few years ago, IPX is better suited for gateway traffic because provides better buffering for the burst fashion of gateway traffic.

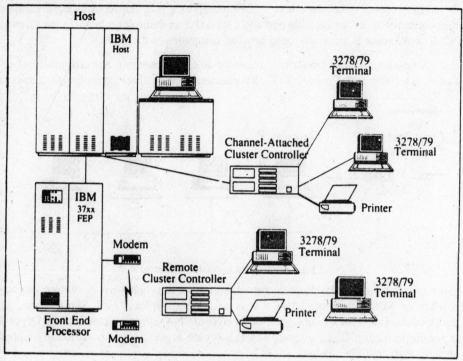

Fig. 20.15 : SNA Terminal-to-Host Diagram

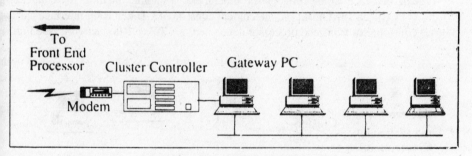

Fig. 20.16 : Coax Gateway

A coax gateway connects to a cluster controller (see Figure 20.16). It is called a coax gateway because 3270 terminals are usually attached to cluster controllers with coaxial cable.

A 3270 terminal can maintain up to five concurrent sessions with a host. A simple, five-session gateway can be created using a 3270 emulator card designed for connecting a single stand-alone PC to a cluster controller. Instead of running the stand-alone emulation software, however, the gateway PC runs gateway software that distributes the five available sessions to up to five PCs on the LAN that are running terminal emulation software.

Many cluster controllers have a 3299 multiplexer port that replaces eight standard coax connections. Using the 3299 port and a special coax multiplexer board in the gateway PC, up to 40 sessions are available to personal computers on the LAN.

A remote gateway emulates a remotely-attached (meaning not channel-attached) cluster controller (see Figure 20.17). By eliminating the cluster controller(s), a remote

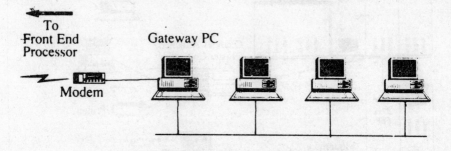

Fig. 20.17 : Remote (SDLC) Gateway

gateway can provide considerable cost savings over coax gateway. A remote gateway requires an SDLC card instead of a coax or coax multiplexer card. SDLC stands for Synchronous Data Link Control, the linkage layer of SNA for remote connections. Depending on the particular SDLC card and gateway software, a remote gateway can usually support between eight and 128 sessions.

Token Interface Connection (TIC) attachment is another method for connecting networked PCs to an IBM host. TIC attachment consists of a Token Ring interface card in a cluster controller or front-end processor connected to a Token Ring network (see Figure

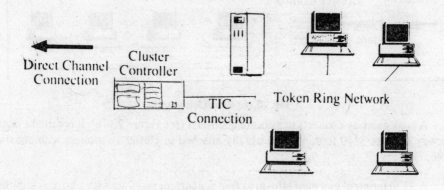

Fig. 20.18 : Token Interface Connection (TIC) Attachment

20.18). PCs on the Token Ring, or on other Token Rings connected via source-routing bridges, can access the host via terminal emulation software without an interve: ing gateway. While terminal emulation software usually communicates with gateways via the **IPX** protocol or NetBIOS applications interface, TIC emulation software comm nicates at the data link layer of the OSI model via the IBMLAN Support Program. A direct TIC connection supports up to 254 sessions.

TIC can also be used to connect to IBM's AS/400 minicomputers.

3270 gateway and terminal emulation software is available from many sources, including Novell, Data Interface Systems Corp., Attachmate, DCA, and IBM.

NetWare for SAA

IBM's computing plan for the nineties is called Systems Application Architecture (SAA). SAA is a set of guidelines for establishing uniform languages, file structures, and processes across all IBM computing platforms. SAA is an ambitious plan and probably will not be completely implemented in the near future, if ever.

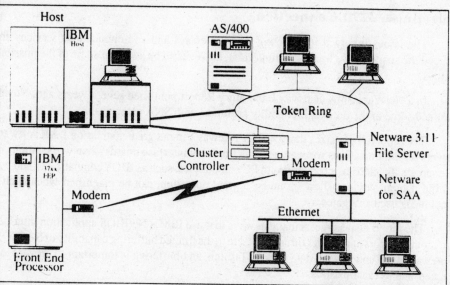

Fig. 20.19 : Netware for SAA

NetWare for SAA is designed to provide comprehensive connectivity between IBM osts and multiple types of LAN workstations. Novell provides DOS and Macintosh onnectivity to IBM mainframes and AS/400 minicomputers, and third-party products allow)S/2 and Unix workstations to connect to those hosts through NetWare for SAA.

NetWare for SAA is a set of NetWare Loadable Modules (NLMs) that run in a letWare 3.11 (or above) file server, or in a 386 PC running the NetWare 3.x kernel. The letWare kernel is a version of NetWare 3.x that does not include file services. The kernel ; included with NetWare for SAA (see Figure 20.19).

NetWare for SAA is built on the NetWare Communication Executive, which adds communications extensions to NetWare 3.x. The Communication Executive is the foundation for NetWare Communications Services, Novell's platform for future communications products, including X.25 and wide area network connections and remote LAN access.

NetWare for SAA supports any combination of Ethernet, ARCNET, Token Ring and LocalTalk from a single file server, and it supports both the IPX/SPX and AppleTalk protocols. By installing multiple copies of NetWare for SAA software, up to 508 host sessions can be run simultaneously. Novell claims significantly increased performance and response times when compared to more traditional gateways.

NetWare for SAA provides integration with IBM's SNA network management system, NetView. It is also supplied with the NetWare Communications Services Manager, a Windows-based graphical network management application that offers monitoring and control of multiple NetWare for SAA servers. Third-party NLMs are already being written for NetWare Communications Services and NetWare for SAA, such as Phaser Systems' NetWare SNA Router.

Selecting a 3270 Connection

The issues involved in selecting 3270 gateways and communications services are beyond the scope of this book. It is important, however, to be aware of some of the possible pitfalls.

In a NetWare SNA Gateway Laboratory Report published several years ago, Novell outlined some of the potential reliability problems with SNA gateways.

The report emphasizes that an SNA gateway can put greater stress on LAN software drivers (communications software for specific LAN interface boards) than workstations or file servers. In addition, problems with PC compatibles, such as BIOS compatibility and bus timing, which may not show up under normal operation, can be magnified when such a machine is used as a gateway.

The report also suggests that gateways that use IBM's NetBIOS application interface are prone to errors and slower throughput due to the limited buffering capability of NetBIOS. Gateways send and receive data in burst fashion, and buffering is important to prevent lost packets and retransmissions.

The report goes on to caution that these problems may not show up in a test-bed environment, but could show up in production situations where the gateway is operating at or near full capacity.

In addition to the potential problems outlined above; it is important to remember that LAN-to-host gateways can differ vastly in the areas of performance, screen display, keyboard mapping, graphics support, and overall functionality. A gateway product that i appropriate for one company's environment may not work well in another's.

Probably the best source for accurate information about gateways is other users Network users' groups, seminars at trade shows such as NetWorld, on-line forums such a

Novell's NetWire forum on CompuServe, or knowledgeable dealers, VARs, or consultants are all possible sources of information.

In any case, be prepared to spend some time tuning and tweaking the prod''ct you end up selecting. Try to locate someone who has experience with it, and make sure they are available to support you. Finally, make sure that any purchase contract has escape clauses.

5250 Gateways

A 5250 gateway provides up to seven local or nine remote terminal or printer sessions between LAN workstations running 5250 emulation software and an IBM System 3x or AS/400 minicomputer. A local connection is made via a 5250 twinaxial terminal cable connected to the minicomputer, while a remote connection is made via synchronous modems. 5250 gateway and terminal emulation software is available from many sources, including Novell, AST, DCA and IBM.

TCP/IP

LAN workstations can connect to Unix hosts, DEC VAX minicomputers, Hewlett-Packard computers, and many others using the Transmission Control Protocol/Internet Protocol (TCP/IP) protocol suite. The TCP/IP protocol suite runs side-by-side with NetWare and the IPX/SPX protocols. NetWare 3.11 provides IP routing, allowing any workstation that supports IP on a NetWare internetwork to communicate with any host on the internetwork that supports IP.

Novell also supplies TCP/IP workstation software called LAN Workplace for DOS, LAN Workplace for OS/2, and LAN Workplace for Macintosh. TCP/IP workstation software is also available from other vendors, including FTP Software, Inc. and The Wollongong Group, Inc. In addition to IP protocol support, the workstation software usually includes TELNET, the standard TCP/IP terminal emulation program, FTP for file transfer, and the Simple Mail Transfer Program (SMTP) for exchanging electronic mail.

TELNET is a generic, universal terminal emulator for TCP/IP networks, and as such does not always support all features of a terminal. Several companies, including Walker, Richer & Quinn, Inc., supply terminal emulation software for specific terminals and for connection to specific hosts, including Hewlett-Packard and DEC.

OTHER CONNECTIVITY OPTIONS

This has not been an exhaustive discussion of all the connectivity options available to NetWare users, many others exist. There are, for example, numerous options for connections to DEC and Hewlett-Packard systems. If you are planning to install a LAN-to-LAN, LAN-to-host, or remote communications link, you should explore the available options. Information about other options is not always easy to find. The NetWare forum on CompuServe and NetWare users groups are good places to start, and dealers, VARs, consultants, and computer manufacturers can also be of help.

21
NETWORK MANAGEMENT

INTRODUCTION

In today's emterprises, the communication resources are complex and heterogeneous and are produced by a wide range of vendors. This is a direct result of computing getting "distributed" -- both functionally as well as geographically. Communications networks today may be built from several different types of dissimilar equipment, and may incorporate several smaller networks of different types. Full network management may require interconnecting management information from all of these networks into a usable form. Managers must now oversee a hetergeneous distributed system involving diverse sets of managed resources which include user and user groups, operating system and application software, workstation and server hardware, databases, printers and a host of communication equipments.

An office needs a variety of control and management functions to make it operate with the correct flow of paperwork. The same is true of a computer network. Some are low-level repetitive functions performed by a clerk each minute he is working at his desk. Others are slightly less repetitive and are needed to initiate the handling of a new customer, terminate the handling of an older customer, and deal with simple problems in a mechanical predefined manner. Others need intelligence and are not predefined. These fall into two categories: those concerned with operation and maintenance, i.e. keeping the existing system working, and those concerned with modifying, auditing or overseeing the existing system.

In discussing computer networks the following four terms are used: control, management, maintenance and administration. These words are sometimes used rather loosely. For clarity we will define them as follows:

- **Control** refers to the second-by-second operation of hardware or software functions that are repeated continuously for an extensive time: for example, the normal flow of data through the transport subsystem; or the normal operation of a session which is already established.

– **Management** refers to software functions which are not part of the second-by-second repetitive control of operations. These functions could cease and the control mechanisms would continue to work, at least for a time. Management functions include the setting up of sessions, the termination of sessions, accounting and charging for sessions, programmed recovery, automatic switchover, and checkpoint-restart.

– **Maintenance** refers mainly to the human activity of keeping the network running -- diagnosing failures, making and testing repairs, routine maintenance. To assist this human function a variety of machine facilities are needed including diagnostics, error logging, and terminals and programs which enable the service engineers to check the network, run the diagnostics, and correct problems.

– **Administration** refers to the human work associated with operating the network. A network administrator starts up the network, shuts it down, monitors its performance, brings up new circuits or reconfigures the network when necessary, brings new user machines on- line, and is concerned with potential security violations. The network administrator requires a terminal and computer programs, and is a special type of network end-user. Software is needed throughout the network to assist in network administration.

NETWORK MANAGEMENT FUNCTIONS

Network management has traditionally been viewed as only a technical problem and has been more of a "fire fighting" approach with little management component in it. Only recently, it has been given its due treatment as a management problem. Many people within an enterprise are often involved with network management -- users of the network who may need access to current network status information, business managers throughout the

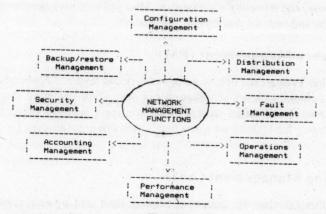

Fig. 21.1 :

enterprise who may be concerned about the effect of the performance of the network on the performance of the enterprise, and the actual network administrator in charge of the day-to-day operation of the network. From a technology standpoint, network management can be depicted as the intersection of eight different functional areas (see Figure 21.1):

1. Configuration and Name Management (CM)

CM facilities deal with the addition, deletion, modification, distribution and browsing of managed resources i.e., it enables a network manager to exercise control over the configuration of a communication subsystem. It allows a manager to close down nodes at will should a fault occur or workload change.

2. Distribution Management (DM)

DM facilities deal with distribution of software in the networked workstations. DM software allows an administrator to plan and distribute updates across the network to the workstations and servers. Afterwards, the changes can be tested and even undone if the test fails.

3. Fault Management (FM)

FM facilities deal with detecting managed resource faults and alerting the appropriate administrators. It also provides isolation, examine error logs, accepts and acts upon error detection notification, traces faults, and corrects faults arising from abnormal operation. Fault management frequently includes automatic program execution to fix or bypass specific faults as and when an end user or program reports that a certain system function is not available.

4. Operations Management (OM)

OM facilities are concerned about the (remote) control of managed resources in a distributed system which may include such activities like stopping and restarting specific application software and rebooting a workstation. Most software packages combine operations management and fault management in one product.

5. Performance Management (PM)

PM facilities evaluate the behaviour of network and layer entity resources and the effectiveness of communication activities. It can also adjust operating characteristics and generate network utilization reports by monitoring a station's performance. For example, monitoring file systems for a disk that is 90% full or monitoring for overloaded print queues.

6. Accounting Management (AM)

AM facilities calculate the amount of network time used by each segment of the network and facilitates a billing system for the usage of resources. Examples include keeping track of how many licenses have been granted to users, enforcing network licenses, and accounting for disk or CPU usage on a server machine.

7. Security Management (SM)

SM facilities provide for the protection of the network resources. It includes authorization facilities, access controls, encryption, authentication, maintenance and examination of security logs. An example might be assigning and checking the privileges of a person who wants to use a printer. This category also deals with putting "fire walls" around sensitive resources -- for instance, securing a host to prevent remote log-ins.

8. Backup/Restore Management (BM)

BM facilities deals with the recovery from disk failure as well as the rollback to previous versions of files to recover data or programs that were lost because of user error.

ELEMENTS OF NETWORK MANAGEMENT

A minimal network management system consists of:

- a central processing unit

- a hard disk or diskette storage device

- an operator's console

- and a set of local and remote monitoring devices.

Let us take the example of an enterprise operating in a LAN environment and using centralized network management (see Figure 21.2). Also assume that the LAN uses a layered

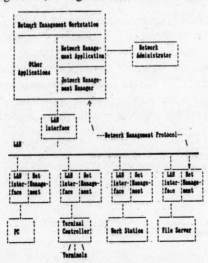

Fig. 21.2 :

communications architecture as specified by ISO in its OSI reference model. Here the elements needed for network management are:

– Network Administrator: person/persons using the network manager to perform network management functions.

– Network Manager Application: is an automated tool with a special human-computer interface that the network administrator uses to monitor and control network activities.

– Network Management Agents and Managers: The network management agent resides in the individual network components that are to be managed. The manager resides only in the network manager station in a centralized scheme; in a distributed scheme, it will reside in multiple stations. The manager provides communication services to the network management application.

– Layer Management Entities (LME): The LMEs interact with each protocol layer to maintain basic information about the configuration and status of the layer.

– Network Management Protocol: This is a means for the manager to communicate with the network management agents in individual network components.

– Managed Objects and Management Information Base: Managed objects define the resources that can be managed. The Management Information Base (MIB) is the concatenation of the information that each agent or LME maintains on its managed objects.

TEST, MONITOR AND CONTROL EQUIPMENT FOR AIDING NETWORK MANAGEMENT

Error free communication is a prime requirement of an effective computer networking system. In a network when error occurs quite frequently, the cause can be ascribed to either a loose connection somewhere in the network or some piece of equipment or software is malfunctioning or it can be combination of all of these conditions. To avoid any cascade effect of the error, it is imperative that the nature of malfunction be identified, the faulty component repaired/replaced at the earliest possible opportunity. There are many devices currently available to the network engineer to achieve the above task. These devices can generally be classified as:

– Handheld test sets

– Analog test sets

– Digital test sets

– Protocol analyzers

– LAN testers

– Fibre optic testers.

Special test equipments are available for testing interfaces, terminals, modems, transmission line, and communications software, as well as for monitoring and managing entire networks. In most network management systems, monitoring devices examine only the status of the modem or multiplexer, its interface with the terminal equipment, its interface with the transmission facility, and the condition of the transmission facility. Information on the modem or multiplexer and its interfaces comes from the presence or absence of signals on various EIA interface leads. Information on the transmission facility comes from the measurement of various analog parameters such as signal level, noise, distortion, phase jitter, and line hits. If a given interface signal or analog characteristic falls out of specification, the system's monitor set off an alarm to notify the operator of a failure.

STANDARDS IN NETWORK MANAGEMENT

In today's enterprises, the communication resources are complex and heterogeneous -- often distributed, with equipments from different vendors each incorporating its own management protocols which does not follow any standards. Managing such diverse resources is the network manager's nightmare. To simplify administration of distributed systems, a consistent and unified approach is necessary.

In an effort to provide the desperately needed consistency and interoperability, industry consortia, standard organizations, and individual companies are taking a variety of actions. We describe here two such major efforts - one by OSF and the other by OSI/NM FORUM.

1. OSF (Open Software Foundation) in Cambridge, Mass., USA, is addressing the distributed management problem through its distributed management environment (DME) offerings, which will provide a common management infrastructure for building distributed systems and network management applications. The infrastructure is based on an object oriented approach and it includes support for standards based technology. The DME will also provide an initial set of applications in the areas of host, print, software licensing, and software distribution management. It includes technologies developed ' by Tivoli Systems, Hewlette-Packard, IBM Groupe Bull, Gradient Technologies, Banyan Systems, and MIT. Already the DME integration effort is under way, and the first delivery of source code of the offering is expected in 1993. When it is delivered, vendors will be able to take the OSF/DME code and build systems and network management products.

2. OSI/NM FORUM (Open Systems Interconnection/Network Management Forum) was formed in 1988 as an open, nonprofit corporation by a number of telecommunications and IT suppliers. The objective of the Forum is to promote the rapid development, acceptance and implementation of standards for interoperable network management. The Forum's work is intended to align with the international standards set forth by the ISO and CCITT. It may be mentioned here that both ISO and CCITT are defining management standards with a focus on managing particular kinds of networks: ISO is defining how to manage OSI networks, and CCITT is defining how to manage telecommunication networks. The OSI/NM Forum is trying to apply those management standards to manage any network. The approach adopted by ISO, CCITT and OSI/NM Forum has been to resolve the open networking problem, starting from the physical hardware and working their way up. They have designed and introduced layers of functionality that make the lower layers transparent, providing well defined services at each layer. This has enabled Original Equipment Manufacturers (OEMs) to select OSI-based products from a variety of vendors rather than a single manufacturer. OSI/NM Forum has defined the concept of a Conformant Management Entity (CME). A CME is defined as a real open system that supports the OSI/NM Forum-defined interoperable interface. Thus, two CMEs communicate across the interoperable interface. Several organizations are now incorporating the architecture being developed by the OSI/NM Forum, into their network management products and systems.

NETWORK OWNERS AND USERS

The distinction between owners and users is important. The owners operate the network as a service for the users. They are not interested in how the users employ it providing that they obey the rules. The owners bill the users for their employment of the network resources.

The owners employ different management facilities from the users. The owners are concerned with billing, network performance, reliability, and fast correction of problems. The users are concerned with end-to-end protocols and file usage, end-to-end session control and services, accuracy control, availability, end-to-end pacing, and security.

The management and administrative functions may be divided into modules serving these two groups.

DISTRIBUTION OF MANAGEMENT

Individual networks differ in the extent to which they distribute or centralize the above functions.

Control decisions, such as which way to route the packets, can be entirely centralized, partially centralized, made by multiple centers, or completely distributed.

Management decisions may be centralized to a greater extent. Some, such as changing the routing when failures occur, could be decentralized. Networks other than simple onces often have multiple management modules which intercommunicate for purposes of setting up and disconnecting sessions, dealing with failures, maintaining accounts for billing, and so on.

Maintenance engineers like to access the network from any user node and run tests or diagnostics. The diagnostic programs may reside only in certain computers, but can be invoked from anywhere on the network. Network information which the engineers need, such as failure reports and error statistics may be transmitted to a central location.

Administration of the network as a whole may take place at one location. This center maintains statistics on network use, congestion, and performance. The staff there may start up and close down the network (though some networks never close). They reconfigure the network, possibly run simulations of it, deal with failures, sometimes telephoning a remote location to get a failure fixed, bring new devices, circuits, and end-users on-line, and are generally aware of the operational status of the network as a whole.

In complex networks there may be multiple administration centers, each dealing with a portion of the network. When a network is a vertical and horizontal combination as in Figure 21.3 the computer at the top of each vertical portion may perform management and

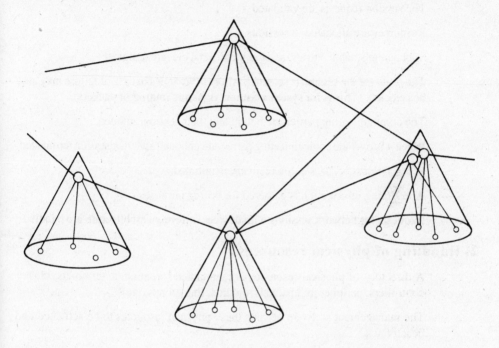

Fig. 21.3 : Separate vertical networks linked horizontally at their tops.

administration functions for that portion. In IBM's Systems Network Architecture (SNA) the vertical groupings are called domains. A host computer at the top of each domain carries out management functions for its domain, and communicates horizontally with management modules at the top of other domains. Administration for each domain may be done at the top of that domain; administration for the horizontal links or the entire network could be done at one specific computer center. There may be multiple administrator terminals, each at any point in the network, and each having jurisdiction over a defined set of links and devices in its own domain or in other domains. The administrator terminals report to a parent (VTAM or TCAM) at the top of their domain.

Security is handled in different ways by different organizations. Sometimes the security officer is different from the network administrator. He or she needs a terminal from which to monitor the network and be provided with reports on network problems, misuse, and violations of security procedures whether they are accidental or possibly deliberate. Sometimes different security officers are concerned with different portions of a network.

The following summarizes the various features for management and administration software that a network might employ.

1. Session services

– Request to have sessions are received.

– The session requests are validated.

– Resources are allocated to sessions.

– Subchannels, table entries, session identifiers, etc. are assigned.

– The route for the session is selected. Alternative routes in case of failure may also be selected. (This is for systems without dynamic routing of packets).

– The communicating parties are bound and their session initiated.

– When it is over the communicating parties are unbound and their session terminated.

– When failures occur, session recovery is initiated.

– Accounting information is gathered for billing purposes.

– Requests for network sessions with devices of foreign architecture are handled.

2. Handling of physical resources

– A directory of physical resources is maintained (processors, terminals, cluster controllers, peripherals, channels, circuits, line groups, etc).

– The management software permits these physical resources to be activated and deactivated.

– Dynamic reconfiguration may take place when failures occur.

– Recovery action may be initiated.

– Information is provided to the network operators to enable them to deal with the physical resources.

– Information is provided to the maintenance engineers about the physical resources.

– Resources are monitored for performance measurement.

3. Maintenance

– Terminal facilities are provided for maintenance engineers to access the network.

– Errors and failures are logged.

– Reports and analyses of the errors and failures are done and made available at the engineer terminals.

- Problems are automatically reported to a network operator.

- Diagnostics and confidence tests are run, possibly triggered automatically, possibly by an operator or engineer.

- Decisions to take down network components or circuits are made, based on the severity or frequency of errors.

4. Security

- A surveillance log is maintained of all security procedural violations.

- The surveillance log is analyzed for the security officer, highlighting occurrences needing immediate attention.

- Triggering of alarms on detection of certain types of procedural violations.

- Files of passwords, cryptography keys, or other security information are securely managed.

- Terminals are provided for security officer functions.

5. Administration

- Terminals are provided for network operators.

- The operators can display details of the network and its various resources.

- The operator can start and stop the network.

- An operator can activate and deactivate network components.

- An operator can start and stop application programs.

- An operator can reconfigure the network dynamically (i.e., without shutting it down).

- An operator can change specifications of network control mechanisms.

- An operator can down-line load programs.

- An operator can initiate a dump of programs in peripheral machines, possibly transmitting the dump to a larger machine for printing.

- An operator can initiate trace or statistics-gathering programs.

- An operator can initiate performance measurement aids.

- Network performance can be measured, analyzed, and possibly experimented with.

- Information is collected for billing users and bills are prepared.

CONTROL MECHANISMS

It is necessary to have error control, flow control and routing control as data pass through Transport Sub-system, and pacing control and control of protocol usage in the Session Services Sub-system.

MANAGEMENT MODULES

Network management often resides in several different places in modules which communicate across the network.

There needs to be some form of manager in or close to end-user environment. It may have to make a request to central management for a session to be set up. If we were concerned only with the transmission subsystem the uscr management would have the task of setting up and disconnecting the calls. It would be a person saying to a secretary, "Get me a call to Suresh Basandra in Hong Kong." With a CCITT X.25 network this could mean sending the packets which set up and disconnect a virtual call, as shown in Figure 21.4. Usually, however, we are also concerned with higher layer functions, and these need various allocating resources and protocol agreements establishing when a session is set up.

As we commented earlier, in setting up a session the management must ensure that the communicating parties:

- are authorized to communicate,

- have the facilities they need to communicate, and

- agree upon the manner in which they shall communicate.

Buffer space must be allocated, control of timing (pacing or flow control) must be agreed upon, security authorization must be checked, use of virtual network terminal protocols or file transfer protocols must be agreed upon, procedures for editing, compaction, conversion, or encryption may have to be agreed upon, and so on.

CENTRALIZED VS DECENTRALIZED MANAGEMENT

Where should the above management functions take place?

In some architectures the setting up and management of a session is done by the machines which participate in the session. In others it is done by a third party -- centralized management.

In general there are four types of approaches to control or management; these are shown in Figures 21.5 and 21.6.

First, there may be no separate manager. The communicating machines take care of their own problems. This situation is shown in the top two diagrams of Figure 21.6.

In this situation there may be a primary-secondary (master-slave) relationship. One of the two machines is designated the primary (master) and the other the secondary (slave).

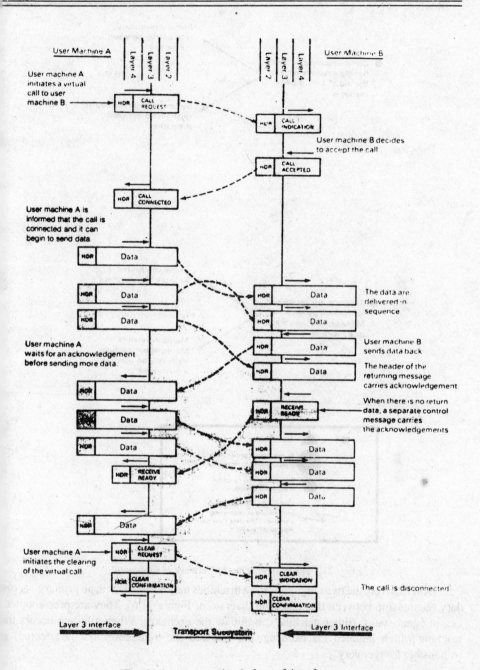

Fig. 21.4 : An example of a Layer 3 interface.

The primary initiates the exchange, and when something goes wrong the primary is responsible for the recovering action.

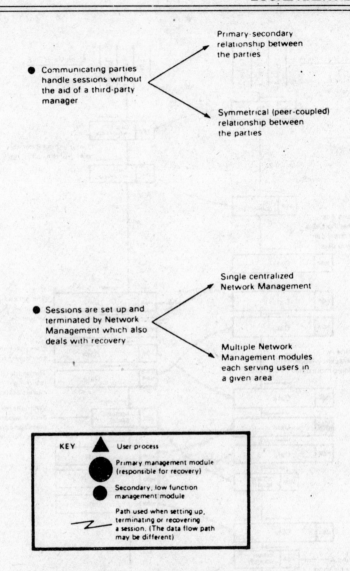

Fig. 21.5 : Four approaches to Network Management.

Alternatively the two communicating machines may be equal, with no primary-secondary relationship between them (second diagram of Figure 21.6). They are peer-coupled i.e., of equal status. Either machine can initiate the exchange. When a failure occurs the machine which initiated the exchange (or initiated the transaction that is affected) is responsible for recovery.

Until the mid-1970's most teleprocessing used a primary-secondary relationship between the communicating machines. This was because usually one of the two machines was rather dumb. It was a terminal or secondary (slave) device designed to respond in

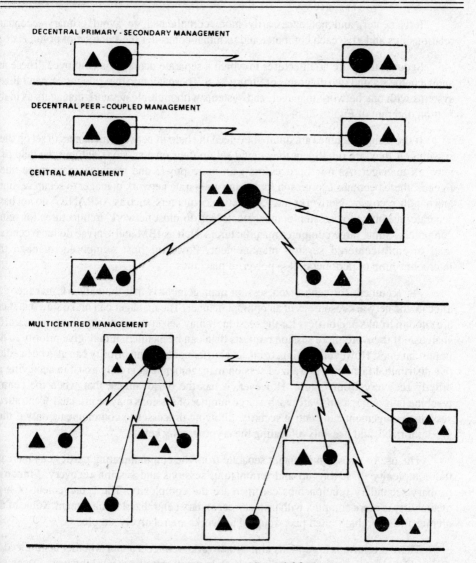

Fig. 21.6 : Four approaches to Network Management.

fairly simple fashion on the commands from the primary (master) which was usually a computer. By the late 1970's intelligent terminals, intelligent controllers, and computer-to-computer communication were common, and so peer-coupled protocols were practical. A peer-coupled protocol is usually a balanced or symmetrical protocol in which both machines have the same algorithms. The advantage of this is that any such machine can communicate with any other and hence there is greater flexibility. With primary-secondary systems one secondary station usually cannot communicate with another secondary, except via a primary. A computer may have to behave as a primary for some communications and a secondary for others.

It is neater, and not necessarily more complicated, to avoid primary-secondary relationships and give each computer and terminal controller the same set of protocols.

Second, there are architectures in which a separate manager is employed. These are shown in the second two diagrams of Figure 21.6. These fall into two categories: centralized systems with one network manager, and systems with multiple network managers as in the bottom diagram of Figure 21.6.

If the using machines are dumb they need the help of network managers to set up their sessions. If they are intelligent they could set up their own sessions without the help of network manager. As microprocessors gain more power and machines gain more intelligence, there becomes less reason for having a separate network manager to set up sessions and handle recovery. Networks interconnecting computers, such as ARPANET, do not have separate machines for session management. Nor do most network architectures for mini computers. Some large computer manufacturers such as IBM and Univac do have centralized or multicentered session management. Powerful host computers manage the interconnection of peripheral, less powerful machines.

An argument for centralized session management is that the network manager can allocate the network resources in an optimal manner. The manager can make sure that there are enough trunks and buffers for the session. It may select the route that the session traffic shall use. If there are more session requests than can be handled, it may give priority to the important ones. However, routing, trunk and buffer control, and priority can also be handled in a distributed fashion. Centralized session management can greatly assist in achieving a orderly recovery from failure. However, it has the disadvantage that when the central machine fails or has a software crash a large number of sessions may be affected. Centralized session management can control security, allowing processes to communicate only if they are authorized, and possibly allocating the cryptography keys.

The use of a session manager separate from the communicating parties can increase the complexity of setting up and terminating sessions and session recovery. Similarly primary-secondary relationships can increase the complexity. The achievement of high availability is more complex with primary-secondary centralized management. Some of the architectures for distributed peer-coupled networks are relatively simple.

There are furious arguments among network architects about whether centralized decentralized session management is the best. In practice both are working well. Decentralized session management appears cleaner and more flexible. Any machine can set up session to any other. But it needs more capability in the communicating parties. The need for primary-secondary relationships and centralized or multi-center management stems from the need to handle nodes of limited power. As the power of microprocessors grows distributed, symmetrical protocols look more attractive.

SYMMETRICAL SESSION MANAGEMENT

As the chips improve session management may increasingly be done in a symmetric fashion with no need for a third-party manager. The type of configuration in Figure 21.7

attractive. All machines have a standard interface to a common network. Any machine can initiate a session to any other machine which has the requisite attributes. Each pair of communicating machines is responsible for its own session security and recovery.

Small, simple machines may have a parent which does session management for them, as at the bottom left of Figure 21.7.

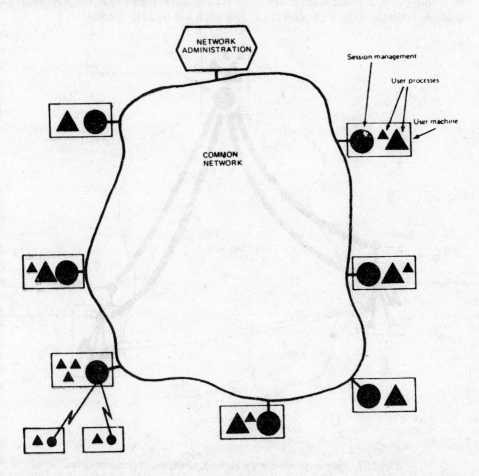

Fig. 21.7 : As chips and networks improve this form of management appears increasingly attractive. Any machine has the capability to have a session with any other machine without third-party management. All are connected to a common network which has its own network administration. Small, simple machines, as the bottom left-hand corner, may have a parent machine to set up and manage their sessions.

The management functions of the network owners are quite separate from those of the network users. The owner functions of network maintenance and administration may be centralized or bicentralized.

PERMANENT SESSIONS

If a management module in a user machine has to contact a centralized management module in order to set up sessions, there is usually a permanent session in effect between these two management modules. Every decentral management module is permanently in session with the requisite central management module. This is illustrated in Figure 21.8. The purpose of this is so that a user can request a session at any time and it will be set up quickly.

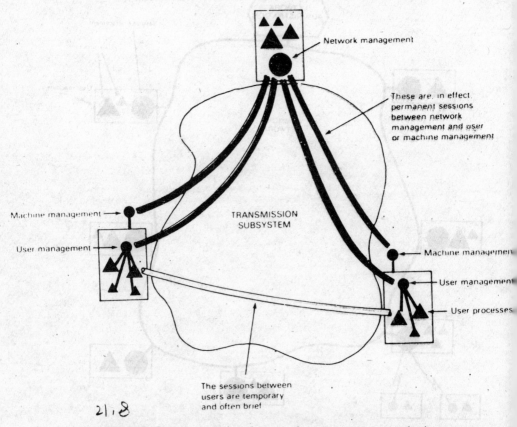

Fig. 21.8 : Permanent sessions for network management communication.

The fact that there is a permanent session does not mean that any transmission capacity or buffer space is being used. That will only be the case when communication takes place over the session path. It does mean that requisite registers, linkages, or table entries are set up to enable the two management modules to communicate without delay.

The central management, in addition to communicating with decentral session management, may also have links to the modules which manage machines. The purpose of this is to deal with problems such as printers running out of paper, machines not ready, storage units having long, unpredicatble access times, and so on. Some architectures have permanent sessions in effect between machine management and network management modules.

If the network administrator module is separate from the network management, there may also be a permanent session between the network management module and network administrator module. Sperry Univac's architecture has three types of network management modules: local, area, and global network management services. The local module is used to serve each major group of machines. The area module serves the user Management (AMS, Application Management Services) with which it is permanently in session. The global module serves the network administrator for the entire network. The user management and local network management modules are permanently in session with the one global network management module.

Figure 21.9 shows a session being set up between two users which report to different network managers. The request for the session is passed on between the network managers,

User A wants to have a session with User B in a part of the network controlled by a different manager. The setting up of the session proceeds as follows:

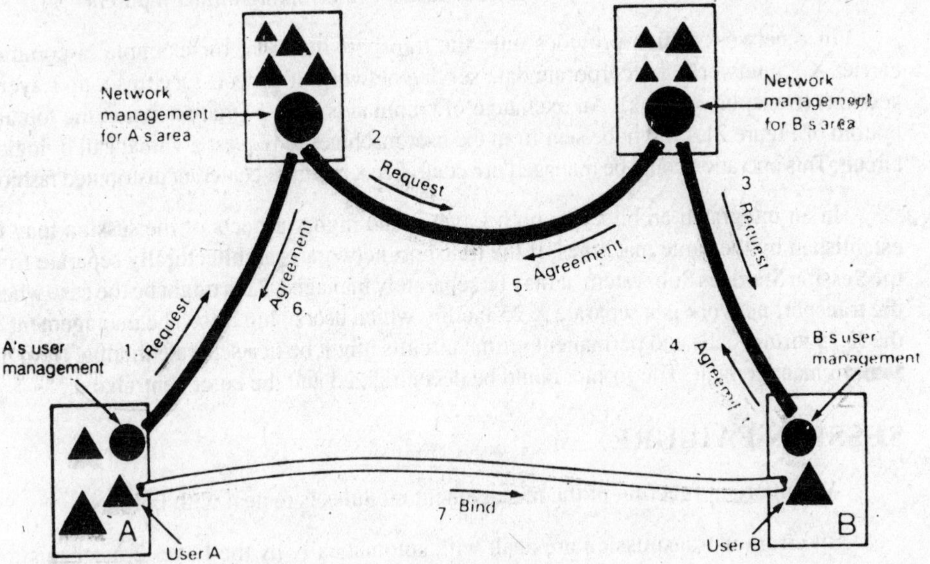

1   (Labeled "1" above) A's User Management uses its permanent session with its Network Management to request the user session

2   The Network Management sends the request to the Network Management which controls B (There is a permanent session between the Network Management modules)

3   The request is passed on to B's User Management

4   B's User Management agrees that B can enter into the session with A. It allocates the appropriate resources and sends a message to its Network Management saying that it agrees

5.& The Network Management modules pass the agreement message to A's User Management,
6.   allocating any network resources that are necessary

7   A's User Management allocates the session resources and issues a BIND command. The session can begin

Fig. 21.9 : Managing the establishment of a session with multicentered Network Management. (Different network architectures use different words for software modules which accomplish this.)

and the agreement travels back by the same route. The user management allocates the necessary resources in the user environment. The network management allocates the necessary network resources and may establish the route through the network that the session traffic uses.

Different architectures use different words for this process. In IBM the network management modules are the SSCP (System Services Control Point) of TCAM (Telecommunications Access Method) or VTAM (Virtual Telecommunication Access Method) residing in the host computers. The modules which act for the users are called Logical Units (LU). In Sperry Univac the network management modules are the area NMS (Network Management Services) and the modules in the user environment are the AMS (Application Management Services).

In a completely distributed system there are no centralized or higher-level facilities for the setting up of sessions. Establishing a session may still be a complex process in which protocols have to be agreed upon and resources allocated. This is the case in the Digital Equipment Corporation's DECNET architecture for interlinking minicomputers.

In a network which provides only the transport function, for example, a common carrier X.25 network or a corporate data service network, it is necessary to set up Layer 3 sessions (transport sesions). An exchange of commands such as that shown at the top and bottom of Figure 21.4 might be sent from the user machines to request a virtual call or logical circuit. This operation could be managed in a centralized, multiple-center, or distributed fashion.

In an integrated architecture both Layer 3 and higher aspects of the session may be established by the same machines. If the transport network is architecturally separate from the Session Services Subsystem, it may be separately managed. This might be the case where the transport network is a separate X.25 facility which users plug into. The management of the X.25 virtual calls and permanent virtual circuits might be in a separate module from the session management. The former could be decentralized and the latter centralized.

SESSION FAILURE

An important function of the management modules is to deal with failures.

Bit errors in transmission are dealt with automatically by the Layer 2 mechanism -- physical link control (HDLC, SDLC, BISYNCH, etc.). Higher-level mechanisms must deal with problems such as lost packets, irretrievably damaged messages, node failures, line failures, security breaches, and harmful errors in protocol.

It is desirable that a management module be responsible for initiating the recovery action. This module will attempt to recover without terminating the session if possible. Failing this, it should attempt to close down the session in an orderly fashion without losing or damaging data, if possible.

THE NETWORK OPERATORS

A network operator has many functions to perform. He or she watches over the network with a console rather like the operator of an on-line computer. The console is often a terminal and can be located anywhere. There may be several network operators in different places, each with jurisdiction over a different set of nodes and facilities. This is often the case where a network serves several divisions of a corporation. Each division has its own computers and terminals, and these are administered separately from any other division.

The operator console is connected to network administration software which is in one or multiple centers. This software permits the network to be controlled in two types of ways. First, it may allow an administrator to define a network and generate the systems programs which control and manage the network. This tailors the network and places an upper bound on its facilities such as numbers of trunks, terminals, and buffers. Second, the software permits a network operator to monitor or control the network or part of the network. The operator can display the status of the various facilities, activate and deactivate nodes, start and stop various facilities, may be able to adjust priorities, and so on.

NETWORK OPERATOR COMMANDS

The operator uses a set of network operator commands. These are provided by the network administration software, for example IBM's VTAM. The commands enable the operator to take actions such as the following:

– Display the status of categories of network entities.

In this way all terminals, all lines, all major nodes, all application programs, or all of the above within a given portion of the network, could be checked.

The display for all terminals might be a list of the names, addresses, types of all terminals, and whether they are active; and for logical units or virtual terminals the name of the associated physical unit and whether it is active, the names of the major node to which the terminal is connected, the name of the line or channel to which it is connected, or entities on the path to an associated host computer.

The display for all line might include a list of the lines in each portion (area, domain) of a network, whether they are active, line type, which nodes they are connected to, which node manages them, and possible summary figures for their load, failures and transmission errors.

The display for applications programs might include the names of all applications programs, which node(s) they reside in, and whether they are active. Another display might show all nodes which can contain application programs and list the programs in them.

From these summary listings an operator could display more detail of individual entities, as follows:

– Display the status of individual network entities.

The condition of a particular terminal, a terminal cluster controller, a line, a trunk group, a part, switching equipment, a network control program, an application program, a session and possibly files could be verified.

The display for a terminal might show whether it is active, whether it has power, the name of the application program (if any) to which it is connected, the name of the node to which it is connected, the name of the line or line group to which it is assigned, details of the path which connects it to a host computer, the identification of the session it is participating in, and possibly a count of its activity.

The display for a line might show its type, whether it is active, what nodes it is connected to, whether it is switched or nonswitched, name of a line group to which it is assigned, which machine controls it, statistics of its traffic load, error retransmissions, and failures, whether its traffic is currently being counted or monitored, and parameters relating to its control such as specifications for polling delay, time-outs, and maximum number of error retransmission.

The display for an application program might include whether it is currently connected to the network software, its job and step names, the terminals connected to it, the terminals with requests for connection queued to it, and statistics of its usage.

    –   Activate and deactivate network entities.

Before a node can be used in a network it must be declared to the control program as "active". The same may be true with lines, logical or virtual units, and so on. The operator can activate and deactivate these.

    –   Start and stop application programs.

Sometimes an application program is started by a user at a terminal with a command such as LOG ON. Others users employ the terminal for a given application without logging on. A bank customer uses a cash-dispensing terminal, for example, without logging on. A network operator must start and stop programs which are not activated by their users.

    –   Load programs into remote nodes.

In a vertical network programs are often maintained and stored in a central node. From there some of them are transmitted and loaded into peripheral machines. In a horizontal network programs may be passed from one node to another. An operator may control the down-line loading of programs.

    –   Activate a remote network control program.

The network control programs in peripheral nodes may be activated, and possibly loaded, by a network operator. A peripheral node may be switched from one host computer to another when failures occur and it may then need a modified control program.

    –   Activate and deactivate files.

Where the network management encompasses distributed files the operator may be able to activate and deactivate files, and possibly create files. This is often in the province of user rather than network management.

    –   Activate and deactivate links to foreign equipment.

It is usually desirable to connect foreign devices to a network, i.e., devices which do not conform to the network architecture. Sometimes these are older terminals or machines with protocols which predate those of the network architecture. The network software may permit these to be linked to the network and the operator can activate and deactivate them.

–   Reconfigure the network.

Additional circuits may be added to a network, additional machines connected, and the connections between machines modified. A peripheral node may be switched from one host to another. In practice many networks grow and change substantially. Within the limits of a given system generation which determines the scope of the software in use, the software changes for these reconfigurations can be made by the operators.

–   Enter messages for users.

The operator may be able to enter messages which will be displayed to users when they log on.

–   Change transmission parameters.

Adjustments may be made to parameters on lines, such as polling delay, limit on negative responses to polling, time-outs maximum number of retries when an error occurs.

–   Start and stop traffic monitors or testing aids.

The operator may initiate the recording of traffic statistics or performance measurement data, and may initiate on-line testing or traces.

–   Initiate a dump.

A program can be down-line loaded from a host computer to a smaller machine. The smaller machine can be up-line dumped, i.e. the contents of its memory at a given time transmitted to the larger machine and printed or stored. The operator may initiate a dump -- either an up-line or a dump on a printer attached to the machine being dumped.

MAINTENANCE

For maintenance purposes the network software should log all errors and failures. The logs should be analyzed and summarized, and prepared for the maintenance engineers. The management software may make decisions to automatically close down certain components or circuits when the severity or frequency of errors or failure exceeds a certain threshhold. It may automatically run diagnostics and confidence tests.

The maintenance engineer needs to be able to inspect the network, examine the error and failure logs, and run diagnostics. This would be done from terminals and so requires some of the facilities listed above for operators.

SECURITY

For security reasons the network may be monitored for procedural violations made by the users. Violations of more than a certain level may trigger alarms at the location of a security officer. All security procedure violations will be logged, and the logs should be analyzed for patterns or usual frequencies of violations. The security officer should be able to inspect the violation logs and analyses at any time from a terminal.

Users may have to key in passwords or secret numbers to gain access to programs or network facilities. These should be maintained with maximum security by the security officer. Similarly, if keys are used for cryptography, these need to be maintained with maximum security.

There may be one security officer or several. There may be one for the network as a whole and other persons with security responsibility in the various user environments. These persons need terminals with secure access to the facilities the network employs the security.

OTHER ADMINISTRATIVE FUNCTIONS

In addition to the functions mentioned, the network should have facilities for billing its users.

Some networks have a center where network measurements are made and performance is studied. Tools may exist in this center for analyzing the performance, and summarizing and charting the network measurements. In some cases experiments are carried out during the quieter periods and weekends and night to test the capacity of the network configuration. Tools may exist for simulating the network and evaluating how to reconfigure it for optimal performance.

SNMP: SIMPLE NETWORK MANAGEMENT PROTOCOL

The Simple Mail Transfer Protocol (SMTP) defines how the mail system on one machine transfers mail to the server on another. Messages sent between the client and server begin with a command (often a 3-digit number) that the programs use, followed by text that humans can read to understand the interaction. This chapter looks at the standards used within the Internet protocol suite for network management.

In the early 1990s, the IAB assumed the lead in setting standards for TCP/IP-based internets and sponsored two network management protocols. One protocol is intended to address short-term solutions and is called the *simple network management protocol* (SNMP). The other protocol proposes to address long-range solutions and is called *common manage-ment information services and protocol over TCP/IP (CMOT)*. This chapter examines these Internet network management protocols with the emphasis on SNMP.

TCP/IP network management consists of three pieces.

(i) A *Management Information Base* (MIB) that specifies what variables the network elements maintain (the information that can be queried and set by the manager). RFC 1213 defines the second version of this, called MIB-II.

(ii) A set of common structures and an identification scheme used to reference the variables in the MIB. This is called the *Structure of Management Information* (SMI) and is specified in RFC 1155.

(iii) The protocol between the manager and the element, called the *Simple Network Management Protocol* (SNMP). RFC 1157 specifies the protocol.

The Internet Naming Hierarchy

Figure 21.10 shows the structure of this tree when used with SNMP. All variables in the MIB start with the object identifier 1.3.6.1.2.1.

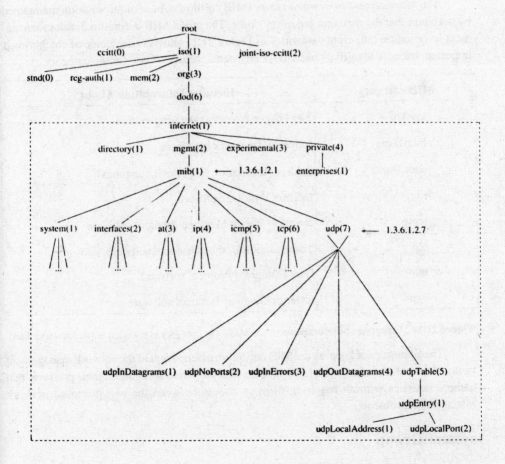

Figure 21.10 : Internet Registration Hierarchy

Each node in the tree is also given a textual name. The name corresponding to the object identifier 1.3.6.1.2.1 is iso.org.dod.internet.mgmt.mib. These names are for human readability. The *names* of the MIB variables that are in the packets exchanged between the manager and agent are the numeric object identifiers, all of which begin with 1.3.6.1.2.1.

An object identifier is a sequence of integers separated by decimal points. The integers traverse a tree structure, similar to the DNS or a Unix filesystem. There is an unnamed root at the top of the three where the object identifiers start.

MANAGEMENT INFORMATION BASE

The *Management Information Base* (MIB) is the database of information maintained by the agent that the manager fan query or set. The initial MIB definition divides management information into eight categories as Figure 21.11 shows. The choice of categories is important because identifiers used to specify items include a code for the category.

MIB category	Includes Information About
system	The host or gateway operating system
interfaces	Individual network interfaces
addr.trans.	Address translation (e.g., ARP mappings)
ip	Internet Protocol software
icmp	Internet Control Message Protocol software
tcp	Transmission Control Protocol software
udp	User Datagram Protocol software
egp	Exterior Gateway Protocol software

Figure 21.11 : Categories of information in the MIB. The category is encoded in the identifier used

The advantage of keeping the MIB definition independent of the network management protocols should be clear - it allows vendors to incorporate software in their products that gathers statistics without requiring them to choose between the two proposed network management protocols.

system Group

Each object group of MIB, as shown in Figure 21.12 is described briefly in this section. Be aware that this general explanation is to give you an idea of the major operations of the groups. RFC 1213 should be studied carefully to appreciate the full functions supported by the MIB definitions.

The *system* group describes:-

- the name and version of the hardware, operating system, and networking software of the entity
- the hierarchical name of the group
- when the management portion of the system was reinitialized

The system group is simple; it consists of seven simple variables. Table 21.1 lists and briefly describes the objects for the system group.

Table 21.1 : Simple variables in system group

Name	Description
sysDescr	Textual description of entity.
sysObjectID	Vendor's ID within the subtree 1.3.6.1.4.1
sysUpTime	Time in hundredths of a second since network management portion of system was rebooted.
sysContact	Name of contact person and how to contact them.
sysName	Node's fully qualified domain name (FQDN).
sysLocation	Physical location of node.
sysServices	Value indicating services provided by node. It is the sum of the layers in the OSI model supported by the node. The following values are added together, depending on the services provided: 0×01 (physical), 0×02 (datalink), 0×04 (internet), 0×08 (end-to-end), 0×40 (application).

interface Group:-

The *interfaces* group describes the:-

- number of network interfaces supported
- type of interface operating below IP (e.g., Ethernet, etc.)
- size of datagram acceptable to the interface
- speed of the interface (bit/s)
- address of the interface
- operational state of the interface
- amount of traffic received, delivered (unicast or broadcast), or discarded, and the reasons

This group also defines a table with 22 columns. Table 21.2 lists and briefly describes the objects for the interface group.

Table 21.2 : Variables in interface table: *if Table.*

Name	Description
ifIndex	Index of interface, between one and ifNumber.
ifDescr	Textual description of interface.
ifType	Type, for example: 6=Ethernet, 7=802.3 Ethernet, 9=802.5 token ring, 23=PPP, 28=SLIP, and many other values.
ifMtu	MTU of interface.
ifSpeed	Speed in bits/sec.
ifPhyAddress	Physical address, or string of 0 length for interfaces without physical address (e.g., serial links).
ifAdminStatus	Desired state of interface: 1 = up, 2 = down, 3 = testing.
ifOperStatus	Current state of interface: 1 = up, 2 = down, 3 = testing.
ifLastChange	Value of sysUpTime when interface entered current operational state.
ifInOctets	Total number of bytes received, including framing characters.
ifInUcastPkts	Number of unicast packets delivered to higher layers.
ifInNUcastPkts	Number of nonunicast (i.e., broadcast or multicast) packets delivered to higher layers.
ifInDiscards	Number of received packets discarded even though no error in packet (i.e., out of buffers).
ifInErrors	Number of received packets discarded because of errors.
ifInUnknownProtos	Number of received packets discarded because of unknown protocol.
ifOutOctets	Number of bytes transmitted, including framing characters.
ifOutUcastPkts	Number of unicast packets received from higher layers.
ifOutNUcastPkts	Number of nonunicast (i.e., broadcast or multicast) packets received from higher layers.
ifOutDiscards	Number of outbound packets discarded even though no error in packet (i.e., out of buffers).
ifOutErrors	Number of outbound packets discarded because of errors.
ifOutQLen	Number of packets in output queue.
ifSpecific	A reference to MIB definitions specific to this particular type of media.

address translation (at) Group:-

The *address translation* group describes the address translation tables for network-to-physical address translation. This group will eventually become obsolete, as its functions now reside in the IP group.

Only a single table 21.3 with three columns is defined for the at group.

Table 21.3 : Address translation table: *atTable*

Name	Description
atIfIndex	Interface number: ifIndex
atPhysAddress	Physical address. Setting this to a string of 0 length invalidates the entry.
atNetAddress	IP address

ip Group:-

The ip group describes

if the machine forwards datagrams

the time-to-live value for datagrams originated at this site

The amount of traffic received, delivered, or discarded, and the resons

information on fragmentation operations

address tables, including subnet masks

routing tables, including destination address, distance metrics, age of route, next hop, and protocol from which route was learned (RIP, EGP, etc.)

The ip group defines numerous variables and three tables. Table 21.4 defines the imple variables.

Table 21.4 : Simple variables in *ip group*.

Name	Description
ipForwarding	1 means the system is forwarding IP datagrams, and 2 means it is not.
ipDefaultTTL	Default TTL value when transport layer doesn't provide one.
ipInReceives	Total number of received IP datagrams from all interfaces.

Table Contd. on next page

Table Contd. from previous page

Name	Description
ipInHdrErrors	Number of IP datagrams discarded because of header errors (e.g., checksum error, version number mismatch, TTL exceeded, etc.).
ipInAddrErrors	Number of IP datagrams discarded because of incorrect destination address.
ipForwDatagrams	Number of IP datagrams for which an attempt was made to forward.
ipInUnknownProtos	Number of locally addressed IP datagrams with an invalid protocol field.
ipInDiscards	Number of received IP datagrams discarded because of a lack of buffer space.
ipInDelivers	Number of IP datagrams delivered to appropriate protocol module.
ipOutRequests	Total number of IP datagrams passed to IP for transmission. Does not include those counted in *ipForwDatagrams*.
ipOutDiscards	Number of output IP datagrams discarded because of a lack of buffer space.
ipOutNoRoutes	Number of IP datagrams discarded because no route could be found.
ipReasmTimeout	Maximum number of seconds that received fragments are held while awaiting reassembly.
ipReasmReqds	Number of IP fragments received that needed to be reassembled.
ipReasmOKs	Number of IP datagrams successfully reassembled.
ipReasmFails	Number of failures by IP reassembly algorithm.
ifFragOKs	Number of IP datagrams that have been successfully fragmented.
ipFragFails	Number of IP datagrams that needed to be fragmented but couldn't because the "don't fragment" flag was set.
ipFragCreates	Number of IP fragments generated by fragmentation.
ipRoutingDiscards	Number of routing entries chosen to be discarded even though they were valid.

The first table in the ip group is the IP address table. It contains one row for each IP address on the system. Each row contains five variables, described in Table 21.5.

Table 21.5 : IP address table: *ipAddrTable*

Name	Description
ipAdEntAddr	IP address for this row.
ipAdEntIfIndex	Corresponding interface number: *ifIndex*.
ipAdEntNetMask	Subnet mask for this IP address.
ipAdEntBcastAddr	Value of least-significant bit of the IP broadcast address. Normally 1.
ipAdEntReasmMaxSize	Size of largest IP datagram received on this interface that can be reassembled.

Table 21.6 is the IP routing table. The index used to access each row of the table is the destination IP address.

Table 21.6 : IP routing table: *ipRoutTable*.

Name	Description
ipRouteDest	Destination IP address. A value of 0.0.0.0 indicates a default entry.
ipRouteIfIndex	Interface number: *ifIndex*
ipRouteMetric1	Primary routing metric. The meaning of the metric depends on the routing protocol (*ipRouteProto*). A value of -1 means it's not used.
IpRouteMetric2	Alternative routing metric.
ipRouteMetric3	Alternative routing metric.
ipRouteMetric4	Alternative routing metric.
ipRouteNextHop	IP address of next-hop router.
ipRouteType	Route type: 1 = other, 2 = invalidated route, 3 = direct, 4 = indirect.
ipRouteProto	Routing protocol: 1 = other, 4 = ICMP redirect, 8 = RIP, 13 = OSPF, 14 = BGP, and others.
ipRouteAge	Number of seconds since route was last updated or determined to be correct.
ipRouteMask	Mask to be logically ANDed with destination IP address before being compared with *ipRouteDest*
ipRouteMetric5	Alternative routing metric.
ipRouteInfo	Reference to MIB definations specific to this particular routing protocol.

Table 21.7 in the ip group is the address translation table. As we said earlier, the at group is now deprecated, and this IP table replace it.

Table 21.7 : IP address translation table: *i pNetToMediaTable*

Name	Description
ipNetToMediaIfIndex	Corresponding interface: *ifIndex*.
ipNetToMediaPhysAddress	Physical address.
ipNetToMediaNetAddress	IP address.
ipNetToMediaType	Type of mapping: 1 = other, 2 = invalidated, 3 = dynamic, 4 = static.

icmp Group

The *icmp* group describes

• number of the various Internet Control Message Protocol (ICMP) messages received and transmitted

• statics on problems encountered

Table 21.8 lists and briefly describes the objects of icmp group.

Table 21.8 : Simple variables in *icmp* group.

Name	Description
icmpInMsgs	Total number of received ICMP messages.
icmpInErrors	Number of received ICMP messages with errors (e.g, invalid ICMP checksum).
icmpInDestUnreachs	Number of received ICMP destination unreachable message.
icmpInTimeExcds	Number of received ICMP time exceeded message.
icmpInParmProbs	Number of received ICMP parameter problem message.
icmpInSrcQuenchs	Number of received ICMP source quench messages.
icmpInRedirects	Number of received ICMP redirect messages.
icmpInEchos	Number of received ICMP echo request messages.
icmpInEchoReps	Number of received ICMP echo reply messages.
icmpInTimestamps	Number of received ICMP timestamp request messages.

Table Contd. on next page

Table Contd. from previous page

Name	Description
icmpInTimestampReps	Number of received ICMP timestamp reply messages.
icmpInAddrMasks	Number of received ICMP address mask request messages.
icmpInAddrMaskReps	Number of received ICMP address mask reply messages.
icmpOutMsgs	Total number of output ICMP messages.
icmpOutErrors	Number of ICMP messages not sent because of a problem within ICMP (e.g., lack of buffers).
icmpOutDestUnreachs	Number of ICMP destination unreachable messages sent.
icmpOutTimeExcds	Number of ICMP time exceeded messages sent.
icmpOutParmProbs	Number of ICMP parameter problem messages sent.
icmpOutSrcQuenchs	Number of ICMP source quench messages sent.
icmpOutRedirects	Number of ICMP redirect messages sent.
icmpOutEchos	Number of ICMP echo request messages sent.
icmpOutEchoReps	Number of ICMP echo reply messages sent.
icmpOutTimestamps	Number of ICMP timestamp requests sent.
icmpOutTimestampReps	Number of ICMP timestamp reply messages sent.
icmpOutAddrMasks	Number of ICMP address mask request messages sent.
icmpOutAddrMaskReps	Number of ICMP address mask reply messages sent.

tcp Group:-

The *tcp* group describes

- retransmission algorithm and maximum/minimum retransmission values

- information on state transition operations

- port and IP numbers for each connection

- number of TCP connections the entity can support

- information on traffic received and sent

Table 21.9 describes the simple variables in tcp group.

Table 21.9 : Simple variables in tcp group.

Name	Description
tcpRtoAlgorithm	Algorithm used to calculate retransmission timeout value: 1 = none of the following, 2 = a constant RTO, 3 = MIL-STD-1778 Appendix B, 4 = Van Jacobson's algorithm.
tcpRtoMin	Minimum retransmission timeout value, in milliseconds.
tcpRtoMax	Maximum retransmission timeout value, in milliseconds.
tcpMaxConn	Maximum number of TCP connections. Value is −1 if dynamic.
tcpActiveOpens	Number of transitions from CLOSED to SYN_SENT states.
tcpPassiveOpens	Number of transitions from LISTEN to SYN_RCVD states.
tcpAttemptFails	Number of transitions from SYN_SENT or SYN_RCVD to CLOSED, plus number of transitions from SYN_RCVD to LISTEN.
tcpEstabResets	Number of transitions from ESTABLISHED or CLOSE_WAIT states to CLOSED.
tcpCurrEstab	Number of connections currently in ESTABLISHED or CLOSE_WAIT states.
tcpInSegs	Total number of segments received.
tcpOutSegs	Total number of segments sent, excluding those containing only retransmitted bytes.
tcpRetransSegs	Total number of retransmitted segments.
tcpInErrs	Total number of segments received with an error (such as invalid checksum).
tcpOutRsts	Total number of segments sent with RST flag set.

Table 21.9 describes the tcp connection variable. This contains one row for each connection. Each row contains five variables; the state of the connection, local IP address, local port number, remote IP address, local port number, remote IP address, and remote port number.

Table 21.10 : TCP connection table: *tcpConnTable*

Name	Description
tcpConnState	State of connection : 1 = CLOSED, 2 = LISTEN, 3 = SYN_SENT, 4 = SYN_RCVD, 5 = ESTABLISHED, 6 = FIN_WAIT_1, 7 = FIN_WAIT_2, 8 = CLOSE_WAIT, 9 = LAST_ACK, 10 = CLOSING, 11 = TIME_WAIT, 12 = delete TCB. The only value that the manager can set this variable to is 12 (e.g., immediately terminate the connection).
tcpConnLocalAddress	Local IP address. 0.0.0.0 indicates the listener is willing to accept connections on any interface.
tcpConnLocalPort	Local port number.
tcpConnRemAddress	Remote IP address.
tcpConnRemPort	Remote port number.

udp Group

The *udp* group describes

* information on traffic received and sent

* information on problems encountered

STRUCTURE OF MANAGEMENT INFORMATION (SMI)

In addition to the MIB standard, which specifies specific network management variables and their meanings, a separate standard specifies a set of rules used to define and identify MIB variables. The rule are known as the *Structure of Management Information* (SMI) specification. To keep network management protocols simple, the SMI places restrictions on the types of variables allowed in the MIB, specifies the rules of naming those variables, and create rules for defining variable types.

The formal specification of SNMP uses *Abstract Syntax Notation 1* (ASN.1) and the actual encoding of the bits in the SNMP messages uses the corresponding *Basic Encoding Rules*(BER). Unlike most text that describe SNMP, we have purposely left a discussion of ASN.1 and BER until the end. When they're discussed first, it can confuse the reader and obfuscate the real purpose of SNMP--network management. In this section we only give an overview of these two topics.

NOTE	
(i)	The TCP/IP network management protocols use a formal notation called ASN.1 to define names and types for variables in the management information base. The precise notation makes the form and content of variables unambiguous.

Fortunately the details of ASN.1 and BER are only important to implementors of SNMP. They are not fundamental to the understanding and use of network management.

SIMPLE NETWORK MANAGEMENT PROTOCOL (SNMP)

The simple network management protocol provides a mechanism to access MIB objects so that they can be read and changed. It also allows a device to send unsolicited messages to an SNMP management station to indicate that some predefined condition has been met.

Simple Network Management Protocol defines only five types of messages that are exchanged between the manager and agent:-

PDU type	Operator	Meaning
0	get-request	Fetch the value of one or move variables
1	get-next-request	Fetch the next variable after one or more specified variables
2	get-request	Set the value of one or more variables
3	get-response	Return the value of one or more variables
4	trap	Notify the manager when something happens on the agent

The first three messages are sent from the manager to the agent, and the last two are from the agent to the manager.

Since four of the five SNMP messages are simple request-reply protocols. SNMP uses UDP. This means that a request from the manager may not arrive at the agent, and the agent's reply may not make it back to the manager. The manager probably wants to implement a timeout and retransmission.

They are referred to as Protocol Data Units (PDUs), as in OSI standards. The get-request PDU is used by an SNMP network management station to obtain the value of a specific MIB variable from the SNMP management agent in a remote node. The get-next-request is similar to the get-request, except it allows MIB values to be received without defining them specifically. get-next-request is used where a table of variables, such as a routing table, exists. The client would not know the number of values in that table.

The get-response PDU is the answer from the management agent to get-request and get-next-request. The set-request is used by the management station to change MIB variable that can be altered in the management agent. One possibility is to set a trap for a defined event or condition detected by the management agent. When that condition occurs on the node, the agent sends a trap PDU to the management station. This message can be generated at any time, so a management station has to be listening for these continuously.

The trap messages use UDP well-known port number 162; other PDUs use port number 161. This allows trap messages to be handled independently of get and set.

Figure 21.12 shows the basic format of SNMP messages. They all start with a version, which is 0 for version 1, followed by a community string. The community string defines a level of authentication which pertains to this message and hence determines whether it will have sufficient rights on a host to make changes or even read the information in the MIB.

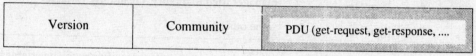

Version	Community	PDU (get-request, get-response, ...

Figure 21.12 : SNMP message format.

The community string is followed by one or more PDUs which define the overall message encapsulated in this datagram. All PDUs, apart from the trap PDU, are the same. The format is shown in Figure 21.13. The normal PDUs start with a request id to help relate requests and responses; these messages are likely to use the UDP protocol and hence there is no reliability.

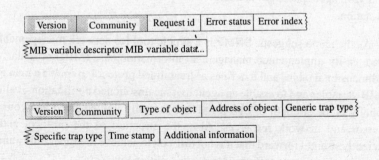

Figure 21.13 : SNMP PDUs: (a) normal; (b) trap.

The *error status* is an integer returned by the agent specifying an error. Table.21.12 shows the values, names, and descriptions.

Table 21.12 : SNMP error status values

error status	Name	Description
0	noError	all is OK
1	tooBig	agent could not fit reply into a single SNMP message
2	noSuchName	operation specified a nonexistent variable
3	badValue	a set operation specified an invalid value or syntax
4	readOnly	manager tried to modify a read-only variable
5	genErr	some other error

If an error occurred, the *error index* is an integer offset specifying which variable was in error. it is set by the agent only for the noSuchName, badValue, and readOnly errors.

A list of variable names and values follows in the get, get-next, and set request. The value portion is ignored for the get and get-next operators.

For the trap operator (a *PDU type* of 4), the format of the SNMP message changes.

SNMPv1 (SNMP version 1) AND SNMPv2 (SNMP version 2)

In August of 1988, the specification for SNMPv1 was issued and rapidly became the dominant network management standard. A number of vendors offer stand-alone network management based on SNMP, and most vendors of bridges, routers, workstations and PCs offer SNMP agent packages that allow their products to be managed by an SNMP management station.

As the name suggests, SNMP is a simple tool for network management. It defines a limited, easily implemented management information base (MIB) of scalar variables and two-dimensional tables and it defines a streamlined protocol to enable a manager to get and set MIB variables and to enable an agent to issue unsolicited notifications, called traps. This simplicity is the strength of SNMP. SNMP is easily implemented and consumes modest processor and network resources. Also, the structure of the protocol and the MIB is sufficiently straight forward that it is not difficult to achieve interoperability among management stations and agent software from a mix of vendors.

With its widespread use, the deficiencies of SNMP become increasingly apparent; these include both functional deficiencies and a lack of security facility. As a result, an enhanced version, known as SNMPv2 was issued in 1993. SNMPv2 has quickly gained support, and a number of vendors had announced products within months of the issuance of the standard.

Surprisingly, SNMPv2 doesnot provide network management at all. SNMPv2 instead provides a framework on which network management applications can be built. Those applications such as fault management, performance monitoring, accounting and so on, are outside the scope of the standard.

What SNMPv2 does provide is, to use a contemporary term, the infrastructure for network management.

The essence of SNMPv2 is a protocol that is used to exchange management information. Each "player" in the network management system maintains a local database information relevant to network management, known as the management information base (MIB). The SNMPv2 standard defines the structure of this information and the allowable data types; this definition is known as the structure of management information (SMI). We can think of this as the language for defining management information. The standard also supplies a number of MIBs that are generally useful for network management. In addition, new MIBs may be defined by vendors and user groups.

At least one system in the configuration must be responsible for network management. It is here that any network management applications are housed. There may be more than one of these management stations, to provide redundancy or simply split up the duties in a large network. Most other stations act in the role of agent. An agent collects information locally and stores it for later access by a manager. The information includes data about the system itself and may also include traffic information for the network or networks to which the agent attaches.

SNMPv2 will support either a highly centralized network management strategy or a distributed one. In the latter case, some systems operate both in the role of a manager and of agent. In the agent role, such a system will accept commands from a superior management system. Some of those commands relate to the local MIB at the agent. Other commands require the agent to act as a proxy for remote devices. In this case, the proxy agent assumes the role of manager to access information at a remote agent and then assumes the role of an agent to pass information onto a superior manager.

All of these exchanges took, place using the SNMPv2 protocol, which is a simple request /response type of protocol. Typically, SNMPv2 is implemented on top of the user datagram protocol (UDP), which is part of the TCP/IP protocol suite. It can also be implemented on top of the ISO transport protocol.

SUMMARY

With the rapid growth of communications technology, both in sophistication and diversity, many enterprises in their effort to capitalize on it have landed up with diverse products and even variety of networks in a single enterprise. To manage such a heterogeneous mix, the current trend is towards development and adoption of an integrated approach to network management. Integrated network management will provide a single, basic set of management tools for all networks in an enterprise. To supplement this, expert systems (e.g. fault management expert system module) are being developed. Thus, network management is also going to be very powerful and sophisticated.

22

OFFICE AUTOMATION

INTRODUCTION

Each of us experiences unfamiliar circumstances that cause us unnecessary concern: the first day of a school year, the first meeting of a new organization, the first seminar, or the first day on a new job. We feel ill at ease because of strange surroundings or unknown customs. Once we find old friends or meet new ones and learn the prevailing social or professional customs, we feel more comfortable.

Office automation (OA) is like that: its unfamiliar terminology and process may cause apprehension, but familiarization removes the strangeness. We soon see that much of office automation is new ways of using old principles, practices, and equipment. Those elements that really are new are soon understood.

In a broad sense, **office automation** is the incorporation of appropriate technology to help people manage information. Technology is considered 'appropriate' when it utilizes the most abundant domestic resources and conserves capital and skilled personnel.

Office automation is a subset of **automation**, a term said to have been coined by D.S. Harder of General Motors Corporation in 1936. The word **office** specifies the sector. But what is an office? To a typist it may be a room full of desks and typewriters. To a salesperson it may be the front seat of a car or a hotel room. To a truck driver an office is the cab of a truck. To a reporter it can be a newsroom or even a telephone booth. All of these has one common element: they are all places where people manage information. In this examination of office automation, an office will be regarded as any place where managerial, professional, and clerical workers are engaged primarily in handling business information.

An automated office system is 'a multifunction, integrated, computerbased system that allows many office activities to be performed in an electronic mode.' The word multifunction is very important. Some people think that automated office systems provide only one or two simple functions, such as word processing. If this were true, there would be no need for this section nor for the many books and thousands of articles written and numbers of seminars conducted on office automation. Rather, office automation does involve the wide range of functions that are discussed below.

OFFICE ACTIVITIES

In a typical office, there are three types of individuals performing three types of activities. **Secretaries** are usually given clerical tasks, which include typing, using the telephone, making photocopies, and filing and retrieving documents. **Managers** make decisions, plan business activities, organize the activities into specific tasks and work groups, hire staff to perform the tasks, and monitor the performance of the staff. **Professionals** are the experts in a given field, such as accounting, architecture, engineering, information systems, law, or medicine, etc. Much of their time is spent with technical details, solving specific problems that are assigned by managers.

These three groups obviously have different needs for work support, but they have some important things in common:

1. All communicate with others in written and oral form.

2. All deal with documents, or 'paperwork'.

3. All have desks or workstations of some sort.

4. All are conscious of calendars and must continually deal with scheduled meetings and deadlines.

These common areas form the nucleus of an office system. Computers are used to support all of these activities and to carry out the common functions.

Office automatiion uses integrated information systems that exist now and are possible and practical, as distinct from systems that are presently unattainable or impractical. The dividing line is reality. The 'office of the future' is the source of ideas that lead to progress. Office automation is the realization of those ideas.

Office automation is a concept, an approach to a new way of handling information. It is not a project with a defined point of completion, nor is it the installation of any single functional element. Rather, office automation is the linking of multiple components or elements in such a way that information, once entered, can be processed and channeled from point to point with a maximum of technological assistance and a minimum of human intervention.

Office automation, then, is not a turnkey product or service that can be purchased, predesigned and preassembled, and simply put in place. It is more than a new type of office system or new technologies or hybridized hardware. A range of available tools must be coordinated and tailored to the needs of a particular organization. If improperly selected and implemented, office automation degrades information systems, causes turmoil, and adds to expenses.

In the 1950s knowledge workers (people engaged primarily in processing information) began to use the computer as a tool for handling numbers. Identifiable, repetitious patterns involved in accounting, inventory control, and similar activities dealing with masses of numbers were systematized and programmed for computerized processing, relieving people from repetitious drudgery. Using an array of technology, including computers, office automation today does much the same for knowledge workers engaged in data, text, audio, and graphic information processing. All four modes of conveying information exist in most offices -- as computer input, typed reports, the telephone, and graphs, respectively. Yet none of these modes has been optimized for purposes of information management.

Basically, data processing forms half of the information management picture; office automation fills the other. A conventional data processing system puts data through multiple processing steps prior to arriving at a result. As processing occurs in a computer, the system recognizes specific circumstances and calls appropriate programs and subroutines into play to meet those needs.

In office automation, people are counterparts to data processing systems. As people process information, they recognize specific circumstances and call into play appropriate tools to meet those needs, ultimately arriving at a result. Data processing converts data (raw facts) into information; office automation assists people as they process (classify, select, and/or arrange) information and convert it to knowledge and action.

Office automation incorporates technology to serve rather than be served by people, for people are more valuable than equipment. Toward that end, system planners are incorporating human-factors engineering principles into the design of both hardware (equipment) and software (programs), resulting in so-called 'friendly' or 'user-friendly' systems.

Technologically, knowledge workers have been neglected. Table 22.1 lists the conventional tools with which workers manage information in offices and the dates of their invention; there has not been a major technological change in office tools since 1946. In some cases, old technology has been adapted to new uses. Except for data processing and photocopying, there has been little concentration on office systems technology. Now, however, technology is flooding the office environment, and with it has come a marked improvement in the design and implementation of tools for information management.

Table 22.1: Tools of the contemporary office with their dates of invention or discovery.

200 B.C.	Ink (Egypt)
A.D. 105	Paper (China)
1040	Movable type (China)
1335	Mechanical clock with dial
1565	Pencil (first written reference to)
1642	Calculator
1714	Typewriter
1809	Fountain pen
1823	Computer (mechanical)
1839	Microphotography

1843	Facsimile
1876	Telephone
1888	Ball-point pen
1899	Magnetic tape recording
.	.
.	.
.	.
1937	Xerography
1946	Computer (electronic)

Anyone who considers his or her office modern uses most or all of the tools listed in Table 22.1 to solve information problems. Yet some of these tools generate still more problems. In many offices, for example, people waste time standing in line waiting to use the photocopier. Locating 'convenience' copiers closer to users or providing copiers that operate that much higher speeds gives rise to other problems, for copying expands to fill the equipment capacity available. When monks laboured for days to copy a short document, no one would have suggested sending 'information copies' to a distribution list of say forty people. Today it is a common practice.

OLD AND NEW SYSTEMS PERSPECTIVE

Narrowly defined, a system is simply a methodical, organized procedure. Systems of this sort are essential to daily productivity. Conventional office systems work from a partial or fragmented approach addressing a small area of the total information landscape. They are oriented to a specific task or set of tasks, and solutions are formulated in terms of a specific user. Generally, if such systems reach beyond their own departments, they do so only within the vertical managerial chain to which the user belongs.

Office information adopts a broader point of view that takes into account the following principles:

1. Some information management functions are systematic or semisystematic.
2. Some information management functions and most data and information are common to numerous users.
3. Conventional systems are actually subsystems.
4. An entire organization (firm, association) is itself a system made up of many subsystems.
5. Ultimately, all organization systems are linked.

Some of the other aspects associated with office automation are:

1. Objective is to increase business effectiveness.
2. Impacts both strategic (what to do) and tactical (how to do it) levels.
3. Information communications is at the heart of all office automation developments.
4. Office automation spans the office spectrum from senior executive to support staff levels.
5. Simplicity and integration are the critical success factors of office automation.

Good automated office systems are modular and highly flexible. They give their users as much freedom of choice as possible. They also provide mobility. Users can carry portable communicating terminals with them wherever they go, so that even away from their offices they can, in seconds, access electronic files and locate specific documents according to subject, author, or date. Terminal users can rapidly communicate with a dozen people in the same building or on the opposite side of earth. One person can take part in ten meetings in different cities in one day without leaving his office.

Office automation has four indispensable components: philosophy, equipment (or technology), systems, and people. The most important component is people; it is they who convert information to knowledge. No brilliance of systems design, no level of capital outlay, no cleverly written report can compensate for the failure of system planners to provide easy-to-use, nonthreatening systems technology. An archaic malady of conventional data processing systems involves just such an omission. In the early years of data processing, computer memory was quite expensive. To limit memory use and conserve costs, designers and programmers encoded commands as concisely as possible, and terminal operators were (and still are) required to learn what amounts to a new language. Memorizing one or even several such enigmatic commands would be no problem, but operators continue to be faced with user handbooks filled with page after page of them.

Today labour is expensive whereas computers are becoming relatively inexpensive. With more computer capacity available, programs can be written to permit the use of natural-language commands, which are much easier to remember and still provide the same system response. Good office automation systems, both computerized and non-computerized, are 'friendly', or approachable.

Even friendly automated office systems occasionally malfunction or, in computer parlance, 'go down.' In a conventional office, if a pen runs out of ink the user can get a new one from a desk drawer or supply cabinet. In an automatted office the user is not always able to solve a problem without a technician. This drawback, however, is being addressed. For example, one computer manufacturer provides three plug-in electronic boards. If the device which they are used fails, the user simply replaces one board at a time until the machine resumes operation, usually within five minutes. The faulty parts are then replaced by the manufacturer.

OFFICE SYSTEM ELEMENTS

Office automation has matured as a concept. Integrated office automation systems have been operational for many years and certain patterns have emerged over time. Because there are functions basic to virtually all knowledge workers, the same functional elements tend to recur in the system designs of office automation planners. These elements, embracing the four information conveyance modes of data, text, audio, and graphics, are:

Word management / Processing
Spreadsheet
Database

4.   Calendar
5.   Electronic Notepad
6.   Phone Directory
7.   Forms Generator
8.   Menu Utility
9.   Calculator
10. Electronic mail systems
11. Electronic filing
12. Micrographics
13. Teleconferencing
14. Integrated office automation systems

Electronic Mail

- Send notes and documents to various users automatically
- User-friendly menus make message creation and delivery simple
- Multiple editor capability
- Multiple mail distribution lists can be created and maintained
- Multiple in-baskets

Word Processing

- Increased office productivity resulting in improved secretarial support for all word originators (including executives)
- Higher quality output resulting from advanced equipment
- Improved human resource utilization with better control and supervision of secretarial personnel through a word processing centre
- Friendly user-interface
- User-definable skill levels
- Sophistication of text composition with the simplicity of word processing
- Adjustable windowing capability
- Records processing

Calendar

- Electronic calendar/scheduler
- Accommodates single users, departments, companies
- Appointments and memos can be added, moved, copied, modified or simply displayed
- Monthly, weekly, daily display
- Alarms and reminders can automatically notify users of important appointments and memos

- Privacy passwords ensure confidentiality

Electronic Notepad

- Writing program for collecting, indexing and retrieving any type of information using an index-card editor format
- Sort and retrieve the information on the card from the database -- instead of searching your desk

Phone Directory

- Create a database of names, addresses, and phone numbers
- Alphabetical, city or category wise

Menu Utility

- Multi-level menu utility for generating and maintaining menus
- Customize your menus without changing source code
- Tie together unrelated programs and subroutines

Calculator

- Full-functionofficecalculator complete withmany memory storage locations and an on-screen 'tape'
- Calcultor functions are displayed on the screen at all times

Forms Generator

- Interactive screen builder, forms manager, and database builder
- Utilize for straight forms design or as a data collection vehicle for other programs such as database or spreadsheets
- Tie together information from other programs using one form

Database

- Powerful, flexible database system with virtually unlimited applications
- Manipulate and access files quickly and easily
- Business-environment oriented

Spreadsheet

- The tool for managerial modeling
- Powerful, flexible modeling of 'what-if' type of business scenarios
- Graphics
- User-friendly design, unlimited applications

COMMON OFFICE SYSTEM FUNCTIONS

The common functions performed by an automated office are document processing, electronic mail, executive support, and MIS interface.

1. **Document processing** involves the functions of word processing, the use of spelling dictionaries, and electronic filing of documents. The documents processed by a typical office include letters, forms, memos, contracts, and descriptions of products, services, and procedures. In addition to the basic documenting functions, some advanced document processing systems check grammar automatically, compile indexes, and keep track of footnotes.

2. **Electronic mail** allows messages to be sent to others. Rather than call or send a short memo, an executive can use the computer to place an electronic message into another's mailbox. Recipients may read, save, destroy, or forward the message. Electronic mail is distinguished from document processing by the length of the average documents and their time frame--electronic mail documents are usually shorter and often require immediate action.

3. **Executive support** is less common than either word processing or electronic mail. It provides a number of features that executives can use, such as computerized calendars and directories, tickler files, and calculators. An executive can use the computerized calendar to schedule a meeting of a specified group of people, and the computerized directories allow companies to update their companywide telephone book continually and give executives access to this information. Tickler files help executives keep list of what needs to be done in order of priority. Calculators allow users to do mathematical manipulations. Many computer systems allow for executive support functions to run in the "background" while the executive is using the terminal for another task. For example, while examining a spreadsheet describing the latest business plan, an executive receives a telephone call that requires consulting next month's appointment calendar. The executive can interrupt the spreadsheet program, consult the appointment calendar (and possibly make changes in it), and then return to the spreadsheet analysis.

4. The **MIS interface** gives executives access to databases and database management systems, private programs, modeling programs, or other systems. It allows executives to share data and work with the same models. Professionals can also use an MIS interface. They can use it to write their own programs or to connect to other systems for special functions. For example, a legal staff member may use it to search for case decisions to use as precedents in court. An architect may use it to gain access to programs used to predict stress limits of building materials. A staff medical doctor may use it to search for possible interactions between prescription drugs and chemicals used in a manufacturing plant.

While these are the main functions of an automated office system, some systems can perform even more tasks. One task is *voice mail storage and forwarding,* which allow people either inside or outside the firm to use the computer system. If someone calls manager when he is not in, the call is handled by an answering machine that tra islates the caller's voice into digital form. After the manager returns to the office, he can play back the messages and forward them to others.

Another task is *facsimile document transmission,* which sends an exact copy of an original document virtually anywhere at a rate of less than 4 minutes per page. It allows users to send not only text but also other images such as pictures, signatures, and handwritten annotations to documents.

Another task involves *micrographics,* a process that sharply reduces the amount of space needed to store paper documents by photographing them and producing microfilm of them.

Since technology is changing so rapidly and since there is such variety in the functions performed by any particular automated office system, we will organize the tasks in a model (see Figure 22.1). The model shows that there are three major types of activity in the system: data processing, word processing, and communication.

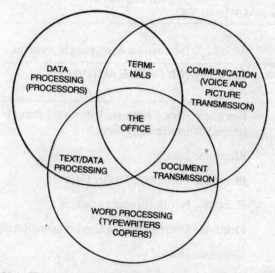

Fig. 22.1 : The three types of activities in an automated office system

Data processing includes the processing power to perform calculations and to store, retrieve, and update data. Word processing combine to integrate text and data; data processing and communication combine when terminals are used; and word processing and communication combine for the transmission of documents. All three types of activity intersect in the automated office.

Tables 22.2 to 22.6 depicts the differences in methods or technologies used for performing normal office operations (- creation, storage, processing, receipt, editing, reproduction and dissemination of information) in conventional offices and electronic offices in the Electronic Message Systems, Information Management Systems and Document Preparation Systems.

Table 22.2: Electronic Message Systems

CONVENTIONAL ACTIVITY	ELECTRONIC OFFICE ACTIVITY
Telephone	Telephone – Voice store and forward – Sophisticated digital exchanges with numerous advanced features (group hunting, call redirect, etc.)
Telex	Telex / Teletex
Telegram	Teletex, Facsimile
Internal Mail	Communicating Word Processors, Computer-based Electronic Mail
Post Office Mail	Teletext Message Services, Private Viewdata Systems, Telepost, Tel
Meetings	Tele Conferencing (Contravision, audio conferencing, Computer conferencing)

Table 22.3: Information Management Systems

CONVENTIONAL ACTIVITY	ELECTRONIC OFFICE ACTIVITY
Filing Cabinets	Electronic Files, Electronic Indexes for Paper Files, Videodisks, Image Scanner/Image Printer
Card Indexes	Electronic Lists
Check Lists	Electronic Checklists, Tickler Files
In-Trays	Electronic Notification and Stacking
Out-Trays	Electronic Distribution and Confirmation Receipt
Diary	Electronic Diary
Planning Boards	Electronic Planning Systems
Written and Tele-phone Enquiries, Catalogues, Time Tables	Viewdata, Teletext, Corporate Databases
The Media, Journals, Abstracts	Access to On-Line Public Information Databases
Microfilm	Access to centrally held Microfilm Libraries
Procedure Manuals	Within - System Aids

Table 22.4 : Office Information Processing Functions

Processing Functions	Office Info	
	Traditional Office	Automated Office
Capture	longhand	shorthand
	shorthand	machine dictation
	keyboarding	
Input	handwritten	typing
	typing	keyboarding
	optical character	
	recognition	
	voice recognition	
Processing	typing	word processing
	calculator	data processing
Output	hardcopy	terminal display
	photocopy	intelligent copier
	typeset copy	desktop publishing
	microfilm	
Storage	paper files	microfilm
	databases on	magnetic media
Communications	mail	telephone
	interoffice mail	telex
	telephone	facsimile
	electronic mail	
	satellite	

Table 22.5 : Some management tools from information systems

TELEPHONE	☐ Voice messaging
	☐ Electronic mail
INFORMATION ACCESS	☐ On line information services
	☐ Corporate and departmental filese
	☐ Personal files
	☐ Laser disk records
	☐ Expert systems

WRITING	☐	*Voice entry*
	☐	*Word processing software*
	☐	*Outliners*
	☐	*Preeentation options (desktop publishing, graphics)*
PROOF READING	☐	*Automatic check on calculations*
	☐	*Voice annotation for comments*
	☐	*Automatic spelling check*
TRAVEL	☐	*Conferencing*
	☐	*Telecommunication*
	☐	*Laser disk records of meetings and seminars*
SCHEDULED MEETINGS	☐	*Conferencing*
	☐	*Presentation options (35 mm graphics, OHP foils, interactive laser desk)*
	☐	*On-line records of meetings*
	☐	*Laser disk records*
	☐	*Appointments diaries with reminders*
UNSCHEDULED MEETINGS	☐	*Ad hoc contact via electronec mail or conferencing*
	☐	*Team appointments diaries*
READING	☐	*Elelctronic mail*
	☐	*Laser disk records*
	☐	*On-line records*
	☐	*Sort/seleclt facilities*
CALCULATING	☐	*Spreadsheets and financial modelling*
	☐	*Data from existing internal and external sources*
	☐	*Presentations options (graphics, inclusion in wordprocessed and/or desktop-published reports)*
INCOMING MAIL	☐	*Electronic mail*
	☐	*Voice messaging*
	☐	*Conferencing*
	☐	*Forward with comments appended*
OUTGOING MAIL	☐	*Electronic mail*
	☐	*Voice messaging*
	☐	*Conferencing*
	☐	*Distribution lists and artomatic routing*
THINKING	☐	*Outliners*
	☐	*'What if' calculations*
	☐	*Expert systems*

Table 22.6: Document Preparation Systems

CONVENTIONAL ACTIVITY	ELECTRONIC OFFICE ACTIVITY
Shorthand	Dictation to personal recorder or to central recording system over Telephone
Longhand	Keyboarding, Voice Recognition
Typing	Word Processing
– Cut and Paste	Text Manipulation / Windowing
– Error Correction Fluid	Word Processing Editing
– Total Retype	Word Processing Replace
Carbon Copies	Photocopy, Disk Storage
Photocopy	Intelligent Copier, Image Scanner/Image Printer
Typesetting	In-House Photocomposition, Desk TopPublishing Services System
Slide Preparation	Personal Computer Based Slidemaker

BUILDING AN AUTOMATED OFFICE

1. Equipment Needed

As we all know, an office can now be viewed as an 'Information Processing Factory' or as a 'Personal Productivity Centre'. Various functions carried out in an office can be categorised into Data Processing, Voice Processing, Word Processing, Image Processing, Communicating,etc. With the advent of rapid industrialisation, geographical expansion and need for quick interaction of business operations, the information processing needs of the offices have incresed tremendously. It has, thus, become essential to introduce automation in the office to meet this challenge. The office automation equipment will manage the information in its various forms -- text, data, voice, image through automation machines. Full office automation will ultimately result in a paperless office.

In an office, from manager to file clerk, all employees have to perform a number of functions, varying from making calls to preparing and transmitting them. For each office function, there is a specialised machine that does a particular job. These machines have evolved as and when the needs were felt. These machines consist of:

- Plain old Telephones, dial or push button type,

- Telex machines,

- Facsimile machines,

- a PABX which may be electromechanical.

The workstations consisting of either of these machines or all the machines may be wired up directly to a central point or connected to the Telex or PSTN networks via a dial up connection or via a leased circuit. These workstations are not at present wired up to each other. Such comunications infrastructure is becoming inadequate to support the requirements of the electronic office. In future more information, of various types, will be held in the electronic form and moved about electronically than at present. The needs of the present and future office are:

– Integration of all the tools of office automation i.e. to have a workstation to do all the jobs.

– Inter-connection of the workstations and host computers through comunication networks at office, regional and at head quarter level.

This will require integration of Voice Processing, Data Processing, Image Processing, with Communication technology to achieve full office automation.

A lot more equipment is involved in an automated office than simply a user and a terminal. An automated office is formed by a web of users, workstations, printers, computers, other equipment, the communication equipment needed to tie them all together, and the software required to perform the various office tasks previously described. Figure 22.2 shows the equipments used in a typical automated office.

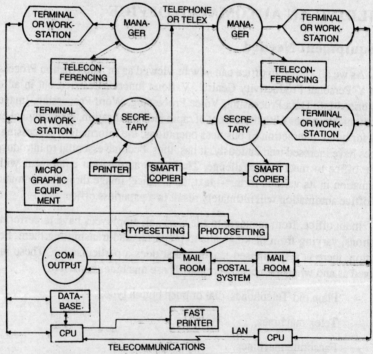

Fig. 22.2 : Equipment in one type of automated office

When an automated office is being built, the designer can choose from a number of options. He can choose different network configurations, main processor, peripheral devices, software packages, and ways of sharing the equipment. Having to choose among all of the options is actually one of the biggest problems in setting up an automated office.

Some of the hardware needed in a typical office automation system are:

Personal computers - PCs, XTs, ATs, Workstations
Printers - letter quality, dot matrix, Laser, Line
Electronic typewriters
Plotters
Digitizer
PABX machine
Telex machine - PC-Telex
FAX machine - PC-FAX
LANs
Optical scanners
Copiers - intelligent
Micrographic equipment
Desk top publishing system with mouse

Every modern office of next decade will require for each executive or file clerk, a general purpose workstation which will be able to process, store and forward any audio, written, mathematical or graphical message. The desirable features of such a workstation are as under,

- Flexibility/configurability
  The workstation should be flexible in terms of software compatibility/configurability to meet the requirements of different categories of users.

- Specialisation
  The workstation should meet the individual but specialised needs with the use of dedicated software/hardware.

- Access
  It should have an interface for access to information system.

- Integration
  There shold be standardisation of software, transmission protocols and data system models to ensure integration and flexibility features of a workstation.

These features are not as utopian as they look. The systems are now available which provide users with workstations which simultaneously handle voice, data and video text.

2. Strategies for Designing an Automated Office

Designers can choose from five major strategies when building an automated office.

1. The *horizontal approach* involves placing the ability to perform one function into the hands of all users in the entire organization. For example, all users may be given word processing or electronic mail.

2.   The *vertical approach* is the opposite strategy. It places the full range of functions in
       one department or group. For example, the marketing department may be given an
       automated office system that allows not only word processing and electronic mail but
       also executive support and an MIS interface.

3.   The *matrix approach* gives one or two functions to everyone in the organization and
       then gives additional tools to selected departments if they are needed. For example,
       everyone may be given electronic mail, but some people may also receive word
       processing and an MIS interface.

4.   The *shotgun approach* involves placing random functions in random departments
       without much overall coordination. For example, the different departments in an
       organization may choose their own functions without consulting each other or a
       company system designer.

5.   Finally, the *chorus line approach* places selected functions in selected departments as
       needed, but as part of a master plan. The functions are added as needed in the order set
       out in the plan. This is perhaps the best approach, since it is based on careful planning.

Having so many options does not make the job of the designer easy. There are so many
options and so much incompatibility between vendors' products that the whole area is very
confusing. In fact, even companies who buy only IBM products are finding incompatibilities
between various pieces of equipment they purchase. Further more, options keep changing.
Each week there are announcements of new hardware, which often presents new, better, and
even less expensive options for automated office design.

So much rapid change and so many options make it very difficult to develop general
software for office automation. Programmers must guess which types of systems to support
far in advance of writing the software. And when a new piece of equipment is connected to
the system, there is the risk that it will not work properly with the software. Further, one
single software package is often asked to support many different types of work.

In addition to these technical problems, there are other problems that managers are
beginning to identify and solve. Here are four main lessons that have been learned:

1.   A piecemeal approach that has an automated office system using separate functions
       in an office without integrating them will not work. Systems developed this way are
       often incompatible or weak.

2.   lans for automated office systems have often been too grand or too limited. Some
       systems are too complex, and others remove critical functions.

3.   Technology has been oversold, so there is an expectation that the computer can have
       greater effects than it really does. At the same time, many human considerations are
       ignored. Having a realistic view of what an automated office system can do leads to
       the building of an effective one.

4.   Finally, the automated office system must apply to the entire company, not only to
       separate departments. The result otherwise might be incompatibility in how the
       company's departments are run, in addition to a weak system.

Designers who keep these lessons in mind when building an automated office system create a system that can help companies carry out their functions quickly and more efficiently. And this is a main goal of office automation.

BENEFITS

The following list shows some of the benefits that businesses and knowledge workers can derive from the proper implementation of office automation technology.

1. Optimize staffing
    Enhance human capabilities
    Conserve human resources
    Compensate for manpower shortages
    Minimize drudgery

2. Increase productivity
    Improve accuracy
    Speed up throughput
    Speed up turnaround

3. Gain competitive edge
    Improve timeliness of information
    Improve decision making
    Conserve natural resources

4. Increase scope of control
    Enhance individual and organizational flexibility
    Make information portable

5. Decrease expenses
    Reduce capital investment in structures
    Reduce or cap off payroll costs

Office automation puts to work the almost daily breakthroughs in communications technology to promote the rapid and efficient transfer of information in the service of human knowledge. Intelligent selection and effective use of the new communications tools requires understanding the important issues that confront modern business, the best way to introduce the new tools to enhance the operation of a business, and the nomenclature and apparatus of communications technology.

COMMUNICATION INFRASTRUCTURE TO SUPPORT OA ACTIVITIES

There are several key issues involved in deciding the type of communications network but before deciding the type of network, it will be worthwhile to examine the desired features of such a network:

  —   the network should be transparent to the users,

-   should be extremely reliable,

-   should be able to carry information from any source voice, data, video text,

-   it should support local area network,

-   it should support all components of OA system,

-    it should have sufficient capacity to support data throughput requirements,

-   Data access should be consistent throughout the network,

-   it should support various protocols for accesses as required.

There are two key issues. First, should public or private networks or both be used? The choice between using public or private networks is largely determined by costs and these depend upon tariffs and the nature and volume of an organisation's external traffic. Existing networks in India are Telex and PSTN. An organisation can construct a private network, with leased circuits for intra- organisation traffic and can provide added value by building intelligence into the network at local switching centres. However, many organisations would prefer the network provided by someone else i.e. public network. The public network will be adequate for transmission of text, voice, data and facsimile between sites and for quite some time, the users will find it adequate for almost all of their transmission requirements. Only for full video teleconferencing between sites require high speed transmission lines than are currently available or likely to be available in future on any public network. For this desirability of using leased circuits on the PSTN will have to be investigated.

The second issue is the internal communications architecture within a site. There are two approaches. One is to have a Local Area Network (LAN) and another is to have a PABX-controlled network. Perhaps a hybrid approach can form the basis for an internal communications architecture to meet an organisation's needs over the next five or ten years.

LOCAL AREA NETWORKING

Local area networking can offer an efficient and cost-effective way of interconnecting within a site the components of the electronic office. Typically a LAN is a circuit which threads its way through an office or factory complex. The circuit may be formed from copper wires coaxial cable or optical fibres -- the latter medium will ultimately become the most popular choice. Sockets are provided at convenient places such as at every person's desk or place of work so that appropriate workstations can be plugged into the LAN as necessary. If everybody is ultimately going to be provided with a workstation, there can be significant cost advantages in using LAN as compared with the conventional approach of a network of wires radiating out from a central point. In an existing office or factory complex, already wired up, the alterations for installing a LAN may be very costly and temporarily inconvenient. In new offices or factories the provision of a LAN should certainly be considered. Speeds in excess of 10 Mbit/s can be achieved, which is ideal for all OA applications. Different approaches have been used for providing LAN, examples are polynet based on four-wire twisted-pair copper telephone cables, Ethernet developed by Xerox, DEC and Intel of US. There are now a number of LANs available using different techniques. Figure 22.3 ilustrates how a LAN can interconnect intra-site devices including a mainframe computer, with a gateway through a PABX to external services, networks and devices.

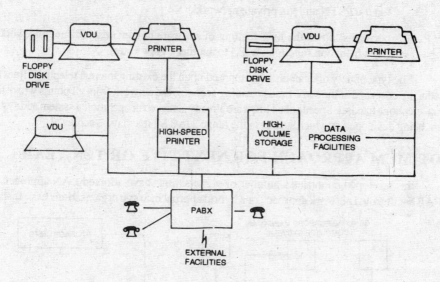

Fig. 22.3 : Local area network architecture

A PABX CONTROLLED NETWORK

A PABX controlled approach is shown in Figure 22.4. In this configuration a PABX performs the following functions:

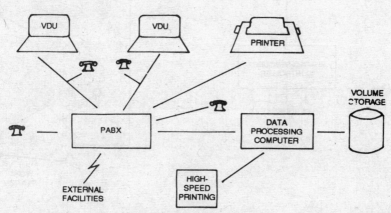

Fig. 22.4 : PABX-controlled network

- acts as a message switch controlling the routing of data and text messages from workstations using the printing and storage facilities of the data processing computer.

- provide sphisticated facilities,

- acts as a concentrators to enable local workstations to access external facilities via the PSTN and via private networks.

- performs 'down the line' loading of software to convert multifunction workstations from one function (W.P.) to another (View Data).

The type of network can be superimposed upon the existing internal telephone lines thus reducing costs and at the same time providing access to the network from all points where there is a telephone handset. Speeds of 64 kBps are already achieved in operational system and system are being developed in which speeds in the range 2 to 8 Mbit/s may be achieved.

OTIMUM APPROACH FOR NEXT FIVE OR TEN YEARS

In developed countries a number of organisations have adopted LAN approach or PABX-controled network approach or a hybrid approach. Some organisations have installe

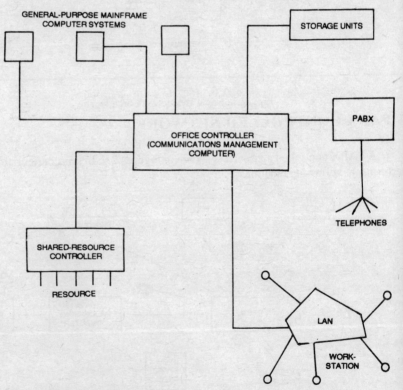

Fig. 22.5 : Communications architecture for the electronic office

or are planning to install coaxial cables. Figure 22.5, illustrates a hybrid approach in which workstations are attached to a LAN which is itself attached to an office controller (communications management computer). In such a hybrid arrangement the following may be connected through the office controller:

- general purpose mainframe computers
  (may be supplied from different vendors).

- share resource controller, controlling resources such as,
  - facsimile machine
  - a graph plotting machine
  - a graphic printer, reader
  - an intelligent photocopying machine
  - an image scanner (high resolution)
  - an image printer (high resolution)
  - magnetic disk and tape storage
  - video disk and tape storage

- A local area network, to which will be attached,
  - word processors
  - data processing terminals
  - multi function workstations

- A PABX to which are attached
  - Telephones
  - PSTN
  - Storage units

- The modern office controller will include,
  - Directoriesgiving addresses and numbers of people and workstations
  - media transformation
  - packet store and forward
  - message switching
  - Information bank containing voice, text and data
  - voice command recognition
  - audio response

Large number of organisations are planning their communication infrastructure -- as shown in Figure 22.6 and 22.7 having short term and long term plans. The organisation shown in Figure 22.6 had kept two local features viz., inhouse view data and archived data.

In the long term infrastructure, message switch controller is shown linked to a modern PABX. The PABX is of course attached to the PSTN and all internal telephones are attached to it.

To establish the OA system with the above features, the long term goal of telecommunication organisation is to evolve Integrated Services Digital Network (ISDN) which

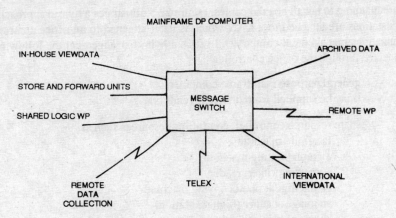

Fig. 22.6 : Communications infrastructure—short-term plan

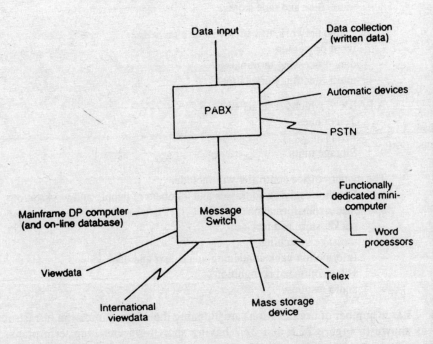

Fig. 22.7 : Communications Infrastructure—long-term Plan

will integrate telephone, data text and video. For the time being the requirements can met with Digital telecommunication network with voice and data integration and implementation requires:

– digital transmission and switching with synchronisation protocols;

– digital link up to the subscribers premises.

As a starting point, digital PABX'S offering a range of facilities and connectability to present and future terminals are available now. Packet switched network services are also being available.

Host Computer

Of all the infrastructure requirements of office automation, this is perhaps most easily understood. The host computer should be such that if additional computatinal power is needed, it can be hooked in the network without any change in software user interface. Also the host must unite all software packages and provide sharable data base for all users of the network.

Standardisation

Integration of the services, network and data processing equipment can be done only they are compatible and compatability can be achieved solely by standardisation in terms Input/Output (I/O) interconnections, machine to machine and man to machine interface c. Standardisation will not only ensure integration but also quality of performance, reduced st, reduced variety of equipment, better maintenance facilities and reduced training and eration costs.

Telecommunication sector was first to realise the need and importance of Internatinal standardisation. International Telecom Union (ITU), International Standardisation Organisation (ISO), International Electro Technical Commission (IEC) are some of the ganisations that have been engaged in evolving standartds in Telecommunication and er related fields for last many years. A full fledged technical committee of ISO-ISO/TC- . Information Processing Systems, has been formulating standards related to information cessing systems for both hardware and software aspects. For the equipment, IEC has med Information Technology Equipment Committee IEC/TC 83 for identifying integra- needs and uses of all Information Technology standards in all disciplines.

CONCLUSION

To make full office automation a reality, unstinted and coordinated efforts of the erts in the fields of data processing networks and office equipment are essential. ecommunication Organisation, in particular, has to play a key role in co-ordination, dardisation and tarrification. In the next decade, we will see sinking boundries between rmation transmission, information processing and information handling and infrastruc- required to achieve this exits to-day.

23

ELECTRONIC MAIL

INTRODUCTION

Electronic mail (often abbreviated to 'e-mail') is the transmission of textual material from one place to another using electronic means for capture, transmission and delivery of information. That information need never assume paper form.

An electronic mail system is a method of electronically sending messages, mail, or documents. It is also known as electronic delivery system or electronic document distribution/communication. The electronic mail seeks to replace the postal mail, telephone conversation and face to face meetings. This has received impetus because of the inadequacy of existing services and the associated high costs. Already most of the offices, businesses are using private courier services and 'speed post', courier services run by Indian Postal Authorities, to deliver letters, reports, samples etc., because of the limitation of the ordinary postal services. But these are expensive. As it is, the cost of ordinary mail has been found to have gone up many folds. The telephone system in India is known to be a very poor communication system. The exchanges are old and faulty, the communication links are extremely bad. Efforts are underway on the part of the government to upgrade the telecommunication system. However, even in the western countries where the communication system is excellent, telephone has posed a problem with respect to achieving meaningful inter-office and intra-office communication due to a number of reasons.

Studies have shown that only 25-30% of the calls go through on the first attempt. Thus an average of four calls are required to complete one. The person being called may not be in office, his number may be busy, or he may be in a meeting and does not want to be interrupted, or the line is lost. Add the time zone problems to this. An office in New York trying to contact Tokyo, finds that there is no time at all during the working hours. Finally there is no authentic record left after the call is over, since it is a verbal conversation. Many businesses and offices insist on records; this is more so in India. An alternative to creating records is to add voice recording system with the telephone. One more disadvantage of telephone calls is that these tend to be long, because of social conventions involving the exchange of pleasantries. It has been estimated that typical 3-5 minute conversation contains much less than 10% of office information. Lastly, the face to face meetings are becoming very expensive since the transportation costs are increasing day by day, as also the travel allowances of the executives and their hotel expenses. These have all encouraged the development of new communication techniques such as the electronic mail.

As such, electronic mail services work rather like the Post Office -- except that messages are stored electronically in a central computer. When you dial up the service, you are told if there are any messages waiting for you: and you get the option of reading them or waiting for a while. You can send messages to other subscribers -- with copies, if required -- by typing them directly or by loading previously prepared work.

WHAT IS ELECTRONIC MAIL?

The term 'electronic mail' could literally apply to any electronic transfer, including simple transmissions between operator- attended workstations like the Telex service. In practice, e-mail more usually refers to a service that includes the following facilities:

- 'Store-and-forward'. Messages are held until they are requested by the recipient. Direct person-to-person contact is not required, and the service can be used by either party at whatever time and on whatever day suits them.

- Copies can be sent automatically to names on a distribution list, including 'blind' copies (where the principal recipient is not notified that others have received the message).

- Advise delivery. The sender can be told (by a confirming message to his or her mailbox) when the recipient has read the message. An immediate reply can also be demanded.

- Off-line working. Text can be prepared in advance of transmission, and incoming messages can be saved for later consideration or for use within word-processed documents.

- 'Gateways'. Most electronic mail services include access to other facilities. They include the Telex system, on-line information services, and electronic typesetting bureaux which accept e-mailed text and return phototypeset masters.

- 'Closed user groups'. These are areas of the e-mail service with restricted access. In some cases they are available to anyone who pays an additional fee; usually they will include extra gateways and more services. Other closed user groups (CUGS) will be specific to members of a particular profession -- Telecom Gold hosts CUGS for solicitors and accountants, for instance; and there are also CUGS for customers of individual companies (handy for disseminating and sharing information or making requests) and user groups for particular computer products.

Electronic mail system provides for information input, transmission and output. An intra-office system located in the same building may use LAN for transmission. An inter-office electronic mail system within a city or connecting offices, located in different cities may use WANs. The mail or messages may be entered using a PC terminal, workstation, OCR reader or even a facsimile scanner. The output may be on a similar equipment or directed to a computer system which may read, file or otherwise take necessary action on the mail.

In addition to these basic functions of electronic delivery systems, most systems provide features related to other aspects of office work. These features include:

- composing messages

- text editing

- message filing and retrieval

- authentication of message authorship

- broadcasting and distribution of messages as per

- specified addresses

- content processing of messages

- message switching

- accounting and billing

- security.

The software is user friendly and helps the user in easily preparing and distributing mail with his name, date and time stamped to the message. The receiver is notified of the pending mail as soon as he logs in and mail is displayed on his terminal with sender's name, date and time of origination of the message. Registered message or urgent mail is automatically acknowledged to the sender. A permanent searchable stored record of received messages can be maintained. The mail system can also provide for addition or deletion of messages and maintaining of on-line files into which he can copy incoming mail for future searches on sender's name, date and subject.

Mail distributed electronically can be distinguished arbitrarily as messages, mail or documents. Messages are generally brief, urgent exchanges between two or more people, which may be discarded readily by the recipient after viewing on his terminal. Mail is likely to contain more information in a format such as a letter, memo, graph etc. It may need to be filed and may be addressed to more than one recipient. Documents, on the other hand, have much more information than mail and are prepared by more than one person, taking relatively longer time. These are considered important from the viewpoint of decision making.

If the documents have already been prepared using word processors, or are created using the already stored digitized images, graphics and the like, these can be assembled without much difficulty and mailed using the electronic delivery system. One may retrieve company forms from computer system, intelligent copiers/printers, archival data from optical disk systems or from other devices. This obviates the need for keeping paper documents or mailing them by postal mail. One may view the received mail message or document on one's terminal without printing the same and store it for future reference. The recipient can view them at his own convenience and send replies to originators. It is because of these reasons that electronic mail holds the potential of greatest advances in productivity and cost savings in the office.

Many e-mail services offer some or all of these:

–   Radiopaging. Your pager will bleep when an urgent message is received in your mailbox. Or you can bleep someone by sending a message to the service's radiopaging mailbox.

–   Telemessages. This replacement for the old-style telegram can be sent from some e-mail services rather than by you calling the Post Office yourself. Delivery the next working day (including Saturdays, usually) is guaranteed for messages received by a set time (which can be as late as 10pm). The Telemessage service can include 'special occasion' formats for birthdays, anniversaries and the like; the delivery can also include a special reply-envelope to encourage an immediate reply.

–   Message translation. Messages sent or received can be translated by the e-mail service into the recipient's native tongue.

–   Courier services. A message placed by you on the e-mail service can be copied and delivered by hand or mailed.

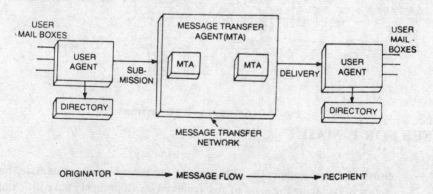

Fig. 23.1 : Functions in a simple electronic mail system

The basic functions involved in an E-Mail system are the message creation, message transfer and post delivery processing. These are provided by the User Agent (UA) and a Message Transfer Agent (MTA). Figure 23.1 indicates a simple block diagram of the technique used in the above E-mail system. Thus, an E-mail system is actually a message handling system. The user agent is responsible for providing the text editing and proper presentation services to the end user. It provides for other activities such as user-friendly interaction (for example, selective viewing on the screen), security priority provision, delivery notification and distribution subsets. The message transfer agent is oriented towards the actual routing of the electronic move. It is responsible primarily for the store-and-forward path, channel security and the actual routing through the communication media. Several MTAs taken together form the message transfer system (MTS).

The E-Mail market can be split into two distinct categories: traditional mainframe/mini host-based systems incorporating E-Mail, and local-area-network-based systems accessed from PCs. There are about 10 million E-Mail connections worldwide, of which four million are LAN-based. A LAN is a local area network communication system that interconnects computers, other electronic equipment and terminals in an office building, a factory or a university. Data, messages and information are transmitted through the network between computers systems (see Figure 23.2).

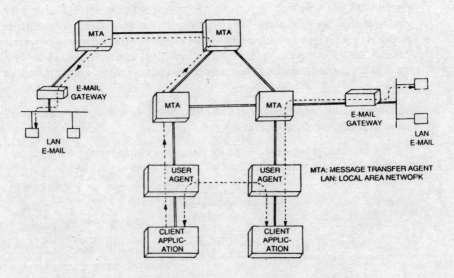

Fig. 23.2 : Set-up of an E-Mail system

USES FOR E-MAIL

—   Business correspondence. This may be the most obvious candidate, but in terms of replacing the mass of post received it will probably have little impact in the immediate future. Crucially, most offices do not yet have compatible text distribution systems; subscribers to different services cannot send messages to each other. The lack of formatting means that e-mail is generally unsuitable for documents where appearance is relevant for comprehension or corporate image.

- Memos. Instead, electronic mail is typically used for time-critical data or for brief memo-style messages: e-mail is tending to replace the telephone.

- Document capture. In cases where content is more important than appearance, incoming text can be saved on disk for subsequent editing and formatting. Internal reports can be circulated and the sender notified of receipt; where a document is being produced on word processors, e-mail can usefully distribute drafts for comment or amendment; a number of newspapers and other publications accept articles via e-mail rather than on paper; gateways to on-line information services can be used to 'capture' information for subsequent use.

ADVANTAGES

- Messages can be sent at whatever time of day suits the user (including times that take advantage of reduced charges). They can also be prepared in advance for subsequent despatch at convenient times.

- Messages will be in the recipient's mailbox within minutes.

- No need to speak to the recipient in person.

- Delivery of messages can be confirmed -- the mailbox principle puts the onus on to the receiver rather than the sender.

- Messages can be marked as 'urgent'.

- A reply can usually be demanded.

- Copies can be sent automatically to everyone on a distribution list appended or previously defined.

- Messages can be read at the user's convenience. Access to the mailbox is available day or night; incoming mail can be stored locally for consideration later.

- Messages do not have to be read in full immediately -- only the sender's name, date and subject need be displayed, allowing the option of reading now or later.

- Incoming messages can be saved (locally on disk, or in a file area of the e-mail service) for subsequent word processing treatment -- for instance, to incorporate into a document.

- Electronic mail reduces the volume of paper that is to be processed.

- Telex services can be provided as part of the electronic mail facility. This removes the need (and the cost) for a dedicated Telex terminal, and it saves most of the ancillary Telex charges.

- On-line information services may also be available.

–   Messages are generally more terse and to the point. Connect time charges, absence of formatting and the fact that the user probably has to handle the e-mail task himself all help minimize the number of characters per message.

DRAWBACKS

–   Recipients must also be an electronic mail user -- and they must subscribe to the same service as the sender, for as yet there is no inter-service communication between e-mail suppliers (but feasible in the future with X400; and availability of Telex improves the range of contacts).

–   Charges can be complicated. It may be difficult to get an indication of actual costs incurred before the bill arrives, and then it can be difficult to check the bill.

–   Only text can be sent. It is normally difficult to transfer graphics files, spreadsheets and other non-text formats.

–   Text formatting is restricted to the basic punctuation and alphanumeric characters.

–   Though illegal on most services, there is occasional use of junk mail. Apart from the time and irritation this involves, there may be charges for unread mail accumulating in a mailbox.

–   Until a mailbox is checked, there is no way of knowing that a message has arrived (unless there is an additional software facility for notifying receipt). As well as a computer, the user must have access to a modem and a phone line.

–   Telephone links vary in quality. Messages may pick up interference and arrive garbled (or worse, with slight corruption that alters the sense); a lower data rate might have to be used, which can make e-mailing costly and irritatingly slow (interference is more likely at higher speeds); and sometimes it may be impossible to make the connection to the e-mail service in the first place because the line is busy or because the modem cannot detect a weak 'carrier tone' sent from the service to indicate connection (these are less likely now that modernization is improving the number and quality of lines).

Communication services in general go for the lowest-common- denominator approach, catering for the simplest possible type of terminal and of transmission. In the case of electronic mail, this is reflected in the type of documents that may be sent and their content.

With an internal service, the likely range of capabilities and requirements will be known and the facilities provided by e-mail will be more extensive. Public services have to cater for the widest possible range of users, which means they have to offer the simplest types of transmission only. In practice this will mean that only text can be sent -- spreadsheets, for instance, cannot normally be e- mailed without first having been transformed into a text-like form. The range of characters will be limited to the basic punctuation and alphanumeric symbols, so not all the keys on your keyboard will produce a sendable character (even tabbing to indent text may not be sent), and few of the formatting functions of a word processor or other package will be acceptable (so some care must be taken to ensure that such controls are removed from a word-processed document before transmission).

What actually appears on your screen may also differ from what the electronic mail service can send. While you may appear to have a neatly laid-out document for transmission, the formatting could well be ignored during the e-mailing.

CHARGES

Charges for electronic mail can be complicated. The overall cost may include some or all of these components:

- One-time registration fee

- Annual or quarterly subscription charge

- 'Connect time' (how long you spend in communication with the mail service)

- Character charge (number of characters sent and, just possibly number of characters received)

- Storage (unread and/or undeleted messages in your mailbox)

- Fees for additional services like Telex

- Telephone bill (PSTN or PSS) for external connections.

USING ELECTRONIC MAIL

The electronic mail systems are easy to operate. The computer based message systems use simple commands to aid mail functions, in addition to incorporating word processing, filing, etc. Some of the commands perform the following functions.

- Review the contents of the mailbox

- Read the contents of the message

- Create a message

- Send a message

- File a message

- Search the file (with respect to originator, date, subject).

With the commercial e-mail services, you are generally given:

- A password that identifies you as a legitimate user. In most cases, individual subscribers can choose their own password.

- A mailbox 'address' to which incoming mail is sent. This may be used for billing purposes by the system.

- A selection of phone numbers to call the service. The different numbers may provide alternative access when one line is busy; more likely, there will be a different number for different modem speeds.

The Dialcom service, owned and operated in Britain under the name Telecom Gold, is the UK's largest e-mail system by far. In most respects it is a typical electronic mail service. When the appropriate number has been dialled and the modem has made the connection, this is the kind of message you should see from the service.

> Telecom Gold Network: For assistance type
> 'HELP LOGIN' at the prompt 'PAD'.
> This is Dial-up Pad 0. line 15 speed 300
> PAD   CALL 81

(The user's input in these examples is underlined). Telecom Gold operates a number of 'systems', which in practice are separate computers on which an individual's mailbox is located; CALL 81 calls the system for this particular mailbox.

> ***Call connected
> Welcome to Telecom Gold's System 81
> Please Sign On
> > ID
> User id: SKB767
> Password:

The 'user ID' is the mailbox number, the password does not appear on the screen when typed. A shorthand form is to enter ID SKB767 [PASSWORD] on one line immediately after the 'Please Sign On' message.

> TELECOM GOLD Automated Office Services
> 19.4I.177(81)
> On At 8:55 24/07/94 BST
> Last On At 8:48 24/07/94 BST
> Mail call (1 Unread, 2 Read, 1 Read express, Total 4)

If the password and mailbox ID match, the service indicates what if anything is currently in the mailbox: in this case there is one unread message and three that have been read but not yet deleted. Messages stay in the mailbox until the user specifically tells the system to delete them altogether. An unread 'express' message is automatically inserted at the start of the mail list.

> SKB>   MAIL

The SKB prompt invites the user to enter a command. A variety of options are available; MAIL enters the e-mail facility, but you can also call Telex or on-line information services at this point.

SENDING MESSAGES

If you opt for Send, a prompt will appear on the screen for a mailbox address to receive the message and a 'subject' line. You can give an individual mailbox as the destination by typing a mailbox ID (or a name, if it has been set up for this by the subscriber). Alternatively, you can circulate the message to more than one user -- in which case you may be able to specify one of several circulation lists that you have previously set up. You will probably be able to apply 'conditions' as well, so that a set of minutes for a meeting might be sent to everyone on a particular list only if they did not receive the last lot.

Thereafter you can type in the text or load on to the screen a previously prepared file from disk.

Once you have completed your message you can send it by typing .S -- most Telecom Gold commands are preceded by the dot to distinguish them from text. Before despatch an urgent message can be marked as 'express' (.EX); other options are 'acknowledgement requested' (.AR), 'carbon copies' (.CC) or 'blind copies' (.BC).

PRIVATE E-MAIL

Users of in-house electronic mail systems outnumber subscribers to the public services by something like four to one. This is partly because most of the computer manufacturers like DEC provides an e-mail system free with its VAX operating system; DEC users account for something like a third of the private mailboxes. Most of these systems run on multi-user minicomputers and mainframes; the market for e-mail on local networks is rather smaller, simply because LANs do not normally service enough users to warrant their having a message facility, but clearly there is scope for e-mail as LANs are increasingly linked to larger computers.

One of the electronic mail systems was implemented by IBM over its VNET connecting over 400 computers located throughout the world.

INTERNATIONAL E-MAIL

There are more than 14 international licensees for the Dialcom system used by Telecom Gold, which means a UK subscriber can e-mail direct to users of these systems.

Country	System name
Australia	MINERVA
Canada	INFOTEX
Denmark	DATABOKS
Hong Kong	DIALCOM
Ireland	EIRMAIL
Israel	GOLDNET
Japan	KDM INC
Mexico	TELEPRO
Netherlands	MEMOCOM

Puerto Rico	DIALCOM
Singapore	TELEBOX
United States	DIALCOM
West Germany	TELEBOX

SUMMARY

Despite the disadvantages, electronic mail can be a cost- effective solution where simple despatch and guaranteed delivery are required. It is quite cheap, not difficult to use, and despatch is fast -- certainly faster than conventional mail or facsimile transmission, faster and more versatile than Telex.

The promise of electronic mail does, however, depend crucially on the availability of cheaper, simpler modems; on better, simpler communications software; on easier, more versatile electronic mail services; and, above all, on the ability for subscribers on different services to talk to each other. The situation is not unlike the early days of the telephone; there is little point in having one yourself if the people to whom you wish to talk do not have a phone.

There are several publicly available e-mail services, and the development of X400 interfaces should allow their subscribers to exchange messages; that will eliminate one key disadvantage of e-mail. There is little to choose between the principal suppliers in terms of the mailbox services they provide. The competition (and much of their income) comes from the other on-line facilities they offer -- such as access to databases -- and their ability to provide purpose-designed packages of services attractive to specific groups of customers. With the resources required for such 'value-added' services, it is likely that only the larger and more visible suppliers will survive as mass- market public mailbox services.

It is important to highlight the fact that computer systems, acting as nodes in the network, control the transmission of messages and provide the message handling features including that of storage. The essential element is a computer network or a store-and-forward message switch, or communicating word processors. The intelligent terminals with local editing capabilities help simplify message preparation, and can interface with corporate databases on central computers. The computer nodes in the network control scheduling, routing, line sharing within the network. With national and international PSTNs interconnected one can connect to one's terminal or workstation from anywhere through dial up connection and view one's mail. An organization may be able to hire mailboxes for electronic mail service, if it does not have a network of its own, from public timesharing networks. For example, in the US, TYMNET provides ONTYME service for renting mailboxes. In India INDONET, NICNET, ICNET, etc. provides this service to its customers.

24

ELECTRONIC DATA INTERCHANGE

INTRODUCTION

Everybody uses business connections of one sort or another to get orders, send bills, make collections, determine and pay what it owes, move goods, and control its money. The business connections used historically to perform these operations have been the Postal Service and the Telephone. A relatively new link is electronic data communications facilities.

In all probability, your company has already installed a computer or computers to help run your business operations -- to keep track of orders, receivables, payables, equipment, schedules, people, facilities, and company money.

Although everything may be satisfactory, there may be a couple of computer problems you want to overcome. One problem pertains to that wall of people kept around the computer to feed it data. Some of the people do their feeding with terminals. Others do it with magnetic devices. All of them have one thing in common -- they receive information brought to the company by its business connection links and transcribe it into a form convenient for the computer.

The second problem has to do with the business connection links themselves. By comparison with what the computer can do at electronic speed the postal service and the telephone are really bottle-necks. Both require human intervention to get the information they deliver into the computer. This slows down the computer feeding process and retards the speed and flow of operational data. In other words, orders, status reports, and other information vital to business operations are delayed days enroute by mail before your company can begin to react. In fact, even though it costs more, you collect some of the more important operational information by telephone to overcome the mail bottle-neck. The Postal Service recognizes the problem and is working on methods to speed up service. But no matter how fast the mail is moved or how much you use the telephone, the problems are still there because neither terminate with the information directly usable by computers. The flow is brought to a halt while the information is transcribed and, during transcribing, errors may be introduced. The penalty for error is potentially wrong business decisions.

Now you have a complete picture. Your links to business connections are limited to the mail and the telephone. Both are slow. Both terminate with that wall of people who feed the computer and who may make errors. Inbound operational information that is produced at the speed of light in somebody else's computer gets to your computer, relatively speaking, at the speed of the turtle!

What your company needs is a better link to business connections and that is what electronic data interchange is all about. To appreciate what electronic data interchange (EDI) means, think about all those orders, invoices, freight bills, shipment instructions, tracing requests, payment instructions, government reports, and the like that your company sends out or receives every day. Think about each as a single transaction. And, think about how you send them and get them! Then:

Imagine - Inbound transactions recorded for action in seconds after they are released by the originator -- with no paperwork or intervening people.

Imagine - Getting operational data so early that planning is no longer an estimation process.

Imagine - The elimination of clerical transcribing errors.

Imagine - Current status reports even when the source of information is another company.

Imagine - Positive control over operational information from origin to destination -- from the time of ordering raw materials until payment for delivered finished products.

Imagine - Payment electronically by data communications with your bank.

Imagine - An information system adaptable for expansion as your needs and capabilities change.

Imagine - A single computer 'window' to the world -- a single set of computer programs to interface your system with the system of any other company on any business subject!

Your imagination has conceived the system for EDI -- Electronic Data Interchange! A system which connects your company's computer to that of a business associate only when and only as long as required for each of you to exchange pertinent operational and status information.

And the system is not a complement of new equipment and dedicated communications facility! Rather, it is a means for interlinking present computer systems by employing standard information structures, standard communications protocols, and a limited number of special EDI interface computer programs.

Incidentally, EDI is also a means to snap the paperwork chain. A means to use electronics as a medium for recording information for intercompany transactions.

EDI is revolutionizing the way corporations are doing business with their trading partners around the world. Companies such as Apple, Chrysler, Caterpillar Inc., Digital Equipment, ESSO, Ford Motor Co., General Motors, Honda, KLM and Mark & Spencer are only a few of the companies who are reaping the full benefits of EDI technology including reduction in paperwork, reduced inventories, lower ordering costs and faster reaction times.

WHAT IS EDI?

Traditionally, the transfer of data from one company to another has been by paper documents. This is known as a paper-based system. These documents have to be manually forwarded and entered to the destination computer.

EDI is the electronic exchange of structured business information, in standard formats, between computers. EDI eliminates the need for a paper-based system by providing an electronic link between companies. This reduces data entry tasks and improves business cycle times.

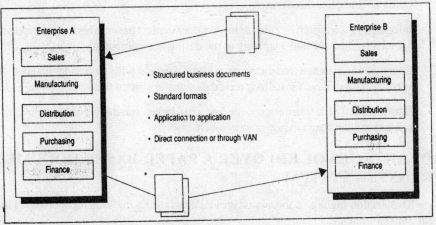

Fig. 24.1 : Electronic Data Interchange

EDI is the electronic transfer of structured business documents in an organization -- internally among groups of departments or externally with its suppliers, customers and subsidiaries (see Figure 24.1). The documents likely to be used in EDI are invoices, purchase orders, shipping requests, acknowledgements and payments. EDI is quite different from generic correspondence like E-mail and involves the exchange of specific documents with management and tracking procedures designed to efficiency.

In EDI information is passed electronically from one computer to another over network without having to be read, retyped or printed. The information transferred mu have a defined structure agreed between your company, and the company or group you ser and receive data from.

Any company or group which uses EDI is called a **trading partner**. The compute that different trading partners use do not have to be from the same manufacturer.

The information that EDI handles includes, for example, purchase orders and invoice However, any type of business document can be sent, providing it conforms to curre industry, national or international format standards.

Examples of current uses of EDI include automatic teller machines (ATMs) in ban where EDI is used for transferring and withdrawing funds between different bank account airline reservation systems, stock exchange transactions and car reservation systems.

WHY USE EDI?

The data from one computer is normally not in a form suitable to be entered direct into another computer. The data may have to be arranged differently before it can be enter into another computer or some items of data may not be needed at all. With EDI, all the da is converted into an agreed standard format before it is sent over the network. The comput that receives the data can then extract the information it requires.

Using EDI implies three things:

1.   Information is transferred electronically rather than on paper. This means that there no need to enter the data manually in the destination computer.

2.   Information is transferred between trading partners who have negotiated tradi agreements and have formalized their data transfer system.

3.   Information that is transferred complies with agreed standards for the format of t content and the transmission control mechanisms.

ADVANTAGES OF EDI OVER A PAPER-BASED DOCUMEN TRANSFER SYSTEM

This section highlights the advantages EDI has over a traditional paper-based doc ment transfer system.

In a paper-based system:

–   A software application generates a paper document on a form.

–   Copies of the document are made. Some are passed to internal departments to filed, other copies are sent to the trading partner via the postal service.

–   The trading partner receives the document and retypes the information on t form into their computer. This retyping often introduces errors.

–   The trading partner generates a paper acknowledgement and this is sent to the originating company.

The transfer of documents in a paper-based system could take a considerable length time.

In an EDI system:

–   The application program generates a file which contains the processed document.

–   The document is converted to an agreed standard format.

–   The file containing the document is sent electronically over the network. This network links the originating company and its trading partner.

–   The file containing the document arrives at the trading partner. It is translated into the correct format and transferred to the recipient's application.

–   A receipt is automatically generated and sent over the network to the originating company.

EDI transmits documents to the trading partner's application in a very short period of ne and with no human intervention.

OW EDI WORKS?

Regardless of the format chosen, companies using EDI communicate with their trading tners in one of two ways: Either they exchange data with several trading partners directly

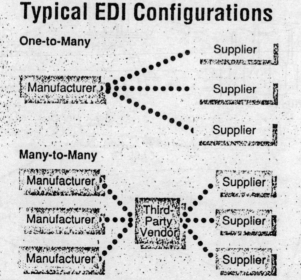

Typical EDI Configurations

24.2 : Typical EDI configurations may involve either direct communication with others (often sing a proprietary system) or the use of a third-party vendor to translate and communicate messages to customers.

or they interact with multiple companies through a central information clearinghouse (see Figu 24.2). In the latter case, all transactions are funneled through a third party's computer syste which routes them to the appropriate receiver's computer. This enables the sender to commu cate with an unlimited number of trading partners without worrying about proprietary syste audit trails, variable transmission speeds, and general computer compatibility.

Basically, here is how EDI works:

1.   Prior to any computer work, representatives of two companies interested in exchar ing data electronically meet to specify the applications in the EDI standard which th will implement.

2.   Each company adds EDI programs to its computer to translate company data i standard formats for transmission, and for the reverse translation on the data it receiv

3.   Then, as often as operationally required the two companies exchange data electro cally in the standard formats.

The data transmitted originates from records in the sender's database after the sen confirms that the receiver is an authorized recipient for such data. The sender compose transmission formatted in the EDI standards; the receiver translates the formatted message computer record to be processed and used internally. All transmissions are checked both electro cally and functionally and the protocol includes procedures for error detection and correctio

TRANSPORTATION INFORMATION PROFILE

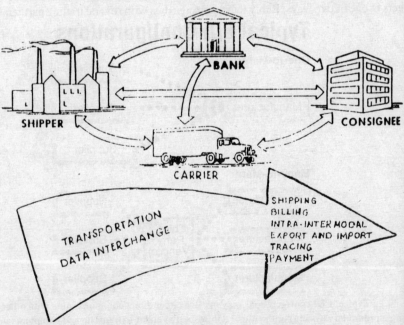

Fig. 24.3 : EDI in its Working Environment

Once a company has established standardized communications with another company, it is now in a position to communicate with any other company that is also using the EDI standards.

Figure 20.3 pictures EDI in its working environment. Notice that the environment may include banks and customs as well as companies and carriers, and the environment may be broadened as needs develop. The information flow in EDI is:

1. A company collects data for its own operational or statistical requirements. This data is edited and added to its own database.

2. Pertinent information is extracted by the company from its data base, summarized if necessary, constructed into EDI transaction sets, and transmitted to the company or organization requiring it for valid reasons.

3. The frequency for preparing this information is determined by the operational requirements of each recipient.

4. A communications link for transmission is established according to the standard communications protocol.

5. The recipient of the information receives the transmission and checks it for its physical characteristics (parity, check character, transmission mode). Re-transmission is requested if an error is detected in the physical characteristics of the transmission.

6. The receiver checks the functional characteristics of the data. A message is transmitted to the original sender to acknowledge the transmission and to identify any errors detected.

7. The receiver processes the information received according to its own internal procedures and timing requirements.

Here is how a typical EDI exchange works (our example assumes the two companies communicate directly with one another). A manufacturer writes its replenishment orders to a computer file instead of printing them. At a mutually agreed-on time, it connects this computer by telephone line, either leased or dial-up, to a processing function and then to the supplier's machine. After an initial "handshake" routine, which establishes the identities of the machines, the manufacturer's computer forwards the relevant orders to the supplier's computer.

Next, the supplier processes the orders, perhaps sending an acknowledgement to the sender. At the same time, the supplier's system generates packing notes and associated documentation for the warehouse and carrier, then produces its invoices as a computer file and forwards them to the manufacturer. The manufacturer, in turn, sends its remittance advice electronically and may even pay the bills through a bank clearinghouse system.

In sophisticated applications, the EDI information flows directly into an artificial intelligence system, where the computer uses it to make business decisions.

EDI STANDARDS

The development of new ways of doing business is often paralleled by the development of industry standards. EDI standards fall under the auspices of the American National Standards Institute (ANSI), which chartered the Accredited Standards Committee X12 (ASCX12) in 1979. The ASCX12 Committee's objective is to develop uniform standards for inter-industry electronic interchange of business transactions.

Briefly, the X12 data interchange standards consist of:

- **Transaction Set Standards**: These define the procedural format and data content requirements for specified business transactions, e.g., purchase orders.

- **Data Dictionary and Segment Dictionary**: These define the precise content for data elements and data segments used in building transaction sets.

- **Transaction Control Standards**: These define the formats for the information required to control the data interchange.

Universal adoption of the EDI standard developed by ANSI/ASCX12 will enable all organizations desiring to conduct multi-industry transactions to use a single standard format for interchanging data. In the US alone, over 10,000 companies, in a wide range of industries, already routinely use EDI and ASCX12 standards. International standards have been established based on the X12 standards as well. These standards are called EDI for Administration Commerce and Trade (EDIFACT) and may be obtained through ANSI.

EDI standards grew from needs in transportation and payment applications and have been extended for use in other business and technical applications. For transportation, the information system parallels the physical movement of cargo and an information transaction accompanies significant events in cargo movement:

- Reservation or pick-up request

- Shipment information from shipper to carrier

- Export/import information for international shipments

- Carrier-to-carrier waybill data exchange

- Tracing information

- Freight bill data, carrier-to-payer

- Payment data - Payer-to-bank, Bank-to-bank, Bank-to-payee.

Each type of information-need requires the formal definition of an EDI transaction set and establishment of user timing requirements. Although the original EDI standards included the transaction formats for transportation applications, formats for other applications are being derived by industry groups. The applications for transportation include shipment information, import/export data, interline and intermodal data, inquiry and reply, consolidation, repetitive pattern processing, invoicing, and payment. Other applications include order placement, commercial invoicing and payment.

For each application, major units of information are defined as 'transaction sets' which are the structure for communicating information between systems. A 'transaction set' in EDI equates to a form in a paperwork system. An application may have several different transaction sets defined. The transaction set is further defined in terms of 'segments' (or lines of information), and the segment is defined in terms of 'data elements' (the smallest information unit other than a character).

All units of information -- transaction set, segment, data element -- may be variable length, but the information is structured so that it may be constructed by one computer system and interpreted and processed by another. New applications and information units may be specified without impacting work previously completed.

Data movement from one system to another may be initiated in several ways:

1.   Inquiry transaction set received from another system

2.   Previously established schedule

3.   Exceptions (management by exception)

4.   Detection of errors in data received from another system

5.   Inquiry transaction set generated in response to management needs.

The interface computer program and the structure of each type of transaction set are part of the EDI standards. EDI does not address a standard which extends into a company's internal system.

EDI standards and documentation for transportation include:

–   Information structure

–   System rules and procedures

–   Programming guide

–   Transaction set formats - Air, Motor, Ocean, Rail

–   Segments, data elements and codes

–   Communications specifications.

The standards were developed by industry work groups at the Transportation Data Coordinating Committee (TDCC).

Variable-Length EDI Standards

The discussion of standards in this section is applicable to all variable-length standards, such as:

TDCC: The Transportation Data Coordinating Committee (TDCC) was formed to develop EDI formats for the transportation industry's four primary segments: air, motor, ocean and rail. This same organization is called EDIA (The Electronic Data Interchange Association) today.

UCS/WINS: The Uniform Code Council (UCC) was chosen to oversee the creation and ongoing maintenance of the Uniform Communication Standard (UCS) for the grocery industry and the Warehouse Information Network Standard (WINS) for the warehousing industry.

X12: The American National Standards Institute (ANSI) formed the Accredited Standards Committee (ASC) X12 as the development and maintenance organization for a generic cross-industry EDI standard, ANSI ASC X12. The Data Interchange Standards Association (DISA) is secretariat for this standards process. The X12 standard is committed to meet the needs of all industries. TDCC, UCS, and WINS are in the process of becoming part of the ANSI ASC X12 standards.

No one industry uses all the capabilities available in the X12 standard. Instead, industries have identified subsets of the standard that their members will use. Some have given their subsets names. References to such standards as EDX (Electrical Data Exchange), EIDX (Electronic Industry Data Exchange), CIDX (Chemical Industry Data Exchange), PIDX (Petroleum Industry Data Exchange), AIAG (Automotive Industry Action Group), ICOPS (Industry Committee for Office Products Standards), VICS (Voluntary Inter-industry Communications Standard), HIBCC (Health Industry Business Communications Council), NWDA (National Wholesale Druggists Association), etc. are actually references to industry-specific subsets of ANSI ASC X12.

EDIFACT: The EDIFACT Standard, EDI for Administration, Commerce and Transport, has been developed for international EDI.

MOTIVATION

The methodologies for communicating business, trade, and transportation transaction data between concerned organizations in the U.S. materialized during the evolution of improved data processing and data communications technologies. Some practical events which dictated that new methodologies be employed are:

(a)   Cost of improved technologies became more acceptable.

(b)   Dynamics of modern business operations relating to time and response constraints, transaction volumes, cost of manual operations, and general growth in complexity brought about increased usage of computer and communications capabilities.

(c)   Corporate 'internal' operations, services, and/or functions were recognized as being dependent on information originating from 'external' organizations.

(d)   Costs were rising for producing, storing, mailing, administering, managing, handling, transcribing and otherwise responding to business information received from external sources on paper.

(e)   Organizations recognized the potential of EDI for becoming more operationally responsive in order to retain a competitive posture in the marketplace.

(f)   Transportation and transportation status information was seen to play critical roles in operating timely, reliable, efficient, and responsive business logistics systems.

(g)   Companies and organizations employing computer technology in the U.S. represented a significant "in place" resource which could productively support EDI operations.

To address the developing technological capabilities and the need for improved inter-organizational electronic communication of transportation data, a broad-based joint government/industry effort was instigated.

Potential industry and government users, computer manufacturers and communications carriers cooperated in this joint effort by way of the following.

(a)   User organizations were asked to define parameters of operational application, functional requirements, data requirements, data standards, and standard methods for data control.

(b)   Computer system and service vendors were encouraged to adjust the traditional 'closed system' design or service precepts to a more open-ended approach in order to be responsive to market demands for EDI capabilities.

(c)   Communications carriers were asked to revise service offerings to accommodate an open-ended, inter-system (inter-organizational) concept of digital data communications.

COST BENEFIT ANALYSIS OF EDI

The demonstrated benefits of EDI include reduced inventories, reduction in purchase and payment overheads and faster reaction times. However, there is an intangible benefit of EDI that cannot be measured in percentages -- improved business relationships with trading partners.

According to Price Waterhouse, the accounting firm, EDI is attractive because apart from eliminating paper and manual processing, if implemented properly it can reduce cost of doing business by as much as five percent of net sales. A complete cost-benefit analysis of EDI should also include the value of increased market share that EDI may bring.

EDI provides many significant business benefits, including:

–   Marketing competitiveness

–   Administrative cost savings

–   Shorter time to market

–   Better quality control

–   Improved corporate trading relationships.

EDI STRATEGY FOR COMPETITIVE ADVANTAGE

Leading organizations around the world are making strategic use of EDI for real cost savings:

Contrary to its name Caterpillar Inc., the world's largest manufacturer of earth moving equipment has a reputation for moving fast to beat worldwide rivals, especially Japanese firms. Caterpillar relies on an X.25 based EDI network to link its supplies around the world. The payoffs so far include a $10 million savings in parts inventory.

At Digital's manufacturing plant in Augusta Maine, EDI has reduced the cost of generating an average purchase order by 25%. The time to process the order has shrunk from 5 weeks to 3 days. Digital's MRP system here is directly connected to the production scheduling system of their supplier, Motorola Corporation in Phoenix. The two companies have increased their trust and reliance on each other to the point where Digital no longer sends purchase orders, but sends forecasting information directly to Motorola's production schedulling system. They have become partners in the true sense of the word.

Norwich Health Authority (NHA) has become one of Europe's highest volume commercial user of an EDI full settlement system.

Using a system built around Barclays EDI Trading Master System and Digital's DEC/EDI platform allows NHA which has major purchasing and payments overheads to transmit all of its payment instructions and remittance information to Barclays as EDI transaction. NHA's suppliers of EDI users and customers of Barclays or Llloyds Banks, then receive payments and remittance advice from Barclays, electronically. The remaining suppliers receive the same advice on paper, but all administration will be handled by Barclays, considerably reducing the NHA's administrative costs.

The International Stock Exchange in London is studying EDI applications, to see whether the technology can be introduced to cover transactions between listed companies and the exchange. Under review are the lodging by companies with the Exchange of such documents as Reports and Accounts, while invoicing of companies by the Exchange is also being considered.

The secretariat of S.W.I.F.T. (Society for Worldwide Interbank Financial Telecommunications) has released details of its new 'envelope' messages. These envelope messages will accompany EDIFACT messages sent over the network in EDI trials due to start soon (see Figure 24.4). These messages will become a permanent feature of the S.W.I.F.T. corpus of messages and will accommodate all the payment message flow scenarios approved by the pilot banks. Banks participating in this pilot project come from nineteen countries.

Shipping Lines are queuing up for membership of EDIship, the UK Shipping Industry's initiative for paperless import/export documentation. The project will enable shipping lines and their customers to exchange messages electronically and replace time hallowed paper trade documentation. EDIship currently consists of the major shipping lines including Campagnie General Maritime (CGM), Hapag-Llyods, Maersk, Nedlloyd, P&O Container and Sea Land.

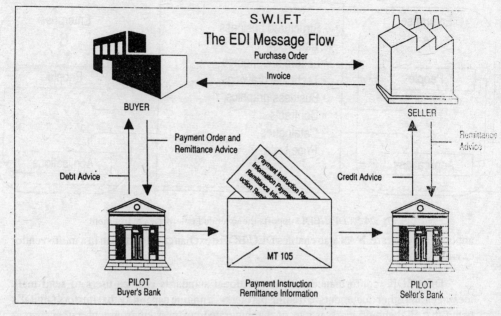

Fig. 24.4 : Swift Pilot Project

At the Italian clothing manufacturer Benetton, for example, computers not only determine what will be included in upcoming production runs, but also designate optimum routing for all finished goods. At each Benetton store, the point-of-sale cash registers maintain a running inventory of item sales, which they transmit via EDI to computers in branch offices. The branch offices, in turn, transmit the data to the central office computer, which uses artificial intelligence and a modeling program to make decisions on production runs. If red sweaters are selling fast, the computer tells the manufacturing system to design and produce more red sweaters. The system then determines how the shipments will be routed to the stores, freeing the traffic department which consists of only six people -- to spend its time researching new routings and handling problems.

DIGITAL'S APPROACH TO EDI IMPLEMENTATION

Digital has taken a non-traditional route with its EDI product offerings. DEC/EDI is a modular product that tightly integrates with all business functions in an organization with the application software the organization uses, and with other kinds of inter- enterprise communications that businesses need for success. See Figure 24.5.

Digital's DEC/EDI solution works with many different VANs. Furthermore, it is based on Network Application Support (NAS) making it easy to integrate with different types of

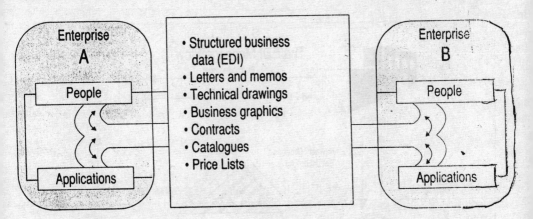

Fig. 24.5 : DEC/EDI supports the extended enterprise environment

application software. NAS also enables DEC/EDI to exchange information in a multi-vendor environment.

DEC/EDI's conformance with international standards enables users to send mail, messages and other documents to trading partners -- a unique capability that mirrors Digital's belief that EDI should work as part of the integrated business environment, rather than as an exception for it.

BEYOND EDI: ELECTRONIC TRADING NETWORKS

Evolving electronic trading networks will bring both opportunities and threats to users. Electronic trading networks (ETN) incorporate the functions provided by EDI, electronic mail, and other services, but go much further to electronically embrace all steps in the trade process, including the trade itself.

· To qualify as an ETN, networks and services must be combined to provide a seamless and open environment for the procurement of goods and services. Thus, an ETN must transparently offer the whole range of interactive data exchanges necessary for inter-firm searching and trading.

These include negotiation, authentication, clearing and settlement, and, of course, delivery. The ETN concept applies to trade for information, goods (including commodities), services and, indeed, a hybrid combining all three elements.

The ideal form of ETN is not a market tied to, or dominated by, one major player but a source of many enquiries with both suppliers and customers, leading to fluid, multiple, contractual alliances. Ultimately, ETNs can be expected to reduce information-related costs, speed the identification and location of customers and suppliers, increase the accuracy of the match between product and service specification and buyer's needs, and facilitate negotiation and delivery.

Interest in ETNs has it roots in research that has challenged the popular belief that information technology alone is enough to provide firms with sustainable competitive advantage. A report by the Massachusetts Institute of Technology, for example, argues that the real benefits of using IT derive from the ways in which organizations are able to integrate information and communication technologies into their commercial structures.

The task of managers, it suggests, is to re-engineer business processes, both internally and externally, and to develop new forms and styles of organization, rather than simply to automate and support existing information systems and processes.

One way organizations can do this is by joining an ETN. These networks could be operated by network service providers, by trade associations or by coalitions of users.

Membership in an ETN can lead to a redefinition of the scope of an organization. For example, access to an ETN could provide small- and medium-sized enterprises seeking to grow their businesses with a mechanism to avoid traditional vulnerabilities.

Most failures have two origins: over-reliance on core business with a dominant trading partner who withdraws, and a cashflow crisis at a time of over-trading due to failure in the arrival of funds or raw materials.

The first problem can be reduced by membership in an ETN, which provides an opportunity for a company to broaden its customer base. The second problem is avoided by an ETN institutional structure that ensures guaranteed payments and delivery of materials. Moves toward the establishment of ETNs can already be observed. Initiatives include networks of customer-service terminals and shopping mall kiosks, some EDI user groups, and alliances of professional trading intermediaries such as brokers and auctioneers.

But if ETNs bring advantages, they also pose dangers. Access to such networks can alter knowledge and power balances between participants. It is difficult to assess whether the benefits of trading on ETNs will be real or illusory in the long term. Simply having access to more information needed to become involved in a trade is not a sufficient guarantee of sustained competitive advantage for users of ETN. The quality, timeliness and security of such information are key ingredients, as are all the rules governing international transactions.

The airline industry provides an example of the kind of inequity that may be created such a system. When American Airlines introduced the first computerized reservation system -- a system that included information on both its own flights and those of other airlines it ensured that information on its own flights was contained on the first page of information. Similarly, selective inputting of information may favour those controlling the information.

Ownership and rules for usage are also key. For example, should one organization be responsible for all the elements of an ETN? The issues here include: who operates the network infrastructure; who operates the market; who controls financial clearing and settlement; and who has the right to access and trade on the network itself?

ETNs are unlikely to bring about a perfectly competitive market. In fact, unexpected asymmetries can be expected to develop. Potential ETN participants can be threatened, for example, by the arrival of new players in previously protected markets; price competition may increase or be suppressed by new market leaders; and the traditional competitive advantages of partnerships might be eroded.

In appropriate regulations and the growing complexity of electronic markets could well result in the proliferation of a new form of black market -- a market that eludes the monitoring and accountability procedures created by national governments to a greater degree than ever before.

The challenges can be considered under four dimensions:

1. **Institutional Dimension**. The ETNs emerging in Europe are doing so in an environment heavily influenced by regulation. Such regulations may promote or hamper the process of building electronic trading user groups. They also affect firms decisions to shift from the use of traditional communication networks, such as telephone and fax, to advanced interactive data exchange procedures such as EDI.

2. **User Dimension**. The potential for ETNs to create opportunities for strengthened competitiveness through improvements in logistics is widely recognized, for example, in shipping and rail transport. But from the users' perspective, the benefits of such networks are contingent on suitable procedures for electronic document certification, clear designation of responsibilities and guarantees, geographical location, firm size and resources, and network and application standards.

3. **Services Dimension**. Traditionally, communication in trading networks has been composed primarily of the telephone, fax and a limited number of relatively simple non-interactive data transmission services. In the 1990s, interactive services such as voice and image processing, electronic funds transfer, EDI, and multimedia applications are expected to combine with open document standards and signature authentication to support interactive data exchange among geographically dispersed and diverse trading communities.

Some of these services have been implemented, others await commercialization, but access, interconnectivity conditions and service functionality will be critical factors in the diffusion and take-up of these services.

4. **Technical Dimension**. Underlying the emergence of ETNs are choices on network interface protocols, software applications, system architectures, and information storage and retrieval methods. Standards are being devised and championed by leading actors in the electronic networking field.

25

X.25 OVERVIEW

INTRODUCTION

With the number of PC LANs increasing at a tremendous pace, one can definitely say that LAN technology is well-accepted by a great majority of PC users. LANs are used today in a wide variety of distributed processing and transaction processing applications and for complete office automation. The main hurdle facing all these LAN users as of today is the issue of connectivity between LANs that are geographically far apart, both within the country and outside. This need can be satisfied by many different ways: normally, using the ordinary telecommunication lines, or leasing telecommunication lines, using a satellite channel et al. All these methods are either quite unreliable or very expensive. After all, it does not make any sense to lease a telecommunication line or a satelite channel for just a few hours of usage of the communication link. Hence, there is definitely a need for a low to medium-cost network to handle traffic lasting from a few minutes to a few hours every day. This requirement is very well-satisfied by packet switching networks.

A packet switching network can be very easily compared with the postal mail system where, for example, several letters are deposited in the mail box every day by an office. Each of these letters consists of an addressed envelope with the matter inside, on the letter. Through mailed from a single location, all these letters take a different route, determined by the address on the envelope. What this means is that the letter is passed on from one post office to the other and finally delivered to the addressee.

The same procedure applies to packet networks, where information is grouped into packets, each packet having data and the address of the destination. These networks are highly reliable, use conditioned commercial lines, and operate at high speed. The best thing about these networks is that the user pays only for the total amount of packets sent and not the total time of use of the network. This is basically possible as the network and the lines are shared.

Also, if there are multiple paths to the destination, the different packets are sent through various paths one after another and the throughput of data transferred increases tremendously. A packet switching network basically consists of nodes (computers, terminals, etc.) and communication lines. Each of these nodes is connected to a packet switching exchange that routes the packets. The incoming packets are stored in the Packet Switch (PSX) and routed to the next PSX depending on the address of the packet. This goes on, till the packet reaches the destination. Note here that the packet does not go from the sender to the receiver in one shot and no direct circuit may be there between the two, unlike a circuit switching network where there is a mandatory need for a direct connection between the sender and receiver. Thus, X.25 networks have many advantages over the conventional way of transferring data and offer the following features:

1. Approved by CCITT, a world body and an international standard being widely used in most European countries and America.

2. Allows sharing of communication lines, hence reducing costs.

3. High reliability data transfer, through in-built error correction of all packets and support for alternate routes.

4. Increased speed through support for multiple routes to destination.

5. Allows heterogeneous connectivity of all kinds of systems.

6. Being used worldwide for applications like resource sharing across LANs, terminal emulations, file transfers and mail transfers.

One of the most important standards for the computer industry is the CCITT Recommendation X.25. This defines the relationship between a transport subsystem, or common carrier packet-switching network, and user machines which employ it. This chapter describes the X.25 techniques, and shows how user machines employ this type of packet-switching network.

Let us now try and understand how the X.25 communication takes place. The X.25 packet switching recommendation formulated by the International Telephone and Telegraph Consultative Committee (CCITT) specifies the protocol to be followed by the user devices (nodes) in accessing public packet-switching networks.

Internationally agreed upon, the X.25 protocol specifies the details of the interactions between any packet-mode device and the X.25 network nodes, as shown in Figure 25.1. The X.25 network node and user packet-mode devices are called Data Circuit-Terminating Equipment (DCE) and Data Terminal Equipment (DTE) respectively. The actual equipment used and the design of the packet-switched network is not of concern when implementing the X.25 protocol. In cases where the communication network utilised does not use packet switching, each DTE is connected to a Packet Assembler/Disassembler (PAD) and the DTE is referred to as a character-mode device. See Figure 25.2.

Figure 25.3 illustrates the concept of X.25 networks. Many user machines are interconnected by **virtual circuits** on which they communicate by means of packets. The

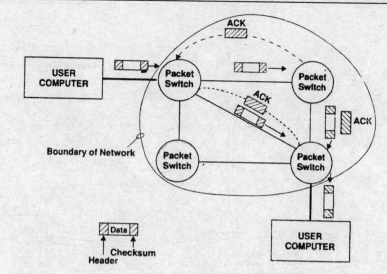

Fig. 25.1 : A simple model of packet switching

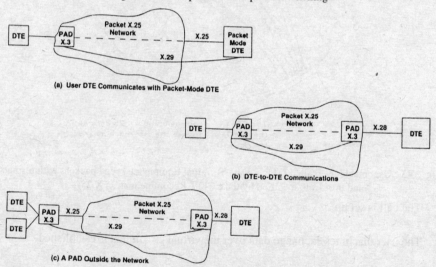

(a) User DTE Communicates with Packet-Mode DTE

(b) DTE-to-DTE Communications

(c) A PAD Outside the Network

Fig. 25.2 : Network configurations using PADs

virtual circuits are derived by sharing common communication facilities. The X.25 Recommendation says nothing about how the network shall be constructed, but it is oriented to conventional packet-switching on terrestrial lines of the types available in today's common carrier tariffs. It may need modification for satellites, packet radio, data broadcasting, or networks in advance of today's state of the art.

The virtual circuits illustrated in Figure 25.3 can be either temporary or permanent. The term **virtual call** is used to refer to a temporary virtual circuit. Like a telephone call there are three phases to a virtual call:

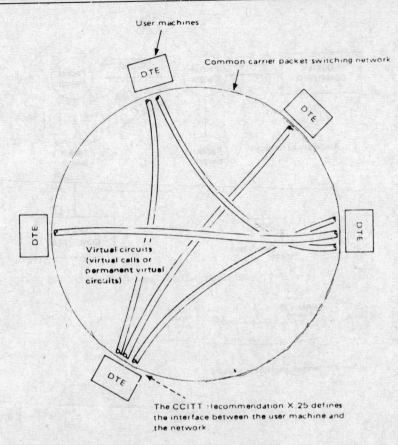

Fig. 25.3 : User machines (called DTE's, Data Terminal Equipments) send packers with formats and protocols specified by the CCITT Recommendation X.25.

1.   The call is set up.

2.   The user machines exchange data over the virtual circuit that is established.

3.   The call is disconnected.

PERMANENT VIRTUAL CIRCUITS

Users of telephone circuits can obtain either a dial-up circuit which they set up when they want and disconnect after use, or they can lease a channel which is permanently connected. Many computer systems have employed leased voice circuits. The X.25 Recommendation gives equivalent options for data. The user can either set up a virtual call when he wants and disconnect it after use, or else can have a **permanent virtual circuit** which is permanently connected like a leased telephone line.

In setting up a virtual call a logical channel group number must be assigned, and a logical channel number within that group. With a permanent virtual circuit the logical channel group number and logical channel number are assigned when the customer leases the facility from the common carrier. The number remains effective for the duration of the lease. A user machine can have up to 15 logical channel groups (addressed with 4 bits) and up to 255 logical channels within each group (addressed with 8 bits). A given user may employ some logical channels for permanent virtual circuits and some for virtual calls, which are, in effect, **switched virtual circuits**.

When a permanent virtual circuit is used there is no call setup operation before data is sent, or disconnect operation afterwards.

ACCESS TO THE NETWORK

When a subscriber signs up with a common carrier employing the X.25 protocol, he will be provided certain access points to the network. He may have an access point at his location. He may dial the network access point on a conventional telephone line. He may sign up for a certain number of permanent virtual circuits interconnecting the user machines, or a user machine may be authorized to use up to a given number of simultaneous virtual calls (temporary virtual circuits). This is like a computer having a given number of ports. The virtual calls may be placed to another user machine and that machine may accept or refuse the call. Some user machines may be inaccessible by the network for security reasons, and may be called only by members of a specified group of machines.

In CCITT terminology the user machine is referred to as a DTE (data terminal equipment). The user machine is connected to a DCE (data circuit-terminating equipment). The DCE refers to the modem or digital interface which links the user machine to the network. The X.25 Recommendation describes the DTE/DCE interface. Figure 25.4 shows the DTE and DCE. The DTE can be a computer like the **host** machines of the ARPA network. It can be a terminal controller or a concentrator which handles remote terminals. It can be a machine which provides an interface to a different form of teleprocessing or network. With the dropping cost of microminiature circuitry, terminals will be built which execute the X.25 protocols themselves.

To avoid excessive use of acronyms we will refer to the DTE as the **user machine** and DTE/DCE interface as the **user/network interface**. We will use the term DCE for the data circuit-terminating equipment.

THE PAD INTERFACE

Many terminals transmit characters rather than blocks of data or packets. In some cases they use start-stop line control. Sometimes they are inexpensive devices. These terminals need to be connected to an interface machine which buffers the data they send and assembles and disassembles the packets needed for X.25 operation.

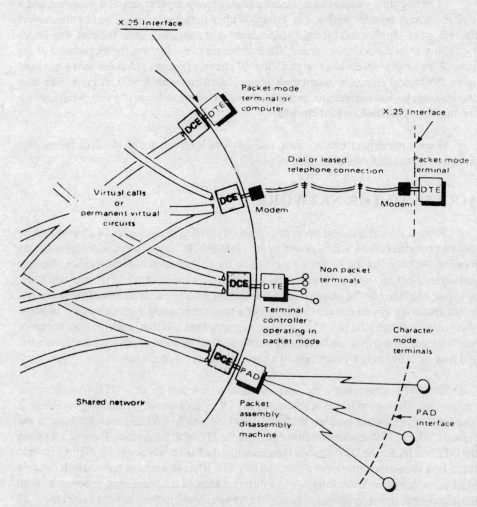

Fig. 25.4 : The user machine, DTE, can be a computer, terminal, terminal controller, or interface to another form of teleprocessing. The PAD, packet assembly/disassembly machine, buffers characters to and from character-mode terminal (e.g., start-stop machines) and forms the requisite packets.

The interface machine could be a control unit controlling multiple terminals, which is part of a computer manufacturer's product line. It could be a concentrator to which remote character-oriented terminals are connected by either leased or dialed telephone lines.

Most common carriers operating X.25 networks provide an interface machine for connecting character-oriented terminals to the network. A standard for such an interface has been proposed. It is an extension to (but not part of) the CCITT Recommendation X.25, and is called the PAD (Packet Assembly/Disassembly) interface. It is illustrated at the bottom of Figure 25.4. The PAD machine receives characters for network transmission and assembles them into a packet. Conversely, it disassembles packets and sends the resulting characters to the terminal which needs them. A protocol is defined for communication between the PAD machine and the character-oriented terminal. This protocol defines how characters are used for indicating the start and end of messages, requesting and confirming connections and dealing with errors.

There can thus be **packet-mode** user machines which execute the X.25 protocols, and **character-mode** user machines which communicate via a PAD interface. Different types of character-mode machines can be used including HDLC machines and start-stop machines which use delimiter characters from CCITT alphabets to indicate the start and end of messages.

LAYERS OF COMMUNICATION

The actual implementation of the X.25 protocol is primarily through the use of a special software in an intelligent terminal, host, or a network processing node. The CCITT Recommendation X.25 specifies three layers of communications: physical, data-link, and network. The user/network interface is concerned with control layers 1, 2, and 3 (Figure 25.5).

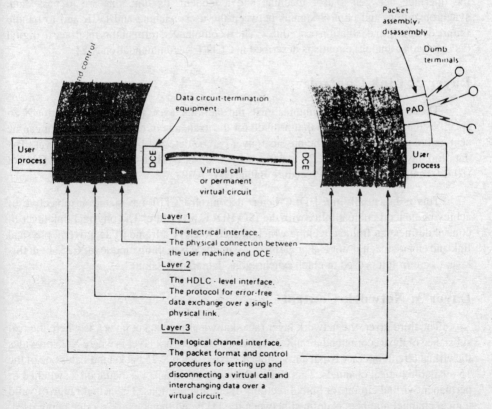

Fig. 25.5 : The CCITT X.25 user/network interface is subdivided into three levels of interface.

Layer 1: Physical Control

The physical layer, in reference to the OSI model, defines the interface between the X.25 network and the Packet mode device. Currently, the bulk of data communications uses telecommunications circuits that were originally designed for voice communications. There are two types of telecommunications circuits available: dial-up and leased line. The signals that travel along these circuits, which are connected by modems, are defined by CCITT definitions such as V.24. In most cases, packet-switched systems use leased lines. If the communications circuit is fully digital, the interface used to communicate on it is defined by the CCITT recommendation X.21. The definition of X.25 also specifies which facilities of X.21 it uses; some of the facilities X.21 offers are not needed by a simple point- to-point X.25 network. Simply stated, the X.21 interface provides for end-to-end digital transmission between DTEs and DCEs.

This describes the plugs and wires for establishing contact and sending bits between the user machine and the DCE. There is nothing unique to X.25 about this layer. It applies to all synchronous data transmission. It defines the interface between the user machine and the line termination of a digital line, similarly to the way the RS #232-C standard defines the interface between a user machine and a modem. Its functions are to pass data, synchronization, and control signals between the user machine and DCE and to handle failure detection and isolation procedures. The recommended form of this interface to digital (as opposed to analog) circuits is described in CCITT Recommendation X.21.

Layer 2: Link Control

The second layer of communication is the data-link layer. The Recommendation X.25 specifies data link procedures that provide for the exchange of data via frames that can be sent and received. Errors in the physical layer can be detected by the data link layer. The data link layer used by the X.25 is defined by a subset of High-Level Data Link Control (HDLC) called Link Access Procedure Balanced (LAPB).

This is essentially the HDLC layer of control. CCITT has stated an objective of achieving general compatibility with the ISO HDLC procedure. The physical link layer of control defines the frame envelope which is used to carry a frame of data over a physical link and ensure that it is not lost or garbled. Again there is nothing unique to X.25 about this layer of control; it is used in much synchronous data transmission.

Layer 3: Network Control

The third layer, the network layer (also known as the packet layer), is where the real substance of the Recommendation X.25 is found. The network layer is where X.25 provides the virtual circuit interace to packet-switched service. Each X.25 packet indicates one of the 15 available logical channels. This channel identifies the packet as being on a switched or permanent virtual circuit for both directions of communications. The actual range of valid logical channel numbers is defined between the DTE and the network service being used. The logical channel numbers are only significant between the communicating DTE and DCE interface pair. Any one DTE may communicate with many other DTEs, each using a switched and/or permanent virtual circuit.

This layer describes the formats of packets that are used for setting up and clearing a virtual call, sending data over virtual circuits, controlling message flow, sequencing and interrupts, and recovering from the various problems that might occur.

This layer of control is unique to X.25 and it is described in the remainder of this chapter. In conjunction with the other layers, it describes what is equivalent to a transport subsystem in manufacturers' architectures, but is intended for large-scale implementation by common carriers.

PACKET FORMAT

X.25 describes the formats of packets that shall be passed between a user machine and DCE in order to set up and use virtual circuits.

The packets have the general format shown in Figure 25.6. This format is included inside the HDLC envelope. There are two types of packets: **data** and **control** packets. The

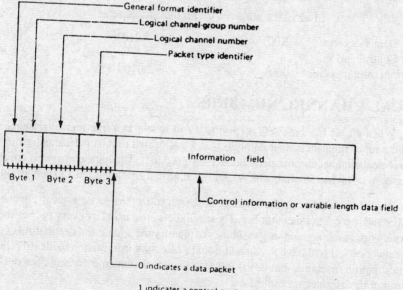

Fig. 25.6 : The general format of X.25 packets. This is included inside an HDLC envelope.

last bit of the third byte indicates whether a packet is a control or data packet. (8-bit bytes are referred to as octets in the CCITT documents. Their bits are numbered 0 through 7. Bit 7, which we refer here as the last bit, is transmitted first in that octet.

A **data packet** has a variable length information field, carrying user data (and possibly user control information for use external to the X.25 layers of control).

A **control packet** can be of many different types, and the type is indicated by the third byte. Some types of control packets have their own information field following the third byte. This may be one or more bytes.

A special type of control packet is called the INTERRUPT DATA packet. This contains one byte of user information, which may be used for user machine control purposes not defined by X.25. This packet jumps the queues of normal flow and travels as rapidly as possible to its destination.

The first four bits of a packet are a general format identifier. The first bit may be set to 1 or 0 on data packets to give two levels of data transmission. This bit is referred to as the qualifier bit, Q. X.25 does not say how the two levels of data packet may be used. One might carry user control information external to X.25. This is the case with the CCITT concentrator (PAD).

The third bit is set to 1 if modulo 128 counts are used. The fourth bit is set to 1 if modulo 8 counts are used. (We describe these counts later).

The general format identifier can thus take the following forms:

	Modulo 8 counts	Modulo 128 counts
Data messages	X001	X010
Control and interrupt messages	0001	0010

LOCAL CHANNEL NUMBERS

When a user machine sets up a virtual call it selects a free logical channel number from the set of logical channel numbers that are allocated to it. A permanent virtual circuit has a logical channel number permanently assigned to it. The logical channels are arranged into groups of up to 255 channels. A user machine can employ up to 15 such groups.

The identification of the channel is therefore in two parts: logical channel group number and logical channel number. These numbers are carried by every packet and enable both network machines and user machines to identify the source and destination of packets. The network itself will have to add additional addressing information to identify the source and destination machines, but this is left to the network implementor and does not concern the user or the user/network interface.

The logical channel numbers constitute a numbering scheme which is logical to a user machine and its network interface. They may be regarded as the numbers of ports for that machine. The machines at opposite ends of the same virtual circuit use different logical channel numbers. The network machine to which the user machine is attached translates that user machine's logical channel numbers into whatever addresses are necessary for network operation.

When a user machine initiates a virtual call it selects a free logical channel from those available to it. The number of this and its logical channel group are passed to the local DCE which then attempts to set up the virtual call using that logical channel. If it completes the set up then the channel is available for data transfer until it is disconnected. In the DATA TRANSFER state there is no difference between a logical channel used for a virtual call and that used for a permanent virtual circuit.

INITIATING A VIRTUAL CALL

When a computer or terminal controller attached to an X.25 network wants to intiate a virtual call, it selects a free logical channel and sends a CALL REQUEST packet to its local DCE. Figure 25.7 shows the CALL REQUEST packet.

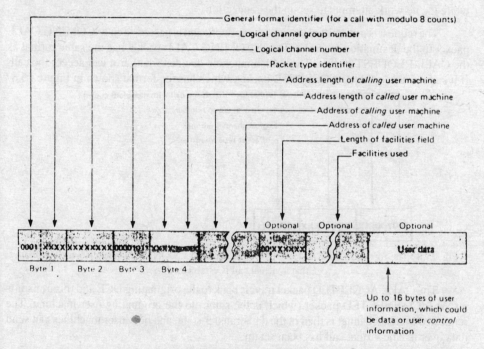

General format identifier (for a call with modulo 8 counts)
Logical channel group number
Logical channel number
Packet type identifier
Address length of *calling* user machine
Address length of *called* user machine
Address of *calling* user machine
Address of *called* user machine
Length of facilities field
Facilities used

Optional   Optional   Optional

| 0001 | XXXX XXXXXXXX | 000001 | XXXXX | | | 00XXXXXX | | User data |

Byte 1   Byte 2   Byte 3   Byte 4

Up to 16 bytes of user information, which could be data or user *control* information

Fig. 25.7 : The format of the CALL REQUEST and INCOMING CALL packets used when setting up a call.

The packet normally contains the address of the destination device and may contain the address of the originating device. Both addresses are variable in length and thus long addresses could be used if necessary. Each digit of the address is encoded in a half-byte in the address field. The address field is preceded by two half-bytes which state how many digits are in each address.

The addresses may be followed by a facilities field which is also of variable length. This field is present when the originating machine wants a call with some operational characteristic which must be communicated to the destination machine. For example, reverse charging may be requested. A maximum data length might be specified because of limited buffer size. A specific window size for flow control might be specified. Other optional facilities may be specified in the future. For each optional facility the facilities field contains a pair of bytes. The first byte of the pair indicates the type of facility request, and the second gives a parameter applying to it, such as maximum data length.

For efficiency, the CALL REQUEST packet may carry user data. This might be control data relating to a layer of control external to the X.25 subsystem (Layer 4) and concerned with functions. However it is used, the X.25 protocol is unconcerned with the contents of the data field.

When a CALL REQUEST is sent on a logical channel, that channel changes its state at the user/network interface from READY to DTE WAITING. The data machine waits while the network attempts to set up the connection.

The request is transmitted through the network and is passed as an INCOMING CALL packet to the destination machine. The INCOMING CALL packet has the same format as the CALL REQUEST packet. The callled machine decides whether it can accept the call. If it can it sends a CALL ACCEPTED packet, which has the format shown in Figure 25.8.

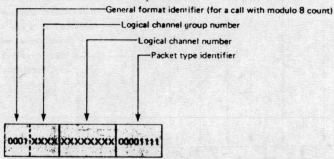

Fig. 25.8 : The format of the CALL ACCEPTED and CALL CONNECT packets which confirm that a virtual call is established.

The CALL ACCEPTED packet travels back to the originating DCE and this transmits a CALL CONNECTED packet (which is the same) to the originating user machine. The requested logical channel is then in the data transfer state, and both user machines can send data over it. The virtual call has been set up.

It is possible that a DCE might receive an INCOMING CALL packet from a distant machine at the same time as a CALL REQUEST packet from a local machine, and both request the same logical channel. It cannot satisfy both requests. It is in a CALL COLLISION state. It cancels the incoming call and responds normally to the CALL REQUEST.

If the attempt to set up a call is unsuccessful, the DCE responds to the calling user-machine by sending a CLEAR INDICATION packet which gives the reason why the CALL REQUEST was not compiled with.

PRIORITY

An optional feature of X.25 allows a virtual call to be set up with two priority levels. A user machine can request that a call it places have high priority. A call for interactive data interchange might be made at the high priority; a call for batch transmission might be made

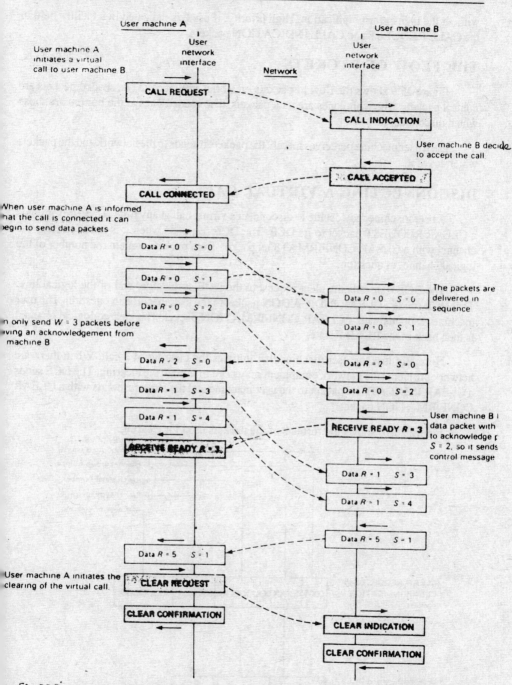

Fig. 25.9 : A virtual call with a window size W = 3. Each user machine perceives merely the packets entering and leaving the network.

without the high-priority indication. High priority, if used, is indicated in a facility field of the CALL REQUEST and CALL INDICATION packets.

THE FLOW OF PACKETS

Figure 25.9 shows the flow of packets on a brief virtual call. The shaded packets are control packets. The white ones are data packets. The shaded ones at the bottom are those which disconnect it.

Each user machine perceives merely the packets it sends to the network and the packets which leave it.

DISCONNECTING A VIRTUAL CALL

A user machine may decide to disconnect a virtual call at any time. To do this it sends a CLEAR REQUEST packet to its DCE. The DCE responds when it is ready to clear the channel with a CLEAR CONFIRMATION packet. Both packets contain the number of the logical channel in question.

The DCE transmits the clear request to the DCE at the other end of the logical link. That DCE sends a CLEAR INDICATION packet to the user machine in question. The user machine responds with a CLEAR CONFIRMATION packet. The cleared logical channel is then back in the READY state.

Normally it is the user machine that initiates the clearing of a call. When there are network problems the network equipment may need to initiate the clearing. The DCE sends a CLEAR INDICATION packet to the user machine and the latter responds with a CLEAR CONFIRMATION packet.

Figure 25.10 shows the formats of the packets used for clearing.

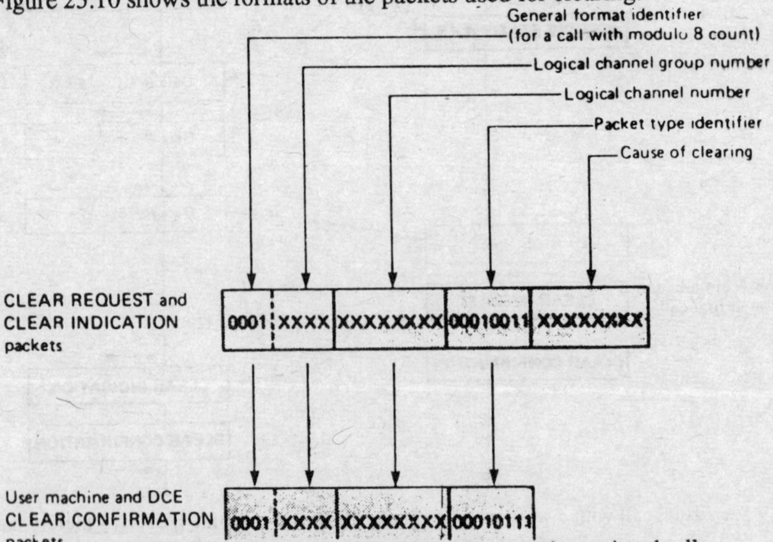

Fig. 25.10 : Packet formats used when disconnecting a virtual call.

DATA TRANSFER

Once a logical channel is in the DATA TRANSFER state, a user machine can send data packets over it. Figure 25.11 shows the format of the data packet.

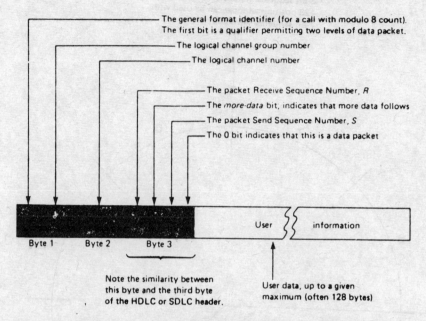

Fig. 25.11 : The format of the X.25 DATA packet (with 3-bit counts).

The data field is of variable length, demarcated by the HDLC flag which indicates the end of the packet. The maximum packet length may differ from one network to another. When a user's data is longer than the maximum packet size, the user divides it into several packets, which the network delivers in sequence. The third byte of the header contains a more data bit which, if set, indicates that more of the same data record follows in a subsequent packet. The more data bit can only be set in a maximum length packet.

CCITT Recommendation X.25 suggests that the maximum data field length should be 128 bytes. It states that some telecommunications administrations may support other maximum data lengths: 16, 32, 64, 256, 512 or 1024 bytes, or, exceptionally, 255 bytes. Different networks may use different packet sizes. In this case the DATA packets may have to be split or combined as they pass from one network to another. The more data bit would be used in conjunction with this.

Data packets can be of two types, as designated by the Q bit in general format identifier. The X.25 Recommendation does not specify how the two types should be used. It is likely that one type will carry normal user data and the other will carry control information employed by the end-user machines external to the transport network.

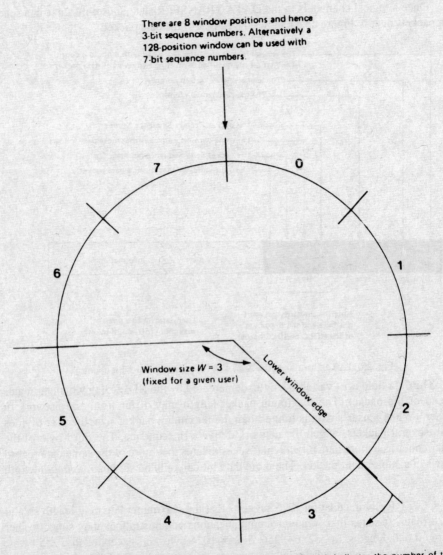

There are 8 window positions and hence
3-bit sequence numbers. Alternatively a
128-position window can be used with
7-bit sequence numbers.

Window size W = 3
(fixed for a given user)

Lower window edge

Packets are acknowledged with the Receive Sequence Number, R, which indicates the number of the next
packet the user machine expects. The lower window edge is then set to R. The sender may send packets up to
but not including R + W (in this illustration R + 3 because the window size is fixed at W = 3). The receiving
network machine arranges the packets within the window into sequence, if necessary, before delivering
them.

Fig. 25.12 : The window mechanism used for flow control.

SEQUENCE NUMBERS

As in the other link protocols, the data packet contains sequential message numbers for flow control. The Send Sequence Number, S, is a sequential message number composed when the messages are sent. The Receive Sequence Number, R, is composed by the receiver when it is ready to receive another message; it gives the Send Sequence Number of the message it expects next. These numbers are usually modulo 8 (3 bits). They reside in the third byte of the header of the DATA packet, which is similar to the third byte of the HDLC header except for the more-data bit.

A window mechanism is used to regulate the flow of data, as illustrated in Figure 25.12. A user machine can transmit packets with sequence numbers within the window. When these packets are received and acknowledged the window rotates.

When a user machine first transmits on a logical channel the lower edge of its window is set to zero, and the Send Sequence Number of its first message is zero. If the window size is W, it can transmit up to W packets before receiving an acknowledgement. The acknowledgement can be either a data message or a control message. It contains a Receive Sequence Number, R, which is the number of the next packet which the receiver expects to receive. When this reaches the sender, the lower edge of the sender's window is set to R. The sender can then send messages numbered up to, but not including R + W.

The window size is fixed for a given user machine and is agreed between the subscriber and the common carrier at subscription time.

Sequence numbers can be used for acknowledgement sequencing, and flow control. In the X.25 protocol these functions are combined into a simple integrated procedure.

Figure 25.11 shows 3-bit sequence numbers giving a modulo 8 count. This corresponds to the modulo 8 window shown in Figure 25.12. If high-speed lines are used (such as T1 carrier or PCM links following CCITT Recommendations A.732 or A.733), or if the propagation delay is long, as on satellite channels, a modulo 8 count is too small. A modulo 128 count can be used by employing a fourth byte in the header in Figure 25.11 to extend each of the count fields by 4 bits.

The general format indicator which starts each packet shows whether a modulo 8 or modulo 128 numbering scheme and window is used. Most networks are being implemented with modulo 8 numbering. When traffic volumes build up so that high bit-rate links are needed, and when satellite links come into use, modulo 128 numbering will probably be employed.

If user machines are exchanging data, the flow control signals containing the receive sequence number can be piggy-backed on the returning DATA packets. If not they must be sent by a separate control message. A RECEIVE READY packet is used to indicate willingness to receive W DATA packets starting with the value of the receive sequence number, R. Figure 25.9 shows a RECEIVE READY packet in use.

A RECEIVE NOT READY packet is returned by a user machine when it is temporarily unwilling to receive further DATA packets. It sends a subsequent RECEIVE READY packet when it is once again ready to receive data. Figure 25.13 shows RECEIVE READY and RECEIVE NOT READY packets.

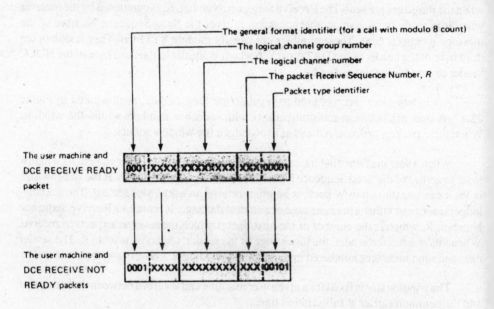

Fig. 25.13 : Packets used to acknowledge a DATA packet (with 3-bit counts).

INTERRUPT PACKETS

A user machine can send an INTERRUPT packet which bypasses the flow control procedures used for normal DATA packets. The INTERRUPT packet contains only one byte of user data. It is transmitted as quickly as possible to its destination, jumping the queues of normal DATA packets. The INTERRUPT packet is delivered to a user machine even when it is not accepting DATA packets.

The INTERRUPT packet could carry user data, but normally it is employed for user control information rather than data. If, for example, a user of a typewriter-like terminal presses the break key to stop a flow of data from a distant computer, this action could be relayed with an INTERRUPT packet to the computer.

The INTERRUPT packet contains no sequence numbers because the sequencing of such packets is of no concern and the packet bypass the normal flow control procedures. Because of this there must be a separate means of acknowledging INTERRUPT packets. An INTERRUPT CONFIRMATION packet is used for this purpose. A user machine is not permitted to send a second INTERRUPT packet on a given logical channel until it has received an INTERRUPT CONFIRMATION packet. Figure 25.14 shows INTERRUPT and

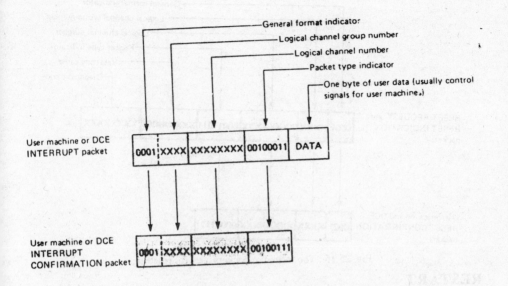

Fig. 25.14 : The format of the INTERRUPT and INTERRUPT CONFIRMATION packets.

INTERRUPT CONFIRMATION packets. These are the same whether they pass from the user machine to the DCE or vice versa.

RESET

Certain types of problems on a virtual circuit can cause that circuit to be reset. Resetting does not disconnect the virtual circuit; it reinitializes it. The lower edges of the windows for both directions of transmission are reset to zero so that the next data message will have a Send Sequence Number and Receive Sequence Number of zero. Any DATA or INTERRUPT packets in transit at the time of the reset are discarded.

A reset could occur for a variety of reasons. For example, the remote user machine might be out of order. The subscriber link might not be functioning. The local or remote user machine might have sent a packet with a procedural error. The network might have congestion conditions on that virtual circuit which temporarily prevent data transfer from taking place.

A reset can be initiated either by a user machine or by a network machine. A user machine does so by sending a RESET REQUEST packet to its DCE. The network indicates that a virtual circuit is being reset by sending a RESET INDICATION packet to the machines using that virtual circuit. This packet contains a byte which gives the cause of the resetting. Machines receiving either of the above packets respond by returning a RESET CONFIRMATION packet. The link is then in data transfer state waiting for new transmission to begin. Figure 25.15 shows these RESET packets.

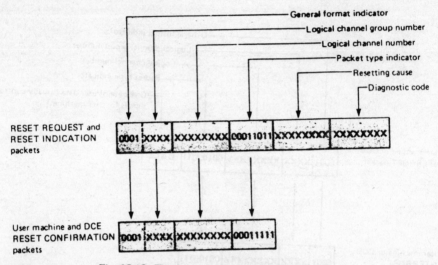

Fig. 25.15 : The format of packets used for resetting.

RESTART

A restart condition is more drastic than a reset. It provides a mechanism to recover from major failures. A restart is equivalent to clearing all of the virtual calls that a user machine has connected, and resetting the permanent virtual circuits (because these cannot be cleared). The user machine may then attempt to reconnect its calls. The restart procedure thus brings the user/network interface to the state it was in when the service was initiated.

A user machine may initiate a restart by sending a RESTART REQUEST packet to its DCE. The network may initiate a restart because of a catastrophic network failure, or because a user has failed to follow a correct restart procedure, by sending a RESTART

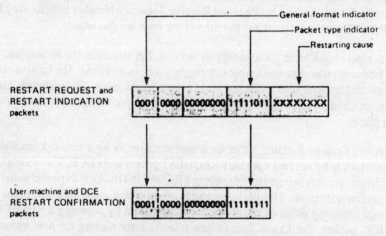

Fig. 25.16 : The format of packets used for restart.

INDICATION packet across the user/network interface. This packet gives a reason for the restart. The response to either a RESTART REQUEST or RESTART INDICATION packet is a RESTART CONFIRMATION packet. These packets are illustrated in Figure 25.16.

STATE DIAGRAMS

Each of the logical channels which a user machine has available to it can be in one of several **states**. If it is free -- i.e., no call is in existence on it -- then it is in the READY state. When a call is in existence it is in the DATA TRANSFER state.

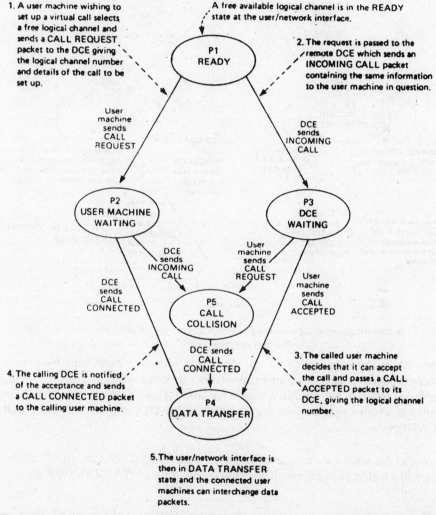

1. A user machine wishing to set up a virtual call selects a free logical channel and sends a CALL REQUEST packet to the DCE giving the logical channel number and details of the call to be set up.

A free available logical channel is in the READY state at the user/network interface.

P1
READY

2. The request is passed to the remote DCE which sends an INCOMING CALL packet containing the same information to the user machine in question.

User machine sends CALL REQUEST

DCE sends INCOMING CALL

P2
USER MACHINE WAITING

P3
DCE WAITING

DCE sends INCOMING CALL

User machine sends CALL REQUEST

DCE sends CALL CONNECTED

P5
CALL COLLISION

User machine sends CALL ACCEPTED

DCE sends CALL CONNECTED

4. The calling DCE is notified of the acceptance and sends a CALL CONNECTED packet to the calling user machine.

P4
DATA TRANSFER

3. The called user machine decides that it can accept the call and passes a CALL ACCEPTED packet to its DCE, giving the logical channel number.

5. The user/network interface is then in DATA TRANSFER state and the connected user machines can interchange data packets.

Fig. 25.17 : A state diagram for the call set-up phase. A normal call set-up follows the numbered steps.

Several other states occur in the transition between the READY and DATA TRANS-
FER states, i.e., in the call setup and disconnect phases. Figures 25.17 and 25.18 are state

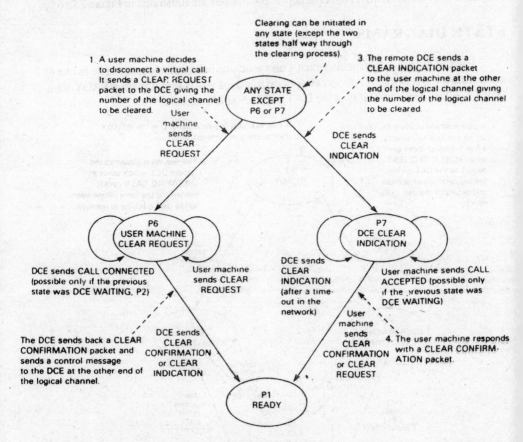

Fig. 25.18 : A state diagram for the clearing process. A normal dis-connect of a virtual call follows
the four numbered steps.

diagrams which show the setting up and clearing of calls. The figures list the normal
sequence of operations. Double-state transition arrows are exceptional circumstances -- e.g.,
call collisions in which two machines request the same logical channel simultaneously, or
a situation in which a user machine does not respond quickly enough to a DCE CLEAR
INDICATION.

Neither the setup nor the clearing operation is used with permanent virtual circuits.
These employ logical channels which normally remain in the DATA TRANSFER state.

There are seven states used for normal operation, designated p1 through p7. They are
listed along the top of Table 25.1. This table shows the types of packets which the user
machine can send in each state.

Table 25.1 : Action taken by the DCE on receipt of packers from the user machine (DTE) in a given state of the packet level DTE/DCE interface: call setup and clearing

State of the interface / Packet from the DTE	Ready p1	DTE waiting p2	DCE waiting p3	Data transfer p4	Call collision p5	DTE clear request p6	DCE clear indication p7
Call request	NORMAL	ERROR	NORMAL	ERROR	ERROR	ERROR	ERROR
Call accept	ERROR	ERROR	NORMAL	ERROR	ERROR	ERROR	NORMAL
Clear request	NORMAL	NORMAL	NORMAL	NORMAL	NORMAL	NORMAL	NORMAL
DTE clear confirmation	ERROR	ERROR	ERROR	ERROR	ERROR	ERROR	NORMAL
Data, interrupt, reset or flow control	ERROR	ERROR	ERROR	See Table 25.2	ERROR	ERROR	NORMAL

NORMAL : The action taken by the DCE follows the normal procedures as described in the text.

ERROR : The DCE indicates a clearing by transmitting to the DTE a clear indication packet, with an indication of Local Procedure Error. If connected through the virtual call, the distant DTE is also informed of the clearing by a clear indication packet, with an indication of Remote Procedure Error.

The DATA TRANSFER state has three substates related to the reset operation. These are FLOW CONTROL READY, the normal condition when a logical channel is in use. DTE (user machine) RESET REQUEST and DCE RESET INDICATION. Similarly, there are two additional states used by the restart operation: DTE RESTART REQUEST and DCE RESTART INDICATION. Tables 25.2 and 25.3 show the types of packets the user machine can send in these states.

Table 25.2 : Action taken by the DCE on receipt of packets in a given state of the packet level DTE/DCE interface: flow control and data transfer.

State of the interface / Packet from the DTE	Date Transfer (p4)		
	Flow control ready (d1)	DTE reset request (d2)	DCE reset indication (d3)
Reset request	NORMAL	NORMAL	NORMAL
DTE reset confirmation	FLOW CONTROL ERROR	FLOW CONTROL ERROR	NORMAL
Data, interrupt or flow control	NORMAL	FLOW CONTROL ERROR	NORMAL

NORMAL   : The action taken by the DCE follows the normal procedures as described in the text.

FLOW CONTROL ERROR : The DCE indicates a reset by transmitting to the DTE a reset indication packet, with an indication of Local Procedure Error. The distant DTE is also informed of the reset by a reset indication packet, with an indication of Remote Procedure Error.

Table 25.3 : Action taken by the DCE on receipt of packets in a given state of the packet level DTE/DCE interface: restart

Packet from the DTE \ State of the interface	Any state p1 to p7 and d1 to d3	DTE reset request state	DCE reset indication state
Reset request	NORMAL	NORMAL	NORMAL
DTE reset confirmation	ERROR	ERROR	NORMAL
Data, interrupt, call set-up and clearing, flow control or reset	See Note	ERROR	NORMAL

NORMAL: The action taken by the DCE follows the normal procedures described in the text.
ERROR: The DCE indicates a restarting by transmitting to the DTE, a *restart indication* packt with an indication of Local Procedure Error.

Note—**See Table 25.1 for call setup and clearing; see Table 25.2 for data, interrupt, flow control, and reset.**

OPTIONAL FACILITIES

We have described the standard features of the X.25 protocol. There are also some optional features, and there may be more optional features in the future. A user machine may request an optional facility when a call is set up, by using facilities byte-pairs in the CALL REQUEST packet (the last shaded field in Figure 25.7). The optional facilities are as follows:

1. **Reserve charging** (already mentioned). A user machine originating a call may request reverse charging. The called machine may be designated as one which accepts reverse charging, otherwise the network will not deliver to it a packet with a reverse charging request.

2. **High priority** (already mentioned). This permits data packets to have a higher priority than normal.

3. **Closed user group**. A closed group of users may share an X.25 network with other users, but members of the closed user group can communicate only with one another. This restriction of network use may be done for security reasons, or it may be done to control costs. A computer with sensitive information on its files may be callable only by certain specified machines. A terminal user may be restricted in the computers he can call.

A user machine can be a member of more than one closed user group, in this case a CALL REQUEST packet must specify which user group that call relates to.

A user machine may be permitted to make unrestricted outgoing calls, but have incoming calls only from a closed user group.

4. **One-way logical channel**. On a logical channel with this optional facility a user machine will be permitted either to place calls but not accept calls from other users, or to accept calls but not place them.

5. **Packet retransmission**. A user machine can ask its DCE to restransmit one or several data packets. It does this by sending a REJECT packet to the DCE containing the

Receive Sequence Number, R, of a packet received. The DCE retransmits packet R and those following it. The number of packets for retransmission cannot exceed the flow- control window size. This is not an end-to-end mechanism. The request for retransmission of a data packet cannot be relayed to the user which originated that packet.

6. **Flow control parameter selection**. A network normally has a given maximum window size and maximum data length. A user machine may optionally operate at less than these because it has limited buffer size or control capability. The window size and maximum data length is referred to as a **throughput class** and may be indicated in the **facilities** field of a CALL REQUEST packet. If there is no such indication, the call is connected with the highest attainable values.

26

INTEGRATED SERVICES DIGITAL NETWORK

INTRODUCTION

The revolution in telecommunications of which so much has often been spoken is now in full swing. On one hand microelectronics and new transmission media present hitherto undreamt of chances to implement new forms of communication, and on the other hand the users' demand for communication facilities is growing appreciably, above all for non-voice services (Telex, Teletex, Telefax, etc.) and combinations of these with telephony.

The public networks are of prime significance in this respect, with discussion focused on the Integrated Services Digital Network (ISDN), which ideally fulfills all the said requirements and which has already largely been standardized by the CCITT.

The Integrated Services Digital Network (ISDN) has been widely discussed at conferences and in the telecommunication industrial circles for the past few years. Organisations like the CCITT (International Consultative Committee for Telephony and Telegraphy) are working towards developing standards for a unified, digital, global communication network. The ISDN standards were recommended by the CCITT as an attempt towards this goal. The conversion of the world telecommunication network to an all digital one will open up exciting changes both to the voice and data traffic. At the same time the overall operating costs will come down.

Initially the ISDN is aimed at combining the various existing forms of communication like telephony, telex, facsimile, and data communication systems which at present have separate networks. But in future it will provide additional facilities like home banking and video conferencing. And above all, it can act as a central framework to be utilised by the new emerging technologies. The CCITT recommendations aim at providing the ISDN services as readily available to a subscriber (through a single standard interface) as electric power is today. ISDN will make it possible to allow a telephone, a computer terminal or a facsimile machine to be plugged into the same interface for communication to the outside world.

TODAY'S TELECOMMUNICATIONS NETWORKS

The historical development of telecommunications has been such that there are now separate, optimized special-purpose networks for the various communication services for speech, text and data transmission. Of these networks, only the "classical" networks, namely the telephone and the telex network, have developed into global open networks, i.e. networks in which every connected subscriber can reach his partner by the same terminal operations and at any time. This advantageous development is due to the great worldwide demand, hence of the large numbers of subscribers, a continuous optimization of the networks during their long development time and a service worth its money.

In the case of the younger data communication networks practically no globally open networks have as yet evolved. This is due to a number of reasons. The data is transmitted at different speeds and with different protocols (interface specifications); the demand for worldwide data communication has so far been smaller as for the telephone service; and the smaller number of users has meant that low-cost networks have hitherto not been feasible. Admittedly, part of the data traffic has been transmitted internationally over the "classical" telephone and telex networks: not optimally, but relatively cheaply.

The recently established radio networks, such as satellite radio and mobile radio networks, can never achieve global proportions, because they are limited by physical restrictions (radio frequencies are limited). Both of these network types can, in principle only, be tied to the terrestrial network and help to optimize it.

THE WAY TO ISDN

Until today, communication users have been generally satisfied with the existing development, because their basic communication requirements could be satisfied. The separate different networks, however, cannot meet certain new communication requirements and the networks themselves are not satisfactory for all demands. For a future communications network the following requirements must be considered (see Figure 26.1):

-   It is not possible at present to simultaneously conduct a call from a terminal and to call down information from a data base via the same terminal, a process that will in the future become a daily need because most information will be electronically stored. We are sure that it must in the future be possible to conduct all kinds of communication in parallel. This "mixed" communication is ideal for the human being, who naturally communicates by various means simultaneously, such as hearing, sight, writing, etc.

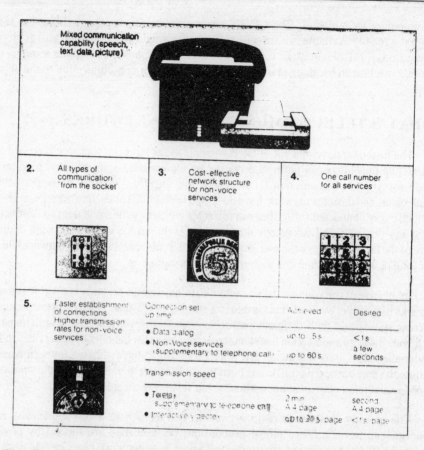

Fig. 26.1 : The five most important requirements in the telecommunications network of the future.

-   Today,communication is tied down to certain locations by fixed cabling to the various terminals. It would be desirable, however, to have "plug-in" communications. That is, every communications socket would permit the connection of terminals for all kinds of communications.

-   The connection and call charges for the non-voice services in special networks are still relatively high compared to the telephone, and are often worth the expense only because the special line units are not used individually by one person but jointly by a whole office or by several subscribers. Lower-priced network structures, and hence cheaper rates for these services, are therefore something to strive for, in order to make it possible for each subscriber to have his own line.

-   Today, the subscriber needs different call numbers and operating procedures for the different communication services. Uniformity would be of great advantage.

-   The performance of today's networks for non-voice services is partially unsatisfactory. There is a need for higher transmission speeds and shorter call set-up times.

To summarize: Now that the paperless office is being developed, and electronic mail is beginning to take over from the letter post and data processing is reaching every home in the form of interactive videotex and personal computers, a subscriber expects a new plug-in subscriber line termination, with which he can operate mixed communication media worldwide. Today's user expects better network performance at normal telephone charge rates; he want to be reachable under only one number and he wants standard procedures for operating the various communication services.

EVOLUTION OF ISDN

The ISDN is envisaged to evolve from the existing telephone networks. In the case of an ordinary analogue exchange where two subscribers are connected together, there should be a continuous physical link between them. But in the case of a pulse amplitude modulation (PAM) type system the principle of time division multiplexing (TDM) is made use of.

As shown in Figure 26.2, switches SW1 and SW2 will sample the lines in synchronisation at least once in every 125 micro seconds. This is the Nyquist sampling rate required for

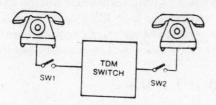

Fig. 26.2 : PAM exchsnge

voice frequency range so that no information is lost due to sampling. For the rest of the time, the physical path can be utilised for transferring information between other subscribers.

Digital switching, Figure 26.3, is an altogether different technique. Here, the analogue voice is first converted to digital form by a codec (coder-decoder). Now this data is directed

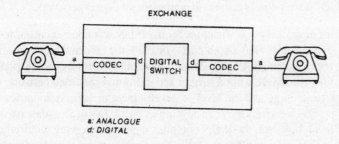

Fig. 26.3 : Digital exchange

to appropriate memory locations under program control according to the destination address of the channel. Data is collected from these memory locations by separate circuitry. Digital switching takes place in steps of interleaved time and space division switching (T-S-T). At the output it is converted back to analogue form and sent to the destination.

The first step in the evolution of an ISDN exchange from a digital exchange is moving the codec from the central switching exchange to the subscriber as shown in Figure 26.4. The link between the user and the central exchange is now digital. This is the common digital link to all the services.

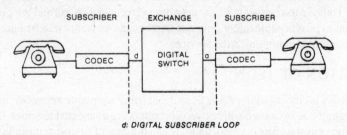

d: DIGITAL SUBSCRIBER LOOP

Fig. 26.4 : Towards ISDN

The ISDN will have an access node at the central telephone office, to which other networks will be connected to offer various services. These services can then be accessed via a standard interface in the user's premises to which different types of equipments can be connected. To a user the whole system looks like a single integrated network. In future, all the segregated networks may be unified into a single network. Even though the whole system appears simple, this is however not the case. Let us take a closer look at the ISDN.

SOME FACTS ABOUT ISDN

A wide spread of all communication services at low cost can only be achieved on the basis of a network with high subscriber density -- such as the telephone network has. That is why telecommunication engineers always wanted an integrated network that could satisfy these conditions. The invention of PCM by Reeves in 1938 was the first important step towards this integrated network. It then became possible for the first time to represent analog signals digitally, and hence to construct a network in which all informations can be encoded in the same digital form. The second decisive step was the development of semiconductor technology, which alone permits economic realization of digital networks.

The work of developing specifications for the ISDN was taken up in earnest in 1978, and since then great advances have been made. In 1984, the essential recommendations for the ISDN were approved by the CCITT Plenary Assembly. According to the present status of the specification, the ISDN is not a strictly and uniformly specified network. By taking into account the technology and the level of development of various countries it offers a framework within which each country can develop its own ISDN in accordance with national needs. At base level, however, the ISDN complies with the following requirements, these being intended to guarantee fulfillment of the above-mentioned demands of a communications network of the future:

- The ISDN is being developed on the basis of uniform 64 kbit/s transmission channels for all types of information -- speech, text, data and video. These channels are through-connected digitally end-to-end. The 64 kbit/s are derived from the coding of the analog speech signals, confirming once again that the ISDN will substitute the present telephone network.

– To permit mixed communication, the ISDN provides two 64 kbit/s information channels and one 16 kbit/s signalling channel per subscriber. The separate signalling channel makes it possible to keep the 64 kbit/s information channels "transparent" for each type of communication. Additionally, the 16 kbit/s signalling channel can be used to transmit telemetry data and as feeder for "slow" data packets.

– The subscriber line circuit specifications provide for a bus interface. Via parallel sockets, any speech, text and data terminals may be connected to the bus.

– With the two 64 kbit/s information channels and the 16 kbit/s signalling channel, the ISDN will be able to handle all conceivable requirements concerning transmission speeds and call set- up times, with the exception of moving picture communication and very fast data transmission.

– Each subscriber will have only one directory number.

– Signalling and procedures will follow the standard protocols, in order to ensure uniform operation and transmission procedures.

– Because the ISDN replaces the telephone network, it should get call charges which are similar or equal and so make non-voice services especially attractive.

– As a substitute for the telephone network, the ISDN will be a worldwide, open network. It will, of course, be necessary to introduce digital links initially at the higher network levels, which, given a suitable introduction strategy, ought to be possible in the medium term.

If we are to promote the rapid spread of the ISDN, it should permit medium-term access to the existing networks. It remains to be decided, however, what points of transition are to be realized and when.

The ISDN is created by adding hardware and software to an existing digital telephone network. The ISDN subscriber terminal, although more expensive than a normal telephone connection, ought to be still cheaper than two connections to an analog network, respectively a corresponding combination of connections to today's analog and digital networks. That is, the basic conditions of technical progress are fulfilled, namely improved services with better performance at lower cost.

OTHER CONSIDERATIONS RELATING TO ISDN

Network transitions

Since the ISDN will replace the telephone network, transition from the telephone network to the ISDN and vice versa must of course be provided from the outset. This will also probably be a simple matter, since the telephone service quality and tariffs will be identical, or very similar, in both networks.

The ISDN is predestined to boost the development of new and efficient non-voice services in combination with the telephone. It is for this very purpose that its transmission capacity has been so greatly increased over that of existing networks. Network transitions to existing non-voice networks can expedite the growth of the ISDN greatly. They permit those subscribers who decided for a connection to the ISDN to continue communication with their partners in other networks. However, new services, on the other hand, should exclusively be offered within the ISDN.

The discussion concerning network transitions will be complex, since not only their technical implementation be achieved, but also an agreement on tariffs. Also, the harmonization of equivalent services and service qualities between the different networks is problematic and will be an important task for CCITT and CEPT to tackle, in order to prevent further service sub-variants being created over a wide variety of network transitions. Nevertheless, at least for new ISDN text services, a transition into the worldwide open teletex network should be provided, over which in most cases the telex network is also accessible.

The topic of network transitions will only continue to be discussed until the ISDN has acquired a certain amount of coverage in the various countries. After this coverage has been reached, the ISDN with its low charges and high performance will very soon supplant the existing networks.

Packet-switching networks, too, will be facing strong competition from the ISDN. As they are offering very favorable services for special applications they probably will exist for some time beside the ISDN, or in combination with it.

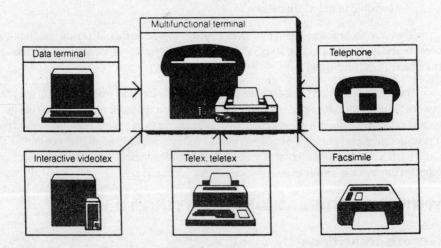

Fig. 26.5 : Mixed communication will be realized ingeniously by multifunctional terminals

Multifunctional terminals

Mixed communication, one of the principal aims of the ISDN, can be achieved in the best manner by multifunctional terminals since it would be inconceivable for one communication station to be equipped with the collection of monofunctional terminals that would be required for the number of services desired.

Therefore, the future main station line takes the form of a multifunctional terminal capable of handling several ISDN communication services (Figure 26.5). Which communication services will be combined in multifunctional terminals will finally be decided by the demand of the market.

In addition there will be a variety of monofunctional special terminals optimized for specific functions. These terminals can then be operated parallel on a new main station line. Owing to the efficient signalling in the ISDN (also from subscriber to subscriber) and the possibility of charge registration depending on the transmission capacity used, the ISDN is completely unconstrained as regards the connexion of terminals.

In order to achieve rapid wide-spread introduction of the ISDN, it may be advisable to include a transition period during which existing terminals would also be connected to the ISDN, though these would then have to be adapted for the functions of the new services. Existing equipment would therefore have to be fitted with a conversion adapter.

Division of functions between terminal and network

As already mentioned, many versions of new mono- and multifunction terminals will be introduced for the new ISDN. Such a range can only be promoted if the network terminations feature high performance and are unambiguously defined, so that every subscriber can be connected.

The division of functional capacities between terminal and network has only been given very vague consideration in previous discussions on standardization, since it is still not known which functions will actually be implemented. However, in this age of the microcomputer we should, where any doubt arises, opt to allocate the function to the terminal. When computer controlled telephone exchange technology (SPC) was being introduced, it proved as the right solution to allocate network-specific functions to the network, and to allocate all other functions to the terminal where this was possible.

The argument that the terminals would thereby become too expensive can be countered by the fact that microcomputers feature extremely high performance characteristics and that subscribers to our communication networks are prepared to pay a lot for attractive features.

ISDN for wideband communication

Interactive videotex is undoubtedly an outstanding invention and a very useful service, but it has a typical weakness, namely, the representation of "analog images". For this we require "TV quality", especially if a moving picture is to be represented. There is therefore a requirement for wideband services in the ISDN.

Unfortunately, the discussions on the standardization of wideband ISDN have not progressed very far beyond the statement that these standards are required. The specification work should go ahead so as to prevent the implementation of different types of wideband channels in different countries, and to agree on a uniform wideband ISDN standard.

It would be prudent to introduce the TV standard for wideband communications with a view to profiting from commercial television through the technology required and the economic production of wideband terminals. One suggestion is a uniform transparent 140 Mbit/s channel with component coding. With this an international uniform transmission -- irrespective of the TV standards PAL, SECAM, NTSC, etc. -- and every form of high speed data transmission is possible. The wideband network could be controlled in parallel with the 16 kbit/s signalling channel of the narrow-band ISDN. This could then produce a wideband ISDN with extremely high performance features.

Standardization of the wideband ISDN is also an urgent matter because the introduction of glass fibers into local networks depends on it. The specification of satellite networks also depends on standardization, these being the means of flexibility and of rapidly achieving a widespread ISDN wideband network.

To bring about a rapid introduction of the glass fiber into the local network, ISDN subscribers should be given priority for connection via glass fiber cable, wherever network development and network planning permit. This would ensure that an ISDN subscriber could also be accorded priority for wideband connection should this be available and desired. ISDN subscribers are the most likely potential users of wideband communication facilities.

Telemetry and remote control

Currently there is a discussion taking place about which means of transmission would ensure the most widespread introduction of telecontrol engineering. The best means would probably be via telephone subscriber lines, because they are the most likely type of line already leading into every household. Rapid introduction via coaxial cable distribution systems would not be advisable as these are laid out in a tree structure and do not lead into every household.

In the context of narrow-band ISDN, there has also been discussion on the subject of transmitting telemetric and remote control data using the 16 kbit/s signalling channel. By its packet oriented mode of operation it is especially suited for solving the task of transmitting alarms and reading meters, measuring equipment, etc.

THE ISDN STANDARDS AND PROTOCOLS

The CCITT published its initial recommendations for the ISDN in the Red Book of I series in 1984. The ISDN is based on the open systems interconnections (OSI) model of digital networks proposed by the International Standards Organisation (ISO). The ISDN defines only the first three layers of the OSI model. The CCITT has defined various channels for carrying information on the network. Also there are two types of interfaces for the customer to choose from: the basic rate interface or the primary rate interface.

The basic rate interface operates bidirectionally at 192 kBps. It includes two 64kBps channels that bear either voice or data which are called bearer channels B1 and B2; a 16kBps data channel (the D channel) used for network signalling and control; and a 48kBps channel overhead for framing and error detection. Voice transmission can be through either of the B channels and customer premises equipment (CPE) negotiates B channel usage with the central exchange through D channel each time it initiates a call. It is expected that this 2B+D basic rate interface will be suitable for residential users because its bandwidth is sufficient for most potential home applications.

The primary rate interface has two structures: 1.544 MBps which can be used as 23B+D in North America and Japan; and 2.048 MBps which can be used as 30B+D in most European and Asian countries. This structural difference in primary rate interface is to make it compatible with the two types of existing digital PCM formats: T1 in North America and Japan; and CEPT standard in most other countries including India. In the primary rate interface, the D channel carries signalling information at 64 kBps. Even though there will be one set of 23B+D or 30B+D channels per physical pair, it is possible for the D channel in one primary rate pair to carry signalling information for B channels in other parallel wires. The primary rate interface is suitable for access to the network by large business customers with a private branch exchange (PBX).

The ISDN standards define four reference points: the RST and U interfaces. Figure 26.6 shows an ISDN architecture. Starting at the central office (CO), the U interface link

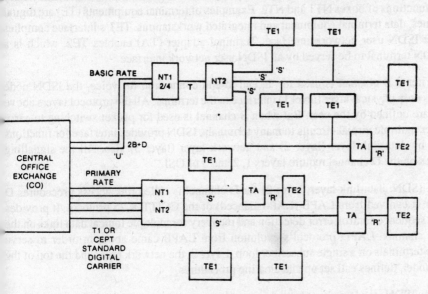

Fig. 26.6 : ISDN architecture.

will transport the B and D channels from the CO to the customers' premises. The U interface uses only one twisted pair to link the CO with the network termination (NT1) box. This interface is called the U interface because it was undefined to accommodate the different needs of various countries. As the national governments of many countries own and operate their telephone systems, the CCITT has left the U interface definition to them.

Network termination box (NT1) terminates the U interface and transforms it into the 4-wire S or T interface. The T interface generally exists between NT1 and NT2. The S interface uses two twisted wire pairs to carry traffic. One pair carries signals from the NT1 box to the ISDN terminal equipment to NT1. A terminal adapter (TA) converts S interface traffic into the R format so as to allow non-ISDN terminals (TE2) to be connected to the network. The R format is similar to RS-232C (CCITT recommendation V.24) interface.

Network termination NT1 is the carrier's side of the connection to the network. It contains logic that properly terminates the transmission and times the data in each digital frame for transmission or reception. NT2 handles the user's side of the connection such as multiplexing and demultiplexing the B and D channels on to each line and switching them to and from their destinations or origins. NT1 includes functions equivalent to the OSI's physical layer. NT2 performs the functions up to layer 3 of OSI model. PBXs and terminal controllers are examples of NT2. NT1 and NT2 can be combined and their functions provided by an ISDN PBX.

At reference points S and T either basic rate or primary rate can be used. As shown in Figure 26.6, enhanced ISDN PBXs can directly access the 1.544 MBps(T1) or 2.048 MBps (CEPT) digital trunk carriers through primary rate interface. This PBX will essentially carry out the functions of boxes NT1 and NT2. Examples of terminal equipments (TE) are digital telephones, data terminal equipment and integrated workstations. TE1's interface complies with the ISDN user network interface. Terminal adapter (TA) enables TE2, which is a non-ISDN terminal to be served by an ISDN user network interface.

When a B channel is used for an end to end connection for voice, the ISDN node provides only physical layer (level 1) interface to the terminal. All the protocol layers above layer 1 are defined by the user. But when B channel is used for packet switching to carry data over multiple virtual circuits to many terminals, ISDN provides interface for functions defined by data link layer (layer 2) and network layer (layer 3) also. All the signalling messages on the D channel require layers 1, 2 and 3 of OSI.

In ISDN, data link layer (layer 2) for D channel is called link access procedures D (LAPD). It evolved from LAPB (LAP-balanced) of the CCITT X.25 protocol. It provides framing sequence control, error detection and recovery for multiple logical data links on the same D channel. LAPD protocol's evolution from LAPB came about in order to serve multiple terminals on a single subscriber loop. Layer 3, the network layer and the top of the ISDN model, defines call set up and clearing procedures.

The ISDN standards have been developed so as to achieve very high flexibility. Thus, a user can structure the primary rate in fashions other than that explained here. There can be three types of high speed data channels H0 (384 kBps), H11 (1536 kBps) and H12 (1920 kBps). The bandwidth of H0, H11 and H12 channels are equivalent to 6, 24 and 30 B channels respectively. Subscribers can mix and match H with B and D channels to suit their applications. Also, a primary rate user can dynamically allocate bandwidth utilising the D channel signalling mechanism up to 31 channels in the 30B+D format and up to 24 channels in the 23B+D format. The signalling between network nodes is using the Signalling System 7 (SS7) recommended by the CCITT.

THE ISDN IMPLEMENTATION

The concept of ISDN is being tested in different countries like Japan, West Germany, Belgium and the US. Japan was the first nation to begin trials with its information network system, although it differs from the true ISDN standards on some points. This is due to the fact that Japan finalised its system before CCITT formulated the recommendations for the ISDN. Many companies like Siemens, Philips, Intel Corporation, Motorola Semiconductors, and Advanced Micro Devices inc, have come out with ISDN chips which can be used for developing an integrated system. The Regional Bell Operating Companies (RBOC) in the US are going in a big way for implementing the ISDN.

Currently the CCITT is working on recommendations for maintenance of the network, for interfaces between the ISDN and the specialised services and many other final details. The existing recommendations may also be modified after feedback from field trials. Broadband ISDN is another field in which studies are going on. Bandwidth of the copper wires in the subscriber loops currently supporting the basic and primary rate interfaces is limited. But data rates of the order of 500 to 600 MBps are possible with fibre optic technology. Potential broadband services include viewdata, video telephony etc.

In India too there are some major developments. Most of India's existing exchanges and circuits are analogue in nature. India first entered the digital telecommunication field by starting the production of digital electronic exchanges by the Indian Telephone Industries Ltd, in collaboration with CIT-Alcatel of France. Then came the indigenously developed digital exchanges from the Centre For Development of Telematics (C-DOT) and those from the Indian Telephone Industries Ltd (integrated local cum trunk exchange - ILT). Now C-DOT has taken up a mammoth project to develop the basic infrastructure required for the ISDN in India.

Finally, a word about the cost factor which the customers will have to bear. Recent studies conducted in the US show that one ISDN line will cost about 1.5 to 1.7 times the price of the average old telephone service line. To users with voice and data needs the formula means they can expect to pay some 15 to 25 per cent less than what they had to pay separately. So the ISDN's initial customers will be businessmen and big officers. Eventually, the cost per ISDN line will come down to 1.2 to 1.3 times. Also, the demand for home data lines will go up, making the ISDN implementation more economical. Anyway, the ISDN will be instrumental in bringing the computer and telecommunication fields together, paving the way for the information revolution.

ISDN CHIPS

ISDN will provide a major innovative impetus to the telecommunications industry. Among the most important innovations with ISDN is the increase in the transmission rate over the public telephone lines from 3.4 kHz for voice and 19.6 kbit/per sec for data to a standardised 144 kbit/per sec. For instance, with current technology, transmission of moving pictures with acceptable quality is possible over 64 kbit/per sec channels. In addition, a multitude of data services can be handled with advanced ISDN ICs, harnessing conventional 2-wire (U interface) and 4-wire (S interface) telephone networks.

Siemens and Advanced Micro Devices (AMD) have signed an agreement to cooperate in the development, production and marketing of such circuits. The foundation of the agreement is based on 15 currently available ISDN ICs from both companies. The agreement represents the continuation of a successful ten-year cooperation in the field of microcomputer ICs, which is supported by more than a dozen individual agreements on integrated circuits.

A wide variety of ISDN terminals, such as telephones, data terminals and voice/data workstations can be realised using the common chip set based on the IOM-2 architecture.

AMD's Am79C30A digital subscriber controller (DSC) integrates in a single chip S-bus transceiver functions, protocol controllers and telephony functions including a codec filter.

Siemens PEB 2085 ISDN subscriber access controller (ISAC-S) and PSB 2160 audio ringing codec filter (ARCOFI) offer a modular approach for similar functions. In an ISDN data terminal the ISACS together with Siemens PSB 2110 ISDN terminal adaptor circuit (ITAC) form an access module for interfacing conventional data processing equipment to the ISDN. The AMD Am79C401 integrated data protocol controller (IDPC) perform similar handling and transfer of packet oriented data, such as X.25.

The network termination, which constitutes the connection box on the customer premises for interfacing to the ISDN, is realised with Siemens' PEB 2080 S-Bus interface circuit (SBC) and PEB 2090 ISDN echo cancellation circuit (IEC). These two ICs perform the functions of transmitting the 2B+D ISDN data rate over the 4-wire CCITT S interface and the 2-wire U interface, respectively.

The currently available IEC is the first IC on the market which supports a national interface standard. This standard was defined by the German Bundespost in 1984 and currently being supported by a number of countries and large communication companies. A version of the IEC for the US T1D1 U interface standard, the PEB 2091, is available. Both IEC versions fulfill the stringent requirements of long distances for local 2-wire loops. low cost 2-wire transceiver for PABX applications is realised with the PEB 2095 ISDN bus transceiver circuit (IBC).

Subscriber line cards in switching systems, both private and public, can be designed in a modular way with the common ISDN chip set. For private exchange systems, the SBC and IBC can be used as transceivers for 4- and 2-wire systems, respectively. Public line cards use the IEC for local subscriber loops. LAPD signalling can be handled locally by the PEB 2075 ISDN D-channel exchange controller (IDEC). Four independent HDLC controllers have been integrated on the IDEC. The PEB 2055 extended PCM interface controller (EPIC) establishes the interface between the line card and system internal PCM highways.

The common chip set is completed by the SAB 82525 high-level serial communications controller extended (HSCX). The HSCX is a powerful general purpose protocol controller which represents an economical solution to much more expensive traditional communications controller boards. The HSCX has special telecom functions integrated to make it an optimal solution for local packet handling on line cards. LAPD signalling for primary rate connections (e.g. T1, CEPT) and X.25 data conversion for ISDN terminals.

All these devices are presently or will shortly be equipped with the IOM-2 interface.

STANDARDIZATION IS DECIDING

With the ISDN, we are approaching a new era in communications which is still difficult to imagine primarily because it offers such an immense range of new possibilities. Such possibilities will only be fully realized once new, multifunctional terminals come into being. One hopes that with the advent of this new world of telecommunications, the ISDN should not be bogged down with technical standardization problems for all existing networks and terminals, but rather, that this new ISDN should be left free to optimally develop its high performance capabilities in the economic and technical contexts. Only afterwards should consideration be given to what additions are required.

It is also to be hoped that the ISDN will be left unhampered during its development phase, because nature, too, could not progress in leaps, without development being impaired. The way for the ISDN has been cleared by the CCITT in 1984. It will now be up to the PTTs and the industry to allow this new world of communications to develop at a reasonable, feasible pace.

27

WIDE AREA NETWORKS

INTRODUCTION

Wide area networks (WAN) are composed of a number of autonomous computers that are distributed over a large geographical area. WANs emerged in the late 1960's, mainly as an academic research project. The idea was to provide efficient communication between sites, allowing hardware and software to be economically shared by a wide community of users.

Wide area networking can be implemented with the help of private networks as well as public networks. Private networks are built within one corporation. The implementors lease circuits for private use which are usually telephone lines and construct a network. On the other hand, public networks are built by government telecommunication agencies. The transmission and switching facilities are shared by several corporations and organisations. Public networks can handle greater volumes of data and are economical. But majority of the organisations use private networks, as the public networks are still in its infancy.

PRIVATE NETWORKS

The first WAN to be designed and developed was the private network, ARPANET, an United States network. The objective was to make the interesting and unique computer facilities available in some computer centres accessible to a large community of users. It has grown from a four-site experimental network to a nationwide communication system interconnecting more than fifty universities and research centres.

A few computer networks link computer centres in multiple locations. To operate these multicorporate networks, a separate service organisation is usually set up and that organisation will take care of creating and operating the network. A leading example is the SWIFT electronic fund transfer network that passes financial transactions between banks.

SWIFT (Society for Worldwide Interbank Financial Transactions) is a non-profit organisation set up and wholly owned by the banks connected to it. The objective of this network is to replace mail, cable and telex and work for 24 hours a day and 7 days a week. It handles over a million transactions per day. It is used to send money, messages and bank statements at high speed between banks and the transaction time is drastically reduced.

SWIFT connects about 3000 financial insitutions in more than 60 countries. Citibank Corp in New York, was the first one to opt for the system and over 40 banks in India have joined the network. The computer-based terminals of these banks are hooked with SWIFT's access centre in Bombay, which is maintained by CMC Ltd. From here, messages are relayed to the overseas communication centre of VSNL, and then transmitted to SWIFT's international receiving centres based in London or Singapore, depending on the location of the receiver, through VSNL's GPSS services. The software needed for the operations has been supplied by SWIFT terminal services, a wholly owned subsidiary of SWIFT and the hardware is being supplied by Tata Unisys, Digital Equipment (India) Ltd. The participating banks finance the system and a tariff structure has been built based on the message, connection charge and annual charge.

SITA is another private network that passes messages between airline computers around the world.

Some of the private networks operational in India are the following:

- CMC's INDONET that offers e-mail services on a subscription basis to the customers.

- NIC's NICNET that connects all the district head quarters.

- SBI's SBINET that connects all the branches of the State Bank of India across the country.

- WELCOMNET, that connects the Welcom Group hotels in India.

PUBLIC NETWORKS

During the mid 1970's the need for building a public data network was realised by the telecommunication administration of various countries, with two specified objectives. One was to provide better services to the computer community and the other was to earn revenue which was enormous. This is the revenue from the switches, concentrators, multiplexers, polling equipment, line control equipment, etc. -- the various devices used in the interconnection of machines. Common carriers operate (this term includes the telecommunications administrations of countries with government- controlled telecommunications - the PTT's) the equipment for switching and routing telephone calls; it seemed natural that they should operate the new equipment for switching routing data.

Once computers were used for switching the desire grew to use them for other functions also. AT&T developed its plans for ACS (Advanced Communications Service) in which the nodes would not only switch data but provide a variety of functions which need processing and storage. The British Post Office created its Viewdata schema (subsequently called Prestel) for operating public data bank accessible with television sets in homes or offices, initially via the telephone network.

CIRCUIT-SWITCHING AND PACKET-SWITCHING

There are two main categories of public computer networks: packet-switching networks and circuit-switching networks.

A **packet-switching** network divides the data traffic into blocks, called "packets" which have a given maximum length (for example, 128 bytes). Each packet of user data travels in a data envelope which gives the destination address of the packet and a variety of control information. Each switching node in a minicomputer reads the packet into its memory, examines the address, selects the next node to which it shall transmit the packet, and sends it on its way. The packets eventually reach their destination, where their envelopes are stripped off. Then, they may have to be reassembled to form the original user messages. It is rather like a postal service in which letters in envelopes are passed from one post office to another until they reach their destination. The typical delivery time on today's packet networks is about a tenth of a second.

A **circuit-switching** network establishes what is in effect, a physical circuit between the communicating machines. The circuit is set up rapidly under computer control; it remains set up while the data passes, which might take a second or less, and may then be disconnected so that other users can employ the same facilities. The reader might think of a copper path, carrying electricity, which is set up for a second or so between the communicating machines and is then disconnected. In fact the path is not a simple copper circuit because time-division switching is used in which many streams of bits flow through an electronic switch, all interleaved with one another. Circuit switching has been used for decades in telephone exchanges and in the worldwide telex network. The difference with computer networks is that the user circuit is set up and disconnected very quickly. The switched connection is often used only for the time it takes one message to pass, or for one message and an interactive response; sometimes it remains connected for the transmission of a batch of data. This rapid computer-controlled switching is sometimes called fast-connect switching.

PACKET-SWITCHING NETWORKS

Many advanced nations now have a public packet-switching network, either working or talked about. These are becoming interconnected into multinational networks so that packets can travel around the world or at least part of it.

The first major public packet-switching network was Telenet, shown in Figure 27.1. This derived its techniques (and its management) from ARPANET, the first private packet-switching network. Telenet was bought by GT&E, the second largest U.S. telephone company in 1979.

Some of the examples of national packet-switching networks are:

1.   Bell Canada's DATAPAC, the X.25 packet switching system of the Trans Canada Telephone System.

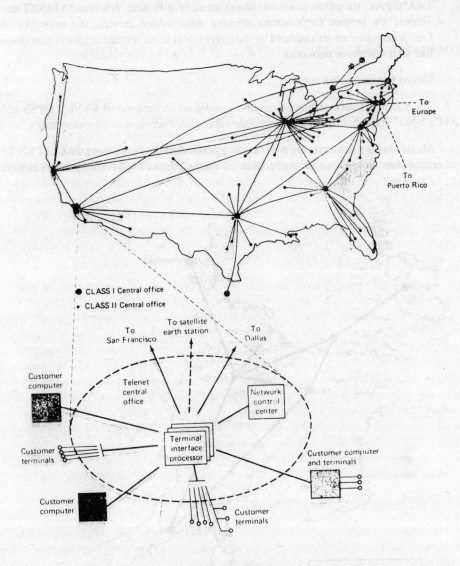

Fig. 27.1 : (a) Telenet's rapidly changing packet-switching network—one of the first "value-added common carriers." (b) A physical map of Telenet.

2.   TYMNET became a value-added common carrier in 1976 and has been growing rapidly ever since. TYMNET competes with Telenet.

3.   TRANSPAC, the public paket-switching network of France. Whereas TYMNET and
Telenet are private corporations offering value-added service, the networks of
European countries are operated by the government telecommunications organisation
like their telephone networks.

4.   United Kingdom PSS network

The public network services available in India are in the form of VSNL's GPSS and
DOT's I-Net. These public networks provide value added services to their customers.

Most industrial countries are now building public data networks using the CCITT X.25
and related standards. These are interconnected via the international record carriers and via

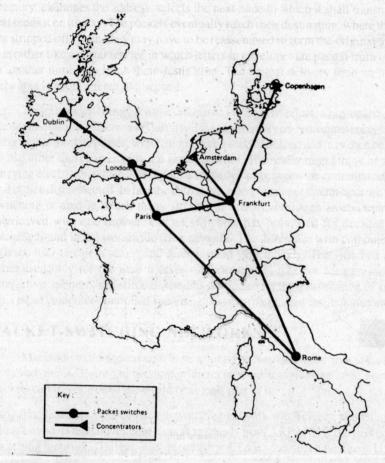

Fig. 27.2 : EURONET, a multinational network capable of interconnection with national networks
EURONET uses packet-switching protocols compatible with TRANSPAC and other national networks.

EURONET. These networks can add new links and switches quickly. Figure 27.2 shows a transnational network, Euronet, which can carry packets between the national networks in Europe.

Many subscribers are a long distance from a switch, so concentrators are used to bring the user traffic to and from the network. The concentrators may form a small start network linked to a packet switch linking many users to the nearest packet switch. Most users are linked to the networks by telephone lines going directly to a switching node or else to a concentrator. This restricts their maximum data rate to that of a telephone line: 9600 bits per second. In North America some users can have higher-speed digital links into their premises.

User machines connected to a packet-switching network need to observe a rigorous set of rules for communicating via the network. It is desirable that networks in different countries should follow the same set of rules so that user machines around the world can employ the same software and control mechanisms, and so that packets can pass easily from one network to another. There has been a high degree of international agreement on the rules -- the protocols and message formats -- for public packet-switching networks, centering around Recommendation X.25 of the CCITT, (Comite Consultatif International Telegraphique et Telephonique) the international standards organization for telecommunications.

FAST-CONNECT CIRCUIT-SWITCHED NETWORKS

The first public circuit-switched network was built by the Datran Corporation in the United States, and was subsequently taken over by Southern Pacific Communications, Southern Pacific no longer offers the Datran type of switching publicly.

Whereas Datran built a digital microwave trunk specially for the purpose, other circuit-switched data networks use conventional wideband circuits between the switching nodes. Figure 27.3 shows a good example, the Nordic data network of Scandinavia. The data switches are interconnected by trunks operating at 64,000 bits per second. Multiplexers

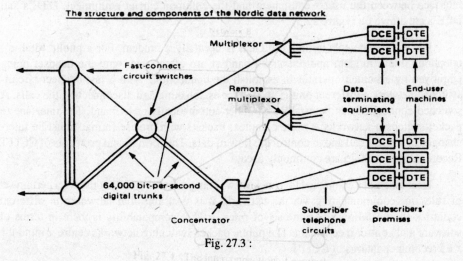

The structure and components of the Nordic data network

Fig. 27.3 :

and concentrators carry users' traffic to the nearest switching node. These also are connected to the network by 64 Kbps trunks. There may be two or more trunks connecting two switches, or connecting a concentrator and a switch. More trunks are allocated to a data network as its traffic builds up.

The network provides switched synchronous data circuits at speeds of 600, 2400, 4800 and 9600 bits per second. Asynchronous (start- stop) terminals at speeds of 110, 150, 200, 300 and 1200 bits per second may be connected to the network.

The call set-up time is normally 100 to 200 milliseconds -- very fast compared with the telephone network, and fast enough to make it economical to disconnect after each message and response in a man- machine dialogue.

Any circuit-switched network can encounter a "busy" condition, just as there are busy signals from the telephone when all circuits are in use. The designer of a circuit-switched network adds trunks and switching facilities until a sufficiently low proportion of the calls encounters a network busy condition. The probability that an attempted call will be unsuccessful is a basic design parameter of a circuit-switched network. The Nordic network is designed so that less than 0.5% of calls will fail to be connected due to network faults or congestion. This figure is determined by the numbers of trunks. Because the call set up time is fast and most calls are brief, the unit which controls the user connection to the network can retry an unsuccessful call quickly and have a high probability of succeeding on that attempt.

DTE's AND DCE's

The end-user machine -- terminal, computer, controller, etc. -- is referred to by the telecommunications administrations as a DTE, Data Terminal Equipment. This machine must plug into a unit which is the termination point of the communications circuit. This is called a DCE, Data Circuit-terminating Equipment. This plug-in connection forms the interface between the user's equipment and the common carrier equipment. DTE's and DCE's are drawn on Figure 27.3.

For a leased telephone line the DCE is normally a modem. For a public (dial-up) telephone line a modem and telephone handset are often used, with the handset being employed by a human operator to establish the connection. With a fast-connect circuit-switched network a different unit is needed for establishing and disconnecting the calls. A switched connection can be established either automatically or by hand. The interface to packet-switching networks is more complex. Packets with precise formats must be interchanged to set up a call and to control the flow of data. The formats and protocols of CCITT Recommendation X.25 are commonly used.

User machines connected to a packet-switching network have to observe a certain set of rules for communicating via the network. It is desirable that networks in different countries should follow the same set of rules, so that compatability is there in terms of software and control mechanism. The public packet-switching networks centre around the x.25 recommendations of CCITT.

CONNECTIONS BETWEEN NETWORKS

Sometimes it is desirable to employ more than one type of network to achieve a given connection. CCITT recommendation X.75 discusses the international gateways. A dialed telephone call may be made to access the concentrator of a packet-switched network. A multinational call may be set up involving a packet-switched network in one country and a circuit-switched network in another. Not all packet networks have identical formats, and messages may need to pass from one network to another.

To deal with network connections, interface machines are needed. The connection between different data networks is called a gateway. It consists of a minicomputer which appears to each network as though it were a normal node of the network. It takes data in the format of one network and puts it in the format expected by the other.

In Figure 27.4 where a machine connected to Network A communicates with a machine connected to Network C, an addressing scheme will be needed which permits the connection to be set up to the right network and also to the requisite node on that network.

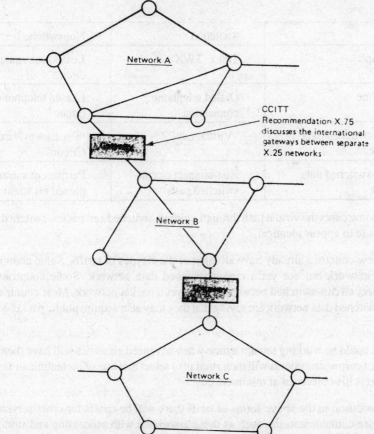

Fig. 27.4 : The interconnection of networks.

Euronet (Figure 27.2) could evolve into a "hypernetwork" designed to interconnect other networks. Worldwide hypernetworks will also be needed if efficient public networking is to take place worldwide.

EIGHT TYPES OF TARIFFS

The switched networks provide two types of connections between machines: first a connection switched through the network so that a machine can request a switched path to any other machine connected to the network; and second, a connection which is permanently established between two machines. A "permanent" connection does not imply a permanent physical path between the machines. On a circuit-switched network it implies a continuous stream of bits or bytes derived by submultiplexing. On a packet-switched network it means that when one of the conected machines sends a packet it is routed automatically to the other machine with no preliminary call set-up.

In the future, then, there could be eight main types of basic tariff associated with telephone and telegraph circuits and the two types of data networks as depicted in Table 27.1.

	Switched	Nonswitched
Telegraph	Telex, TWX	Leased subvoice-grade circuit
Telephone	Dialed telephone connection	Leased telephone circuit
Packet-switched data network	"Virtual call"	"Permanent Virtual Circuit"
Circuit-switched data network	Fast-connect circuit-switched path	Permanent submultiplexed bit stream

In some cases the virtual path through a circuit-switched and packet-switched network can be made to appear identical.

A few countries already have all eight of these types of tariffs. Some countries have a packet network but not yet a circuit-switched data network. Some countries have a fast-connect circuit-switched network but not yet a packet network. Most countries with a circuit- switched data network are saying that they may also acquire public packet-switching facilities.

We could be working toward a time when advanced countries will have them all. The designer of corporate systems will then attempt to select that mix of communication facilities which meets his objectives at minimum cost.

In addition to the above forms of tariff there will be tariffs for other services which are not pure communications, such as those associated with processing and storage in the nodes as in AT&T's ACS.

NEED OF PACKET SWITCHING AND X.25

The packet switching concept was first proposed in the early 1960s for military communication systems, mainly to handle speech. It was proposed that speech should be digitised and transmitted in short bursts (packets) using a mesh type of network. It was subsequently realised that the technique with additional refinements might be ideally suited to the requirements of remote access computing systems. From the mid-1960s the technique was widely explored, initially almost entirely in the academic and research communities.

The benefits of packet switching were seen as follows:

- the subdivision of information into individually addressed packets in conjunction with alternative routing arrangements enabled the transmission path to be altered in the event of congestion or individual link failure;

- the employment of additional intelligence within the network enabled more sophisticated error control and link control procedures to be applied;

- packets associated with different users or calls are clearly distinguishable and this provided the basis for an efficient form of statistical multiplexing, making variable speed transmission available to users according to the demands of their applications.

- by employing wide bandwidth circuits for the trunk network, substantial economies through extensive sharing of capacity could be achieved.

Apart from any other advantages, packet switching was seen as providing a relatively low-cost means of improving the reliability of analogue transmission networks.

PACKET SWITCHSTREAM (PSS) SERVICE

Packet SwitchStream (PSS) was introduced in the UK in 1981 and is now one of the many well-established data communication systems currently on offer from British Telecom.

PSS is a national, public network designed and equipped specifically for the transfer of data by computers and terminals throughout Britain and with connections to networks in many overseas countries. It aims to complement, rather than supersede, other British Telecom data transmission services. PSS provides full-duplex working and it can also provide intercommunications between terminals which operate at different speeds.

Nationwide availability of PSS is assured by a special network. PSS exchanges are located in large towns and cities for convenience of installation. PSS has a distance-independent tariff, so new exchanges can be added to the network whenever growth demands, without the changes resulting in a revision of charges to individual customers, or any need for individual customers to review their arrangements.

The present network which has a hierarchical and modularised structure served approximately 4,000 customers at the end of 1984 and is doubling its X.25 port capacity each year.

All PSS switches are duplicated as a matter of security policy and have the protection of three levels of power supply. Network control and management is focused on Network Management Centres (NMCs) in London and Manchester. Each is a fully-duplicated computer system and is capable of running the complete network in an emergency.

Customers' Equipment

All PSS customers have to provide their own terminal equipment. British Telecom does not recommend any models, nor does it designated approved suppliers.

All devices connected to PSS are referred to by BT as terminals in preference to the CCITT term Data Terminal Equipment (DTE). Terminals can be packet devices or character devices.

Permission to Connect

Permission to connect is generally sought by manufacturers who submit their new products to British Telecom. The equipment must have BABT approval to ensure that it cannot harm the functioning of the BT networks. In the case of intelligent devices, those parts of the software which affect the network, directly or indirectly, are examined by PSS.

Access Facilities

PSS supports a wide range of terminals, from teletypes to host computers. Access facilities are categorised by type of terminal (packet or character) and type of connection (dial-up or dataline).

A packet terminal is capable of constructing the package for transmission and reassembling the stream of incoming packets into messages. This type of terminal uses the CCITT X.25 protocol, which enables it to connect directly to PSS. Character terminals are simple devices, such as teletypes, which connect to PSS through a PAD (Packet Assembly/Disassembly) unit. The PAD performs the tasks of packet assembly/disassembly and call control.

Packet terminals are connected to the network by datalines- dedicated links to the packet switching exchange (PSE) - these are referred to as 'packet datalines'. Three line speeds are available: 2400, 9600 and 48,000 bits per second (bps)

Dial-up character terminals access is via the public switched telephone network to the PAD at either 300 bps, 1200/75 bps or 1200/1200 bps. The caller may use a modem (rented from BT or otherwise) or an acoustic coupler.

Packets and Calls

In PSs, 'octets' (8 bits) of data are assembled into packets, each packet normally consisting of a 'wrapper' of control information and up to 128 octets of user data. Longer packets can be requested by any user, up to a maximum of 1024 octets, by using the optional 'extended formats' facility.

For charging purposes, each packet is counted using the unit called a 'segment'. This is 64 octets, or part thereof.

A number of packets transferred between two points form a call. PSS has two types of call - the datacall and the minicall.

The datacall is defined as having the three distinct phases referred to earlier: call set-up, data transfer, call clear. Call set-up involves the calling terminal sending an initial 'call request' packet to the distant terminal. If it is accepted, a 'call accept' packet is returned. The data transfer phase covers the flow of packets of user data, whilst 'call clear' is a final packet which terminates the datacall. Datacalls are available to 'packet dataline', 'character dataline' and 'dial-up' terminals.

The minicall is a short message (up to 128 octets) in the 'call request' packet. An equally short response may be included in the returned 'call clear' packet. Minicalls are available to 'packet dataline' and 'character dataline' terminals but 'character dataline' terminals can accept but not make minicalls. Dial-up 'character terminals' cannot make or accept minicalls.

Addressing

All terminals on PSS have a Network User Address (NUA). PSS will bill all charges to NUAs, and for this reason dial-up users are notified of the NUA which will be used by PSS for billing purposes.

All NUAs consist of 12 decimal digits as shown below, and two optional extra digits which are available for packet terminals only to use for sub-addressing.

DNIC												Sub-address	
1	2	3	4	5	6	7	8	9	10	11	12	13	14

National Number

The first four digits of the NUA are known as the DNIC (Data Network Identification Code).

The first three digits of the DNIC identify the country, the fourth identifies the service within that country. The rest of the NUA from digits 5 to 12 identifies the particular dataline termination. In the UK the DNIC is 234 with a fourth digit '2' to identify PSS.

A packet terminal user must quote the full NUA of the number called, including the DNIC, whether calling a character terminal or another packet terminal.

A character terminal (dial-up or dataline) only needs to quote the 'national number' part of the NUA, digits 4 to 12, of the number called. This saves the trouble of entering the first 3 digits; the PAD will do this when it passes on the call request, but for international calls a prefix and full international number must be used.

INTERCONNECTION OF PUBLIC AND PRIVATE DATA NETWORK

In countries where private data networks are permitted there is a growing requirement for their interconnection with public packet switching network.

As the number and size of private at a networks increase, the maturing system of national data networks with standard X.25 packet mode interfaces and international X.75 connections offers new opportunities for national and worldwide inter-communication.

X.25 concentrators have proved attractive in reducing the customer cost of terminal access to public networks and, when combined with switching capabilities, have enabled cost-effective networks and sub-networks to be built. More specifically, the use of an X.25 switch as a gateway between the public and private networks provides a cost-effective means of sharing relatively expensive X.25 access lines to the public data networks.

Public networks access from private networks can provide increased geographic networks coverage, provide extra network capacity on demand, or provide an alternative form of low-cost back-up to private circuits.

For small private networks requiring wide geographic coverage with low data volumes, long-distance transmission over public networks may be cheaper than dedicated facilities. For large networks dedicated connections on heavily used routes can be supplemented with public network switched connections to permit economical wide geographic coverage.

The term 'gateway' is now commonly used to define a facility which interconnects two networks so that users on one network may communicate with users on another network.

The term 'gateway' is thus broad but here we are solely concerned with a 'gateway' which provides interconnection between private packet switching networks based on OSI principles and the public packet data networks based on the X-Series Recommendations.

There are two fundamental requirements of private-to-public network interconnection methods which need to be provided in gateways. First, universal accessibility for private network Data Terminal Equipment (DTE); and second, adequate cost control mechanisms for administration of the private networks.

Active discussion of private network interconnection is proceeding within the various international standards committees. X.25 is seen as the best protocol available to private packet switching networks but interconnection poses problems of addressing, routing, availability and accounting that are beyond X.25 and must be resolved in the private networks.

Interconnection depends upon the method used to assign addresses to private network DTEs. The standards bodies have placed high priority on finding suitable private network addressing methods. Proposals for addressing extensions through the X.25 facility field and X.121 numbering plan extensions to permit private network addressing are under study.

Private network requirements initially have been met without any special interconnection mechanisms beyond X.25. There is a growing consensus of opinion that public/private network interconnection must be provided for and that X.25 is the appropriate protocol.

The ideal technical solution would be to directly attach private networks to the public services, thus becoming in effect a subset of the public network. However this does present both regulatory and practical difficulties.

CCITT Recommendation X.121 defines the international numbering plan for public data networks; it provides for international addressing within the 15 digit limit of X.25. Three or four digits (the DNIC) are used to identify the country, and possibly a network within the country. Up to 11 or 10 digits are available for use as national addresses. These are given significance and allocated by the network; on PSS they are structured as follows:

digits	5 – 7	area code
	8 – 12	terminal number
	13 – 14	sub-address digits (for use by the user)

In the case of PSS the top 12 digits of the 14 digit addresses (NUAs) are unique, the remaining two digits being available to the user.

If that user is in fact a private network there is an immediate problem of how calls originating on the public network are further routed through the private network. Three approaches to private network numbering which are compatible with X.121 have been proposed: shared address space, private local numbering, and private network national numbering. 'Shared address space' assigns addresses to private network DTEs within the numbering plan of a single public netowork; 'private local numbering' assigns DTE addresses that are chosen independently from the public network plan; 'private network national numbering' is similar to an integrated national numbering scheme except that one or more separate four-digit Data Network Identification Codes (DNIC) are assigned to cover all the private networks within a given country, and each private network has a nationally agreed Private Network Identification Code (PNIC). Although this is the basis of a draft amendment to X.121 a number of drawbacks exists:

– there is, as yet, no UK registration authority for number plans;

–. there is doubt as to whether there is sufficient range of available numbers to accommodate the spread of private networks envisaged;

– the existing public networks do not support this facility.

Althouth there is currently no standard to define the services to be offered by a gateway, explicit standards for interconnection between private and public packet switching networks are actively understudy. As mentioned earlier X.25 as presently defined can be used to provide standard gateways to public networks although the systems being implemented are usually application specific. For example, X.25 concentrators/switches can be effectively used as gateways between public and private networks.

In this role, X.25 gateways provide methods for the routeing and transmission of incoming and outgoing calls from or to a public data network. Both functions differ from previous uses of X.25 as a purely DTE/DCE protocol for public network access.

An incoming call from a public network can address a DTE on the private network using the sub-addressing feature of X.121. This means that the public network does not examine the entire destination address but passes all the information to the private network where further address analysis is carried out. Incoming calls from a public packet network to a private network are thus forwarded by the gateway to the private network terminal identified by the desination sub-address in the call packet.

FEATURES OF PUBLIC PACKET SWITCHED NETWORKS

The most salient of these features are listed below:

— switched service

— variable network propagation delay

— provides for standardised X.25 call multiplexing

— improved error performance

— simpler physical host computer interface

— functionally complex X.25 interface

— speed matching and terminal matching capability

— low level protocol conversion

— centralised network management support

— high integrity

— ease of network reconfiguration

— distance independent access

— traffic dominated usage chage

ROLE OF PSS

There has been much speculation about the role of PSS in the marketplace, and the benefits it can offer compared with the alternative services. In this context, the broad conclusions which have historically emerged are based largely upon the features.

The total cost of using a service can be specified in terms of a selection of variable and parameters which between them describe the particular properties of the service, the facilities which are used, and the extent of the usage. The usage of a service will be strongly influenced by the amount of traffic and traffic patterns. For example it may be appropriate to describe the traffic as that of high volume, long duration, or 'bursty'.

Depending upon the particular service and its associated tariff structure, some particular collection of parameters will be significant. Parameters which directly affect costs will be represented among the cost components of the relevant tariff structure.

A user of the X.25 public data network such as PSS is faced with a rather more complex tariff structure than that for the more traditional circuit switched and leased line services. Leased circuit charges are based upon the length and speed of the circuit and are totally irrespective of the amount of traffic which is being transferred and the time taken for the transfer of the traffic. Circuit switching relates to a usage charge which is dependent upon the total connect time and the distance involved in the individual call. For a specific service the usage charge would typically be obtained from the distance tables for a given type of leased circuit, or the staged tariff for a dial-up connection. With PSS, however, the usage charge is predominatly related to the volume of traffic which is transmitted and to the duration of the call.

BENEFITS OF PSS

PSS is particularly suited to those applications with the following characteristics

- bursty traffic

- low communications intensity

- widely dispersed terminals

- multiple remote host or applications accessed by a single local access circuit terminal and circuit

- access to international packet switched services

Cost saving opportunities arise from the unique PSS tariff structure which is totally independent of distance but related to actual traffic volumes and as such favours low traffic intensity calls. Other cost savings arise from the connection and interfacing arrangements of X.25, X.3, X.28 and X.29, such as:

- standardised multiplexing

- single line local access which leads to a reduction in point-to-point circuit costs

- increased freedom of choice of terminals which alleviates multiple terminal provision

Further savings can result from:

- ease of reconfiguration and attachement of new devices

- network management facilities including standby provision

Chief opportunities for cost reductions at a mainframe site lie in reduced local line interface cost (and modern costs) together with a reduction in network management costs. The X.25 interface provides opportunities for simplifying the line interface particularly for dial-up lines. All dial-up traffic to PSS, instead of being presented at the customer mainframe site as distinct low-speed circuits, is concentrated onto a far smaller number of higher speed synchronous circuits. Apart from simplifying the physical distribution and access arangements, there will be a corresponding reduction in modem and computer port requirements. Furthermore, through the adoption of X.25 the interface is also standardised, thus increasing the interconnection potential of the network.

For a sizeable terminal population and associated mainframe line terminations, these cost savings may be quite significant. However, the price that has to be paid for the above advantages is a greater functional complexity in the interface. This requires substantial intelligence and as such may possibly require major modifcations to the mainframe computer systems software. This would particularly apply to suppliers' older product ranges.

Network management facilities are being increasingly regarded as a major benefit of PSS. For PSTN access they provide a facility which is not currently available and for some point-to-point and multipoint private circuit configurations they could possibly swing the balance towards PSS for those organisations who wish to minimise their network management overheads. Multipoint circuits in particular have always presented special problems for network management and fault diagnosis. The potential value of PSS network management support which is inherent in the service should therefore not be ignore and should be included in any evaluation of the service.

Finally, with BT committed to packet switching as a major 'Open Systems' service which complements the advances in digital circuit switching and digital private circuits, and with the growth of applications which involve inter-organisational data communications, the opportunities of OSI and the adoption of X.25 has great strategic significance for interworking opportunities. It also provides access to those value-added services for which packet switching may be either the most economic or even a mandatory form of access.

As the core X.25 network, PSS alone cannot meet all the cost/performance requirements of the marketplace. The introduction of the local distribution network (MultiStream) enhances the basic PSS service to provide more flexible and effective support for smaller hosts and terminals. Further enhancements result from links to other networks through the InterStream gateways.

PSS offers some significant cost saving opportunities when it is regarded purely as a direct substitute for the traditional PSTN and leased line services. However, an evaluation which is based only upon cost-saving criteria takes a far too narrow a view of the potential benefits and also of how the role of PSS might develop in the medium and long term. A much more broadly based assessment should give great weight to the unique features of PSS, and to the new business and application opportunities which it may present. How the role of PSS is likely to evolve must obviously be considered within the context of both the existing traditional services which have been referred to earlier and the newly emerging digital services such as KiloStream and ISDN.

KiloStream is enabling BT to gradually replace analogue Datel private circuits by digital private circuits and as such is being offered at extemely competitive cost terms compared with analogue circuits with modems. This is attractive at all data rates and over all but the shortest distances, and is substantially cheaper at the higher data rates than the specially provided wideband circuits.

VALUE-ADDED NETWORKS

The concept of value-added common carriers was important in the development of computer networking. A value-added carrier leases communications facilities from conventional common carriers and uses these in conjunction with computers to build a network which offers new types of communications services and tariffs. These are called value-added networks (VANs). Graphnet offered services for delivery of documents, often in facsimile form. Telenet built a network for the interconnection of data processing machines, like the ARPA network although the software and hardware mechanisms eventually became substantially different from ARPANET. Telenet delivers packets of data between computers or terminals in a fraction of a second, and charges by the packet. TYMNET offering similar services evolved from a private time-sharing network to a value-added common carrier.

In 1971 the United States Office of Telecommunications Policy recommended a policy of first-tier and second-tier common carriers. The first-tier carriers construct and own telecommunications links, and lease channels to their customers. They typically own 50% to 100% of the channel miles in service and lease the remainder from another carrier. The second-tier carriers are the value-added carriers. They add equipment including multiplexers and computers, to channels leased from first-tier carriers and sell services that they create in this way, including message-delivery services, computer networks, and possibly information retrieval services and computer timesharing devices. It seems likely that second markets will develop in many telecommunications areas. The second-tier carrier may minimize investment in terminals by letting the customer provide these.

Legislation in favour of second-tier carriers has increased the diversity and competitiveness of the telecommunications industry in those countries where it has been passed. In most countries, such legislation does not yet exist.

Telecommunications systems use computers in different ways. Some use them for switching; some for sorting messages which are transmitted; some for processing the data transmitted. At one extreme the computer merely switches the circuits; at the other the circuits are merely links into a data-processing system. The term "computer utility" became used for describing public access to computer networks, and in 1966 the United States Federal Communications Commission (FCC) initiated a lengthy inquiry to determine whether public computing services should be regulated. The inquiry terminated in 1973 and defined the six categories of operation shown in Figure 27.5 (FCC Docket #16979). Local and remote data processing services are not to be regulated, whereas communications systems are. There is a hybrid service between these two in which a subscriber sends data, which is processed and transmitted to another subscriber. If the data processing is the primary part of this operation, it is not regulated. On the other hand, if the operation is primarily one of communication between the parties, it is regulated. The former is referred to as hybrid data processing and the latter as hybrid communications. There is a gray area between these two about which lawyers will argue. The FCC is now conducting a new inquiry into the subject partly because of the uses of distributed intelligence. It is difficult to say whether certain intelligent functions are "computing" or "communications" functions.

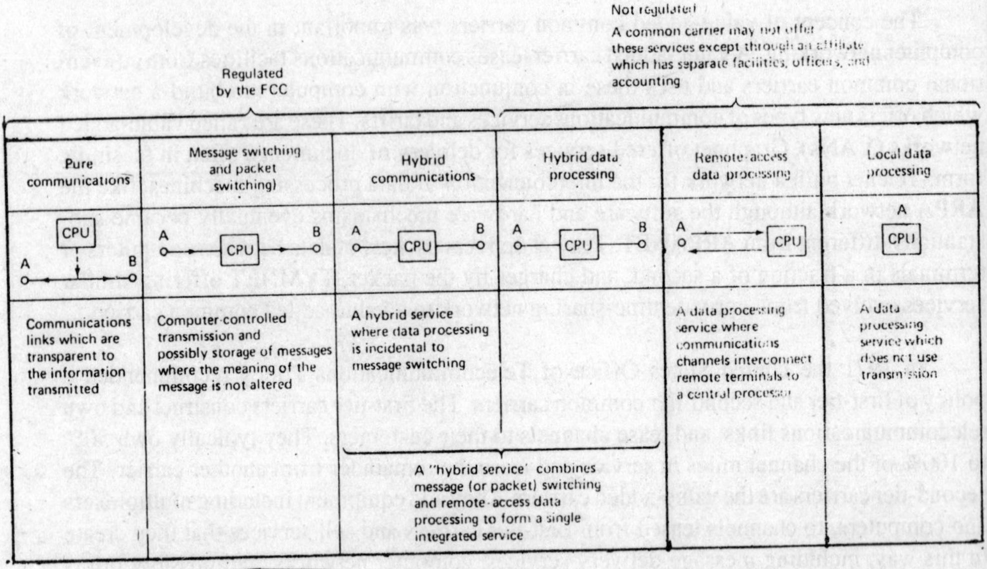

Pure communications	Message switching and packet switching)	Hybrid communications	Hybrid data processing	Remote-access data processing	Local data processing
CPU A ——— B	A o———[CPU]———o B	A o———[CPU]———o B	A o———[CPU]———o B	A o———→[CPU]	A [CPU]
Communications links which are transparent to the information transmitted	Computer-controlled transmission and possibly storage of messages where the meaning of the message is not altered	A hybrid service where data processing is incidental to message switching		A data processing service where communications channels interconnect remote terminals to a central processor	A data processing service which does not use transmission
		A "hybrid service" combines message (or packet) switching and remote-access data processing to form a single integrated service			

Regulated by the FCC (spans first four columns)

Not regulated — A common carrier may not offer these services except through an affiliate which has separate facilities, officers, and accounting (spans last two columns)

Fig. 27.5 : Range of services defined by the first FCC computer inquiry final decision.

Hybrid communication services must be completely tariffed and regulated by the FCC. Common carriers may not offer data processing services (hybrid or otherwise) except through a separate corporation with separate facilities, officers and accounting. AT&T has been excluded from offering any such unregulated services under an earlier consent decree.

Most countries do not have these legislative problems because the state telecommunications authority rigorously enforces its absolute monopoly over all telecommunications, no matter how bad its service may be.

STANDARDS AND CAPABILITY

For computer networks to be useful as possible it is desirable that they should employ standard interfaces so that many different machines can connect to many different networks. Just as telephone devices can connect to telephone networks everywhere, so data devices should be able to connect to data networks everywhere, and the data networks themselves should be linked up worldwide.

The interface to a data network is likely to be more complicated than that to a telephone network because it cannot rely on any human intelligence as does the making of telephone calls. It must be completely automatic. However, if the interface is rigorously defined it can be built into mass-producible VLSI machines and quantity production will make the cost low. It can reside in inexpensive terminals and in computers. One of the distributed logic elements employed by a computer can be the standard network interface unit.

Perceiving this, as we mentioned earlier, telephone administrations (common carriers) of the world used their international standards organization, CCITT, to agree upon an internationally recognized set of protocols for making calls on data networks. This is referred to as CCITT Recommendation X.25. X.25 defined the formats of packets of data which will be used both for carrying information and for setting up and disconnecting calls on data networks, and for dealing with the errors and failures. It is likely that many countries of the world will build X.25 data networks in addition to those already in use. A wide variety of machines using the X.25 protocols will be manufactured.

Producing a standard interface to data networks is complex, and requires different layers of control. X.25 does not attempt to define all of the protocols that are desirable for computer communication or distributed processing. It is concerned with the sending of packets across the network interface. Further, it would not be suitable for all types of transmission networks. Other protocols are likely to continue to exist for inexpensive machines like AT&T's transaction terminals, or the British Post Office's Prestel television sets. Other protocols will exist for circuit-switched networks and wideband networks.

Other protocols will continue to exist in computer manufacturers architectures for distributed processing, and for new or specialized forms of data networks including networks using communications satellites, simple inexpensive networks, networks for facsimile transmission, networks with radio terminals, networks using cable television, and so on.

Network protocols have been created by the following types of organizations:

- CCITT and standards authorities.

- Common carriers with networks simpler and cheaper than X.25, like AT&T's TNS network and leased line networks.

- AT&T, with the introduction of its Advanced Communications Service (ACS)

- Common carriers with technology different from that for which X.25 was created, e.g. communications satellite networks.

- Value-added carriers such as Telenet, TYMNET, Graphnet.

- Computer or minicomputer manufacturers with architectures for interconnecting their software and hardware products, e.g., IBM's SNA (Systems Network Architecture), DEC's DECnet, Sperry Univac's DCA (Distributed Communications Architecture).

- Industry groups creating protocols for specific applications such as electronic fund transfer or airline reservations.

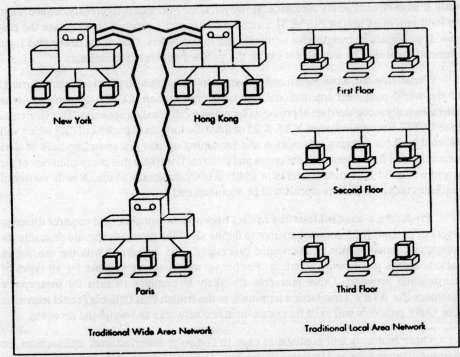

Fig. 27.6 : Differences between traditional Wide Area Networks and Local Area Networks.

- Large corporations which develop their own computer network and networking software (sometimes purchased from a software vendor).

COMMON PRINCIPLES

In spite of the diversity of network types, there are many common principles which can be applied to these networks. The different networks have problems in common such as flow control, transmission errors, user interfaces, congestion, recovery from failures, network management, security, etc. Often they use similar mechanisms for solving these problems. The similarities among ARPANET, new common- carrier networks, DECnet, and IBM's SNA are as striking as the differences.

WAN APPLICATIONS

Wide area networking has its own caveats and concerns. And when your goal is to make a WAN out of LANs, the job gets even more complicated! Often a company starts building LANs that work fine within the head office, only to find a huge job and a lot of compromises facing them when the time comes to connect all those LANs together.

WANs evolved from early telegraph networks and grew up to enable computers in widely dispersed locations to communicate. WANs predate LANs, partly because in the early days there usually were not enough computers in one location for a LAN to make any kind of sense.

WANs and LANs have many things in common, but they differ in important ways too (see Figure 27.6). While LANs are usually built for speed, WANs tend to emphasize reliability. LANs are designed to connect lots of computers for quick communication over short, reliable lines; traditional WANs, those that grew up with the telephone system, have features to deal with unreliable lines, complex meshed networks, multiple paths between modes, and a variety of communications technologies. LAN manufacturers are steadily adding WAN capabilities to their products, though the job is not complete.

But what are WANs good for in today's networking environment? E-mail probably first springs to mind. Companies with offices spread across town or across the world often can benefit from a single, global E-mail system that lets any user easily send mail to any other user. Files can be attached to E-mail messages, allowing a limited form of file transfer.

Another important use of WANs is in data collection. Organisations with large numbers of retail outlets, such as fast food chains and convenience shops, benefit by being able to collect sales and inventory data from each location either at the end of or during the day. This allows central computers to plan for restocking and to get accurate information on the state of the company. Public utilities are also making use of data collection to read meters remotely, reducing the need to send people out into the field.

By making file transfer easier, WANs are allowing work groups to be spread across the globe. In one typical application, a securities firm has financial researchers in major cities such as Tokyo, HongKong, London, and New York. Each researcher adds his analysis to the growing report via a distributed desktop publishing system, and the document is formatted and published in New York.

A more advanced application is the networked database, which allows users all over a network to access and update a single, consistent view of data. Depending on the sophistication of the database, it may either store the data in a central location, or it may distribute and replicate data at various sites. A centrally stored database is easier to write and implement, but it has the disadvantages of requiring heavy network usage to access the data, of being a single point of failure, and of being totally inaccessible if the WAN link into it is down. A distributed and replicated database puts data where it is most often used and keeps copies of frequently used data at each local network. The database application then communicates between nodes, keeping records in each location consistent and fetching requested records from remote servers as needed. If the WAN is down, users can generally use the database locally, though data on remote nodes can not be accessed.

WANs have many other uses, including software distribution; the ability to use expensive resources, such as compute servers and high resolution colour graphic printers, remotely; and, importantly, the ability to manage networks centrally.

As networks get bigger and more complex, and as corporate management begins to realize how strategically important LANs have become, there is often a desire to incorporate LANs into the existing corporate information structure in order to assure that they are managed competently. Also, by centralizing network management, it becomes less necessary to have permanent employees with network management expertise at each remote LAN location, possibly saving money. Remote network management lets this centralization happen.

DESIGN CONSIDERATION

OK, WANs have their uses. So what seems to be the problem with just connecting all those LANs anyway? Well, some of the issues in setting up WANs out of LANs are the same as those confronting any organisation with a large LAN. Managing all those users and servers can become a daunting task if the tools provided do not take on some of the burden. Users and application developers can find that accessing resources and addressing other users is difficult without some sort of system-wide naming service: preferably one implemented with a distributed, replicated database.

Constructing a WAN out of LANs, though, brings up a set of unique problems as well. In WAN planning, guidelines from network and application software vendors are helpful, and learning about the experiences of other users who have done similar installations with the same products can prove invaluable. Before committing to a large WAN installation, though, there is no substitute for trying it out on a pilot basis, using the actual hardware, software, and communications connections being considered. Constructing large scale networks is still an art.

What applications do we plan to across the WAN?

What data rate do we need to support these applications?

Depending on what applications will be used across the WAN, different data rates will be acceptable. In the simplest case, if low-volume E-mail is all that is required, 9.6 kilobits per second (Kbps) asynchronous dial-up may suffice. An E-mail network can be constructed by just having each node call the others when it has mail to send.

When traffic gets heavier, a permanent connection is desirable. For remote file access or distributed database usage by a fairly small number of users, 56 Kbps may be called for. And with heavier use of remote file servers, with distributed databases, or with larger numbers of users, it may prove necessary to use one or more TI (1.54 megabits per second [Mbps]) lines to connect the LANs.

Do we need permanent, or can we use temporary connections?

Currently, if an application demands more than about 9.6 Kbps throughput while it is running, leased lines are pretty much required.

In the best of all possible worlds, bandwidth would be automatically allocated on demand. The network OS would detect a request for a given resource or file, determine what node the resource resided on, see if there was an existing connection with enough bandwidth available for the intended application, and if not, create a new connection with sufficient bandwidth. In reality, most current systems do not yet have the smarts for this, and high-speed dial up connections are not particularly widespread.

Though AT&T has been offering a rather expensive switched 56 Kbps service for some time now, allowing on-demand calls to predefined locations within the USA. Integrated Service Digital Network (ISDN) will probably be the technology that will make high-speed dial-up more common. It is faster, at 64 Kbps for Basic Rate, and because it is an international standard it will eventually be possible to use it for international data calls. By that time, though, it is a good bet that higher inter-network speeds will be required for many common applications (as distributed databases and graphics gain importance). This should make the faster Primary Rate 1.54 Mbps ISDN service fairly routine for temporary connections in a few years.

What types of connections are available between our locations?

Within the U.S.A., we have a variety of low and high-speed connections available to us, but in some overseas locations it can be difficult to get a leased line, or there may be a long wait for one. Since nearly every major city in the world has local access to a Public X.25 Data Network (PDN), it can be fairly easy to set up links using them.

Getting a connection to a local PDN in a foreign country is often far easier than getting a leased line, since less permissions are required from local government telephone agencies. Also, since the user's network and the PDN are connected through a local call, data errors may be lower, hence, throughput may be higher.

On the downside, it can become quite expensive to use a PDN, depending on the data rate and type of data transmitted. Since some PDNs charge per packet as well as by the number of characters transmitted and the connect time, the actual cost of using a PDN can be highly influenced by the characteristics of the Network OS being used. If it sends many small packets, the cost will be higher than if it sends fewer large ones. Additionally, PDNs can introduce delays into the communication process, as packets are switched through the network. Depending on the network operating system's protocol, as we will see below, this may or may not cause problems. Finally, the amount of available bandwidth on a PDN may be quite limited in some localities, making leased lines essential for medium or high bandwidth applications.

Corporate LAN/WAN builders often find that the corporation already has a private WAN, using multiplexors and leased lines or satellite links. Many of these networks were set up years ago to provide remote offices with access to mainframe computers. While there usually is not a lot of spare bandwidth available, low-speed LAN connections can often be provided by adding cards to existing multiplexors and reallocating some of the bandwidth for these new channels. The new channels can be used for permanent or temporary asynchronous, synchronous, or X.25 connections, and if there does happen to be sufficient spare capacity on an existing network, this is very cost-effective.

It is also possible to route WAN/LAN traffic through existing host-based IBM Systems Network Architecture (SNA), Digital DECnet, or TCP/IP networks, again with varying results depending on the available bandwidth and underlying network operating system and host-network protocols. Since this usually entails encapsulating LAN packets into host-network packets, additional processing and bandwidth overhead is incurred. Still, if there is a large host-based WAN in place that has sufficient excess capacity, this option is worth exploring. LANs are usually hungry for bandwidth, and care must be taken to ensure that the LAN does not eat up all the capacity of the host network, interrupting essential applications.

What throughput do we get over the different available communications technologies: that is, Asynchronous, Leased 56KB, TI, X.25, etc.?

This is another important question, because some network protocols provide better throughput than others, and some work much better with one communications technology than with another. For example, the throughput with one vendor's protocols on a 9.6 Kbps line may far exceed, under certain circumstances, another vendor's throughput on a TI line! So after deciding what data rate is acceptable, it is necessary to see what data rate you actually get using a given network operating system, application, and communications link.

What protocols will we use on the WAN?

The same protocol that works beautifully on a LAN may fail miserably on a WAN. So know your protocol, and know how it will behave across the WAN. On a LAN, the simplest protocol is often the fastest. This is because sending data from one machine to another across the network is extremely fast, while processing a complex protocol can add delays.

Across a communications link with inherent delay, such as a public X.25 network or a satellite link, the tables are turned, and the more complex Sliding Window/Asynchronous Acknowledge protocols easily outperform simple Request/Response protocols. A long-delay communications link can be thought of as a long pipe to get high throughput it must be kept filled, and by sending multiple packets without waiting for an acknowledgement for each one, it can be. Sometimes there is a choice of protocols on a given network operating system, and we can pick the best one for the job. At other times, the communications method or the network operating system itself has to be reconsidered.

Do we use transparent bridges, server-based connections, or routers/brouters?

Each of these, of course, has its advantages and disadvantages. Transparent bridges are just that: transparent to the network. They operate at Layer 2 of the OSI Data Link Layer (see Figure 27.7), and have the ability to send packets of all protocols across the communications link. This makes it easy to set up a smaller sized WAN/LAN using bridges. When the network gets larger, though, unnecessary multicast traffic tends to build up; messages that are really of local interest to a specific LAN, but which get set all over WAN because the bridges do not know not to send them. Most bridges can be configured to ignore specific classes of multicasts, but this usually has to be done by someone well versed in the details of the particular protocols in use in a given installation, and even then it is not always possible to totally filter out superfluous multicasts.

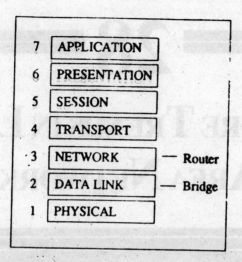

7	APPLICATION
6	PRESENTATION
5	SESSION
4	TRANSPORT
3	NETWORK	— Router
2	DATA LINK	— Bridge
1	PHYSICAL

Fig. 27.7 : OSI levels that are addressed by several different interconnect products.

And, since bridges are transparent, servers and workstations are unaware of their existence and assume that nodes which are really remote, on the other side of one or more bridges, are local. This can cause timeouts and retransmissions, wasting valuable bandwidth.

Server-based connections and routers have a lot in common. They typically operate at Layer 3 of the OSI Network Layer, and their existence is known to the network. This usually means that nodes (servers and workstations) that communicate over the link are aware that there is a slower link between them and can adjust their timeout/retransmission counters and their transmission rates appropriately.

Also, routing often allows the use of standard methods for load balancing and for providing multiple paths between nodes. While some bridges also offer load balancing and allow multiple active paths between nodes, they do so in non-standard ways and require that bridges from the same manufacturer be used exclusively in those parts of the network where these functions are to be provided.

One difference between server-based routing and standalone routers is that the standalone boxes often support more protocols. Another difference is that standalone routers can often be set up as brouters (bridge/routers) when necessary. This lets them route some protocols while bridging others. Since several important protocols like Digital's Local Area Transport (LAT) are not routable, brouters are sometimes the only viable choice besides transparent bridges.

Server-based routing would seem to have a cost advantage over other methods of WAN connectivity. The same server used for LAN file services, for example, can be used for WAN communications. Sometimes that advantage is real, but sometimes WAN communications processing overhead is enough to significantly slow LAN service response times.

28

FUTURE TRENDS IN LOCAL AREA NETWORKS

INTRODUCTION

This book is intended to give some idea of the development and present state of local area networks, and the way they impinge upon other aspects of modern communication technology. However, the nature of the field is one of constant change (and hopefully improvement) and even the time this book has been in preparation has seen major alterations, both in local area network technology and in the way it is perceived by users and potential users. It therefore seems appropriate to look at the way the technology will develop, and the way it will be used in the future. The following points all have some bearing on future trends in LANs.

COMPATIBILITY

The complete dominance achieved in recent years by IBM and its emulators in the personal computer market now makes it unwise for any manufacturer and supplier of local area networks to ignore this section of the market. LANs for IBM PCs and compatibles automatically have a large customer base. LANs not catering for these machines automatically lose access to this lucrative market. The same is, of course, true for all kinds of peripheral systems such as printers, memory backup systems, MODEMs and the like, and this circular process of peripheral supporting PC supporting peripheral has edged other hardware and software systems out of contention.

One-make LANs such as Acron's Econet and Apple's Appletalk will be successful only insofar as their host computer systems will succeed and it is likely that more LAN manufacturers will produce PC compatible interfaces, even those closely associated with competing microcomputer systems. Even the early leaders in the microcomputer field, such as Tandy and Commodore, are now producing machines with varying degrees of IBM compatibility.

Wide-range LANs, other than those supporting previously established communication standards like RS232C, will also base their product ranges around IBM PC-compatible interfaces. This preponderance of all things IBM will influence thinking in low-cost LAN development for the forseeable future and can be seen, in some ways, as the standardisation micro users have been clamouring for since the second microcomputer appeared. However, this standardisation by default leaves aside the thorny subject of standards for LANs rather than for the equipment they interconnect.

STANDARDS AND THE HIGH-COST, LOW-COST SPLIT

Local area networks are continuing on two development paths, which do not seem to be converging. These two paths can be described as the high-cost, high-performance path, and the low-cost, low- performance path, bearing in mind that cost and performance in this context are purely relative terms.

The high-cost, high-performance development, typified by Ethernet and its myriad supporters, implies strong adherence to whatever national (USA) and international standards are applicable, ensuring that different manufacturers and suppliers can provide compatible components and complete systems. In general the standards involved are mostly the IEEE 802 committee's and the International Standards Organisation's OSI model. Both these standards are well-established and well supported, and to a large extent compatible.

This kind of standardisation is very attractive to large business users who view continuity and second sources of supply as more important than low cost. The relatively high performance of these types of LANs is also essential as the standards were originally produced with large scale business and research organisations in mind. There is no doubt that these standards and networks will flourish and provide the technological lead in the LAN field, as data rates increase and the number of potential users expand rapidly.

Meanwhile a new class of users has appeared, brought into the LAN market by the proliferation of low-cost computing power and the need to connect it all together in order to use it efficiently. Schools, small businesses and research organisations all come into this strategy. The common denominator in this class is perennial lack of funds, making high-performance, high-cost networks impractical as a solution to their communication problems. These users are more inclined to choose a solution in which standardisation and compatibility come a very poor second to cheapness. Most of this group of users will be willing to sacrifice operating speed if it saves them money and more inclined to either work with limited facilities or devote time and effort to circumventing problems inherent in the design of low-performance, low-cost networks. Bottom- end users are a growing group, both in real terms and more rapidly, as a proportion of LAN users. So far, they have not exerted any substantial effect on general LAN development as they are not the customer base towards which research and development is directed, but it is likely that the market they represent will not be ignored by the main LAN developers for long.

This may give rise to a new standard for low-cost, low-performance LANs, conforming perhaps to the OSI 7 layer model but fundamentally different from the high-power LANs currently leading the standardisation drive.

The British Microcomputer Manufacturers Group (BMMG) are currently proposing a standard which may go some way towards this but as the BMMG consists mostly of small manufacturers, and their proposals do not yet have any international acceptance it remains to be seen whether their efforts will bear fruit. It is important that manufacturers do cooperate to produce agreed standards, but it is equally important that the agreement is international and that its backers have sufficient influence to promote it.

One new proposal that will undoubtedly find favour is the Manufacturing Automation Protocol (MAP) developed for General Motors. MAP has been around for some time but has been restricted to the automated manufacturing environment where networking is still in its infancy. However, the recent announcement that an office automation subset called Technical and Office Protocols (TOP) has been developed has been greeted with enthusiasm by manufacturing and computing giants alike. On the industrial side, General Motors are backed by international organisations like Boeing, Volkswagen and British Aerospace, whilst computer manufacturers including IBM have agreed to support MAP.

MAP is also said to conform to the International Standards Organisation OSI seven-layer model, making it compatible with most other high performance networks. This widespread support and compatibility, together with the tremendous potential for networking in industrial and manufacturing applications, could mean that MAP may emerge as the one network standard on which everyone can agree in the future.

FUTURE OPEN SYSTEMS STANDARDS

It is already clear that the International Standards Organisation's efforts to produce open systems. Interconnection standards have a great deal of support in official Government circles in many countries. The United States government, for example, which has an estimated IT budget of $16 thousand million per year, has drafted a Government OSI Procurement document (GOSIP), which may become mandatory in future government systems specifications. Manufacturers are also grouping together to speed up the development of the standards, notably within the Corporation for Open Systems, which contains all the major US manufacturers, and is now linking with the European Standards Promotion and Applications Group (SPAG), and the Japanese Promotion Conference for OSI (POSI).

The major problem, however, is that there are already in excess of 30 ISO standards which have reached at least the draft stage, plus a similar number in production. As noted earlier, each of these standards may have several classes, and within each class many options, such that even when two systems claim to conform to the same protocols they may not be able to interwork. This problem is being addressed by the above groups and others, with the resultant promotion of functional standards.

Functional Standards

A functional standard is a set of detailed recommendations, usually based on the ISO protocols, defining how one or more of the standards should be used in combination to meet a particular requirement or function. In general a functional standard ties down the details of which options shall be used within which protocol class for a given layer of the model. It normally comprises a list of specifications for each layer, i.e., a vertical slice through the OSI model. This is known as a protocol stack, and will fill in many of the details which the basic standards leave to the implementor. For example, many protocols do not specify maximum data field sizes, but this can be crucial for good performance.

The agreement of many manufacturers to adopt a functional standard has many advantages. First, it provides a stable development environment: even when some standards are in draft form it is possible to select a stable subset for implementation and thus provide early practical experience of a protocol. Second, it greatly simplifies the conformance testing problem. If two products conform to a functional standard, then they will be guaranteed to interwork for that function, e.g. for document interchange, but not necessarily for any other function.

In Europe, the lead for this work has been taken by the CEN/CENELEC manufacturers' groups, along with the CEPT, the grouping of European PTTs. They have produced a set of ENs (European Norms) which specify not only which protocol options to use, but also the tests for conformance which any product will have to undergo before being able to claim conformance to the standard set. Unlike most other functional standards, ENs do not normally define an entire protocol stack, but concentrate on individual layers of the model. One very relevant standard for LANs, for example, is numbered T/611 and concerns the use of CSMA/CD LANs within the Connection Oriented Network Service.

In USA, functional standards have been developed from two different sources. The National Bureau of Standards (NBS) has produced a functional standard for the message handling application called OSINET, in much the same way as the European efforts. Secondly two major users, General Motors and Boeing, have, by virtue of their vast purchasing power, been able to specify two sets of standards, MAP and TOP. These have generated great interest, as they are unique in being defined by users, rather than by manufacturers or standardisation bodies.

Manufacturing Automation Protocol

MAP, the Manufacturing Automation Protocol (MAP 2.1 1985), is a set of proposals originally promoted by General Motors, who were faced with the problem of automating their factories. As in the computer communications arena, the manufacturers of process control and robotic equipment were each locked into their own methods of communications, largely based on point-to-point links. Thus large manufacturers, like General Motors, had a mixture of separate partly communicating devices, which could only interwork by the development of very complex gateways, between what General Motors termed 'islands of automation'.

In 1980, therefore, General Motors set up a task force to study their existing factory automation procedures and recommend alternatives. The task force discovered that a large part of the factory cost was in practice computer communications, as most automation equipment was computer based. They therefore concluded that costs would be reduced, cables eliminated, maintenance simplified and productivity increased if all automated equipment were attached to interconnected LANs, and all ran the same software.

The result was the production of a functional standard in the form of a vertical protocol stack, as shown in Figure 28.1a. They decided on a bus topology, as this is simpler to wire round a factory, and the token passing access method, as this could guarantee the timed delivery of messages which is necessary for process control. Thus the MAC layer was chosen to be the IEEE 802.4 token bus, using the two channel 10 Mbit/s option. The use of broadband also enables factory video security and environment monitoring systems to be carried on the same cable. The MAP specification is intended, however, to be media dependent, and thus baseband MAP networks are possible.

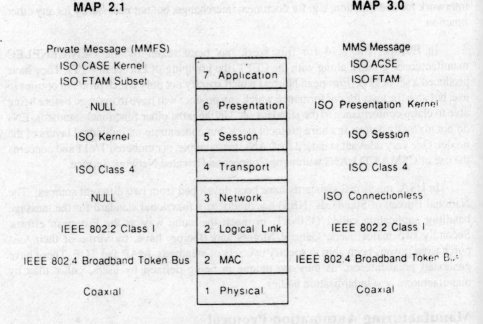

Fig. 28.1 : MAP 2.0 and 3.0 protocol stacks.

General Motors then selected the protocols and services, and the options within the protocols, at each layer of the ISO model from what ISO had defined at the time. This early stack was identical to Figure 28.1a, with the exception that the network layer was left as null. The stack shown, known as MAP 2.1, was soon produced, and has become the first generally available set of protocols. The MMFS protocol (Manufacturing Message Format

Standard), is a non-ISO protocol which was in use within General Motors for driving some devices.

Since General Motors have a budget of several thousand million dollars to devote to factory automation over the next few years, many manufacturers have been keen to develop products, and many other users are keen to adopt any standard which presents itself. The potential success of the approach has been demonstrated, firstly at the US Autofact show in November 1985 when 21 different suppliers took part in demonstration of interworking. By the end of 1986, a similar demonstration at the UK's CIMAP show involved no less than 60 co- operating companies.

Not all manufacturers and users have jumped onto the MAP bandwagon yet, however, as there are two main problems. First MAP is not static, but is still developing along with the ISO protocols, and the projected MAP 3.0 will not be compatible with MAP 2.1 as it will replace the MMFS protocol with another called RS511. Second, current MAP installations, being broadband based, are expensive compared with other LANs, and manufacturers are concerned that smaller users will not be willing to pay the necessary start-up costs.

There is also a rival, European-based, grouping of manufacturers and users, called the Communications Network for Manufacturing Applications (CNMA), which are promoting a different MAP 3.0 stack. This is shown as Figure 28.1b, and shows the inclusion of more of the ISO higher layers, plus yet another message passing protocol, called MMS (Manufacturing Message Service). As these message protocols are responsible for the delivery of the driving commands to the automated equipment, they are obviously crucial to the future success of MAP. There is, however, an International Federation of MAP User Groups, which hopes to impose a single version of MAP 3.0.

CNMA are also promoting a 'collapsed architecture' version of MAP, known as EPA (Enhanced Performance Architecture), in which layers 3 to 6 inclusive would be removed completely when used within a very local network, as they will be superfluous. Furthermore, because there are relatively few broadband networks in Europe and a great many baseband LANs already installed in factories, they are suggesting the option of running the protocol set over the IEEE 802.3 CSMA/CD bus. It can therefore be seen that, even with a strongly promoted functional specification, there will be a considerable settling down period before true interworking is achieved.

One final benefit of MAP is that it is intended that all the computer based communications of an organisation, including terminals and computing resources, be attached to one cable, as well as programmable machine tools. This is forcing many organisations to rethink, or determine for the first time, their corporate communication requirements, an exercise which should result in improvements throughout the organisation.

Technical and Office Protocol

TOP, which stands for Technical and Office Protocol (TOP 1985), is another application-specific protocol stack based on the ISO model. It addresses the area of office systems, particularly technical office work which requires advanced graphics. The initiative for TOP came from the Boeing Company, and they have since been joined by General Motors, Ford Motors and others. The TOP choice of protocols is shown in Figure 28.2. Although the work is not as far advanced as the MAP developments, indications are that many manufacturers are interested.

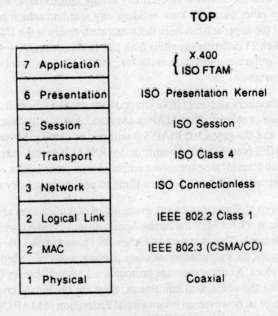

Fig. 28.2 : TOP protocol stack.

The main differences between MAP and TOP are at the MAC layer, which for TOP is the CSMA/CD bus, and at the message passing application level, which for TOP is the CCITT X.400 protocol, which is the forerunner of the ISO protocol for message passing. As there are obviously some installations with a need for both MAP and TOP, there is every possibility of some common subsets being defined in the future, or even a total merger of the two. Table 28.1 presents a comparison of TOP and MAP protocols.

Table 28.1 : Comparison of TOP and MAP Protocols

	TOP	MAP
Layer 7 Application	ISO FTAM 8571	ISO FTAM 8571
Layer 6 Presentation	null	null
Layer 5 Session	ISO 8327	ISO 8327
Layer 4 Transport	ISO 8073/Class 4	ISO 8073/Class 4

Layer 3 Network	ISO 8473	ISO 8473
Layer 2 Data Link	IEEE 802.2	IEEE 802.2
Layer 1 Physical	IEEE 802.3	IEEE 802.4

Even with the above efforts in functional standards, it can be seen that there is much room for confusion, and ISO themselves have announced a new initiative to try to clarify the situation. They are proposing that regional workshops convene to produce proposals for International Standardisation Profiles (ISPs). ISPs will list those options from within the ISO standards which must be implemented for specific applications. They will thus form a functional standard of functional standards. Because of the regional differences of approach, however, particularly between Europe and USA, there is a possibility that more than one ISP could exist for a single application.

FUTURE HARDWARE

The one certainty concerning the future development of LANs is that the technology will not stand still. In particular there is now a considerable blurring of the categories of LAN, particularly with regard to topologies and media, and this can be expected to continue. To take two recent examples, experiments have taken place, and a few products announced, in running 10 Mbit/s CSMA/CD over ordinary twisted pair cable, rather than the more expensive coaxial cable. This would permit the use of existing telephone wiring, in the same way as the StarLAN network, but at ten times the speed.

The second example of this blurring of dividing lines is the linking of broadband networks by joining the headends in a star configuration. This is particularly being promoted for MAP, as the star configuration reduces the dependence on a single headend. The increased initial cost over a tree topology can thus be offset by the considerable savings when only part of the network fails, rather than the whole thing.

Another factor worthy of consideration is that the technology of traditional wide area networking is not static either. When LANs were introduced in the mid 1970s, their data rates of 10 Mbit/s were many times that economically achievable on point-to-point circuit or packet switches, 64 kbit/s being considered a fast line. Now, however, packet switches can handle lines running at 1 Mbit/s, and at least one 10 Mbit/s X.25 chip is available. Thus the speed advantages of LANs are being eroded, and the cost advantages of switches - they are generally cheaper than LANs in large installations - may affect the LAN market.

It can, however, be reasonably predicted that the physical standards outlined earlier will be augmented by others, with the possibility of radical changes unforeseen by ISO. It is therefore appropriate at this point to introduce one new MAC layer development, which is designed to be compatible with the ISO LLC layers. This is the Fibre Distributed Data Interface (FDDI), which promises to be the first LAN developed specifically for fibre optic cable, and thus to restore the speed differential over wide area networks.

FDDI - a Future Fibre LAN

FDDI is being promoted by the American National Standards Institute's X3' working group, which is charged with examining high speed communications. They h concentrated on the physical and MAC layers, along with station management, choosir model the LAN on the IEEE 802.5 token ring. There are many dissimilarities, however first being that there are no absolute limits on the number of stations or on the size o ring. This will vary depending on the application, but rings of five hundred stati spreading over 100 km, will be possible. The raw data rate of 100 Mbit/s will n significant performance differences over current LANs.

The network is configured as two fibre rings, with the data flowing in opp directions in the primary and the secondary circuits. In some cases, both rings can be simultaneously, but normally the secondary will only be used if the primary fails. Bec it is expensive to connect each station to two rings, two classes of station have been def Class A stations (Figure 28.3a) will be able to connect to both rings, but the simpler (B stations (Figure 28.3b) will only connect to one or other of the rings.

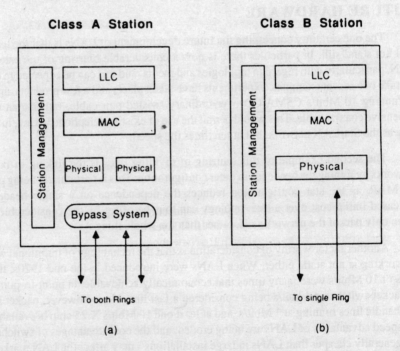

Fig. 28.3a & 28.3b : Class A and B FDDI station schematics.

An extension of the Class A station, shown in Figure 28.4, has also been defi give the same sort of functionality as the wiring concentrator of the token ring. The enable several Class B stations to be logically attached to both main rings, concentrator will route the traffic to whichever ring is in use. The concentrator is a(

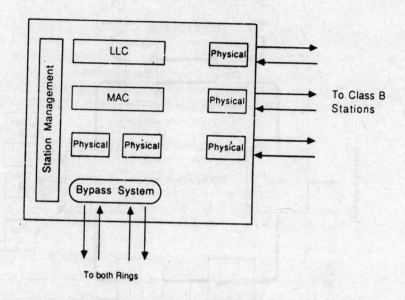

Fig. 28.4 : Class A FDDI station configured as concentrator.

being seen as enabling star or tree style topologies to be adopted, where this is more convenient than the ring.

Because of its very high speed, FDDI was originally seen as a type of back-end network, used to connect mainframe CPUs to fast peripherals, such as discs, usually within a computer room, or even several computer rooms many kilometres apart. As it has developed, however, it is apparent that the concentrator mechanism will permit FDDI to be used as a high speed backbone LAN, connecting a number of the slower ISO LANs. As all the LANs are compatible from the LLC layer upwards, and as the FDDI data rate could support traffic from several such LANs without degradation, a configuration such as that shown in Figure 28.5 becomes a possibility.

Figure 28.5 shows a PABX connected to the FDDI backbone. This is possible if the most recent work, dubbed FDDI II, is adopted. In this scheme, the 100 Mbit/s channel would be divided up into 16 channels of 6.144 Mbit/s channels, plus a control channel. As this is a convenient multiple of both the US and European voice rates, it is being pursued with great interest.

FDDI development is proceeding very quickly, with the first products already available, although the complete specification of the ANSI standard is not yet published. As this is the only fibre optic standard being promoted and as the fibre manufacturers have no entrenched positions to defend, it is likely that FDDI will be one of the fastest standards to gain widespread acceptance.

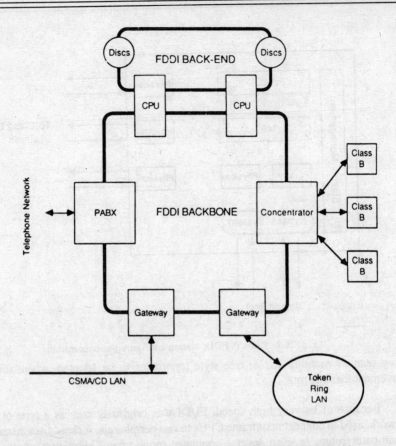

Fig. 28.5 : Example of FDDI as back-end and backone LAN.

INTEGRATED SERVICES DIGITAL NETWORKS

One final aspect of standardisation must be mentioned when the future is under discussion, namely ISDN. Integrated Service Digital Network is a standard being developed mainly by the PTTs, to enable all communications, voice, data and video, to be transferred down a single logical cable.

At present, a large company will have separate connections to the telephone network, possibly several wide area data networks, telex, facsimile and possibly video conference networks. This results in a great deal of physical wiring, plus the complications of dealing with many network service suppliers. The idea behind ISDN is that each site will have one line to the international ISDN network, in the same way that telephones are currently on the international telephone network. Because the latest generation of telephone equipment works with digital transmission, there is no difference to the carrier between voice and data.

ISDN, however, requires an upheaval for every country, as each exchange has to be upgraded, and thus it will take many years for ISDN to become widespread. The necessary signalling standards have been defined, however, and many pilot networks exist. It may be some years before ISDN becomes relevant to LANs, as the basic local connection to a user's building is currently only rated at 64 Kbit/s. Higher speeds are part of the requirement for ISDN, however, with primary access being set at 2 Mbit/s and some limited high speed access is possible now. Part of the UK's Alvey Project, for example, is using a 2 Mbit/s ISDN link for bridging between remotely sited LANs. This is one of the most likely future uses for ISDN, as applied to LANs.

FALLING COSTS AND CHIP SETS

One of the accepted pieces of wisdom about local area networks is that as more of the network functions are integrated on a chip the cost of the network will fall. But will it? It is true that one integrated circuit will cost less than five of the same circuit, but whereas the integrated circuits currently used in most LANs are mass- market devices produced in thousands if not millions, and sold at competitive rates, chips specifically designed for networking have a much narrower market, which must mean that costs per chip will remain relatively high until every intelligent digital electronic device has a network node installed as standard during manufacture. However, there are other advantages to be gained by using specially-designed networking integrated circuits, particularly where size and power consumption are critical factors. Using custom integrated circuits allows powered systems, as well as allowing more space for other things in desktop computers and peripherals.

Manufacturers are now offering networking chip sets: Intel has an Ethernet set, and Texas Instruments has a set for use with the much- heralded IBM Token Ring LAN, and there is no doubt that these integrated circuits will be generally used to produce a new generation of networking equipment, but LANs lend themselves very well to another branch of integrated circuit technology, the Uncomitted Logic Array (ULA). These devices can be produced to perform a particular function in relatively small numbers, without incurring any of the cost penalties usually associated with small-batch manufacture of semiconductor devices. This has made them popular with smaller LAN manufacturers.

ULAs and specially-designed chip sets will contribute to a reduction in the cost of high-powered, high-cost LANs, but the cost reduction per node often mentioned by manufacturers and analysts may be misleading. Node costs are not the only cost in a network. In fact, cabling cost may well exceed the other hardware costs in some situations; and no amount of custom integrated circuits is going to shorten the cable. High-performance baseband LANs, such as Ethernet need high-quality cable and whilst the economies of scale apply to cable just as they do to semiconductors, the LAN market's relative smallness, and the intrinsic expense of the material in the cable may combine to thwart the sought-after price reductions. Cabling and installation costs for this type of network are likely to remain relatively high in the forseeable future.

In contrast, cost for broadband LANs are concentrated in the node, which must include a modem. Cables and connectors used are produced in huge quantities for the cable TV market and are, therefore, relatively cheap already. Hopes for drastic cost reductions in broadband LANs centre on the increasing demand for modems and the possibilities of integrating modem functions onto chips. There is speculation that broadband systems may become as cheap as equivalent baseband networks if this happens. Broadband LANs would then be a very attractive alternative, considering their inherent versatility.

Low-cost, low-performance baseband LANs will continue to exist, using cheap components and cheap cabling or in some cases, no cabling at all. One British LAN, Nectarring, transmits its signals through the cables providing AC power to the network, thus eliminating the need for any additional cabling costs. This sort of cost-conscious approach is bound to find favour with users.

The high-cost of high-performance baseband systems has been recognised by some manufacturers as a problem and a reduced form of Ethernet, popularly known as 'Cheapernet', is now available. It is, however, still a much more powerful and expensive system than many of the low-cost baseband networks.

NETWORK-TO-NETWORK CONNECTIONS

Once equipment is connected together using a LAN, users invariably find that the whole system would benefit from connections to another system. The logical step is to install some kind of network-to-network connection, either to allow two systems to share facilities, or to allow a small, low-performance LAN to act as a feeder to a bigger network. This larger network might be a high- performance LAN, a WAN using radio and telecom links, or a distributed mainframe computing system. The term 'bridge' is normally used for a connection between two similar networks, whereas 'gateway' is normally used to describe a link between two dissimilar networks.

It is obvious that bridges and gateways will proliferate in the near future as users seek to make the best use of the available resources, and these inter-network products are likely to become almost as common as the networks they support. Already manufacturers are producing equipment to link LANs to public networks such as the X25 Packet-Switched network, an indication that the future of low-cost LANs may lie as much in acting as front end for larger systems as in stand-alone operation. In future, the usefulness of a local area network will be judged, among other things, on the number of other systems it can be connected to.

GENERAL

As a general rule, local area networks of all types are going to become more common, and at the same time, more invisible. Microcomputer manufacturers will eventually come to some sort of agreement about networking and start to include LAN facilities within their equipment as standard, in the way Apple are currently doing with the Macintosh and Laser-Writer. This facility has been largely ignored in the general speculation about the Macintosh, but it represents a significant step forward in terms of integrating LANs with the systems they are meant to serve. When other manufacturers adopt this approach LAN software will be contained within the normal operating software of the computer, and networks will be designed as single entities rather than as a group of individual units with various interconnections. The LAN will cease to be an afterthought and become the starting point from which all systems are planned.

However, the integrated approach to local area networking requires both manufacturer and customer to see things the same way, and it may take some time before the general level of awareness of the subject is such that integrated systems from single or multiple sources become a common occurrence. In the meantime, users must continue to pick and choose the network that best suits their particular needs from within whatever budget constraints exist, and struggle against the difficulties imposed by all manner of incompatible and inadequate hardware and software.

In conclusion, it seems inevitable that computer networks will play an increasingly important role in all our lives. Local area networks will play a large part in network development, although one can expect the divisions between local and wide area networks to become increasingly blurred.

29
WIRELESS LANs

INTRODUCTION

Wired LANs provide a logical and efficient choice for most networks. Where the users operate from a fixed desk in a standard office environment, the wired (or cabled) LAN is a natural choice. If the user is highly mobile and not used to a fixed location of operation, then the wired LAN will be a restriction and a handicap. However, some buildings do not lend themselves to being wired or cabled, posing some physical restrictions on the wired (or cabled) approach.

Wireless LANs provide a new layer of flexibility and services to environments and users that cannot be well served by the traditional wired LAN. As more and more users are becoming highly mobile within their building environments, the wireless LAN could be the most effective way to couple the mobile users to their information and communication services. Removing systems tethers from users will enable them to increase their flexibility and productivity to tackle logical business actions and communications wherever they are within the contact space provided by the wireless communication system.

The future of wireless LAN systems will depend upon success of meeting user needs and expectations. The technology will continue to mature and the wireless services will complement the wired world to make a seamless integrated internetwork process.

Wireless LANs represent a spectrum of capabilities that support limited distance local coverage, moderate distance metropolitan coverage, and longer distance coverage. Depending on the power of the transmitters and the sensitivity of the receivers, wireless LANs may become the first truly universal form of virtual LAN (VLAN.) by coupling wireless LANs with other wireless communications forms such as cellular or satellite, the user connectivity can be almost limitless.

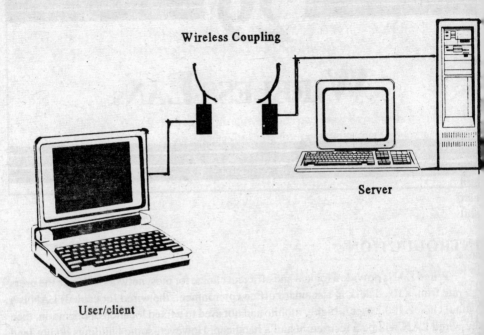

Fig. 29.1 : Wireless LAN

NEED OF WIRELESS LANs

Wire has been the chosen medium for LANs since they were invented in the ea~ 1970s. The need for and interest in wireless developed over the past few years is in the f~ that some applications have found it difficult or impossible to implement LANs. F example, consider a warehouse, where there is a need to track vehicles, movements of goo~ locations, etc. in support of a logistics and distribution activity. Wiring LANs for such environment would be difficult to impossible. Yet with wireless LANs, the roving users c be in direct two-way contact with the full resources of the enterprise's information systen~ Similarly, in the situations in which people move around to various locations to perfo~ their work as opposed to staying at a fixed desk that can be easily wired, are candidates ~ wireless LANs. Such situations would include manufacturing stations, assembly lin~ researchers, testers, health care providers, and a host of other.

The wireless LAN opened up the coverage of LAN services to a host of applicatic that have been isolated from the wired world. The answer to "why wireless" is that it fulf~ a need that has heretofore gone unanswered. The wireless LAN is also opening up n~ applications that had not even considered the possibility of being part of a LAN. Howev~ several previously wired applications are now considering the potential of going to wirel~

The wireless LANs can also move to higher power plateaus which will extend their distances from hundreds of feet to several tens of thousands of feet. In fact, with multimile capability of some of the wireless networks, this technology may be more far ranging than the wired world. Add in wireless satellite broadcasting, and you have a global capability. These alternatives can make the wireless LAN world more flexible and support longer distances than the other options.

COMPONENTS OF WIRELESS LANs

The wireless LANs have two components different from those found in a wired LAN. These components are the waveform transmitter and the receiver that handles the data transfers from the user client and the servers to the air space. The transmitters and receivers can use a variety of media and frequencies to support their services. The wireless LAN will still need all of the components that are used in a wired LAN, including a network interface card, a network operating system, application programming interfaces, network-compliant software, and various operational procedures.

The waveform transmitters and receivers for the wireless LANs will vary with the specific technology and wave frequency used. The radio frequency wireless LAN is different in level, form, power, and other factors from the infrared units or the microwave stations. These differences will result in different power requirements, different antenna systems, different tuning and operational support requirements, and different performance values. The differences will also cause variations in user operations, transparency, ease of use, the scalability.

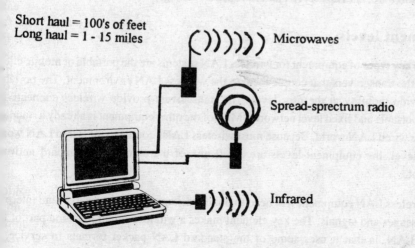

Short haul = 100's of feet
Long haul = 1 - 15 miles

Microwaves

Spread-sprectrum radio

Infrared

Fig. 29.2 : Differences of wireless LANs

The waveform transmitters will convert the signals of the computer system into the waveform motions at the correct frequencies and send them into the air medium at the proper time and signal level. The waveform receivers will extract the signals from the air and perform review, recognition, and acceptance processing on them. The transmitters and receivers will require external antennas to enter and receive the waveforms from the air medium. In addition to the different components of the wireless LAN configuration, there is the added requirement of careful design and setup of the equipment and the tuning of its sending and receiving operations. Issues such as facility obstructions, antenna locations, signal tuning, electromagnetic radiation testing, and movement patterns must be evaluated and taken into account before committing to a wireless LAN installation. There may be conditions and situations that would limit the usability of the wireless LAN technology and restrict the success of the investment. It is also possible that one wireless LAN technology may work better than other in given situations. A trial setup or a pilot installation may be needed to make the final verification of wireless LAN feasibility.

The wireless LANs use various pieces of equipment that are unique to the network world. The transceivers, monitors, client units, and the interfaces between technologies are unique parts of the wireless LAN world. These technologies are new in their packaging, infants in their operation, unstable in their forms, and developing in their connectivity.

The wireless LANs also use the established components of networks and telecommunications to accomplish many parts of their operations. Hubs, bridges, network operating systems, servers, and other elements are often the same as those used in the wired LAN. Some components may be extensions or modifications of wired products such as user interface software, backup servers, and transaction managers.

Equipment levels

The key types of equipment for wireless LAN systems are the portable or mobile client units and the transceivers that couple them to the wireless LAN environment. The portable units provide mobility at the user level. The transceivers provide wireless connectivity between portable and fixed level networks. Most of the other equipment is already a standard part of the wired LAN world. Because most wireless LANs couple to the wired LAN world at some level, the equipment levels are a full mix of the unique and standard network equipment.

Wireless LAN equipment will need to build, package, transmit, receive, and interpret LAN messages and signals. The key element makes a wireless communication part of the wireless LAN, is that it uses some of the standard LAN packet formats to service transmission process.

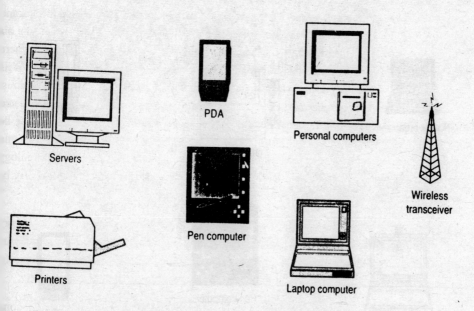

Servers

PDA

Personal computers

Pen computer

Wireless transceiver

Printers

Laptop computer

Fig. 29.3 : Wireless LAN Equipment Spectrum

Mobile Equipments

The mobile equipment units for wireless LANs are portable computing devices that can act as full or partial client systems and interface to a wireless LAN communications unit. The typical range of units includes:

LAPTOP Computers - Standard personal computers in a laptop form using a wireless LAN transceiver unit usually attached to a standard PCMCIA slot.

Personal Digital Assistants (PDAs) - Small handheld (palmtop) computer units that support some type of communications capability.

Pen-Based Computers - Small handheld wiring slates that can connect to a communications network.

Speciality Units - Specially built (purpose-oriented) computing, data entry, and communications units that can perform specific functions and communicate to different network services. Included in this category would be radio frequency (RF) data collection units, portable bar code scanners, special data collection instruments, medical equipment, security control devices, etc.

Portable Bridges and Transceivers - Units that can support the interconnection from one LAN to another at the wireless layer. These can be PCMCIA transceivers, portable satellite ports, and other communication units that provide bridging services.

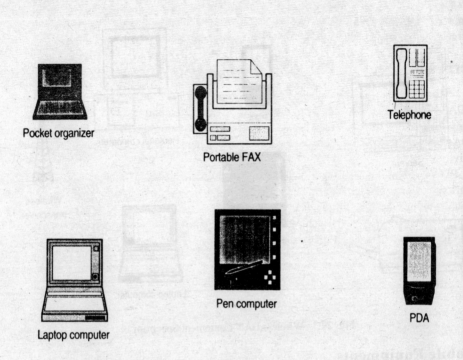

Fig. 29.4 : Mobile client spectrum

WIRELESS RECEIVING DEVICES

The wireless LANs will support the layer between the end user and the higher orders of the information resources of a organization. In few cases traditional desktop personal computers can become wireless devices by adding a transceiver board in place of wire connection. The more popular and heaviest uses of wireless LAN technology is likely to be in support of new user interface devices that are built for the wireless world. Some of these devices are described as follows:

Laptop or Notebook Computers

The evolution and popularity of laptop and notebook computers provide a ready platform for the interconnection to a wireless network. These devices are highly portable, battery run, and built to go anywhere, and run anytime in the hands of a mobile worker. They are being built with one or more standard personal Computer Memory Card International Association (PCMCIA) facilities. These small credit cardsized devices can contain modems, storage resources, transceivers, etc. to support interconnectivity to a wireless network.

Laptop and notebook computers are also an accepted commodity in many jobs. They can support a first-order one-to-one connection and can be expanded to work in a one-to-many format. As the popularity of these devices grows and their production volume increases, their price will drop, increasing their popularity.

Personal digital assistants (PDAs)

The next level of miniaturization of computers will be the personal digital assistant (PDA). These units are handheld, calculator, cellular telephone-sized, battery-operated computers. Using touch screen or voice-activated technology to replace keyboards, the PDAs can put mobile workers into contact with a wide variety of information support activities that are stored within their memories. By adding the wireless LAN connections to the PDAs, the mobile user can have access to the total world of information. The only restriction would be that the information has to be formatted and sized to fit within the capabilities of the PDA.

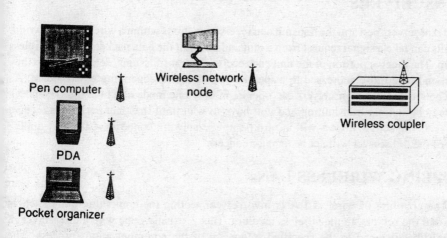

Fig. 29.5 : Various types of wireless LAN receiving devices

PDAs are the nearly perfect receiving product for wireless LANs. They are highly portable but of limited self-contained capability. This makes them dependent on using a network to reach and interact with organizational information resources. Wired networks would certainly perform the required services, but they would remove the flexibility and portability of the PDA, restricting the key values the user is seeking. By using a wireless LAN connection, the user can increase the usability of the PDA as a window into the information resources appropriate to the individual user. PDAs and wireless LANs will make a most appropriate marriage. Each needs the other to ensure their success. As PDAs move to more capabilities and power, they will include built-in wireless LAN connections which will ensure this bonding of technologies and services.

Wireless resource interfacing

In addition to personal user connections, the wireless LAN receivers can be attached to fixed service resources. On popular example is to have a remote printer that is shared via a wireless connection by all users or clients in the coverage area. The device will provide its standard resource services, but the users will be able to select and access the unit via the wireless network. Similar connections could be made to data recording stations and fixed information servers that contained local reference information. An example would be a wireless product or warehouse location server that provided query, access, and return information to a community of mobile users within a defined building envelope space. Whenever the user made a product request, their personal unit would send a fixed message to the wireless server, which would perform the required lookup and turn the information to the mobile user unit.

TRANSCEIVERS

Transceivers perform the transmit and receive functions within a wireless LAN world. The units can take a signal request from a unit and transmit the data packet into the wireless medium. The receive portion of the unit can receive the transmissions, determine who they are for, and take those addressed to a specific station into its operating environment. As dual-function devices, transceivers can operate in only one mode at a time (half- duplex). They may be tied up transmitting and will have to wait until they can perform a receive process. As the active process will in turn tie up the network connection, the half-duplex nature of the transceiver will not be a major concern.

COUPLING WIRELESS LANs

The coupling of wireless LANs involves connecting the computing units such as clients and the servers, to the wireless medium. This is usually done with a transceiver of each unit that it tuned to the specified frequency of the communications process. The transceivers form a combined unit that is capable of both transmitting and receiving the signals for the wireless medium. The units is also capable of formatting and recognizing the transmission packages that are being sent over the wireless medium.

The coupling of units for wireless LANs can be done at many levels. The simplest is a one-to-one coupling between a portable client and a fixed server system. The next level is one-to-many, where a portable client can have wireless connectivity to a series of servers. The most extensive level is many-to-many, where several portable users can interface to many remote servers and services.

The wireless LAN transceivers will have to convert the network data packets from the internal computer format to the format defined by the transceiver vendor. The standards at the transceiver level are limited, with most of the wireless LANs depending on the unique format defined by the producing vendor. At the receiving end, the vendor's transceiver reconverts the data packets to the standard format for the computer system.

WIRELESS LANs VS WIRED LANs

Wireless LANs will offer the same user or client services available from wired LANs. The client or user can access files on servers, perform remote operations and applications, transfer data, share resources, and interact with other facilities and users within the enterprise network. Users will be able to communicate, interact, transfer, transact, query, and initiate actions and reactions from within the organization. The major difference between wireless LANs and wired LANs is that they are not connected to wire or cable and users have extensive flexibility to move about and still receive services from their LAN world. It is important that the wireless connections be reasonably transparent to the end user. Many users will find themselves moving from the wired to the wireless environment and back again. If the systems were different in their operational form, function, and user interfacing, they would not be acceptable in light of the moves to seamless integrated information systems. As the wired LAN world sets new services and standards, the wireless world will need to implement and remain consistent.

However, the user will not be able to discern the boundaries of the wireless LAN world, which requires some form of notice be given when they reach the limits, or the system will have to support some type of roaming that allow to user to move from one area to another and still retain services from the LANs environment.

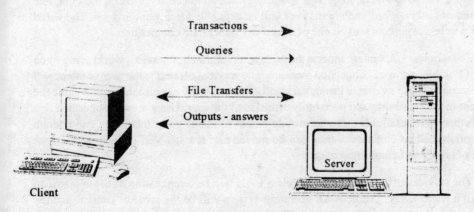

Fig. 29.6: Wireless LAN Services

As compared to wired LAN, wireless LAN services will be found in the slightly slower speeds of information transfer, the problems of security of transmission, and possibly error to noise factors. Many of these differences can be overcome with advances in technology and the evolution of specific wireless components that address these restrictions. For example, by using the available frequency space more aggressively, technology can not only improve the transfer reliability of wireless LAN communications but also improve the security of the information transfer at the same time.

In addition, some of the perceived problems of wireless LAN technology may be patently false. For example, the air waves used by the wireless systems are considered very open and unsecured. However, the spread-spectrum radio format of wireless communications was developed by the U.S. Department of Defense to support battlefield-level secure communications. Other limitations may also be overcome with aggressive reengineering of the technologies.

The security concerns over wireless LANs can also be addressed via the use of encryption techniques and other means of scrambling the contents of the information transferred over the network. Given the ease with which someone can tap or copy the contents moving over copper wire with minimal chance of detection, the wireless LAN world may provide improved security by forcing the users to take steps to assure the safety and accuracy of the communications over the wireless world.

Wireless LANs will never replace fixed wiring media. This was never the intention of this technology. However, there are several applications that are not well served by wired media. These applications may be served by the wireless systems. The wireless and the wired media systems will be integrated at some level. The higher levels of enterprise networks will continue to the primarily built of wired media. The wireless LANs will operate at the lower levels and interface to the wired networks for the higher levels of service.

The issue should not be wireless versus wired in local area networks, but rather when one should use which technology and where they interconnect. Eventually, the complete spectrum of LAN options and alternatives will be available for any application. The wired versus wireless argument will be one of adaptivity rather than competition.

The wireless LAN interconnects the users to an information services world using some form of flexible, nonwire connection medium. The services offered to the user or client will be the same as those available through a standard wired LAN or close thereto. What is the different in the flexibility and portability afforded to the user. Users are no longer tied to a fixed tether. Wireless LANs, can be mobile within limits of geography, they can operate with portable client computers, they can be moved and reassembled quickly without the hassle of laying and connecting wire.

The services offered through a wireless LAN will be a replication of those provided through a wired LAN. The network operating system will be the same or similar, and the commands and actions will be the same. The differences in the user's view will be minimal. The differences from an installer and an operational support view will be more dramatic and significant. But these differences will be in the background and remote from the user. The differences will occur only at installation or change times, so will be nearly transparent most of the time for the operations level.

ADVANTAGES OF WIRELESS LANs

Wireless LANs can be used within the building environment. Installation in historic buildings where wire installation would be costly or historically inappropriate can be supported by wireless LANs. Organizations with dangerous or hazardous conditions that could not be supported by wire networks may be amenable to the use of wireless LANs. Emergency situations in which there is no time to lay wire or to establish stable network operating procedures can be supported by an instantaneous setup and implementation of wireless LAN systems. In other words, wireless LANs provide LAN words, services and internetwork access for a number of unique settings and situations.

The benefits of the wireless LANs will include flexibility, portability, modest cost, movable installation, and multiple system interconnectivity. The wireless LANs will bring mobile workers into the information world as full-time partners. They will also allow other workers to migrate to mobile operations to improve their performance and productivity within organizations.

The wireless world is oriented to supporting mobility. If the user or client did not move, then the tried and true wired approach would be the preferred choice. But in many situations, as workers are mobile by nature and/or would like to become more mobile by choice, the wireless world provides the technological linkages to the established data and information services available in the wired world.

Mobile operations can be conceived in many different forms and implementations. A telecommuter is a mobile worker, as is a traveling salesperson. In the wireless LAN context a mobile worker has to be within the physical area of contact that can be maintained by a wireless LAN. This can include the inner space of a building, a local campus or a multiple facility environment that is within a line-of-sight connectivity zone.

Mobile operations usually mean that the individual users cannot easily be connected to or use the traditional form of wired desktop-supporting LAN. The mobile user is moving about too much to be able to connect via a fixed-location client station. As mobile users move about in their environment, it is important to take note of the fact that the level of mobility and the spatial areas covered by today's wireless LANs are also limited and contained. The tighter the user's roaming space, the better for most wireless LANs.

The infrastructure consideration for mobile workers is that they operate within a fairly tightly constrained area of the organizational facility. Wireless LANs are meant to be limited-distance support products. They cannot support open and un-limited roaming of the users. The supported infrastructure is more oriented to a department area or a small section of a facility, not unlimited space or the total facility unless it is very small.

The infrastructure limits of wireless LANs are also difficult to live with in many organizations. The boundaries are ones of going beyond the limit of the communications technologies; they are not hard and fast limits like the walls of a department or building.

What happens is that the user simply fades out of contact with the wireless world or may sense a cutoff type of disruption in services as they reach beyond the established limits. Due to interference and spatial considerations, the break in service may vary by location, direction, time of day, and other random factors. In other ways, what may have worked yesterday, may not work today.

Flexible connectivity means that the users can choose how and when they want to be connected to the wireless LAN services. Some will choose to remain in such a contact state on a continuous basis, and others will make the connections on an occasional as needed basis. The key concept is the ability to obtain services where and when they are needed without regard to the specific positioning or location of the servicing units.

Flexible connectivity also means the ability to connect to a broad range of services and/or to different networks as the need or location may dictate. The wireless LANs can support flexible connectivity by providing an automatic recognition of roaming users and the ability to hop across various networks (wired and wireless) to obtain information and services to which the user is entitled.

The wireless LAN is not intended for all applications and situations. The technology is stable and cost effective and it is appropriate for selected applications. Where the technology is appropriate, the wireless LANs are a most logical choice. When the situation is marginal, other choices may be more effective.

The advantage of covering previously unsupported applications with wireless LANs allows for the opening up of numerous areas, applications, and users to becoming full partners in the information services worlds. These people had previously been denied access to this world or had to make access through inconvenient means and techniques, thus limiting the effectiveness of the connections. With the wireless LANs, these users can access almost any layer and element of information processing while still maintaining their mobility and flexibility within the organization.

The another advantage of wireless LANs is the ability to initiate a fast setup or a quick move of the technology and continue to offer connectivity services. This is critical for emergency services and users who must relocate themselves while still needing access to organizational information. The flexibility of wireless LANs to be installed quickly and come up running with minimal setup and initiation makes them a logical choice for most emergency or temporary settings. Whether at a fire or a wedding or a sports event, the wireless LAN can supply data transfer services at reasonable speeds with minimal setup time and effort.

Wireless LANs should be considered as having two layers of capacity. One of the limited coverage of a local area, where the wireless capabilities compete with those of wired LAN technology. The second layer is the remote services where the distances are beyond the coverage space of any wired technology. By using microwave transceivers or portable satellite dishes, the wireless LAN distance can be almost limitless. In fact, the longer distance wireless LANs will end up competing with traditional communications services such as data communications lines, frame relay, and other telecommunications services. The advantage is that the wireless LAN services will be user and application dedicated and may use less costly communications components, those supplied by the traditional telecommunications firms. For example, a satellite office could be coupled with a long-distance wireless LAN and then take advantage of all of the services provided at its primary business location. The remote users could exchange data, tap into the corporate PBX system, use remote databases, communicate to corporate personnel, and maintain apparent contact as if they were a physical part of the central organization rather than a small satellite facility.

The longer distance wireless LANs may be very appropriate for telecommuting and other remote user operations. If the costs of the wireless services are competitive with those of alternative communications, then the flexibility, reusability, and scalability factors will make the wireless form the best way to go.

DISADVANTAGES OF WIRELESS LANs:

There are numerous disadvantages to the use of wireless LANs. They include:

— Lack of reliability

— Errors

— Long waits

— Incomplete returns

— Contention

— Slow response

— Unpredictable timings

— Instability

— Variable space coverage

The disadvantages of wireless LANs are found mostly in their environmental limits of connectivity and in their reliability of operation in all areas and at all times. At the edge zones, the connections between clients and the network can become error prone, easily broken, and/or distorted. As long as the wireless mobility is kept within tight limits of the capabilities of the installation, the fault of wireless LANs should be equivalent to those of wired units.

The biggest fault for wireless LANs is when they frustrate the end user. The user wants reliable and effective services from all of their computing world. If the wireless LAN is unable to deliver reasonable services when the user demands them, then the product will be avoided. There is little patience or sympathy for an un-reliable and non-performing technology today. Uptime and service are the watchwords for all systems. Quality, performance, and above all, user service is the only survivable game.

Because of new technology, wireless LANs still have teething problems. They can operate erratically and are subject to many forms of interference. If these fault are not overcome, then these products will be unsuccessful in the marketplace.

The other key fault is in the limited speed and transfer rates of the wireless systems. The limits of 1 or 2 million bits per second (Mbps) could hamper the use of wireless as a high-speed file transfer service. Plans for 10 to 16 Mbps transfer speeds would put the wireless technology in the same range as most current LANs. However, as the wired technology moves up to the 100 Mbps range, it is unlikely that the wireless systems will be able to reach this new high speed plateau. Speed, however, may not be that much of a limiting factor, especially in situations where the client is a small (and limited capacity) laptop or notebook computer and the transferred data are small transactions with limited movement of large data blocks and files.

The low-speed individual wireless links can also be partially overcome by the user of dedicated channels and frequencies for each user similar to hub switching on wired LANs. This would gives dedicated private line couplings from user to the server worlds where the 1 to 2 Mbps speeds would be higher than the shared services rates on party-line wired LANs. The real key lies in the ability of wireless technology to move information reliably and accurately between the users and the service facility. If users are satisfied by remote coupling via a 9600 baud modem, then they will be ecstatic with a 2 Mbps wireless LAN connection.

DISTANCE & SPEEDS LIMITATIONS

Local area networks are limited in their coverage area. The use of a wireless medium will impose other limits and restrictions on the distances and geography of the network. The use of air transmission signals for the passage of information in the wireless LAN will be dependent on their strength, local interference, travel through the medium, contention and competition, collisions, and other characteristics of the physical and operational environment.

Typical distance limits for localized wireless networks are in the order of 80 to 300 feet between components. This can be extended with relay servers and other design alternatives. This limit is not unlike those of wired networks such as twisted pair (10BaseT), which is 300 feet between a unit and its wiring hub.

The distances for the open-space varieties of wireless LANs are the reverse of those for the localized forms. These systems can move information at higher speeds over distances that are tied to the physical line of sight through the air space. Some of these systems can move information over 2 to 3 miles of space, and others that use more powerful transmitters can send information over 15 miles. These forms of wireless LAN are far longer than the 1500 meter segments of a typical wired Ethernet and far exceed the individual link wiring of 300 feet for token ring networks. If one then moves into the arena of wireless satellite connectivity, the wireless LAN can couple an individual user in a remote location using a portable satellite dish to almost any point in the universe. There is no other technology that can cover this level of distance.

The nominal speed for wireless LANs will be in the range of 500,000 to 3,000,000 bits per second. The new 802.11 standard calls for a speed of 2,000,000 bits per second. Although 2 Mbps is not the fastest speed for a LAN, various systems provide multiple channels of available frequency, allowing different users or client to have concurrent dedicated connections of a full 2 Mbps bandwidth.

The new infrared transmission systems being developed by IBM are striving to establish new speed levels for wireless LANs in the 16 Mbps range. This would make these systems compatible with the 15 Mbps token ring systems. Although speed is important in any data communications and distribution system, the types of usage for wireless LANs may provide opportunities to constrain the loads and volumes of communications to fit within the limits of the technology and even then offer good user services. It is very application and usage dependent. It is accurate to indicate that wireless LANs will work better with limited amounts of data transfer, rather than as volume traffic systems.

COSTS AND BENEFITS OF WIRELESS LANs

Cost and benefits will still be a part of the consideration of the use of wireless LAN technology. The good news is that the air medium of wireless systems is less costly than the copper or fiber medium of the alternative technologies. However, the transmitter and receiver products are still more expensive than the same functional units in the wired world. This is primarily due to the popularity and volume of the wired products and the novelty of the wireless units. As the popularity and acceptance of wireless technologies grow, the prices of the transceivers will drop and the economics will shift to favor the wireless world. In addition, if the vendors begin to build wireless capabilities into their basic system units, the costs will drop even further. Now, consider the large number of notebook computers that are coming with builtin infrared wireless capapbilties. Stay tuned; as the popularity of wireless grows, the volume will build and the prices will drop. This will in turn change the economics of the decision and tilt it in favor of wireless. Given the other advantages to be derived from wireless LANs, the current extra costs can often be overcome with reasonable valuation of the other additive benefits such as flexibility, speed of installation, and scalability.

USES OF WIRELESS LAN APPLICATIONS

Many work situations require the worker to move around in the work environment, making it hard to make use of a standard computer. Flexible workers can be serviced by portable computer units that are connected to a wireless LAN to give them communications and server access. Wireless LANs can support a number of applications in a wide variety of organizations and industries. Most of the applications focus on the mobility of the user or the temporariness of the application. When the application fits the characteristics provided by the wireless LAN, then the system can be successful as long as it fits within the physical limits of the wireless technology.

Health Care

Health care work is one typical form of flexible work that can benefit from wireless LANs. The provision of health care services is centered around the interface of the patient and the health care provider. As medical providers usually go to many patients, it would be difficult, expensive, and inconvenient for them to constantly shift from one computer to other. It will be difficult to provide a tethered system, because the care givers often have to move long distances between patients. Thus a wireless LAN can be one answer for a health car or hospital environment.

With the help of small portable computers such as personal digital assistants (PDAs), palmtop computers, or pen tablet computers the care giver has portability and a sufficient system platform to input and output the information needed to perform and deliver the patient services. The connection over the wireless LAN will take the individual user or client units to a local server where patient data and service information is stored and retrieved. Input transactions can be validated at this local server and the data passed to other LANs and servers for processing and formal file updating. The wireless LAN provides support for the mobility of the health care provider and the capture of information at the point of origin. It also distributes appropriate information from networked servers into the hands of the health care provider at the time it is needed. Because of the volume of patient information involved and the frequent necessity of responding to unexpected events in the health care environment, the wireless connectivity to the LAN provides more complete and navigatable information access than if the data were simply down and uploaded from a portable PDA device.

Most of the focus of wireless services in health care is aimed at the care provides. The administrative side can also be benefit from some process reengineering and the use of wireless LAN technology. Health care services are known for their heavy loads of paperwork and numerous lines and administrative forms that must be completed before the medical services are provided. This process can be difficult and stressful for someone who is waiting for the medical procedures (already a stress-inducing situation).

Several hospitals are changing their admissions process by using laptop computers and wireless LANs. When planned patients arrive at the hospital they are identified and immediately escorted to their rooms, introduced to the area staff, and invited to become comfortable with their surroundings. A health care admissions representative arrives at the patient's room equipped with a laptop computer coupled to the area wireless LAN. The representative will take all of the data and patient information interactively and complete the form using the computer. Access to files and records and updating of the results to the departmental computers are done over the wireless LANs link.

Educational System

The educational system are logical candidates for the use of a wireless LAN. The campus facilities of most schools lend themselves to a zone type of wireless LAN setup and the teachers are highly mobile as they bring their teaching efforts to various groups of students. The use of a wireless LAN would provide the teachers access to student information, grade books, teaching resources, lesson plans, attendance, messaging and a host of other information systems and services. It would allow the teachers access to data at any location within the teaching campus and the ability to take their client workstation to any location where they would be dealing with the teaching process or their administrative duties. As teachers are a highly mobile workforce yet stay within a contained campus environment, the wireless LAN would provide direct support for most of their data processing needs. Additional services such as access to the Internet and other teaching services would also be available through the wireless LAN.

Temporary Setup

Temporary work situations are excellent candidates for the use of wireless LANs. The systems can be set up quickly in most compact locations, operated while needed, and then taken out when the temporary situation is over. Typical temporary situations include:

— The Sporting events

— The Entertainment programs

— The Political campaigns

— The Fund raising campaigns

— The Special events

— The Training camps

— The Seasonal events

— The Sales campaigns

— The Security operations

— The Special sales

— The Management events

— The Emergency situations

— The Conventions

The temporary application of wireless LANs would require the ability to orchestrate a rapid connection to the existing wired LANs. This would include a physical transceiving station to make the connection to the wired world and the ability to test and validate the connection. It will also be necessary to identify and validate the users who will be signing onto the system via the temporary wireless units.

The temporary applications can literally be here today and gone tomorrow. The temporary setup and the necessary equipment would probably be stored as a library unit, so it could be quickly acquired and implemented. Pretesting and trial runs at setting the temporary services up and using them would be mandatory to prevent any glitches from developing when a real temporary use was being implemented.

Emergency centers have a tendency to be here today and gone tomorrow. They are often highly localized, command center- oriented situations that need coordination and control of diverse resources working to correct a defined emergency situation. A fire, follow, disaster, accident, or other catastrophe would qualify as an emergency service situation. The emergency itself could last from a few hours to many weeks. The efforts could involve rescue efforts, medical attention, property modification, relocation support, service provisioning, and emergency restoration services. The key in servicing emergency centers with information is the speed of setup and the flexibility to maintain information services between a diverse set of mobile workers. The unpredictability of the coverage area, the condition, and the area for services provisioning and management are variable and seldom ideal. The operation of an emergency-oriented wireless LAN would be based on using a mobile service headquarters that would provide the nucleus of the services and operate the transceiving equipment for the site. The mobile service unit would also establish the communication coupling with other remote or local services using traditional or wireless network connections. The local emergency site wireless LAN could be coupled to the remote LANs using wireless LAN bridging or wireless satellite communications.

General Services

The emergency support wireless LAN can provide a host of other services to the emergency workers and crews in addition to the access to emergency data and instructions. These services include:

- The Task management
- The Person location
- The Operation control
- The Logistics management
- The Facilities control
- The Provisioning for food and refreshment
- The Scheduling of backup support
- The Time tracking and triggering
- The Messages and electronic mail
- The Management reporting
- The Media interfacing
- The Bulletin board messages

The administrative support services may be inactive while the emergency is tended; as soon as the situation is under control the support services would be engaged and used to document and complete the summary of operations.

FUTURE EVOLUTION OF WIRELESS LANs

Wireless LANs are still in their infancy. They will move through several generations of new and improved technologies on their way to maturity. The evolution for the future of wireless LAN's will include:

- Higher speeds
- Improved security
- Multiple frequency hopping
- New vendors
- Seamless end-to-end protocols
- Better error control
- Longer distances
- Home systems
- New devices

30

WIRELESS LAN MEDIA COMPONENTS : AIR

INTRODUCTION

The media components of wireless LAN systems are the air through which the transmission waves will travel. Unfortunately, the air medium is subject to many variations and pollutants which cause deterioration in the performance of moving signals through the medium. In many cases the medium will require cleaning and conditioning to support a reliable signal transfer. There is very little that wireless LANs can do to change the air medium through which their signals will travel. They must constantly monitor the air quality and the accuracy and strength of the wireless LAN signals that are passing through the air. The continuous monitoring process will be build into the transceivers for the wireless connection. When the performance of the air medium fails or drops, the transceivers have to switch to alternate forms of operation to sustain the accuracy of the communications.

The following steps are involved in conditioning and signal control:

— Suspend operations

— Switch to other frequencies

— Move to other forms of signaling

— Retransmission of the messages

— Multicasting

The key process is to get the messages accurately through the air medium to and from the client-sever components. When the air medium is optimal, such services may be dormant, when the air quality deteriorates, these conditioning alternatives need to come on line automatically and expenditure.

The communication of information between two computer systems requires some form of connecting medium. The wireless LAN uses air as its medium rather than a physical wire. Air is a part of the fluid world and behaves according to defined laws of physics. The principal physics for communication is the pulsing of the medium in such a way that the pulses travel across the medium and can be detected and reliably received at specified points in the medium. The medium must carry the signal with accuracy, reliability, continuity, and quality.

The physics of the use of the air medium is actually the same as that used in the wired world. Pulses are generated at one connection of the wire, and they travel through the wire medium and are received at other points along the wire. The difference between the wire versus air medium, only dictates that the means of generating the pulses may be different. In a wire medium the pulse is set and maintained by electrical current turned off at specified intervals and maintained at a set power level. The air medium is also pulsed, but with waves that can be transmitted by broadcasting into the medium using predefined frequencies. The available frequencies are defined by wave mechanics and physics and the spectrum of frequencies allocated by laws and regulation for various purposes. The three basic levels of pulsing are used for today's wireless LANs:

1. The radio frequency band space.

2. The very small wavelength area known as microwaves.

3. The frequency area just above visible light, which is known as infrared.

Several other frequencies are available in the air medium pulsing arena, such a low-frequency heat variations, frequencies just out of the human audibility or hearing range and several others.

The use of the air medium requires that wireless LANs have a transmitting and receiving capability to pass high-reliability, high-speed, error-free messages and contro information between one another within their prescribed geographic area. The *local* of loca area networks will have precise meaning in terms of distance and power and accuracy of th wireless system.

The air medium is not as "clean" and reliable as a contained wire medium. The wir environment is dedicated to the communication process and is a carefully defined physic world. The air is common and shared by many uses and users. Air is also not a particular clean world. Continuous and dynamic disturbances are placed on the air which can cau disruptions and problems in its use as a communications transfer medium. The moveme of heavy physical objects through the air causes the air to move in different patterns a waves. Thus vehicles, people, machines, etc. can move the air medium in different ways a induce distortions in the flow of the communication waves through the air medium. Usuall air is an unstable, multiuse, multiuser environment that is not particularly friendly to t hosting of communications signals. The air can be contaminated with foreign particl distorted by operations and movements, and disrupted by influences such as electric interference, lightning, and other phenomena. In some respects it is amazing that air can used at all for the reliable transmission of communications signals.

The physics of the air molecules is also different from that of the wired world. Air is composed of loosely coupled molecules containing a variety of different components. To pulse these molecules requires more power and patience, as the separation of the air components is greater than that of tightly packed copper atoms.

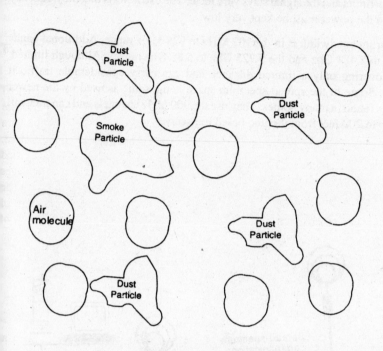

Fig. 30.1 : Air signal movement problem

RADIO WAVE LANs

The use of the radio waves for the wireless LAN medium is the simplest and most logical way to interchange information between local computers. The problem is that all radio frequencies are carefully managed and controlled by the federal governments. However, most of the radio frequency spectrum is already in use by other applications and assigned clients. Radio wave LANs have been granted usage of three frequency bands that are small unused niches in the spectrum. Known as the spread-spectrum areas, these frequencies can be used without license for low-power, limited- distance communications that stay within the confines of a building.

Radio wave LANs provide a broad range of flexibility and portability. They require little tuning and can be used within a reasonable area. They are susceptible to local interference from equipment and other electrical devices.

Radio wave wireless LANs operate in the 900 MHz range. They utilize from one to three segments of this band to transmit and receive signals between units. The bandwidths are very limited and are in the ISM band. This band is known for its susceptibility to interference from radar, microwave ovens, medical equipment, and other devices.

The good news is that no license is required in the spread- spectrum bands at long as power is kept within limits and the signal stays very local. The bad news is that the frequency space is limited and the power must be kept very low.

Spread-spectrum bandwidth is in the 902 MHz to 928 MHz range. **Additional bands** are in the 2.4 Ghz to 2.484 Ghz and the 5.725 Ghz to 5.85 Ghz ranges. Although limited, these bands are covering only a limited distance and can carry considerable traffic if managed properly. Some of the spread-spectrum space is the same as used by the newer portable telephones found in many homes. They use the 900 MHz channels and can transmit their voice calls up to 200 feet from the line-based transceiver.

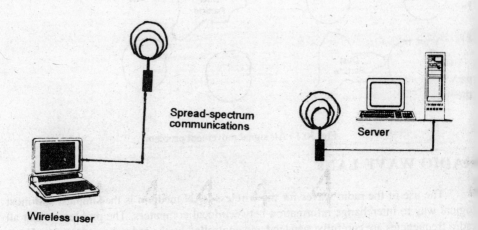

Fig. 30.2 : Spread spectrum operations

Wireless LANs are mostly used for limited distance, local services. It is possible to use the same concept with higher power broadcasting levels and travel over several miles. The Air-Bridge system from Persoft has the capability to extend LAN-based devices and services to distances of over two miles. The Air-Bridge maintains 2 Mbps speeds between the remote connections. The LAN- LAN wireless connections offer higher speeds than wired telecommunications facilities at lower costs. Radio spectrum wireless LANs can split the frequency up into multiple channels, or they can use a single channel and dedicate the total bandwidth.

Frequency Hopping

Communications on one channel of the radio spectrum can be transferred from one to another available channel as the traffic passes from one radio zone to another on its way to the final destination. This is known as frequency hopping. The frequency hopping is performed automatically as the signal is received and retransmitted across the network nodes. The process is very similar to the one used in the cellular network as a user passes from one cell into another.

Frequency hopping has two basic advantages in wireless LANs:

1. The system can use the available bandwidth more efficiently.

2. Frequency hopping makes it very difficult to eavesdrop on spread-spectrum data traffic, because only the transceivers know which channel is carrying the next block of communications.

By the time an eavesdropper was able to shift to another channel, the communications traffic would be gone. Frequency hopping is built into the transceivers of a spread-spectrum wireless LAN. It may be selected as an operating option at the time of installation and setup. Many of the systems operate in this mode as their default state.

Direct Sequence Coding

The passage of information through the wireless LAN network will move across the network nodes using the spread-spectrum bandwidth. Direct sequence coding happens when the traffic is directed between specific nodes for passage into other network media.

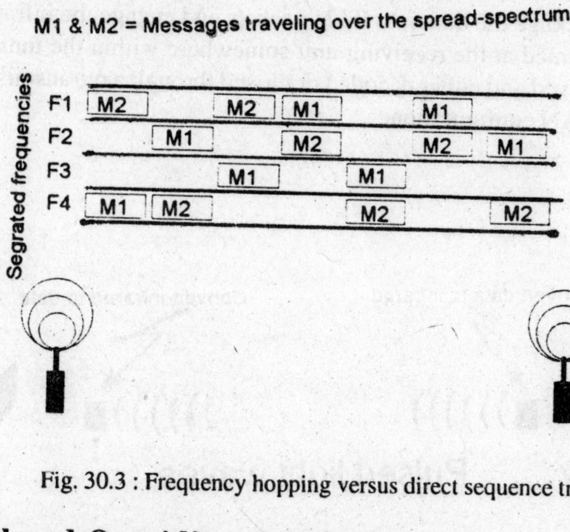

Fig. 30.3 : Frequency hopping versus direct sequence traffic

Directional and Omnidirectional Antennas

The connection of a mobile client to a wireless LAN will require a physical device to generate the waveform pattern that will travel through the air or space medium. Various types of antennas will be used to fulfill this physical medium conversion step. Some of the antennas will be directional. These will require tuning the wave beam from the transmitter to the receiver. The tuning may require space entry (microwaves) or it may require direct line of sight (infrared couplings).

Omnidirectional antennas will beam the wave transmissions up into the space around the transmitter and the transmissions will radiate uniformly in all directions around the antenna. The pickup receiving antenna need only be within the wave transmission area of the signal to receive and convert it.

INFRARED LANs

Infrared LANs use the nonvisible portion of the light spectrum. The wavelength is in the range of 900 nanometers. This is the spectrum used by remote controllers, TV remotes, and some security detection units. The wavelength provides short signals with good resolution but very short range, with tuning required. In the LAN operation the infrared systems will use a broader spectrum of wavelength to provide a less critical tuning connection between the LAN nodes and the network transceivers.

The infrared beams are waveforms just outside the visible light frequencies. The beams are still generated frequency levels in this spectrum, with their data contained in pulsed encodings. The sending and receiving are different from those at radios frequencies because the light beams are unidirectional rather than omni-directional as the, leave and enter sending and receiving units.

The sending of infrared signals requires the network operating system (NOS) to interrupt the request for LAN services and send the data to the network interface unit. The interface unit will package the data into LAN packets and engage the infrared transmitter. The transmission is aimed at the receiving unit somewhere within the tunable space. The infrared signal is received and either decoded or passed through a retransmission to another unit in the wireless LAN configuration.

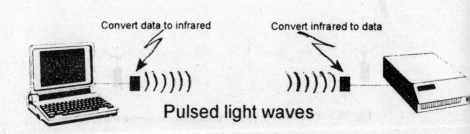

Convert data to infrared   Convert infrared to data

Pulsed light waves

Fig. 30.4 : Infrared light beam transmissions

The sending of infrared signals can be a direct one-hop transmission or it can be set to be multihopped between transceivers until it reaches the specified server or user in the wireless environment.

The receiving of infrared LAN signals requires that the receiving sensor be located within the line of sight of the transmitter. The angle can be fairly wide (± 30 degrees), but the beam must reach the sensor with adequate strength and continuity. The straighter the beam and the more directly it is aimed at the receiving sensor, the better the reliability and throughout of the information transfers.

The infrared LAN signals are directional signals. The radiation pattern is focused from the transmitting source in a straight line form in the direction in which the beam is pointed. The signal pattern spreads out as the signal travels; however, the spread at the end of the receiving distance is about 3 to 4 feet, which means that the beam must be in line-of-sight alignment from the transmitting source to the receiving point.

The receiver for the infrared beam can be mounted in any location where there is a clear path from the transmitter to the receiver. A common practice is to mount the receiver in the ceiling in a corner of the usage area. This makes a convenient pointing space for the user to aim at with a high likelihood of reaching the target without interference.

The infrared signals can be operated at relatively high speeds. Current laptop-to-laptop infrared services are running at 16 Mbps. The theoretical limits of the technology are up around the 100 Mbps range. This can make the infrared services the fastest of the wireless LAN technologies.

The optical frequencies used by the infrared LAN signals are below the visible lightwave spectrum. These light beams are not visible to the naked eye and they are not harmful to humans. As part of the optical spectrum, these signals are immune to electrical interference and they are relatively immune to eavesdropping because of their tuned send and receiver nature. The light signals can also support a relatively high speed of data traffic within their bandwidth.

Infrared power requirements are very low. The infrared remote controllers use small batteries that last for several years. This makes infrared ideal for portable, battery-operated computer units.

Infrared signals are very susceptible to physical forms of interference. If a human body enters the infrared beam space, it will absorb the signals and the receiving antenna will be blocked. Other forms of interference can be caused by signal deflection, bouncing signal interference, and a host of other physical space distortions.

Infrared transfer services are also being used for very short distance intercommunication. Many new generation laptop computers are coming with built-in infrared transmit and receive capabilities. IBM, Texas Instruments, Hewlett-Packard, and others are making infrared the first level of interconnectivity for their laptop computers. When a laptop user needs to move data to or from the laptop computer to another computer such as a desktop unit, the user would simply position the devices within 3 to 8 feet of one another, perform some send-receive tests, and then open up to systems for rapid transfer of the chosen data and information. The data movement speeds for this form of infrared wireless LAN are in the region of from 600 kbps to 16 Mbps. The key is to support the bus speed of the slowest unit so that it forms an almost continuous service capability between its internal resources and those available via the infrared LAN.

Infrared communication has various positive characteristics. It is low power, requires no license, needs an area tuning, but provides some security from eavesdropping. The short distance is not a problem when the units are in close proximity anyway. Infrared is the least expensive and most reliable form of short-haul wireless interconnection. It will continue to grow to become the connection of choice for personal digital assitants (PDAs), laptop computers, and other protable data collection and service units.

MICROWAVE LANs

Microwave wireless LANs use the frequencies in the 18 GHz to 24 GHz range to encapsulate and transfer the LAN data packets. These frequencies are is shortwave form are very high. They will pass through most things without loss or distortion. This makes microwave a viable form for wireless LANs and other forms of open distance communications. Microwave has been used for decades in long-distance transmission services, and by reducing the power it is now being applied for wireless LANs.

The microwave frequencies used for wireless LANs are in the range of 18 to 24 GHz. These frequencies will pass through most things, like tissue and walls. They are capable of a multiplexed traffic load and can be used beyond building limits, if permitted by the license.

Microwaves have been used for long-haul, high-speed communications for many years. They formed the original backbone of the long-distance network in the United States. They were also the foundation of companies like Microwave Communications, Inc. (now known as MCI). Long-haul microwave requires territorial licenses and uses high-power microwaves. The wireless LAN microwaves are a specialized part of the microwave spectrum which is licensed for limited distance, lower power operation.

Like the infrared LANs, microwave systems must be in a line of sight type of relationship. The tuning is, however less critical than for the optical wave beam, which must hit the optical receiver. The microwave beams spread out in a fan, and as long as a sufficient level of the beam hits the receiver the information transfer can take place reliably.

Microwaves are also easier than infrared signals to capture and retransmit in a multihop configuration. In most of the cases the sending station will aim the microwave to a receiver up at the ceiling level of the source room. From here the receiver can be aimed at other receivers at ceiling level around the building. The receiving station will then retransmit the signals to the next level station and create a multihop distribution service.

The distances for microwave LANs depend on the number of hops between transceivers. The single-hop distance is on the order of 80 to 100 feet. There can be as unlimited number of hops in the overall network as long as the single hops conform to the distance limitations. Long-distance microwave towers can send their waves to around 30 miles, depending on the height of the towards. This is done with high-power microwaves, whereas the wireless local area network systems use far lower power and thus must limit their distance.

The dispersion of microwave signals from the transmission antenna is a dispersion pattern that is elliptical in shape. There is some edge distortion in the signal, which increases as the signal travels through the air. This distortion is not a problem, as long as the main signal is received rather than the edge portion. If the relationship angle is off between the transmit and receiving antenna, then distortion or errors in the received signal may occur. When such errors are detected the signals will have to be retransmitted.

The error correction for most of the microwave systems is built into the transmission hardware. This makes it possible to sample the quality of the transmissions continuously and quickly respond to any faults or needs for retransmission.

The main interference in microwave signals is due to the existence of stray microwave signals from other licensed users. Many areas of the United States are already saturated with microwave signal licenses and very active patterns of microwaves being beamed through the airspace. These signals, which are usually intermittent in nature, may stray or bounce into the spectrum space of the microwave wireless LANs. This is especially true of higher floors of buildings in major metropolitan city centers.

In their basic form, microwaves are transmitted through a high- speed pipeline that moves data between a transmitter and a receiver using a narrow beam of space and compressed high energy waves. In some of the situations, such as moving the microwaves through odd spaces, it is possible to use square metal tubes that are hooked together and serve to bounce and guide the microwaves from one location to another. The tubes are called waveguides, and they will contain and direct the microwave signals. This provides two valuable results; the signals are following a known and clean track, and they can be given higher power without problems of interference with humans or other possible signal blockages.

31
WIRELESS LAN OPERATIONS & CONNECTIONS

ONE-TO-ONE OPERATIONS

One-to-one wireless LAN operations will take place when a single portable unit wants to make data contact with a single fixed server unit. A typical example would be a laptop or notebook computer coupled to a fixed desktop computer station. This would allow for the intertransfer of data, files, programs, and other information between the portable unit and the fixed station. The fixed station can be the connection to a wired LAN world and form a bridge or conduit for passing requested information between the user or client station and the rest of the information world. The one-to-one wireless connection may become the most numerous implementation. The growing number of personal digital assistants, laptop computers, and other portable devices can all use the one-to-one connection.

The one-to-one wireless LAN would cover limited space and traffic. It would be under the direct control of one user, who would most likely control both the portable unit and the desktop system. The simplicity of the one-to-one coupling will make it easy to operate and manage. The use of the capabilities of the wireless communications will be limited to the creativity and needs of one individual.

ONE-TO-MANY OPERATIONS

When wireless LAN users want to access several servers within their networked, they are coupling to a one-to-many relationship. This connection is more complex than the one-to-one relationship, as described earlier. The user, or the system administration process, will have to know where and how to navigate the network and the attached resources to locate and return the services requested by the user. One-to-many operations will also have to be cognizant of the traffic patterns of other users and applications, determine service facilities and performance factors, control the accuracy and reliability of the operations, and be vigilant for any faults which could occur while the user is interacting with the other resources.

One-to-many connections will probably be the most common connections from a user view of point. This allows the user to have apparent access to a full range of resources via the wireless LAN technology. This will allow the coupling of the user to a wide variety of systems resources while still retaining the mobility and flexibility of the end user. The one-to-many connections will be defined by the user operations and actions and controlled by an administrative management process that is built into the overall network control level of the system. As one-to-many may use of a combination of wireless and wired connections, the control levels will need to be logically rather than physically defined.

MANY-TO-MANY OPERATIONS

Many-to-many operations would consist of various mobile user clients coupled to a variety of resources over a wireless LAN. The many-to-many operation is an extension of the one-to-many situation. It will again add complexity and management requirements to keep the users straight and their service requests properly addressed and handled. As multiple mobile users are being supported in most organizations, this form will end up as the most typical form of connectivity.

The major aspect of many-to-many couplings will be the management of the requests and returns of information to and from the mobile end users. The services may be performed via a mix of wireless and wired networks from resources that could be anywhere in the organization's networked world. Many-to-many management will have to keep track of all users and their network activities at all times and under all loads and conditions.

PLANNING OF WIRELESS LAN

The planning of a wireless LAN installation needs more analysis and evaluation than the wired LAN. One part of the extended planning is to be certain that a wireless LAN is the correct solution for the users and the application. Another part of planning is to determine that the environment will support a wireless LAN installation and provide an adequate operating environment. Once these feasibility issues are determined, there are additional planning steps for the facility, locations, operational procedures, and the implementation of a wireless LAN.

The first planning step is to determine whether a wireless LAN is a good solution for the application, the users, and the environment. The key factors to be evaluated are the level of mobility needed, the types of data to be transferred, the operational facility space, and the characteristics of the users. The answers that would favor the use of a wireless LAN are:

Mobility of the users- Untethered movement is required within a physically limited area which could be served with a wireless service.

Facility space- The spatial area should be well defined, contiguous, and self-contained with enough openness to support wireless transmissions without interference or constrictions.

Data transmitted/received- Wireless systems work best with short bursts of data being moved. This would include transactions or file reference records and not transfers of large files or big blocks of information.

User competence- The users should be computer-adaptable persons who can interact with a network service environment that might have delays or minor disruptions or discontinuity of services.

The second step of planning step after the successful determination of the feasibility of using a wireless LAN is to evaluate the facility space and do some preliminary layout of the wireless LAN environment and service locations. It is useful to obtain architectural layout drawings of the facility area where the wireless LAN will operate. These diagrams should show the major structural components, such as walls and supporting columns, and the temporary additions such as partitions, partial walls, and false ceilings. It is often useful to have access to diagrams that show the power, heat, ventilation, and other utility services in the area including telephone, wired LANs, and other communications services. If the facility already has wired LANs installed, these diagrams may already exist with the LAN components drawn in place on the diagrams. Always start with the most complete reference diagrams possible. Ones with the current LAN layout are best because the wireless LANs will likely be connecting to the wired world at one or more places.

The next step is to plan the usage or wireless layout of the spatial area. The determination of logical transmit and receive points to be within the distance limits of the technology and easily accessible to the users will take some amount of trial-and-error positioning and evaluation of the possible operations of the wireless LAN. The key factors in the positioning decisions are:

Clear access - Can the points be reached and used without having any restrictive building components in the way between the transmit and receive facilities?

Logical user interfacing- Can the access points be conveniently used by the application users without difficulty or blockage of their efforts to communicate using the wireless technology?

Natural warning locations- Does the spatial area have natural borders where warnings can be posted or issued to inform the users they are at the boundary of the wireless LAN's service coverage?

Possible voids in service- Are there any places where there will be likely difficulty or possible inability to maintain services to the wireless LAN? Known as voids, these areas should be minimal to nonexistent. If they are present they should be in places where it is unlikely to be necessary to transmit or where the voids will be a minimal problem. Too many likely voids may invalidate the idea of using a wireless LAN.

Locational movements- Can the users move comfortably through the environment and still be able to be in send/receive contact with the wireless LAN?

Roaming- Are there places where one wireless LAN can detect and hand off services to another LAN? Roaming connectors should be placed where they have the greatest area of coverage and can efficiently move users on the limits of one LAN to another without loss or disruption.

In few situations it may not be possible to predetermine the feasibility of a wireless LAN. In such cases a trial evaluation implementation may be required. By setting up a small wireless LAN in the physical environment, it may be possible to confirm or reject the potential for a successful full-scale operation.

SETUP OF WIRELESS LAN

The setup of a wireless LAN system involves the physical delivery and establishment of the send and receive units. This may include facility preparation and organization, determining the location of transmit and receive equipment, and review of expected applications for the wireless system.

Setup also involves defining the server units and the client units in terms of their capabilities, services, identity, and locations on the network. The interfacing to existing computer resources and wired LANs will also need to be evaluated. Such systems will also need to be reviewed for the adequacy of their resources to service the loads from the wireless LAN world. The added loads from the wireless world could have major impacts on the use of available memory and disk space.

Once the physical and logical elements have been determined to be adequate for the wireless LAN installation, the setup plan is complete and the physical installation can begin. The information for the setup should be documented and made a part of the systems definition and management file.

INSTALLATION OF WIRELESS LAN

The installation process for a wireless LAN varies slightly with the chosen wireless technology. The common elements include:

(1). *Install the transceiver units* - Installation may consist of installing a network interface card into the computer unit and coupling wires from the card to the transceiver unit. The transceiver units will need to be aligned and tested according to the instructions provided by the vendor. Usual placement involves keeping the antenna in a higher space that is clear of people and physical interference.

(2). *Tune the send and receive elements of the system* - The tuning process consists of selecting the starting frequency levels and running some self-tests to see if the units can establish and maintain contact with one another. Adjustment of the tuning alignment consists of moving the locations and aiming the transmitters and receivers connected to the various computer units. The tests would then be rerun to determine whether any improvements were generated. Other tuning can be done with a multifrequency signal strength meter. This unit is placed in various locations within the intended signal space to measure the level of received signal when the test units are transmitting.

(3). *Load the software into the clients and servers* - Once the transceivers are in reasonable tune and the units can transmit and receive to or from one another, it then becomes time to set up the software that will connect the applications and the user to the wireless LAN world. The loaded software is usually a vendor-developed version of a mini network operating system. This software requires to trap data operations that must move over the wireless network and develop the proper data and messaging formats to be used for communication over the wireless LAN. This software will require resident space on the client and the server systems. It will trap user requests for remote services and format these requests into forms that can be recognized and serviced by the wireless LAN.

(4). *Test the components for proper operation* - This level of testing will involve both the application and the wireless network components. The application level on the client should set up a request or an information transfer that is intended for a remote server reachable over the wireless LAN. The test should involve observing the client and sever relationship over the wireless LAN. The steps, actions, and timings of the client generating the wireless LAN transaction and the server responding to it would be tracked and evaluated. Once the tests are functionally complete and deemed correct, the next level of testing will come when the system is operational and multiple transaction loads begin to challenge the system's performance.

(5). Test the connectivity components - The test of the connectivity components will validate the ability of the wireless LAN to sustain reasonable throughput under varying situations and conditions. Tests for loads, continuity of service, through-put timings, and other performance characteristics should be run and evaluated. If the performance is not deemed adequate, then adjustments should be made to priority schemes, network segments, reliability characteristics, speed incre-ments, and/or other adjustment factors.

(6). *Training the users* - Most of the operations of a wireless LAN should be transparent to the users. However, there are several unique operations and steps that the user will need to know and support to make the wireless LAN a success. One area of training is in the setup and maintenance of the physical arrangement of the wireless units. The placement of antennas, transceivers, and other coupling components is critical. The locations for the units that are known to work best should be identified by the users. In the event of decoupling of the wireless LAN, the user will need to know what to do to attempt to reconnect and initialize the services of the wireless LAN.

(7).   Document the system - The operation of the wireless LAN and any work the user will require to do to keep it running will need to be put into written form. This documentation could be provided in an on-line file format, an interactive help service, and hard copy. The material should be clear in format and well indexed so that users or client can find the documentation portion that is relevant to their needs.

(8).   *Set up the operations support services* - The wireless LAN installation process is a short one-time effort for each node. A few hours are all that is required for the opening, connecting, and testing of the wireless LAN. Most of the time will be taken up with the installation and testing of the software components. This may require reallocation of memory space, modification of user files and systems specifications, and adjustment of user applications.

(9).   *Final operational testing* - The total installation must be tested under realistic operating conditions. Sometimes user applications programs will not run as the network modules have taken up resident memory and prevent certain user applications from loading into their normally expected areas. Considerable adjustment and shoehorning may be needed to make the system properly operate all user applications and services.

WIRELESS-TO-WIRE CONNECTIONS

The wireless LAN will seldom be a self-contained environment in which all elements are coupled only via a wireless system. The normal situation will have wireless clients coupled to a server level, which is in turn coupled to the wired world. This allows the wireless user the best of both worlds. They will be able to be mobile and wireless from their client systems and still receive the benefits of connectivity to the wired world.

Wireless-to-wired connections will involve signal recognition and translation from one form of medium to another. They should also be transparent and provide the users with information services that do not identify themselves as being handled by a wired or a wireless world. Full operational transparency where the wireless and wired worlds interact with seamless and transparent interfacing is a key measurement criterion for the wireless-to-wired coupling.

Very few wireless LANs operate only in the wireless mode. The usual configuration is to have the wireless LAN operating as the local connectivity layer for the mobile users and then couple the system to a wired LAN via a common server node. This provides the best of both the wireless and wired worlds. Users at both ends of the spectrum can have access to shared resources and each other.

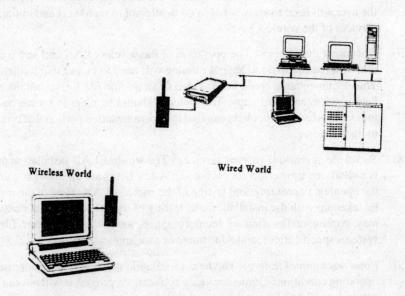

Fig. 31.1 : Wireless to wired couplings

Wireless-to-wire LAN connections are relatively easy to set up and maintain. A selected server is configured to be a part of both the wireless and wired LAN worlds. This server functions as the intermediary for both environments.

Remote Access

The provisioning of remote access to wired networks via a wireless link involves tightly managed relationship. The provisioning of security controls and careful screening of the data flows is needed to maintain the integrity of the environment.

Remote access will provide flexible access to a broad range of services, however the remote access connection will probably be slower and more error prone than local coupling.

Resource manager

The resource manager have to identify the request of a remote wireless user and determine where and how to provide answers to the request for services. The resource manager have to know the following details:

Authorized users

— Location of resources
— Access codes and directions
— Service possibilities
— Alternate routings
— Validation and security permits

The resource manager will probably be vested at the wireless-to- wired interface point or in a shared server that is somewhere in the wired world.

Bridging and Routing

Bridges allows traffic to pass from one network to another. The bridge is nondiscriminating and will pass all of the traffic presented. A bridge takes traffic and moves it to the other side of the bridge onto the connected network. In wireless LANs, the bridge may be connecting the wireless world to the wired environment. Bridges could also be used to couple one wireless work group to another.

Routers are more intelligent than bridges, they contain tables of legitimate addresses and network locations. When presented with a message, the router will examine the address and determine that the addressee is a known entity in the network. If the address is unknown, the router will eliminate the message as erroneous. If the message is bound for a remote network, the address would be a known connector port within the router's knowledge space.

When a wireless network hands a message to a router, the unit could determine the best way to proceed with the message's movement in the network, as the router also knows the links and conditions within the network. Routing would seek to send the message by the most efficient and least congested connections.

Bridges and routers will be natural points of interconnectivity between wired and wireless networks. These devices natural role in interconnecting networks will work in both wireless and wired media. The use of standard protocols such as Ethernet and token ring, within the wireless world will allow the bridges and routers to function as a wireless coupled device with minimal change.

Central servers

Within the wired world, there is a tendency to build and maintain some central repositories and servers. For examples include data warehouses and electronic image filing cabinets (optical jukeboxes). These central servers can be coupled to the wireless world through the use of bridges and routers and/or locator servers that would direct requests from wireless users to these central servers.

The difference between accessing central servers versus local or distributed units is that the waiting lines of users may be longer, making it more difficult to assure reasonable response times to the mobile wireless user. This could be improved by assigning priorities to the wireless user to minimize the waiting lines and delays. Other considerations would include caching wireless requests or making them into a delayed call-back type of response.

Locations

The location for making the connection of wireless to wired is very important. The wireless distances are the constraining part of the equation, so that the location of any interface device will have to be within the distance domain of the wireless world. However, the wired world also has distance limitations varying with the medium being used. If the connection from wireless-to- wired is using 10 Base T cable then the wireless to wired coupler cannot be more than 100 meters (330 feet) from the coupling hub of the wired network. Although these distances are greater than those used in the wireless network, they can still represent severe constraints in the layout of the interconnections.

Loads

The coupling between wireless and wired networks will suffer some form of speed imbalance. The wireless network will probably top out at 2 Mbps, while the wired network will perform at 10 Mbps and above. This speed imbalance will cause some buildup of load at the connections points. The wired network will have to buffer data to support the slower speeds of the wireless network, and the wireless network will require some form of concentrator to bring its speed up to that of the wired system.

In addition, the loads between the two networks will be subject to the fact that wireless users will use small request packets for the information they need from the wired servers and will likely receive a large number of packets from the server to answer their requests. This will mean a greater high-speed load feeding into a lower speed wireless network. Again, buffering and load balancing will be necessary at the interface point.

Control

The connection between the wireless and the wired networks will need some form of management control. As the wired world is treated as the senior environment, control will most likely be vested in this sector. Control will consist of the mechanics to log and manage the processing of a message and/or the management of the request and answer between the client and the server(s).

Control will consist of:

— Message management
— Traffic logs

— Audit logs

— Error logging

— Corruption detection

— Retransmission management

— Other support services

LAN TO LAN OPERATIONS

Some wireless LANs will be stand-alone operations; however, most of them will involve coupling one LAN to another. The couplings may be wireless to wireless or wireless to wired. There may be many levels of LAN-to-LAN couplings as the wireless units become accepted parts of the enterprise network integration. In some of the couplings, the wireless LAN connection will become a key part of bonding other network layers together.

Although many wireless LANs will provide user-level services, others will be devoted to the interconnection of one LAN to another. For example, wireless LAN bridges can supply long- distance, high-speed, wireless data connectivity between one LAN and another. At the lower speed of this spectrum, between 1 and 2 Mbps, these wireless LAN bridges will compete with T1 communications lines but with less cost and simpler LAN-based administration. At higher speed levels, 16 Mbps and above, the wireless LAN couplers will compete with T3 lines and other services such as frame relay.

Key factors in the use of wireless LAN couplers will be support for longer distances 'up to 15 miles' with lower costs and the use of internal LAN management techniques. Wireless LAN-to-LAN couplings may become a major playing card in the building of cost-effective enterprise networks.

Very few wireless LANs operate as stand-alone entities. Most of them are the local user front end to a fixed wired network environment. The wireless LAN may support the mobile workers, but it will at some point connect to a wired LAN of the organization. Wired LANs have been the traditional form of LAN and make up most of the connectivity between the offices and operational facilities of an organization. The wireless LANs are more recent introductions that are used to service special classes of users and provide them with capability for both the wireless and the wired world of data and information.

The merging of the wireless and the wired worlds will logically happen at one or more server nodes within the networks. Either special connector nodes or extensions of a working server will be used to couple the wireless and the wired worlds. From this coupling information can flow bi-directionally from the users to the server and form the server to the users. The traffic will flow over whichever technologies are used to connect the units together.

The operation of the wireless-to-wired LAN interface will require the merger of two different worlds. Although both worlds are part of the LAN environment, their operations and controls are different. The framing of the data packets may be the same, Ethernet or token ring, but the speeds and the actual operations of the networks will be vastly different.

Recognition

The wireless and the wired LANs must be able to recognize the signals from one another. The interface device between the two networks must be able to be a participating member of each network and handle the specific protocol format and signal level needed for each native network. When a signal arrives that is destined to cross over between the two networks, the interconnect device must recognize the request and convert it from one format to another.

Recognition consists of being able to accept the signal in one format and then convert and manage the signal in the second network environment. As the signal reaches the interconnect device, the device must be able to identify, accept, and convert the signal to the proper format.

Acceptance

Once a signal is recognized as moving between the two different types of networks, it is necessary for the receiver to accept the signal as valid. If it finds the signal or message is not up to its requirements, the signal must be rejected and some flag or message sent to confirm the rejection.

The acceptance process will occur at the interface point between the two networks. In a passive coupling the signal will be passed directly to the receiving network and the final terminator or the addressee will have to determine acceptance. In an active network the acceptance would be conducted at the port of entry.

Speed matching

The wire and wireless networks will probably have speed differences. Today the wireless average 2 Mbps while the wired networks are seldom less than 10 Mbps. The difference will increase as the wired networks raise their speed levels to 100 Mbps.

Speed matching will require considerable buffering to support the return flows from the higher speed wired worlds to the lower speed wireless systems. The inbound matching will be less of a problem.

The speed matching will probably occur at a server type of node which will be able to store the total communications from the wired world and dribble them out to the wireless network.

Packet conversion

Packet conversion is the process of reframing the packets from one network environment into those required by another. Even though the wireless and wired networks might both be running Ethernet formats, the detailed headers and packet controls may be different in the two networks. The packet conversion process can be done along with the speed matching and the acceptance process.

Flows

The flow of messages from the wireless and wired worlds will have to be carefully managed. The matching of speed differences, format conversions and audio trail tracking will disrupt the continuity of the flows. The use of message techniques such as electronic mail will provide some form of flow management and control.

The flows between the two network worlds will probably be somewhat discontinuous due to the large variations in capabilities. Buffering or holding the messages to perform the necessary balancing and matching will be part of the design process. Flow control and conversion can be performed by an intelligent server or a large buffer-oriented protocol conversion unit.

Errors

Errors may occur at the point of coupling of the wireless and the wired worlds. Such errors will have a high probability of being errors of interpretation or conversions. If the data are received properly, then the conversion process could be flawed. If the conversions process is made active rather than passive, then the errors should be small and identifiable and correctable before the message is retransmitted.

Losses and reconstitution

There is always the possibility that a message or transmission will be lost in transit. This is possible in any medium and more probable in the wireless world. If the message is missing as defined by a sequential packet identity being open and unreceived, then the system will have to locate and retransmit the missing message.

The loss identification and retransmission process scan be largely automatic within the send and receive functioning of the system. The receiver will check the message identities and validate and sequential consistency of the received packets. It will also validate the packets to be sure they are of acceptable quality. If any are unacceptable or missing, the receiver will make requests for retransmission.

LAN-To-LAN COUPLINGS

Wireless LANs can also provide services directly to the internal parts of networks, rather than always to end-user situations. In these operations the wireless LAN can cover longer distances, operate at higher speeds and perform in competition with many wide area network services (WAN). For example, the wireless LAN bridge which can be used to couple one LAN to another that is up to several miles away. Using line-of-sight paths and either radio beams or microwaves, these systems can transmit large volumes of data at high speeds with excellent reliability.

The LAN-LAN couplings are usually tuned and nonmobile. This means that once they are set up and validated they will maintain their alignment, can support higher intensity signal power, and simply use the air space as their working medium, rather than wire. Given that any outsider intervention with the signal would change the signal itself in easily monitored and measured levels, the overall security of this form of wireless LAN is very good. For those with some fear and reluctance to transmit sensitive data over open air space, encryption and decryption processes are available.

CROSS-COUPLINGS

Very few wireless LANs will be independent stand-alone devices. Most of them will be cross-coupled to wired worlds to make up a total integrated virtual organization. These crossover points will require special attention as there will be a conversion of technologies and signals from the wireless to the wired medium and return.

Cross-couplings may bring together different vendors and different protocols. Any necessary conversions and translations should be done quickly, reliably, and transparently No user intervention should be required, once the systems is set up and thoroughly tested.

Wireless-to-wireless to wired LANS

In some situations the cross-coupling will not be directly from wireless to wired. There may be several levels where one wireless LAN talks to another wireless LAN. For example in a remote site operation the site wireless LAN could talk to a long-distance wireless LAN and the second wireless LAN could make the connection to the wired world.

Such connections may involve two or more levels of wireless technology with multiple vendors and differing protocols. Automatic connections and end-to-end continuity and error management would need to cover all of the wireless layers.

Multiple couplings

LAN traffic has to cross over several LANs to reach the intended server or service i involved in the process of multiple couplings. The path could take the packets from a wireless network to another wireless to a wired and back to another wireless LAN. The multipl couplings could involve conversions and bridging to travel over the various layers.

Multiple couplings will increase the overheads of the conversions between the variou wireless systems and services. They will also complicate the reliable communication o messages between the calling parties. Multiple connections should be able to be automate and buried the connection management layers of the protocols or the products.

Protocol conversions

Protocol conversions is not necessary if the wireless-to-wireless-to-wired worlds all run the same type of data packaging. Ethernet or token ring formats should follow the world standards and be used throughout the network layers. There is little justification for adding a new and unique protocol to the wireless layers. However, many organizations used token rings at their wired layers and wish to use Ethernet at the wireless levels. This will necessitate conversion of the message packets just as would have to be done in a wire-to-wire network with the variant protocols.

These conversions are well defined and can be performed in hardware via a multi-protocol bridge or within some part of the hardware coupling logic. Error management and packet control should be an integral part of the conversion logic.

Security

The security of message passage over different coupling points between networks and protocol conversions will require careful attention and control. These are points at which taps or external capture could take place. The detail of message frames and contents such as passwords and other details could be exposed at the points of coupling. The use of encryption of passwords and some camouflage of the message framing should be sufficient to maintain the integrity of the security of the total system.

GLOBAL INTERCONNECTIVITY

The ability to go from the wireless LAN to a central communications hub that can in turn be coupled to existing networks is a key advantage of the wireless LAN. It can be the conduit that allows any emergency worker to be in communication with anyone else in the contactable world. This could be extremely valuable in retrieving emergency condition information, remote expert advice, stored procedures, information on sites, terrains, past efforts, etc. All of this can be delivered from anywhere to the emergency site and then to the individual emergency worker in a timely and usable fashion.

The use of the facilities of the Internet and other emergency services networks would be the provisioning key to these services. The wireless LAN would provide the link from the individual emergency worker to a local intermediary server that would coordinate and manage the global interconnectivity.

LAN-LAN HOPPING

LAN-to-LAN hopping involves a message generated on one LAN being able to move onto other LANs for delivery to its final address destination. As more and more LANs are interconnected, the hopping connect become the vehicle for making the overall intercon-nectivity seamless and contiguous. In long-distance wireless LANs, the hopping concept would involve the coverage of the longer open segments of the network and the move from a WIN (wireless inside networks) to a WON (wireless outside networks) to another WIN and finally perhaps to a wired service.

The short-distance wireless LANs are mostly all within a building envelope. These are known as WINs or wireless inside networks. The external networks are knows as WONs or wireless outside networks. The WINs are limited distance, localized systems and the WONs are longer distance (mostly limited to a line of sight of approximately 15 miles) metropolitan area networks. By coupling these two forms of wireless LANs together, it is possible to cover a wide area and provide coverage to a multiple building campus environment.

This WIN and WON variation, is described as follows:

Wireless Inside Network	Wireless Outside Network
Local	Long haul
Limited distance	Line of sight
Mobile services	Load matching
Roaming	Bulk transfers
Area services	Internetworking
Load sensitive	Load leveling
Transparent hopping	Bridging
Transactions	
Queries and requests	
Messages	

LAN-to-LAN hopping should be performed as an automated services that is seamless and reliable. The use of intelligent bridges and routers, which can integrate the different network technologies, is the key link in this level of enterprise data movement.

Interlinking

The interlinking mechanics will involve the ability of a LAN to recognize signals that are destined for another LAN world. Once recognition is made, the message would need to move to the interlinkage point and flow smoothly from the source LAN over the interlinkage onward toward its ultimate destination.

Interlinking requires access to the level 3 or 4 OSI information which defines the network and transport layers or alternately to the TCP and the IP contents. With this information the interlinking process can determine the movement and possibly the routing of the message to its proper destination.

Integration

The use of short-and-long-distance wireless LAN services can support the efficient and reliable integration of information flows across the enterprise. The integration will take place through LAN-to-LAN interfaces and the merger of wireless and wired network technologies. The integration will also be supported by the abilities of the information management process to direct messages and user requests to the proper service locations.

The overall concept is to build an integrated network services world that can traverse different technologies and provide responsive user services. This integration level should be focused more on the provisioning of user services with the integration of the technology layers handled as a seamless and transparent background process.

Local to global

As wireless technology moves from local limited services into providing longer and longer distance services, it will become a major link in the overall information services spectrum. With the growing use of satellites and the demands for anywhere, anytime communications couplings, the wireless world could become the dominating technology in the overall equation.

The key is that wireless connectivity can be local, metropolitan, wide-area, and global in form. Although the technologies vary, the wireless implementation provides flexible, untethered couplings between the users and their service systems. The fact that wireless can go anywhere and provide a broad range of services makes it a logical building block for an enterprise information environment.

Mixing of technologies

Most enterprise networks will be an intermix of various technologies. The mix will range from various forms of wireless to different types of wired to a variety of wide area forms. The mixing will provide the unique services and coverage of each type of technology to support the needs and applications of the organization. The network management system and services will be responsible for the conversion, translation, speed matching, and other interconnectivity services. To the end user the intermix of technologies should be transparent, efficient, reliable, and consistent.

LONG - DISTANCE WIRELESS LAN TECHNOLOGIES:-

Wireless LANs are usually thought of as being localized, limited-distance systems. However, there are several versions of wireless technology that can provide longdistance wireless connectivity between LANs. These technologies are all wireless and operate in similar fashion to the localized wireless LANs. However, some of them can extend the connecting distances to several miles and others can literally link systems around the globe. This section will cover the long-distance wireless LAN services.

Cellular connections

Cellular services are based on wireless radio wave networking. Primarily oriented to voice communications and built on analog waveforms, the cellular services networks provide limited- distance cell-to-cell connectivity and interfacing to the wireline communications world. Like voice or analog networks, the cellular system can be used with analog modems to transmit and receive user data communications. If the remote cellular users connect to a LAN and use LAN services from a remote client computer they are a part of the wireless LAN services environment.

Cellular connections can be treated as a special remote extension of a wireless LANs. They can provide limited-speed connectivity and data services to a variety of remote users.

The key to cellular services for connecting to a remote LAN is that they are relatively distance insensitive. There is complete cellular coverage of most modern population centers and the major transportion corridors. In the United States there is also good cellular coverage of rural areas, where farm and service managers are highlevel users of cellular services.

With the roaming services, users can have a broad spatial coverage for their travels and still maintain some form of contact with their remote data services environments.

Cellular service coverage can extend from transportation facilities to the open spaces. Remote field sites, vacation spots, and walk-in location such as remote work sites, can usually be covered with cellular services. This means that wireless contact can be maintained with LAN data systems from almost anywhere via the cellular services.

It is possible to build and maintain remote radio wave services for connecting remote users to their organizational networks. These links will be built around the Specialized Mobile Dispatch Radio (SMDR) systems that have been used for years by utilities, construction companies, taxi fleets, and other mobile services units. SMDR is now being converted from local service to an integrated national network with higher speeds and quality for the movement of data between remote users and their data systems Most of the cellular and radio link services will connect to traditional wireline services at some point. Some users may contact other cellular users for local client-to-client data transfer, but most users will be contacting a fixed organization location for most of their data services. This means they will be interfacing to plain old telephone services (POTS) for some portion of their routing and traffic movement.

Wireline services will convert the data signals to their modulated format and then move the data through their network routing system to the addressed location. The wireline data services will be readily available, reasonable in cost, slow in speed, and moderately reliable in their delivery of the data.

Cellular Digital Packet Data (CDPD) is a new format for packaging digital data for transmission over the analog cellular network. The messages still travel over an analog network, but they are packaged and managed in a digital format. This will increase the reliability, error control, and signal management within the existing cellular systems capabilities.

Cellular services are now moving form their analog base to a full digital signal process. This will provide more channels of service and greatly improve the reliability and management of the signal flow processes. The all-digital cellular service will also make it easier to transfer data between cellular users and their remote LAN environments.

Personal Communication Services

The personal communications services (PCS) may have a significant impact on the wireless LAN world. PCS is a low-power, localized cell service that is intended for person, rather than vehicle, mobility. This is the same market covered by wireless LANs. The main difference is that PCS will allow roaming is a wider geographic area than those provided by the wireless LAN. PCS will also be a commercial carrier service rather than a user-owned service.

Personal communications services may be offered as packages that can be implemented within building envelopes. One option would be to connect a PCS server to the internal Private Area Branch Exchange (PABX/PBX) and allow roaming users to be able to couple to any internal or external telecommunications service. Such a coupling would be directly competitive with or complimentary to the concepts of wireless LANs.

The PCS will operate in a newly allocated range of frequencies in the gigahertz bands. The frequencies are radio frequency and capable of both voice and data traffic. These frequencies were previously used by emergency services for reliable local communications.

The PCS power levels will be very low to allow limited coverage of the areas without interference with other nearby cells using the same frequencies. Cell hopping and roaming will be provided in a fashion similar to that in use within cellular systems. The PCS will be all digital from the start, thus avoiding the conversion from analog to digital that the cellular world is now going through.

The key service from the PCS products will be a single communications device with one identifying number that works on everything at any location. The concept of a singular truly universal telephony connection is very attractive in today's convenience-oriented market.

The new PCS will also provide integrated services for voice and data communications and may eventually be expanded to video. Remember the Dick Tracy wrist communicator that handled radio, video, and messages? Well, PCS is the arrival of that old comic strip prognostication. A truly portable, go anywhere, connect anytime communications system would provide an efficient and easy-to-use interface that would depend on internal network services to direct and handle the provisioning of the data, message, and information deliveries. PCS may become the universal communications appliance. Many firms are bidding for the air wave space to run PCS systems in the hope that they will become the wireless communications base for the future.

Personal communicator systems are normally considered a low power, out-of-building communicator service. If the PCS cells are set up so that they are within a building envelope, then you have an in-building PCS service. Such a service could provide wireless connectivity to internal users from any location within the PCS coverage space. As the PCS is within the building envelope, it would not need licensing and it would be the dedicated property of the organization.

The in-building PCS would allow users to take their desk telephones with them throughout the building. They would be reachable by normal call processes anywhere they roamed within the covered space. PCS would replace the desktop telephone and all of the in-wall wiring.

The PCS service can also handle data, so it could interface to portable personal digital assistants and provide another wireless data link. This could make dual-function devices like the Bell South Simon product, the telephone or PDA of choice in many organizations.

The private area branch exchange, PABX or PBX, can be a logical coupling unit for wireless LANs. The PBX is the connector between internal and external networks. Longer distance wireless LANs will require to interface between the internal service networks and the longer distance worlds. This is the same type of connection being managed by the PBX in the wired world. Extending the PBX to provide interconnection to long-distance wireless LAN services will use standard services of the PBX and provide support to a broad range of users.

Low-power roaming of mobile users involves the use of personal communicator products that can make connections to local PBXs within building envelopes. The low-power systems will provide in-building connections to networks and data servers. The user can roam around the building and make calling connections to the LANs the data servers. Data and message services can be moved from the networks to and from the user mobile devices.

By staying at low power, the units should not require licensing and can be used as owner-operated networks without time service contracts. The low-power roaming units should provide low-cost, low-volume data interfacing services.

The PCS will open up new bandwidth communication channels that will support a wide range of wireless data services, including connections to wireless LANs. PCS will provide low-power, cellular-type services using digital channels.

Low Earth Orbiting Satellites (LEOS)

One of the new distance services for LAN-to-LAN interconnection is the use of satellites travelling in low earth orbits to receive upward transmissions, hop them between other satellites in the same orbit, and then beam the signals back to earth and the receiving system. Known as LEOs, these projects will provide low-cost, high-performance digital communications services that are distance insensitive.

LEOs will not only provide wireless linkages to another networks and services, they will also strive to be worldwide. This is not fully possible, but they will band the earth will their satellite coverage and be able to hit any 3000 mile wide space in either half of the globe, north or south, depending on where the satellites are placed.

The LEOs will offer a broad range of services that will include anywhere, anytime access by users to their larger data networks. Also to be offered will be voice and video communication services plus news updating and other communications services. The concept is a general communications network that puts the user in contact from any point within the near-global service view of the satellites.

The linkage in LEO projects is wireless from the base level user environment up to the local satellite that is passing overhead at the time of transmission, wireless from satellite to satellite to satellite until the signal is over the receiving territory, and then wireless down to the addressed receiver.

The connections from ground-level users to the LEO environmen will be through channel access contention. The requesting users will signal their LEO interface that they need to communicate over the satellite loop. The interface will arrange for circuit bandwidth and make the connection to the overhead LEO satellite using an open channel. Once the communications packet is released to the LEO environment, the service will become a datagram routing process with the LEO managing the setup and movement of the communications packets between LEO satellites and the eventual ground receiver.

Once the traffic has moved to the receiving LEO zone, the local LEO will contact the receiver's ground interface and download the communications packets into its buffer memory. Movement to the internal computer systems will be by awaiting message notices.

As the communications packets move across the LEO world they will be handled by a sophisticated satellite hopping and space management system. The switch has to know the destination of each packet and compute the correct positioning satellite for the downlinking based on time to travel the hops to the correct receiving location. Errors, retransmissions, load buffering and other traffic must be taken into consideration. Depending on the number of parallel satellite arrays, there is an opportunity to use alternate routing for the messages. However, if there is only one planar sequence of satellites, the traffic would have to hop in order to get from one satellite to its next neighbor.

The satellite hopping and space switching process will be the most complex part of the LEO operations. These processes will have to take place up in the satellites and their control systems. If they fail or cause errors, they will be difficult to repair. Backups and tandem processes will be a critical part of the overall LEO configuration. Ground control and management of the overall traffic will also be very important.

One of the advantages of the LEO system is that it will have to provide global service within the apogee of its satellites. This means that the costs of sending a message across the street or around the world are nearly the same. With the wireless LEO system much of the external WAN distribution of data and information could move to this service and be distributed by the LEO system anywhere within its worldwide coverage area. Multidrop communications would likely become a speciality of the LEO systems.

LEO systems are evolving as a hot property. They are being supported by many large organizations and governments. All of the concepts needed for the LEO systems are in use in other systems. Cell hopping is similar to satellite hopping, other orbiting satellites can control the sending and receiving of high speed communications, frame relay is a protocol similar to the one proposed for LEOs, and the network management for ground satellite interfacing exists in many forms.

What will need to be proved with the LEOs is the market acceptance, reliability of services, and cost competitiveness with alternative forms of traffic. The significance of the organizations backing this approach and the amount of investment being collected probably make this a more sure bet than the introduction of cellular telephony was ten years ago. Time will tell.

Medium Earth Orbit Satellite (MEOS)

MEOs are a close cousin to the LEOs, except that they are placed into a higher earth his allows fewer satellites to cover more surface space. However, the trade-off is that each satellite will have to handle more traffic and the timings to and from and higher orbit will need to be factored into the transmission equation. It will also cost more to launch the higher orbit satellites, but the trade-off is that there will be fewer of them.

The satellite hopping and space switching process will be similar to that of the LEOs. MEOs will also offer communications and interconnect services on a global basis.

VSAT Satellites

The very small aperture satellites (VSATs), which use small 18-to 30-inch dishes on the ground are another attractive form of wireless LAN communications. These will use high-altitude geostationary satellites and provide a range of medium and high- speed interconnectivity services.

The coupling to the VSAT network is via a tunable small satellite dish. Such units can be portable and battery operated, providing some level of flexibility in setting up and operating a wireless local LAN and using the VSAT to interconnect to the rest of the world. The military successfully used this concept in the Desert Storm engagement and plans to increase the information couplings via VSAT for its mobile deployment forces.

The LEO and MEO products and services will provide an extended range of coverage for physically remote sites. Depending on their placement, these systems can cover large sections of the globe with their services. Being moderate speed wireless services, they can provide remote uses with access to a complete communications, messaging, and data world.

Physically remote sites will now be able to be connected to other parts of the organization and share services with the rest of the world. These sites can access data, provide messages, input transactions, perform communications deliveries, and be queried by other parts of the organization.

The connection of satellites to remote locations will be done via portable satellite dishes. The VSAT dishes are in the 18-to 30- inch size. Such dishes can be moved about easily and assembled and focused to the satellite transponder in a few minutes. Once set up, the VSAT portable dishes can provide a high-speed intercommunications services.

The use of satellites and VSAT technology can provide global coverage of interconnection to remote information services and resources. This means that a user can move to any spot on the globe and set up a connection to the satellite system. From the satellite services, users can move information and data to and from their location to the processing points.

Global coverage will increase the flexibility and mobility of information systems users. They will be able to make contacts and interfaces from any mobile position. Although the systems will require physical set up through the satellite dish, they will provide high-speed, reliable data transfer services.

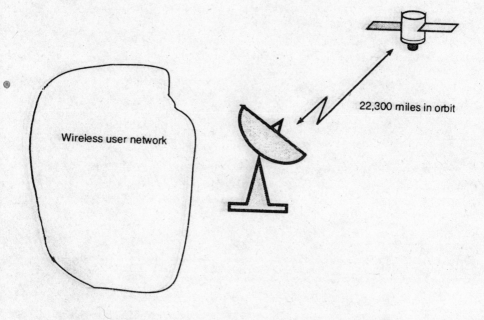

Fig.31.2 : VSAT Connections

The portability factors of VSAT systems will involve the mobility of the VSAT dish and the availability of adequate space to set up and tune the dish and satellite alignment. Portability will also be influenced by air space interference, tuning alignment, and signal quality.

If the satellite service cannot be quickly and reliably set up, the users will be denied access to their information resources. Speedy set up and easy tuning of the dish to satellite alignment will be key to portable connectivity.

The mobility of portable satellite systems will allow them to be used in support of remote projects and missions. Situations such as field operations, emergency efforts, remote project sites, military operations, and other missions can be serviced by these systems. Their support will allow these remote missions to maintain connectivity with their command centers, transfer data and messages, exchanges files, and maintain data communications.

The satellite implementations of wireless LANs will need to pay special attention to the security of the data transfers. The satellite services cover large distances using open space that can be trapped and scanned by technically astute individuals and organizations. Most satellite messages will need to be encrypted to allow message handling with reliable security.

APPENDIX A

QUESTIONS AND ANSWERS ON LANS

QUESTIONS AND ANSWERS ON LANS

Q. Is it possible to network standalone PCs with a Unix mini, and have a facility for file sharing? We also want to connect our laser printers to this network so that everyone can use them. What is the best possible way to achieve this?

A. The first step should be to connect all the PCs to the Unix mini using an Ethernet medium. Next, you would need Network File System (NFS) -- on both the Unix mini (if it is not already bundled with the operating system) and on the nodes (PCs).

NFS is a collection of networking services which provide:

–   transparent file sharing between networked computers.

–   transparent resource sharing by distributed applications.

–   executing commands on remote systems.

–   managing large networks.

Most Unix vendors support NFS. It allows file system operations between Unix and other environments. PC-NFS allows PC users to access the file systems of larger computers as if they were PC files. Connect the laser printer so that it is identifiable as a node. This will enable anyone on the network to use it effectively. See Figure 1.

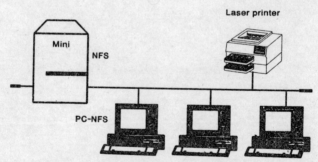

Fig. 1 : Connecting PCs to a UNIX mini

Q. We have a Netware LAN at our Bombay office and another in New Delhi. Is it possible to connect both these LANs in such a way that anyone on the network can log in to the other LAN? Presently, there are four nodes in Bombay and seven in New Delhi. Please suggest the most effective solution.

A. You could connect both your LANs through routers -- one placed in Bombay and the other in New Delhi. Routers operate at the network layer (layer 3) of the OSI model. They route packets using the network layer addresses assigned by a network administrator. Routers can support and connect different network layer protocols. They can also communicate with other routers on the network that support the same set (or subset) of network layer protocols. Routers which support both LAN and WAN lines to the network, can be connected to the modem and finally through lease lines between Bombay and New Delhi. See Figure 2.

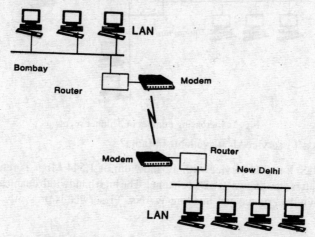

Fig. 2: Connecting two remote LANs together

Q. We are expanding our 20 node Arcnet LAN. At present, we plan to upgrade the server only and add eight to ten more nodes. We are concerned about the degradation in performance that may occur with the additional nodes. Even though the server will be more powerful, we cannot afford to change our Arcnet investment immediately. Could you suggest a solution that gives the best performance now and will allow us the flexibility to expand in future, including replacing the existing Arcnet setup.

A. A powerful server would definitely give better performance. However, there is no doubt that more nodes would actually degrade the overall performance if you stay stuck with Arcnet. Since you do not want to replace Arcnet (which operates at only 2.5 Mbps) immediately, it is suggested that you keep the existing nodes on Arcnet as they are. To add the new nodes you could include an Ethertwist/Ethernet adapter card in the server. By connecting the new nodes on to this, you will be able to achieve a bandwidth of 10 Mbps, while your existing setup keeps working as it is. In future, you could shift all your old nodes on to this new media by replacing the Arcnet adapters -- without affecting your overall LAN setup.

Q. How can we split up a Thinnet cable to get more Thinnet segments?

A. The easiest way to get more segments of Thinnet is by using a Thinnet hub. A standard Thinnet hub can help you connect nearly eight Thinnet cables together. You can then connect your server, nodes, peripherals, etc. See Figure 3.

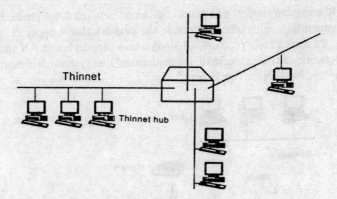

Fig. 3 : Increasing number of Thinnet segments

Q.   What is a T1 service? Is it available in India?

A.   In the US, a digital service with a bandwidth of 1.544 Mbps is referred to as a T1 service. It is also known as a DSI channel. The high bandwidth enables users to support their own data, voice and imaging WANs. T1 service is presently not available in India.

Q.   We are planning to replace all our internal office cabling from Thicknet to Thinnet. However, our Ethernet adapter cards have only AUI ports. We understand that nodes having such adapter cards will connect only to Thicknet. What should be done? Do we have to replace these cards with those having BNC ports?

A.   By replacing Thicknet with Thinnet, the bandwidth would not increase. You could consider replacing Thicknet directly with Ethertwist cabling. The best thing about it is that it has a bandwidth equal to that of Ethernet. Also, you do not need to replace your adapter cards having AUI ports with newer cards. You could use transceivers which plug into your old adapter and give you either a RJ45 or BNC connection. Depending on the choice of your media, you can connect the existing adapters to it.

Q.   We would like to convert our existing thin Ethernet LAN to Ethertwist. We have a 486-based server with 19 nodes connected to it. What are the changes we have to make? Can you give us the specifications of the Ethertwist cable?

A.   Ethertwist technology is definitely more reliable, flexible and cost-effective than thin Ethernet. To change your existing LAN technology to Ethertwist you will have to change the bus topology to star topology with the help of Ethertwist hubs. See Figure 4. Ethertwist cabling should have the following specifications:

   –   Type: Unshielded twisted-pair.

   –   Number of Twists: At least six twists per meter.

   –   Attenuation: Less than or equal to 10dB from 5Mhz to 10Mhz.

   –   Characteristic Impedance: 85 to 110 ohms between 5MHz to 10 MHz.

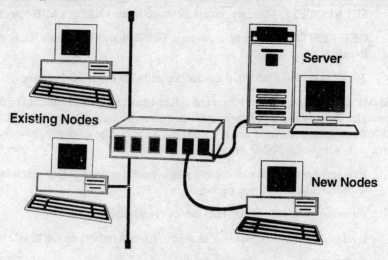

Existing Nodes

Server

New Nodes

Fig. 4 : Thin Ethernet and Ethertwist

– Pair-to-pair crosstalk: 30.5dB at **5MHz**, 26dB at 10MHz for four pairs of cable.

– Multiple Disturber Crosstalk : 27.5dB at 5MHz 23dB at 10MHz.

– Maximum Segment Length : 100m.

It would also be necessary to replace the thin Ethernet adapter cards in the systems with Ethertwist UTP port adapters. However, converting a technology this way becomes very expensive. Since you need to take into account your existing investment on thin Ethernet, it would be advisable if you keep your existing LAN as it is and expand with Ethertwist. In such a case you could keep everything the same and probably connect the server to the Ethertwist hub and all future nodes can be added through the Ethertwist hub.

Q. We are concerned about the sudden problems that bring our network down now and then. And at critical moments we do not know how to bring the network up again. We understand that network management can help us solve our problems. Could you let us know more about this and how to implement it?

A. Current network management environments range from simple work- group LANs to complex site and multi-site LANs. Simple Network Management Protocol (SNMP) has become the de facto industry standard protocol for network management, and has been implemented by many vendors on hub, repeaters, bridges, routes and other devices. SNMP uses a simple fetch and store command philosophy. It fetches data from a data item, called an object, in the managed device and stores data into the data item. SNMP has the following operations.

– GET REQUEST: Manager queries agents on the status of the objects.

– GET NEXT REQUEST: A Get Request steps through the management information base subsequently.

- SET REQUEST: Manager directs a change in the value of a MIB object.

- GET RESPONSE: Agent answers a Get Request, Get Next Request or Set Request.

- TRAP: Agent notifies manager that a significant event has occurred.

SNMP uses a transport level protocol called User Datagram Protocol (UDP). UDP provides a connectionless delivery service that uses Internet Protocol (IP) or Novell's IPX management software and it's managed devices. The advantage of using SNMP lies in its simplicity. SNMP provides the following:

- It minimizes network traffic using single-packet request or response transactions without using connection packets.

- Firmware code size in managed devices is minimized.

- It allows the network manager to control its own retry rates and device timeouts.

- It allows the manager to enable a network management operation called a trap object, on the managed device. This allows the managed device to report on pre-defined events that can occur at any time.

Q.   Our Netware-based LAN is on the ground floor where our computer department is. We have used thin Ethernet and have eight nodes connected to it. We would now like to extend this LAN to other departments. How can we extend the length of this thin Ethernet cable?

A.   All you have to do is remove the terminator from the segment end of the Ethernet cable, that you would like to extend. Using a barrel connector, connect the additional cable length to it. Make sure you add a repeater after 185m of thin Ethernet. This Ethernet, sometimes regenerates them, and then re-transmits them to all ports, except the one they were received on. See Figure 5.

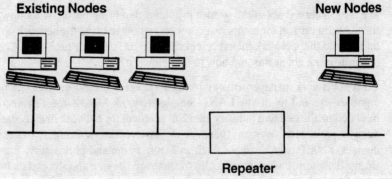

Fig. 5 : Using a Repeater

Q.   We are planning an e-mail on our Netware-based LAN. We understand that some mail packages need an additional product to make e-mail work. Do we need to make any modifications in our existing LAN to have the e-mail facility?

A. Some of the popular mail packages need Netware Mail Handling services (MHS) to run on Netware networks. However, the vendors for such e-mail packages usually bundle a copy of Netware MHS. This product uses Standard Message Format to provide DOS-based messaging services on Netware networks. It transfers information containing addressed text, and other data from an MHS-compatible e-mail to other locations. Netware MHS runs on a server running Netware V 2.1 and above, and requires at least 1.5MB or free disk space and 200 free directory entries for storing Netware MHS programs, drivers and other files. See Figure 6.

Fig. 6 : Netware MHS and E-Mail

Q. What is the difference between SMA and ST connectors used with fiber optics?

A. Both SMA and ST type connectors are used to terminate fibre optic cables. The difference is in how you install them. An SMA connector has threads on the barrel and must be screwed on and off, while the smooth barreled ST simply snaps and twists on.

Q. Exactly what is a 3270 environment?

A. Interconnecting hardware for data communications in an IBM mainframe setup is known as 3270 environment. IBM's 3270 information display system was introduced

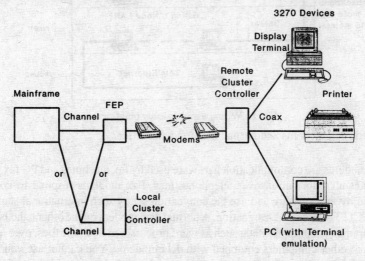

Fig. 7 : Elements of the 3270 environment.

in the early 1970's. The 3270 environment provides local connectivity for terminals, printers and PCs via coaxial cable for direct connection to a cluster controller. Remote connections are made through the Front End Processor via IBM's Synchronous Data Link Control (SDLC) for WANs, and via gateways for LANs. Coax-connected devices operate at 2.34Mbps while most SNA/SDLC connections transmit at 9600kbps. See Figure 7.

Q.   We have an eight node LAN set up on our first floor. Our building has a total of five floors. Please let us know how we can extend our network to all the floors without disturbing our existing set up. Our present network is based on thin Ethernet.

A.   You can extend your existing thin Ethernet from both sides through barrel connectors. If the total distance exceeds 185 m, add a repeater in your backbone. This will enable you to extend the distance of your thin Ethernet cable. And your existing network will not be disturbed. You can connect more terminals on the ground floor. For other floors, it is advisable to use Ethertwist hubs which can connect on to the thin Ethernet backbone and provide easy connectivity to nodes. Ensure that your backbone and floor connectivity does not run near the power transmission lines otherwise you will experience data distortion. See Figure 8.

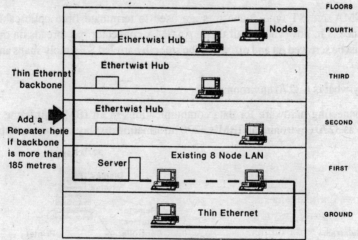

Fig. 8 : Wiring a multi-storey building.

Q.   How do fax modems and normal data modems differ?

A.   Fax modems are communication hardware used by fax machines and PC fax products to transmit information over telephone lines. Fax modems respond to commands issued by fax software and use the convention set by such international standards as the CCITT's Group 3 Designation. A normal data modem on the other hand is a device that transmits computer data, such as word processor and ASCII files, over telephone lines to other computers equipped with data modems. You cannot use your existing normal data communication as fax modems by simply running the fax software. Nor can you use a fax modem with data communication software for transferring computer data. However, there are dual function fax/data modems that are now available, which work with both fax and data communication software.

Q. How does the AppleTalk network work?

A. AppleTalk is Apple's proprietary, peer-to-peer protocol for interconnecting printers, workstations and other devices. The AppleTalk network uses a bus topology with information travelling at 230kbps. It supports several different media types, including AppleTalk cabling and unshielded twisted pair cabling.

To interconnect two or more Apple devices you either need an external connectivity box or pre-installed wall plates. Usually, the external connectivity box has three connectors. One connection is usually a 5" or 6" pigtail terminated with a connector which attaches to your Apple device. The remaining two connectors are for the daisy chain. Guidelines for AppleTalk cabling are:

– The AppleTalk cable is a twinax type of cable with a 78 ohm impedence.

– AppleTalk networks are typically set up in a star or bus configuration. Never configure your AppleTalk network in a closed loop.

– When using an external connectivity box, a cable segment can support up to 32 devices and it cannot exceed 1,000 feet.

– With pre-installed wall plates, a cable segment can support up to 24 devices and cannot exceed 3,000 feet.

– The last device on the daisy chain must be terminated using a terminator.

AppleTalk networks in India presently have an installed base of less than 2 percent.

Q. What are 10BaseT networks and how popular are they?

A. The 10BaseT network provides the advantages of a star-wired cabling system for easy moves, changes and additions. It uses a low cost, unshielded twisted pair cable, while still allowing the devices to operate at full 10Mbps data rate. Changes can be made quickly and easily by simply moving a modular patch cord on the hub or the patch panel. One of the most important advantages of 10BaseT is that other devices on the network will not be affected by a change of the node or a failure. You can use your existing internal telephone cables if they are of data grade to form a 10BaseT network. The guidelines for configuring a 10Base network are:

– The maximum length of 10BaseT link segment is 100 m.

– Use 22-26 SWG unshielded twisted pair cable.

– Devices are connected to a central hub in a star configuration.

– Hubs usually have an Ethernet port for backbone.

– Existing nodes with Ethernet cards can also be converted to 10BaseT using transceivers.

–   Hubs may be concatenated to form larger networks.

The 10BaseT is growing in popularity worldwide and is expected to have a greater demand than Arcnet or Ethernet in the near future.

Q.   What are the advantages and disadvantages of using UTP cable versus thin Ethernet cabling in any LAN.

A.   The UTP has a major advantage of using the same wiring infrastructure as the internal telephone systems. The cabling is of data grade type. UTP is less expensive to maintain because making moves and changes is as easy as switching on phone extensions. However, the thin Ethernet cable for LANs does not allow changes too often and is quite cumbersome to manage.

Q.   What does media speed bridge mean?

A.   In a bridge. media speed operation is defined as the ability for a network device to transmit and forward data packets as fast as the physical layer rate. Take the example of the physical rate for IEEE 802.3 networks which is 10Mbps. When data frames appear at the fastest rate possible on the networks attached to a bridge, the bridge is fast enough to process each frame before receiving the next one. This ensures that the bridge does not become a traffic bottleneck during peak network loading times.

Q.   What are wireless LANs?

A.   LANs using radio or light waves to connect PCs and printers are known as wireless LANs. They are gaining world-wide popularity due to high labor charges involved with ordinary LAN installations, maintenance and moves, additions, and changes. There are basically three types of technologies used in wireless LANs. These are:

–   Spread Spectrum Radio

–   Infrared Light-Wave

–   18GHz Microwave

Spread spectrum radio technology operates at 2Mbps and involves spreading out a radio signal over a range of frequencies. This spreading may be continuous or it may involve jumping rapidly from one frequency to another. Either way, spread spectrum radio behaves quite differently from conventional radio.

Infrared light-wave technology on the other hand, offers greater security and immunity from interference. It operates at 16Mbps. The biggest disadvantage is that its signals are easily blocked. A 186GHz microwave technology promises high bandwidth, security and immunity from interference. It has the capability to operate at 15Mbps. However, the connectivity boxes in this type of technology are not yet compact enough. See Figure 9.

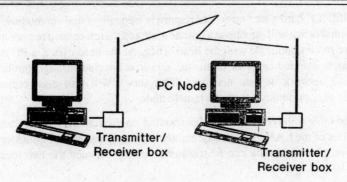

PC Node

Transmitter/
Receiver box

Transmitter/
Receiver box

Fig. 9 · Wireless LANs

Q. When should I use a router as against using a bridge?

A. Routers can select another available path, if one path in a network fails, just like a bridge. This gives a network fault tolerance. An important feature of routers is their ability to handle parallel active links. With bridges however, only one parallel link is allowed to be active at a time. Routers can use the combined bandwidth of the links making them an excellent choice for complex network technologies. Routers also provide greater LAN isolation capabilities than bridges. A bridge on the other hard will filter out some packets, but normally will not filter out those broadcast packets or packets with addresses it does not recognise. Routers can provide greater isolation of broadcast traffic and can filter out packets addressed to unreachable destinations. They allows greater control over network traffic than a bridge.

Q. What is SNMP?

A. Simple Network Management Control is to treat the network as a collection of cooperative and communicating entities. A manageable network consists of one or more management stations and a collection of agent systems or network elements. A management station executes network management operations that monitor or control the agent systems. An agent system is a device that has an agent responsible for performing the network management operations requested by the manager. The Management Information Base (MIB) is a collection of management information that can be accessed through SNMP. The SNMP agent contains the intelligence required to access MIB values. MIBs are organized into modules and objects and can be defined by standard bodies such as the IETF MIB-II, or by specific vendors (enterprises specific MIBs).

SNMP communicates management information between a manager and an agent. SNMP allows a manager to retrieve management information from or to alter (set) management information on an agent. An agent can also emit unsolicited messages (called traps or events) to alert managers of noteworthy local events such as a systems reboot.

Q. Our head office has a Novell-based LAN. We want to connect one of our PCs at the regional office to this LAN so that the data processed can be transferred between the two locations. What are the additional hardware, software and accessories required?

A.   The additional hardware you would require is basically a dial-up modem. The PC at the regional office will operate as a remote node and therefore need remote node access software to communicate with the head office. At the head office, a PC can be used either as a non-dedicated or dedicated server connected through public switched telephone network or data networks. This server will also need communication software to communicate with the remote node.

It is advisable to have the .EXE files residing on the remote node. When using the .EXE files of the LAN through the remote node, response will be considerably slow. However, processed data can be transferred easily between the two locations. See Figure 10.

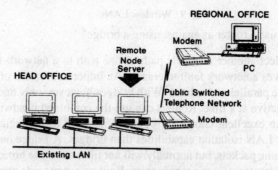

Fig. 10 : Connecting A Remote Node

Q.   Our existing set up consists of a Unix-based LAN and a separate departmental Novell LAN. How can we link the two so that the user has a choice of operating either in the Unix or Novell environment. Both LANs are based on Thinnet.

A.   Unix networking is possible due to the TCP/IP support available. The communication media is either Ethernet, Arcnet, FDDI, CDDI or even serial ports (i.e., SLIP connections using various WAN hardware). The difference between a Novell-based LAN and one using TCP/IP is that Novell LANs use client/server structured control protocol (IPX/SPX) in which the server program resides on the file server and the client program runs on LAN PCs. On the other hand, each processor on a TCP/IP LAN has a complete control program that communicates with other processors on a peer-to-peer basis. Another difference between the two is that Novell-based LANs were created to share expensive peripherals among PCs whereas in TCP/IP LANs, expensive processors are made to communicate with each other.

For a single processor to access information from both environments, it must include software drivers, known as protocol stacks for IPX/SPX (Novell's transport protocol) and TCP/IP. A dual protocol stack can be run on the file server -- dual stacking the server, or on LAN PCs -- dual stacking the client.

A node from the Novell-based LAN is used to bridge the two networks together. This node has two network adapter cards to dual stack client software. See Figure 11.

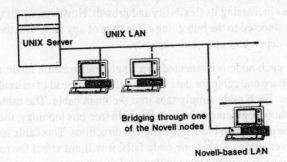

Fig. 11 : Linking UNIX And Novell-based LANs

Q. What are multiplexers?

A. Multiplexers are devices that connect more than one communication equipment through a single composite link. The biggest advantages are the considerable saving achieved by using only one communication link and reduced number of other devices such as modems. See Figure 12.

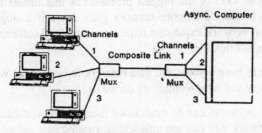

Fig. 12 : Multiplexors

Q. We need to take a decision on the best network topology available today. Please let us know which would be better, star or bus topology? Is there any other type of topology also?

A. LAN topology commonly refers to the physical layout in which nodes are connected to one another by cable. Each topology has its own advantages and disadvantages, and the suitability of each depends on individual requirements. There are three types of LAN topologies: star, bus and ring.

Star: It has an active or passive device as the central hub. All connections to the network emanate from the hub as separate point-to-point connections. Initial networking topologies were all star-based. Any communication between devices must go through the hub. The cost of such a network is initially high, but decreases incrementally as more nodes are added. Though, the outward appearance of this topology looks like a star, the way it actually moves data across the network can have the characteristics of either bus or ring topology. This is known as the network's logical topology. A major advantage of this topology is its centralized approach to network management. The entire network can be monitored and problems diagnosed from the hub. This topology can also allow a number of technologies such as a PBX to be used as the hub, thus increasing its flexibility and growth. However, its disadvantages include all nodes connected to the hub going off in case of any fault with the hub. The number of nodes is dependent upon hub capacity.

Bus: Here, each node is connected to a single transmission medium such as a cable. All nodes share one cable for data communication instead of individual point-to-point connections. Each node simply taps into the main cable. The cable can be extended by adding more segments or by branching. In tree-bus topology, the cable can be split allowing the network to branch in different directions. This cable splitting can happen over and over again. And if one node fails, it will not affect the rest of the network. The initial cost of a simple bus topology is low when compared to star topology since only a single cable is used. However, its limitations include its inability to be managed centrally. No single node has central control of the network. Some bus topologies are also limited by distance restrictions which can be overcome by additional devices such as repeaters.

Ring: The third network topology, the ring type, is not too popular in India as yet. In ring topology, each node is connected to the next with a point-to-point link in one continuous circle. One of the biggest problems is that unless bypass circuits are installed at each node, the entire network goes down if a single node fails. The limitation is that network expansion requires cabling and software changes at every node. Also, it is not flexible.

Q.   We would like to have a voice and data network in our office. Which would be the best possible way and what technology do we use?

A.   Data and voice networks can be established using Ethertwist-based technology. For this type of network you can use unshielded, twisted pair cables. Data PBX can be used in conjunction with an analog PBX in two ways.

The first method is the data over voice connection (see Figure 13). Here, the telephone

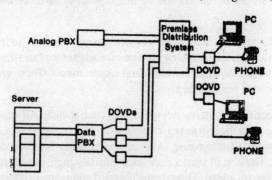

Fig. 13 : Data Over Voice Connection.

and the PCs are connected to a Data Over Voice Device (DOVD). The DOVD module converts the PC's data to analog signals which operate at frequencies above the voice range. At the Premises Distribution System, the cable is split into two individual cables. One cable connects with an analog PBX and the other connects to the data PBX. The analog PBX ignores the computer's data since it is not in the voice frequency range.

Another method is to construct two separate networks, one for data and the other for voice. The analog PBX switches only voice traffic and the data PBX routes only data traffic. Here, the terminal and telephone can be used simultaneously. See Figure 14.

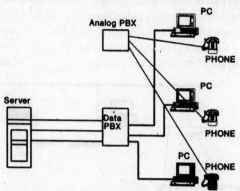

Fig. 14 : Analog/Data PBX Connection

Q. What are the ARPA and Berkeley services in networking?

A. ARPA and Berkeley services were two de facto networking standards developed outside the OSI model. These standards are commonly used over Ethernet LANs.

ARPANET is one of the networks operated by the US Department of Defence, connecting major research facilities. Its architecture was developed long before the OSI model. In 1982, a set of protocols was approved for use over all networks supported by the US Defence Data Network. Two of these protocols, the Transmission Control Protocol (TCP) and the Internet Protocol (IP), are being used as the transport and network layer protocols for multivendor networks.

ARPA services include File Transfer Protocol (FTP), TELNET and Simple Mail Transfer Protocol (SMTP). FTP allows a user to transfer, delete, rename and display a remote file anywhere on the network. TELNET is a terminal access protocol which lets a user access remote systems as if the connections were local. SMTP is a simple e-mail facility which allows a user to read, print, delete, store and send messages to other users connected to the network. E-mail programs running on host systems store and forward messages to users on other systems. These programs also recognize incoming mail for their users and translate the message to a form which is readable by the user.

TCP/IP protocols are being widely used for inter-networking computers outside the DDN. TCP at the transport layer ensures that data packets are delivered to their destination in the same sequence in which they are transmitted. IP at the network layer controls communications between two computer systems which reside on different networks. Both protocols are used for wide area packet switching and local area baseband networks.

Q.   Is it possible to expand out Thinnet-based LAN through the Ethertwist media without actually disturbing the existing set up? We have a 486-based server running Netware and 11 nodes. We would like to add at least five more nodes.

A.   You can add a Ethertwist hub which has a BNC connection and RJ 45 outlets to expand your network. The existing network can be taken from the RJ 45 connections available. The hubs usually come with 8 or 12 outlets. In case your demand for new nodes increases further, you could cascade another hub. It is also possible for you to use bigger hubs with 48 RJ 45 outlets if the initial cost is not a constraint. See Figure 15.

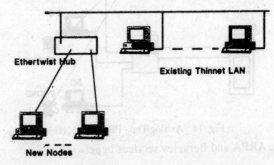

Fig. 15 : Adding Ethertwist to Existing Thinnet LAN

Q.   We presently have a Novell network-based on Arcnet. We would like to add newer technologies such as Ethernet without discarding our existing investment. Please let us know the quickest way to adapt Ethernet to our existing network.

A.   Ethernet is the right topology to choose if you require higher throughput and reliable performance. It links easily with other topologies. Ethernet's maximum throughput speed is 10Mbps. It uses the CSMA/CD (Carrier Sense Multiple Access/Collision Detection) access method to ensure accurate transmission. The quickest way to add Ethernet topology to your existing set up is by adding an Ethernet adapter card in your server and expanding your network from there. But first verify whether your server has a vacant slot for the additional adapter. See Figure 16.

Q.   What are the major factors that influence the performance of a PC server in any network?

A.   Disk speed and I/O (input/output) sub-system are the two major factors that influence PC server performance. The effects of very high speed CPUs or even adapter cards are less noticeable if the server's disk sub-system is slow and inefficient.

Q.   What does multi-protocol support mean with reference to Novell Netware 3.11?

A.   Multi-protocol support means that the NetWare 3.11 Network Operating System (NOS) supports both IPX and TCP/IP communication protocols on a network.

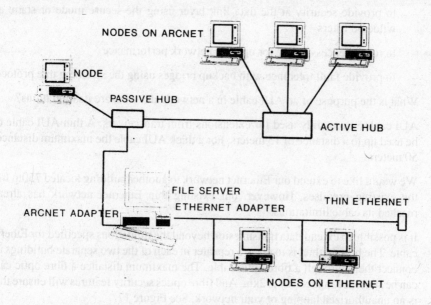

Fig. 16 : Extending Arcnet-based LAN with Ethernet

Q.   While selecting an Ethernet adapter card for an EISA-based server which is better --
     a 32-bit card or a 16-bit one? And does choice really matter when the maximum
     throughput of Ethernet remains 10Mbps?

A.   A 32-bit Ethernet adapter card for EISA has twice the memory and faster throughput
     when compared to a 16-bit adapter card. In heavy network traffic, adapter card could
     become a bottle-neck. A 32-bit adapter card can accommodate heavier traffic loads.
     Adapters with more memory (usually 64kB in 32-bit EISA adapter cards) have low
     utilization of server CPU. Percentage of CPU utilization represents that portion of the
     CPU bandwidth taken up by an adapter card to complete data transfer in the network.
     Lower utilization of server CPU by an adapter card means better network performance.

Q.   We have to take a decision on the type of thin Ethernet cabling for our organization.
     Which should we select, PVC or FEP?

A.   Thin Ethernet cable usually comes in two types of jacknet material, PVC (polyvinyl
     chloride) and FEP (florinated ethylene propylene). PVC is cheaper that FEP and is the
     most commonly used cable for networks located within office environment. FEP on
     the other hand, is fire-resistant and usually recommended for floor-shops and other
     factory environments.

Q.   When do I need to use a bridge in my network?

A.   You need a bridge in your network only when you want:

     –   to join two LANs or to extend a LAN beyond its physical configuration limits

–   to provide security at the data link layer using the secure mode or static and wildcard filters

–   to reduce excess traffic for optimal network performance

–   to provide fault tolerance with backup bridges using the spanning tree protocol.

Q.   What is the purpose of an AUI cable in a network and what are its limitations?

A.   AUI cables are mainly used for extensions from transceivers. A thin AUI cable can be used up to a distance of 15 meters. For a thick AUI cable the maximum distance is 50 meters.

Q.   We would like to extend our Ethernet network to another building located 750m from the existing premises. However, our existing thin Ethernet network has already reached its cable limitations.

A.   It is possible to extend data transmission beyond the limitations specified for Ethernet cable. The best method is to place a repeater in each of the two separate buildings and connect them through a fibre optic cable. The maximum distance a fibre optic cable can be stretched in this way is 2km. And fibre optics security features will ensure there is no unauthorized tapping of your network. See Figure 17.

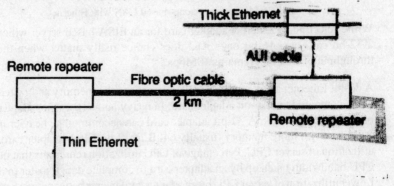

Fig. 17 : Extending Ethernet LAN with fibre optic cable

Q.   What is the ideal solution for connecting terminals to a multi- vendor network?

A.   In most cases an active device such as a terminal server is the most cost-effective solution. A terminal server lets you connect a bank of terminals to a network. You can use these terminals to log on to any host computer on the network and access its files, provided the host supports these terminals. Since a terminal server gives you transparent connectivity, you can work as though connected directly to the host computer.

Q.   What are the configuration guidelines for Ethernet cabling in a network?

A.   The most popular Ethernet cabling in India are thick Ethernet and thin Ethernet. Thick Ethernet is widely used as a backbone for networks, while thin Ethernet is used in a more general layout. The guidelines for configuration are:

Thick Ethernet:

- The maximum length of a single thick Ethernet coaxial cable is 500m

- A maximum of three repeaters can be connected

- The maximum length of the transceiver cable is 50m

- The minimum distance between transceivers is 2.5m

- No more than 100 transceiver connections are allowed per segment

- Both ends of each segment should be terminated with a 50 ohm resistor

- Each segment should be grounded at one point only.

Thin Ethernet:

- The maximum length of a thin Ethernet coaxial cable segment is 185m

- A maximum of three repeaters are allowed

- Devices are typically connected with T-connectors

- If a BNC transceiver is used to connect a device, then the maximum length of the transceiver is 50m

- The minimum distance between transceivers is 0.5m

- No more than 30 device connections are allowed per segment

- Both ends of a segment should be terminated with a 50 ohm resistor

- It is not necessary to ground the cable.

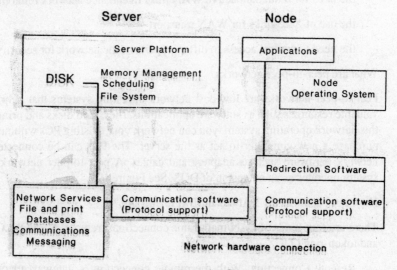

Fig. 18 : Network Operating System

Q.   What exactly is a network operating system and why is it necessary for a network?

A.   The network operating system (NOS) resides in the server and creates the network environment. Some of its functions are file and record locking, security, print spooling and interprocess communications. The NOS also determines performance, multivendor support, security and reliability of the network. See Figure 18.

Q.   What is a backup cable link? And when is it useful?

A.   A backup link is a separate cable that usually runs between two hubs to provide fault tolerance to a network. The backup link is automatically activated when the connection designated as the primary link fails. The primary link and the backup link are run over separate conduits through different paths. And even if a cable gets damaged the network still keeps running.

Q.   What is a Router?

A.   Routers operate at the network layer (layer 3) of the OSI model. They route packets using network layer addresses assigned by a network administrator. Routers support different network layer protocols such as TCP/IP, DECnet Phase IV, IPX/SPX and XNS.

     Routers communicate with other routers on networks that support the same set or subset of network layer protocols. Routers are designed to meet various network needs such as:

     –   connecting networks that use different media types and network layer protocols

     –   supporting LAN and WAN links

     –   the need for redundant active WAN links to enhance network reliability

     –   the use of X.25 links for WAN transport

     –   the need to control access to different parts of the network for security.

Q.   What are peer-to-peer networks?

A.   Peer-to-peer networks are low cost network operating systems that help you share valuable resources such as software applications, files, hard disks and printers. Using this network operating system, you can network your existing PCs without having to purchase a new computer to act as the server. The PCs can be connected through network hardware such as adapters and cables. A peer-to-peer network operating system operates as an extension of DOS. See Figure 19.

Q.   How can I connect my LAN to an IBM mainframe?

A.   There are four kinds of LAN/mainframe connections: remote, X.25/QLLC, Coaxial, and token-ring (TIC).

     –   Remote Connection. With the remote connection, a gateway adapter card is located in one PC on the LAN and emulates a remote 3X74 controller. The

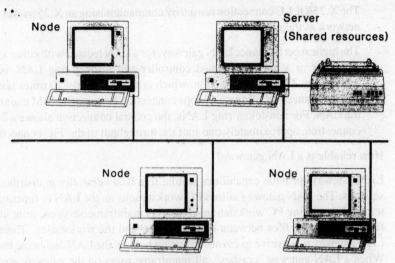

Fig. 19 : Peer-to-peer network solution

connection to the host is made with a synchronous modem through dial-up or dedicated telephone lines. The other workstation PCs on the LAN are connected by the LAN to the mainframe through the gateway PC, and operate as 3270 terminals.

– X.25/QLLC. With the X.25/QLLC connection, a gateway adapter card is located in one PC on the LAN and emulates a remote 3X74 controller. The connection to the mainframe is made through an X.25 packet-switched network. Similar to the remote connection, the other workstation PCs on the LAN are connected to the mainframe by the LAN through the gateway PC and operate as 3270 terminals.

– Coaxial Connection. With the coaxial connection, a gatway adapter card is located in one PC on the LAN, and is connected to a port on the 3X74 controller. The controller can be either locally or remotely connected to the host. The gateway PC directs mainframe sessions to other workstation PCs on the LAN.

– TIC connection. With the TIC connection, either a 3X74 controller, a 37X5 front-end processor, or a mainframe (9370 or AS/400) processor is connected directly to a token-ring LAN. A PC on the LAN is designated as the gateway PC and directs sessions to the workstation PCs.

Q.   Which connection should I use?

A.   The appropriate connection for a LAN depends on many factors. However, the following general guidelines are appropriate in many situations.

– The remote connection is used for LANs that can be connected to the mainframe only via a telephone line. Remote connections are possible with line rates up to 56 kbps.

- The X.25/QLLC connection is used by companies using an X.25 packet-switched network as their WAN.

- The highest performance LAN gateway, for a LAN located with either a front-end processor or a locally attached controller and a token-ring LAN, is the TIC connection. The TIC connection, which is approximately 70 times faster than a remote connection, allows a 4 Mbps connection between the IBM mainframe and the LAN. For non-token-ring LANs, the coaxial connection allows a 2.35 Mbps connection, approximately one-half the throughput of the TIC connection.

Q.   How reliable is a LAN gateway?

A.   LAN gateways provide capabilities similar to a host controller in distributing 3270 sessions. The LAN gateway allows PC workstations on the LAN to function as 3270 terminals, enabling PC workstations to display mainframe sessions, print mainframe files, and transfer files between the mainframe and the workstation. Therefore, the LAN gateway is sensitive to events occurring both on the LAN and in the mainframe. When a LAN gateway "crashes", all mainframe users on the gateway are affected. Thus, the reliability of the gateway is extremely important.

LAN gateway software reliability requires the ability to handle emulation errors/exceptions in a fashion identical to the real device, a 3174/3274 communication controller. Therefore, the software design needs to follow IBM's system network architecture (SNA), allowing it to handle mainframe exceptions and errors. The gateway design should incorporate Netview support for gateway monitoring and control.

Q.   What LANs do the gateways support?

A.   Most LAN gateways utilize the NetBIOS transport facility for the gateway to communicate with the workstations. All PC/LAN vendors, including 3Com, Novell Banyan, UB, and IBM, support NetBIOS as an application transport protocol. However, each LAN vendor has implemented NetBIOS slightly differently. Therefore, it is important to make sure the LAN is supported by the gateway vendor.

Many LANs support a proprietary transport protocol which provides performance and other advantages. For example, Novell provides the IPX/SPX protocol. The IPX/SPX protocol performs three functions: reduces your workstation memory requirements by approximately 20 kbytes per workstation, increases performance, and allows bridged workstations to access the gateway. Support for a network's proprietary protocols allows the LAN gateway to take advantage of these features.

Q.   What mainframe computers can I connect to my system?

A.   Mainframe computers are designed to communicate with terminals. IBM mainframes are designed to communicate with 3270 terminals. Therefore, any IBM mainframe that supports 3270 emulation can be connected to LAN. These mainframe computer families include 360/370, 308X, 4300, 9370, and the AS/400. Communication is handled by the mainframe operating environments MVS/TSO, VM/CMS, or CICS. Each environment has its own unique characteristics.

Q. What mainframe protocol do I use for the LAN gateway?

A. IBM mainframe systems use two primary protocols to communicate with 3270 terminals: SNA and Bi-Synchronous Communication (BSC). A third protocol, referred to as non-SNA, is used by smaller mainframes not implementing SNA.

The mainframe protocol (SNA, BSC or non-SNA) used by the mainframe is the appropriate protocol for sessions delivered to PCs on the LAN. An SNA/LAN gateway cannot directly connect to a BSC mainframe or vice versa.

Q. How many mainframe sessions can I access at may PC?

A. Multiple mainframe sessions allow connection to several different host applications at the same time, as well as exchange of information between the various applications. Therefore, it is possible to look at several different databases without having to log out of one application to look at another. Most LAN gateway vendors allow a user to access from four to eight host sessions at one time.

Q. What model 3270 terminals are emulated?

A. All models of 3270 terminals, including graphics terminals, can be emulated by PC workstations on the LAN. Table 1 shows the 3270 terminal models that IBM provides. Most 3270 vendors provide emulation of all 3278/3279 terminal types. Large-screen capability can be provided either as a full-screen display or by displaying only a portion of the screen at one time, allowing the user to scroll to view the other portions of the screen.

Many enhanced-graphics adapters and advanced-video adapters are capable of displaying two and four full-screen Model 2 sessions simultaneously. This allows the user to view the information from multiple applications at the same time.

Table 1. IBM 3270 Terminal Models

Model 3278/3279	Screen Size (characters)
Models 2A, 2B	24 × 80
Models 3A, 3B	32 × 80
Models 4A, 4B	43 × 80
Models 5A, 5B	27 × 132

Q. How much memory does the workstation software require?

A. Workstation memory is a scarce resource in LAN installations due to the 640-kbyte limitation of MS-DOS. LAN gateway vendors are endeavoring to provide the maximum amount of functionality with the minimum amount of memory usage. While PC application programs generally have been increasing their memory requirements, LAN/gateway workstation software memory requirements have been decreasing. Currently, most vendors offer workstation software requiring from 64 to 150 kbytes of memory. The memory requirements are dependent on both the number of sessions and the type of session.

LAN gateway workstation users must load MS-DOS and the network operating system in addition to the workstation software. Many users desire to "hot-key" between their host session(s) and their DOS application. This requires that the DOS application fit in the remaining PC memory.

Q. Do I need to dedicate a PC to function as the gateway?

A. Intelligent communication adapter cards are designed to off-load the gateway PC to the maximum extent possible. The gateway PC is available for the LAN administrator to monitor gateway activity and for local copy printing. It is not desirable, in a large LAN, to run a gateway in a user's workstation PC. Problems with a user's programs running on a gateway PC will affect the reliability of the gateway. If the user needs to re-boot the gateway PC, then the gateway will need to be restarted.

Q. Can I have multiple gateways on my LAN?

A. Most vendors allow multiple gateways on a single LAN. Each gateway can talk to a separate mainframe or the same mainframe, be of any protocol, and use any of the four types of host connections.

This enables users to have concurrent access to mainframe sessions from different gateways. Subsequently, this allows the user to integrate host data from different mainframes at the workstation.

Q. How do concurrency and multiple mainframe sessions increase my productivity?

A. Concurrency allows a DOS application to continue to run while the user is in a mainframe session, and vice versa. Therefore, the user can be either compiling a program or recalculating a spreadsheet while querying a mainframe database.

Multiple mainframe sessions allow access to several mainframe applications simultaneously. This enables the user to hot-key from one application to the next. The hot-key prevents having to log off one application to access another application.

Q. How can I transfer files between the LAN and the mainframe?

A. There are three types of file transfer between a LAN and mainframe: editor file transfer, IBM (IND$FILE) file transfer, and proprietary fast-file transfer programs.

–   Editor File Transfer. The mainframe TSO or CMS editor is used to transfer files between the mainframe and the LAN. This method of file transfer is both slow and limited to transferring text files. Binary files from popular PC applications, such as spreadsheets, can not be transferred.

–   IBM (IND$FILE) File Transfer. IBM markets IND$FILE (Send or Receive) for VM/CMS, MVS/TSO, and CICS environments. This mainframe software is inexpensive to acquire and provides high-speed file transfer of both text and binary files with error correction. Most LAN gateways provide PC-workstation support for IND$FILE file transfer.

- Proprietary Fast File Transfer. A number of third-party software vendors provide packages to provide data compression and repacking to enhance IBM's file transfer programs. These programs consist of both mainframe and PC software.

Transferring host information through file transfer is an important LAN gateway application. Therefore, there are several advanced features which increase performance and user productivity during file transfer.

- Multiple File Transfer. This allows users to transfer more than one file at a time. The file transfers can occur from either the same mainframe or different mainframes.

- Background File Transfer. This method uses the host session to do file transfer, allowing file transfer to be a back- ground task. This enables the user to run a DOS program (i.e., doing word processing while host files are being transferred).

Q. How do I interface my PC applications with my mainframe applications?

A. Application program interfaces (APIs) provide communication between programs running on the LAN workstations and the mainframe. These APIs allow the development of cooperative processing applications, using the processing capability of the PC.

APIs can automate mainframe log-on procedures transfer files, create screens, and integrate applications. IBM has defined several PC APIs for communicating with mainframes: 3270 PA API, HLLA-PI, and SRPI. These APIs support PC programs written in Assembler, C, BASIC, COBOL and Pascal.

Q. Can I display mainframe graphics on my LAN PCs?

A. Mainframe application programs that display graphical images on 3X79 terminals can have these images displayed on LAN workstations. IBM uses two techniques to display graphics, programmed symbols displayed on 3279 S3G terminals, and vector graphics displayed on 3179-G terminals. Mainframe graphics can be edited and enhanced by the user at the PC workstation, and then printed or plotted by either the mainframe or a LAN printer.

Q. Can I print host files on the LAN printers?

A. LAN gateways support 3270 printer emulation, both LU1 and LU3. The printed output can be directed to any printer on the LAN. In addition, most LAN gateways provide print screen and local copy features.

There are two important printing capabilities to look for. First, how are host printer control sequences (EBCDIC) translated into PC printer control sequences (ASCII)? Is this translation user-configurable, so that one can specify the proper control sequences for the printer? And second, how does the printer route its output to printers on the LAN? Does it support PC/LAN printer spoolers?

Q.   How are the 3270 special functions made available to PC users?

A.   The keys of a 3270 terminal are mapped to the PC keyboard. A configuration program provides the ability for the user to change the mapping easily. Keyboard templates aid users with the 3270 keystrokes. Macros can be defined to enable users to replace multiple-keystroke sequences with a single keystroke.

      Several vendors have developed an on-line keyboard template, which conveniently displays a picture of both the user's keybaord and the 3270 key assignments, eliminating the need for the physical keyboard templates. The on-line keyboard template also provides the keyboard layout, allowing the user to develop keyboard macros and reassign keys easily.

Q.   What kind of support can I expect before and after the sale?

A.   Each company's LAN/gateway requirements have their own unique issues. Therefore, the gateway vendors should have a thorough knowledge of both mainframe and PC-connectivity environments. They should be prepared to offer a full range of services, including consulting, systems integration, planning, training, installation, testing and both telephone and on-site support.

Q.   Can you put some light on remote bridging?

A.   A remote bridge basically links two remote networks together. The DE-2000 hub's built in remote bridge allows two IEEE 802.3 Ethernet networks situated apart to be linked together over a dial-up telephone line. Ethernet nodes on either networks thus can communicate with each other as if they were on one single network.

      The advantage of a built in bridge is of course, you do not have to neither purchase nor install a separate bridge. The DE-2000 thus saves you both the cost and the installation trouble.

Q.   Can LAN's have Arcnet and Ethernet on the same network?

A.   Yes, both the topologies can co-exist in the same network by using the concept of bridges. Novell Netware 3.11 and 2.2 has built in capability to offer bridge.

Q.   Is it possible to Connect a Laptop to an existing LAN?

A.   With D-link pocket LAN adapter it is possible to connect a Laptop to an existing LAN. Separate adapters are available for Ethernet or Arcnet configuration, which is connected to the parallel port of the Laptop.

Q.   What is Network Management?

A.   Network Management involves one or more systems that manage the network, and a number of managed systems. We call the system that manages the network the manager console, and systems that are managed the agents. The network manager can be a PC that runs a network management software program. Agent systems can be hubs, bridges, gateways or host that contain an agent, or Component that responds to requests from a manager console.

The components of the hubs allow them to be part of a manageable network. These component include a CPU, memory for data storage, other related hardware and the agent firmwork. With these components, activities on the hubs can be monitored, while the hubs can be manipulated to carry out specific tasks. Among the principal tasks, performed by the agent are;

– Statistics: The hub collects statistics at specific Ethernet for determination of the hub's network traffic load and pinpointing at problems.

– Traps: The hub periodically sends information to the manager console to automatically alert you of changes occuring in the hub, such as a change in configuration.

– Reset: From a manager console located far away, you can reset the hub for a quick diagnose or reset the hub to its default configuration.

– Port Management: From a manager console, the ports of the hub can be disabled or enabled for the purpose of problem diagnosis.

Q. I have a small training institute and want to connect my DOS nachine with the UNIX host to transfer the files and use my DOS machine as a UNIX terminal. My friends tell me that using TCP/IP we can establish this connection. Can you tell me something about TCP/IP and how to use?

A. Connectivity between DOS machine and UNIX host can be established using TCP/IP (Transmission Control Protocol/Internet Protocol). It is a layered set of protocols. The four layers of this protocol are (i) Application (ii) TCP (iii) IP (iv) Protocols needed to manage specific physical medium such as Ethernet. The major function of TCP is to break the message into datagrams and that of IP is to route them through the best available route. This set of protocols uses the Internet Protocol Address (IP Address in short). It is a 32 bit number, that looks like 132.145.160.09. It is normally written as four decimal numbers each representing 8 bit element. Information is transferred as a sequence of datagrams. You can use File Transfer Protocol (FTP) to transfer the files across the two machines. Two modes of transferring the files are available, i.e., Net ASCII and Binary. Net ASCII mode can be used for transferring text files and for transferring executable files Binary mode is used. Telnet utility can be used for emulating a UNIX terminal.

For establishing the above connectivity, you have to install TCP/IP for UNIX on the DOS based machines. On the hardware side you have to install Ethernet LAN Adapters on both the machines. Apart from this you have to create HOSTS file on both the machines specifying the IP address of both machines. You can specify the IP addresses of the hosts. Then you can use FTP and TELNET features to transfer the files and remote logins.

Q.   When a number of workstations, some of which are even diskless are connected to the
     server, does the speed of the server goes down drastically?

A.   No. The speed of the server is not at all affected, when it offers its resources to be
     shared. Actually, Network operating system uses a number of techniques to speed up
     its response time. One technique is directory hashing, which can be likened to an
     efficient indexing system. The software maps all the directory files and keeps all of
     this information in RAM. When a workstation requests a file the file server need only
     examine the few directory entries to locate the particular file. Since this information
     is in RAM and not on disk, the procedure is very fast.

     A second technique is, disk caching, in effect, the file server anticipate future
     workstation file requests and keeps an image of frequently requested positions of its
     drive in RAM. When a workstation requests additional material from this area of the
     servers hard disk drive, the information is already located in RAM and does not require
     access to the hard disk. Since disc access is in milli seconds and RAM access in micro
     seconds, a significant time is saved for the network users.

Q.   What is the advantage of using a LAN when a multi-user environment can be achieved
     using mini computers?

A.   LAN has got various advantages over Mini Computers. They are summarized in
     following table.

MIN Versus LAN

MINI	LAN
1. Single CPU-Time Sharing	Multiple CPU-Load sharing
2. Proprietory OS-Limited Software	Standard OS-popular user Software
3. Centralised resources	Central and local resources
4. Single function terminal usually dumb	Multi function work station. Basically computer.
5. Upgradation in quantum jump	Upgradation in single units
6. One time Block investment need	Staggered investment, system grows with your needs
7. Fear of obsolescence	Workstation procured as required with latest technology
8. Technology upgrade implies replacement	Implies changing or adding workstation
9. Practical limit on number of terminals is 16, in extreme cases 24	Upto 100 workstations numbers per server, total 8-225
10. Degradation in response with addition of terminals	Practically no degradation with more work-stations.
11. Cabling distance upto 2-4 km	Cabling distance upto 64 km

Q.   When you share your resources to the network. Are there any provisions by which you can control the access to your shared resources?

A.   When you share your resources, you set an access right for other users so that you can control the way they use their resources. Five different access rights are.

   –   Read, write and create (RWC)

   –   Read and write (RW)

   –   Write and create (WC)

   –   Read only (R)

   –   Write only (W)

Q.   Can simultaneous voice and data signals be transmitted using LAN, if yes, how?

A.   Yes, simultaneous voice and data signals can be sent through LAN using Broad band coaxial cable.

Q.   What should be the criteria of the selection of LAN?

A.   A LANs effectiveness depends on its applications programs and how well those programs take advantage of the specific environment that only a LAN can provide.

SELECTING PERSONAL COMPUTERS

INTRODUCTION

Personal computers that in recent years were available mainly to professionals in science, engineering and business, are now available to millions of users all over the world. The Information Age is no longer dawning, it is here. But how do you choose the right tool for your Information Age Job?

In the first instance, it is important to have a good reason for wanting to use a microcomputer at all, and it is important for people who buy them to obtain tangible benefits. Buying computer is relatively simple, but buying one that is right for particular requirements is not so easy. There is an enormous range of products on offer, and a confusing array of variations in packaging and in terminology. For most people, a microcomputer is a relatively expensive object, perhaps intended to last for a long time. As with all decisions, it is best to define objectives before opening the cheque book. Some reasons for obtaining a computer are given below. A microcomputer may be required:

1.   As a means to understanding computing or programming.

2.   As a means for home entertainment.

3.   To maintain files of relatively slow-moving information (e.g. name and address files).

4.   To maintain primary accounts for a business (nominal ledgers, etc.).

5.   To handle on-line transactions from multiple users.

6.   To control a process, such as a heating or lighting system.

7.   To communicate with a database stored remotely on a mainframe or minicomputer.

The first step in choosing the right tool for your job is deciding what type of computer is right for your job environment. The next step is to analyze your job in terms of how computer solutions might be applied for greater productivity and an easier, more fulfilling workday. Begin your comparison shopping by determining which software will carry out your desired applications and which computers can run that software. Use the selection factors defined here to help you choose a personal computer system that meets your present and future needs.

Some of the essential considerations in choosing a personal computer are discussed here. Begin by deciding which factors are must in terms of your own needs. This enables you to quickly eliminate models that, no matter what advantages they may offer, do not meet your real requirements.

. SOFTWARE

Software refers to programs that can be run by a computer. It is generally distributed
in media such as floppy disc or magnetic cassette or cartridge for use on various computer
systems and is available from your dealer or software vendor or the manufacturer. Software
can also be user-written for specific applications.

The software you intend to use will determine the hardware you will need. Suppose
you want your computer to replace your typewriter and maintain all your personal or
business records and accounts. For openers, you might choose software for word processing,
file and information management and accounting.

Your dealer or sales representative can provide literature about the software available
for your intended purpose. The documentation on a given software package will tell you
what type of computer system is required to run it and how much primary and secondary
memory is needed. For example, CP/M (Control Program for Microcomputers), a widely
used operating system on which thousands of business programs and languages have been
used, requires a dual floppy disc drive for full efficiency.

The performance of any computer system depends on the quality of the programs
controlling it. Good software has to perform as many of your required tasks as possible. It
executes major functions quickly and correctly, cutting the time you spend waiting. It
provides on- screen help such as user-friendly menus, or multiple choice prompts to guide
you through problems without constant reference to the manual.

Good software should also accept all possible input errors and notify you without
crashing (stopping suddenly), in which case data can be lost. It should be able to guide you
out of trouble with on- screen commands and resume program execution with all data intact.
In other words, a good software writer will anticipate potential problems and provide
routines to cope with them.

Another point about good software is that it should be thoroughly tested and debugged
the software author. In many cases the software author is not the manufacturer of the
computer you are using. Many manufacturers provide their own tested applications software
for their personal computers, designed to utilize their expanded capabilities such as screen-
labeled softkeys. Additional sources drawn upon include independent authors who produce
additional applications programs or add-ons, and PC users, whose innovations become part
of the PC Users' library and available to all.

The language in which the software is written is the set of commands that comprise
the dialog between the programmer or user and the computer and all its peripherals. Many
different languages exist, each with its own level of complexity and power and were written
for a different purpose. Examples of some of the popular high-level languages include
BASIC, FORTRAN, COBOL, C, Pascal, Ada, LISP, SNOBOL, FORTH, Algol, PL/I, APL,
. BASIC (Beginners All-purpose Symbolic Instruction Code), was written to enable more
people to operate and program computers through simple statements derived from common
English. The Standard and Enhanced versions of BASIC onboard certain personal computers

contain extra built-in commands that transform sequences of steps into one-step operations. The result is easier operation and greater programmability.

As you observe various software categories, learn which languages are popular in your field(s) of interest. Try to learn the characteristics of popular languages and determine the ability of each to solve your problems. FORTRAN (Formula Translation) is a high-level programming language often used in scientific applications. COBOL (Common Business Oriented Language) is designed to handle large amounts of data and was written for use in business environments. FORTH is a complex, very effective programming language that enables the user to compile a dictionary of routines that comprise program "kernels". Pascal is an English-oriented language written to be compatible on many computer systems and to encourage more logical programming practices. Excellent programs can be written in any of the higher-level languages described here.

Languages vary in efficiency and speed of execution the same tasks take less time in faster languages. Assembly language produces machine code instructions represented by a list of binary numbers. This is the simplest and fastest form for the computer to understand and execute but the most difficult for the programmer.

Learning about software can be a complex endeavour, but having a single source of software, hardware and information can make it easier. The range and quality of software and hardware offered by many computer manufacturer provides the right tool for the job in many fields. The growing library of programs includes such "best-sellers" as:

WordStar   :   A word processing system from MicroPro International Corpora
                    tion, USA using the power of CP/M or MS-DOS to produce your
                    letters, reports and documents.

dBASE IV   :   A database system from Ashon-Tate, USA that helps you collect
                    and manage information and data.

VisiCalc   :   Electronic spreadsheet from VisiCorp, USA that can graphically
                    highlight data that might otherwise buried.

SuperCalc   :   The supercalc spreadsheet and graphing concepts can be used
                    for an almost unlimited range of financial, engineering and
                    scientific applications.

Sidekick   :   It helps you to organise your work and keeps your desk free of
                    the eternal file of paper notes, pencils, hand-calculators, phone-
                    directories, and what not that gets lost all the time anyway.

Lotus 1-2-3   :   It is an integrated package having an electronic spreadsheet,
                    graphics and data base creation facility. Most suitable for
                    financial applications.

Windows 3.1   :   1989's most successful software from Microsoft Corporation,
                    USA. Facilitates working on multiple softwares, files and tasks
                    with total ease.

Excel	:	The package from Microsoft that integrates a spreadsheet of unparalled power with a lightning fast database and outstanding business graphics.
Works	:	The four tools in one package, with Database Management, Spreadsheet, Wordprocessing and Communications. Available from Microsoft Corporation, USA.
File management	:	For organised entry and retrieval of information, better record keeping and decision making.
Communications Terminal Emulation	:	For modern control and filetransfer or communication between other terminals and a host computer.
Training Courses	:	On-screen training in computer use and programming.
Graphics Power	:	Software utilising built-in commands to easily design visual displays and control colour plotter reproduction.
Harward Total Project Manager	:	A specialized software package for project management activities.

2. MEMORY/MASS STORAGE

Memory storage capacity is measured in bytes. A byte is a group of eight binary digits (called bits) that represents one character. To the computer a byte represents a number from 0 to 255 that is interpreted according to the program being run. For example, a word processing program may interpret a byte of data from a disc as a letter "T", whereas a graphics program could interpret it as part of a shape.

Data storage systems are measured in Kilobytes or Megabytes. K = 1024 bytes, M = 1,046,576 bytes.

Personal computers contain varying amounts of memory onboard (internally) in the form of Random Access Memory (RAM) and Read Only Memory (ROM). As your demands increase, onboard memory can be added with plug-in modules or chips upto the system limits. More read/write memory can be accessed externally via mass storage media such as disc or cassette tape. Mass storage is any form of hardware capable of accepting groups of data, or files, from the computer and retaining it for later access.

The amount of memory your system will require is determined by your applications. In entering text, for example, you might use 4000 bytes (80 characters per line, 50 lines per page). Consult the documentation on your desired software to determine the storage requirements of your largest jobs. 256 K bytes of onboard memory and dual 5-1/4" floppy-disc drives may be sufficient memory for many small business uses of a personal computer. But because everybody's applications differ, so do their needs. Larger jobs involve programs that can handle larger files and call for greater amounts of onboard and mass storage memory.

Cassette tape is a relatively inexpensive, high-capacity medium for memory storage. Information is stored on a cassette tape as a series of magnetic pulses representing binary data. A cassette drive enables a computation device to access memory on tape.

Magnetic discs, handled by peripherals called disc drives, are the most widely used form of external memory for storing and retrieving programs and data. There are two basic types: flexible discs made of mylar, known as floppies and rigid aluminium discs called hard discs or Winchesters (after the powerful rifle). Standard disc sizes are 8", 5-1/4" and 3-1/2" diameter "microfloppy". Discs have a smooth magnetic surface on which information is stored as a series of pulses along lines called tracks. Information is transmitted to and from the spinning disc by a read/write head on the drive unit. Because the head can go to any part of the disc directly, discs are random access storage devices and provide faster retrieval than cassette tape, which has to be positioned to the exact point being accessed. Winchester discs rotate faster than floppies and hold much more data.

The mechanical functions of a disc drive are controlled by software called a disc operating system (DOS) which enables the computer to read, write, or erase to modify the contents of the disc under software control. To accommodate the varying needs of users, the computer manufacturers makes a wide range of drives capable of handling various combinations of disc sizes and types.

Micro floppies come in a hardcase with a sliding cover that protects the media surface. Some micro floppies have a unique "media monitor" that warns you if the disc is about to wear out protecting both your data and the read/write heads of your drive unit.

Magnetic cards are another form of mass storage. They are magnetically encoded strips that can be written to or read from by a small device called a card reader. They provide an inexpensive, easy way to store programs and data.

An optical wand is a peripheral that transforms printed bar codes into data that can be transferred to the computer making paper available as an indirect, inexpensive mass storage medium.

3. KEYBOARD/EASE OF USE

The keyboard enables you to communicate with the computer. Some of the major conveniences to look for are:

1. USER DEFINABLE SOFTKEYS. Let you type in frequently-used multi-character commands that can then be executed with the touch of a single softkey. In word processing, programming or any use on a regular basis, this timesaving feature means more creative time and less typing time. Some of the personal computers not only have a full set of softkeys but provide inverse-video blocks on your screen for labeling the softkeys according to your definitions.

2. A NUMERIC KEYPAD. Simplifies entry of long lists of numbers. The layout resembles that on a standard business calculator. Essential if your job requires arithmatic input as in accounting, statistics or cash management.

3. A DISPLAY EDITING SYSTEM. With single keys for full-function display and editing operations such as cursor positioning, scrolling, rolling, clearing the screen and deleting and inserting characters and complete lines in programs and text.

4. SYSTEM COMMAND KEYS. Enable entry of commonly used commands such as LIST, RUN or PAUSE with a single key stroke.

5. 'FEEL'.Comfortable spacing, molded keycaps and tactile feedback are desirable features. But there is no substitute for a hands- on evaluation in this area.

6. QUALITY AND DURABILITY. Varies greatly. It is safest to choose a manufacturer that employs vigorous testing methods to produce machines that receive daily use in business environments.

7. DETACHED KEYBOARD. You may prefer the compactness of a built- in keyboard but if your applications require that the keyboard be separate from the main unit, the right tool for the job is a detached keyboard.

8. ROTARY CONTROL KNOB. It can be used for fast program editing, cursor positioning, analog like input and fine adjustments during testing or drawing.

4. VIDEO DISPLAY

The display, also known as the video monitor (although monitor may imply an external device) is a Cathode Ray Tube (CRT) with circuitry to decode text and graphics information from a computer and present it in the form of dots activated on the screen. The quality of the video display will determine how easy it is to use your computer for long periods. High resolution displays produce legible characters, reducing eyestrain. Some offer the added convenience of variable brightness.

The right video display for you depends on your job. The software you intend to employ will make demands on your display. For example, many CP/M based programs require an 80 character by 25 line display to be used to their full effectiveness. The main criteria for selecting a video monitor are:

1. DISPLAY SIZE. The overall size of the display is usually given as a diagonal measurement in inches or centimeters. Preferences are highly subjective. Some people want compactness; others feel its "the bigger the better". Common ones include 12" and 14" displays.

2. DISPLAY MATRIX. This refers to the number of characters that can appear on the screen at one time. Common display matrices range from 16 lines of 32 characters to 24 lines of 80 characters per line.

3. CHARACTER MATRIX. Characters appear on the CRT as groups of dots within a rectangular matrix. The more data that can be activated within the matrix, the greater the legibility provided. A 5 by 7 dot matrix capable of producing "true descenders" (g,j,p,q,y) is considered a prerequisite for good legibility.

4.   OTHER MONITOR FEATURES. To look for are glare prevention and a tilt/swivel base that allows you to adjust the screen to the most convenient viewing angle.

5. GRAPHICS CAPABILITIES

If your work can be enhanced by charts, graphs or other visual displays, your computer should be capable of generating high- resolution graphics. Graphics software interprets data entered by the user to activate dots on the CRT screen, thereby producing patterns. The greater the number of displayable dots (also known as pixels), the higher the resolution. High-resolution displays produce smoother curves and finer lines. Typical high-resolution displays start at 250 dots horizontally by 200 dots vertically.

Graphics software differences among personal computers can be determined by studying the commands that a given system makes available. Look at the instruction set provided in the documentation: the more graphics commands resident on a system, the better. Find the commands that pertain to onscreen or hardcopy graphics control. There should be enough to draw lines, plot points, draw circles and squares, fill shapes, erase, manipulate, save to disc etc. Each of these routines should be written to run as fast as possible. Your computer dealer or sales representative will let you compare the graphics capabilities of the models you are considering.

Versions of BASIC provided on typical Personal Computers contain extensive commands for designing screen graphics and controlling hardcopy devices. They are designed to enable you to generate fast, accurate drawings and plots. Sophisticated graphics software cuts design time and enhances the effect of your artwork.

In order to produce colour hardcopy of your graphics designs your system should include a colour plotter, a peripheral that uses coloured pens to reproduce, on paper or transparent film, shapes transmitted via the computer. In choosing one you should ask these questions:

1.   Is it easy to understand and operate ? Is paper loading and positioning a simple process?

2.   Is the resolution fine enough for your applications ? Do you get truly straight lines and smooth curves ?

3.   Can it produce complex plots in a matter of minutes ?

4.   Can you plot on transparent film for overhead slide presentations?

5.   Does it contain different software-selectable typefaces and styles for text and graphics mixtures ?

6.   How many pen colours are available ?

7.   How readily will it interface with your computer ? Is your computer capable of utilising the full capabilities of the plotter ?

Efforts to bring artists and designers closer to the computer have led to the development of devices such as the digitizer, which converts a position on a flat surface to data understandable by the computer and the graphics tablet, a pad-like surface that can be drawn on with a stylus.

6. INTERFACES

In order to use the right tool for the job, you need the right connections. Over the years people have learned to apply computers in many environments requiring different interfaces. Serial and parallel, the two main types of interface common on computer systems today, exist in many configurations. Some require an Input/Output (I/O) port for every peripheral you use, which can limit the uses of your system. Many computers are sold without the necessary interfaces for mass storage and for a printer peripherals essential to many personal computer systems. Acquiring interfaces, if they are not built-in or available from the manufacturer, can be very time consuming and costly and with some personal computers it may not be possible at all.

Standard interfaces available are HP-IB (Hewlett-Packard Interface Bus), industry standard IEEE-488 bus, GP-IB (General Purpose Interface Bus), RS-232C serial interface, Centronics parallel interface, etc. These interfaces can control various modems (modulator-demodulator), printers and equipments. Because the interface itself does not appear as a peripheral, its hidden importance, can be overlooked resulting in inconvenience, extra costs and a system with limited abilities. It cannot be overemphasized: in order to use the right tool for the job, you need the right connections.

7. PERIPHERALS

Any device external to but interfacing the CPU (Central Processing Unit) is a peripheral, including the keyboard and display. Two widely used peripherals, mass storage devices and plotters, have been described above in reference to memory and graphics. Your intended applications will determine whether these and/or other peripherals should be included in your system. To maximize your flexibility now and in the future, your computer should provide easy access through its interfaces to as many peripherals as possible. For ease of use, your peripherals should be able to run off of a common bus. As explained above, there should be no hidden costs or inconveniences involved in adding peripherals to your computer. The advantage of buying all your gear from a single vendor is that you are guaranteed that all the devices were designed to work with each other as an integrated system for maximum efficiency.

Most personal computer applications require that hard-copy be produced by a printer. The three main types are dot-matrix impact, dot-matrix thermal and daisy wheel printers. If your system does not include a plotter and you want some graphics capabilities, dot-matrix printers enable you to reproduce simple designs. If you need "letter quality" hardcopy for business or other purposes, you should choose a daisy wheel printer.

Many applications involve the use of a modem, a peripheral that enables a computer to interface wth telephone lines. Users can connect or "log on" to other computers to exchange messages, data and programs. You can access an information network for such services as news. A typical model provides automatic answering, dialing and log-on for easy connection to a host system. It enables you to easily access the resources of your office from home or any outside site.

8. QUALITY, RELIABILITY AND SUPPORT

Buying a personal computer is like buying a car. What you want are high-quality products that do not break down and a dependable seller who will make life easier if and when you need repairs, parts, accessories or advice.

Reliable products are the result of workmanship, experience, rigorous testing procedures and an overriding commitment to quality control on the part of the manufacturer. Reliability is not easy to determine at the point of sale, but the manufacturer's overall reputation is significant.

It is important to bear in mind that quality determines the economic soundness of any computer purchase. Low price must not be confused with high cost-effectiveness. Computation gear that does not breakdown, that is readily expandable and for which the manufacturer provides first-rate service and support is the ultimate bargain.

9. SPEED AND POWER

These aspects of computer performance are especially important in laboratories and other technical work environments. The speed at which the microprocessor steps through memory and carries out its instructions is controlled by the system clock, a high-frequency signal measured in Megahertz (MHz). Power refers to direct memory- addressing capability. It is determined by the computer's internal architecture the width of the data path and the length of the programmable registers contained in the CPU. A wide data path enables more complex operations in single steps (as opposed to sequences of smaller steps). Most personal computers available today are 16-bit machines.

10. CONVENIENCES/INTANGIBLES

The actual amount of space a personal computer occupies on your desk its "footprint" is an important selection factor. Some will occupy your whole desk, making it difficult for you to function effectively. Some take up floor space, too.

Well-designed personal computers and peripherals should run a self-test at the start of operation a diagnostic program to confirm that all parts of the system are working properly.

Portability is another useful convenience, even if it is not your main prerequisite. You might not need a battery-operable portable for use on the road or in the field; but you might on occasion want to take your personal computer home, bring it to a different work site, or have it on hand to make a presentation outside your office. Portability is determined by weight, overall size and whether or not a carrying case is made for the model. Battery-operable portable computers should be rechargeable.

A highly subjective factor, important nonetheless, is appearance. You might prefer a striking console or an unobtrusive model that seems like "part of the furniture". The point is, you are going to be spending a lot of time with your computer and it should not be an eyesore. If you are expanding your system, remember that peripherals should be compatible with your computer visually as well as electrically.

Another intangible worth considering is the likelihood that the manufacturer will be on hand tomorrow to offer the hardware and software enhancements you desire.

11. DOCUMENTATION

The quality of the systems, applications, users manuals and guides, etc provided by the manufacturer of a given hardware or software product will affect how long it takes you to get the product working and whether you will be able to take full advantage of its capabilities. Good documentation tends to be brief and informative. It generally includes complete examples of operations, relevant illustrations, an index of key terms and either a glossary or clear definitions integrated with text. Good documentation is written in a style you can understand, helps you carry out your intended applications and may even suggest applications you had not considered. Manufacturers and dealers will supply you with documentation on the products you are interested in. Study documentation as a short-cut method of comparison shopping.

12. PRICES

If a computer is bought for a specific purpose, the purchaser should seek a combination of hardware and software which fulfills that purpose alone. However, if a computer is to be purchased for use in several applications, it is likely that it will need to be expanded or enhanced later, by adding additional features or peripheral units. It therefore pays to consider the price of these additions and perhaps plot several stages of enhancement, so that prices of different expansion paths can be considered and compared before a specific machine is selected.

Some manufacturers make the price for their entry-level systems quite low; but they may then charge relatively high prices for additional features which the average user doesn't order first time around. It has been noticed that some home computers are priced in this way; the technical literature, for example the programming manuals, required for the more serious applications of such systems, is often expensive. It, therefore, pays to look at prices in detail, including all the ancillary goods and services required to support the intended use of the computer system.

13. IBM PC COMPATIBLE COMPUTERS

PC Compatibility has become an important topic, with many computer manufacturers claiming it, and much confusion as to what compatibility really means. Here we examine why compatibility with the IBM Personal Computer can be important, in what forms it is claimed, and what to consider when checking for compatibility. We see that the most important form of compatibility is software- compatibility, where software written for the

IBM PC will run without flaw in another MS-DOS (MicroSoft Disk Operating System) computer.

Compatibility - Why it matters

In the world of 8086/8088/80286/80386/80486 based computers, most software is written first for the IBM Personal Computer. If you want a general-purpose personal computer, you want one that will run the software written for the IBM PC. More than 90 percent of IBM PC users use MS-DOS. Excellent packages have been written to run under other operating systems, and on other computers, but the greatest variety of software is found running under MS-DOS on the IBM PC.

Another aspect of the current marketplace is that you cannot sell computer hardware without software. A manufacturer who can build a computer that runs software written for the IBM PC will avoid enormous software development expense. However, the IBM PC, although sturdy, reliable and popular, does not have all the latest technological advances. Newer computers can be better than the IBM PC; the manufacturers have a tough time balancing probable sales against the desire to introduce new technology.

Compatibility Claims

PC Compatibility is widely claimed. It is also made hazy by the yearnings of people who sell computers based on the Intel 8088 family. The claim can be based on as little as the fact that the computer, when it is not running its regular operating system, can run MS-DOS, or, at the other extreme, the claim can be based on the fact that the new computer can run any and all software written for the IBM PC.

"MS-DOS Compatible" is often used as a name for the first type of compatibility. The potential for confusion between MS-DOS compatibility and IBM PC compatibility is not entirely to the disadvantage of people selling an "MS-DOS Compatible" computer. However, the second type of compatibility is what counts; such a computer is, ultimately, a software-compatible machine.

Compatibility that Counts

If your computer dealer can show you a list of several hundred programs written for the IBM PC that, without any patching or other adaptation, run on an MS-DOS computer, and that list includes Microsoft's Flight Simulator and Lotus 1-2-3, then that computer is compatible with the IBM PC.

Even though we use the term software-compatible for such computers, a considerable degree of hardware compatibility is implied. The copy protection scheme for some versions of Lotus 1-2-3 (among other applications) depends on certain operational features of the IBM PC's disk drive. If those hardware features are not duplicated in other computers, those other computers would not even be able to load Lotus 1-2-3, let alone run it.

Data Compatibility

Other levels of compatibility are less valuable, but cannot be dismissed. You may want to transfer files of information from one manufacturer's computer to another. If the computers are software- compatible as defined above there will be no difficulty in making the transfer. But even if they are not, at least you will want them to be data-compatible. Fully data-compatible computers can read disks written by other computers, and write disks that can be read by other computers.

Sometimes commercial software vendors will come to the rescue when you want to transfer files between machines that are not data- compatible. Xenocopy, for the IBM PC, reads files from, and write files to, disks of different format. Sometimes the computer manufacturer will supply software that allows you to read files prepared on other machines. Xenocopy, by the way, is so specific to the IBM hardware (it addresses specific locations in ROM BIOS (Basic Input Output System)), that it is one of the very few pieces of software that will not run on any PC compatibles.

Hardware Compatibility

Another category of compatibility is associated with hardware features. If pieces of the hardware are interchangeable with the IBM PC, then programs written for the PC that use the interchangeable hardware will most likely run well.

ROM BIOS

The ROM BIOS chip in the PC is unique to IBM PC. Other manufacturers can use the same interrupt locations as IBM to point to software functions that accept the same parameters and provide the same software services, but they cannot exactly duplicate the BIOS. Few programs make use of the routines found in the BIOS other than by way of the standard interface through an interrupt location, but when they do, the chances of those programs running perfectly on any PC- compatible is close to zero. IBM sues manufacturers who copy their ROM BIOS.

Other companies make alternative ROM BIOS chips, e.g., Pheonix ROM BIOS. Their command interface is sometimes perfectly compatible with IBM's ROM BIOS, but not always.

ROM BASIC

The IBM PC has a subset of BASIC installed in a ROM chip. The disk based BASIC (or BASICA) makes extensive use of the ROM BASIC capabilities. Programs written in BASIC on the PC will not run on computers that do not have the same set of capabilities. However, GWBASIC (also supplied by Microsoft, who wrote BASIC for the PC) is supposed to run progrms written in BASIC for the PC. Some commercial software manu- facturers supply AUTOEXEC.BAT files that start operation of their programs. That batch ile would contain the line.

BASICA HIGAME

If the batch file is changed to read

GWBASIC HIGAME

Software compatibility may be regained.

Expansion Boards

Computers that are most hardware-compatible accept memory expansion boards, device-controller boards, and other add-on boards made for the IBM PC. As usual, statements that one computer will accept boards made for another computer may not mean that the two computers are hardware-compatible; the boards might fit in the slots but they may not always do what is required of them.

However, if you do find an MS-DOS computer that works just fine with IBM PC boards, and vice-versa, the chances of the MS-DOS computer being software-compatible are high.

Keyboard Compatibility

The IBM PC keyboard has odd key placement, and a selection of keys not always found on other computers (e.g. Alt, PgUp, PgDn, Numlock). To run IBM software, the keyboard layout does not have to be the same (we can adapt to a difference in key positions) but access to all the keys has to be possible!

Display-Handling Compatibility

The IBM PC displays gets its characters from a buffer at a specific address in the memory of the computer (B0000H for the monochrome display, B8000H for the colour/graphics display). The adaptor boards are built to output specific characters of a specific resolution. The set of 256 characters used by the PC is made up of the first 128 standard ANSI characters, and a selection of IBM-chosen characters for the other 128. If an MS-DOS computer uses a different memory address, or does not use memory-mapped displays, if it forms character sets at a different dot-resolution, or sends out characters different from the IBM PC, it won't be software-compatible.

Disk Compatibility

The PC uses 5 1/4 inch disks formatted with 9 or 15 sectors per track, and 48 tracks per inch. Some noncompatible MS-DOS computers use disks of a different physical size, or with a different number of tracks per inch, or both.

Do you Need Compatibility?

This repeated use of the word compatibility might obscure the fact that you may not need it! A computer might have unique features (for example, the touch-screen hardware) or it might serve specific applications so well that you choose to buy it without PC compatibility. In addition, a manufacturer may have the resources, or market-share, to convince the creators of popular software packages to tailor them for its machine. Remember that your choice of machines may not be strictly limited to whether or not they are software-compatible with the PC.

14. BENCHMARKING

Benchmarking is a technique to gauge the speeds of computers. They can be broadly classified into two categories - Analytical Models and Simulated Models. In the case of Analytical Models, one can collect information from the manufacturer regarding CPU speeds and peripheral efficiencies, analyse them and find out which system is more effective. In the other case, a set of user programs can be run on selected computers and the efficiency can be compared.

To gauge the CPU speed, some sort of thumb rule is always used. With the advancement of general purpose application programs supplied by the manufacturer many new factors came into the picture in evaluating the performance of computers. When reliability, availability and serviceability became prime factors, a 1/3 ratio was applied, i.e. use 1/3 for system efficiency, 1/3 for serviceability and 1/3 for application programs available on the system.

Various types of job mix like Gibson Mix, Flynn Mix were used to compare computers for scientific and engineering applications. Usually the CPU speeds are expressed in terms of Millions of Instructions Per Second (mips). For efficiency in commercial applications, sorting and file manipulation are taken as prime factors. In the case of microcomputers, program run time need not be viewed as a prime factor. More weightage should be given to error- free behaviour of the system. One can measure efficiency of computers only by defining a suitable job mix for a particular user. The conventional formula used to gauge the efficiency against the cost of any system is:

$P2 = 2(P1)*(C2/C1)$

In other words, if the cost of a computer (C2) is twice that of another computer (C1) then the performance (P2) should be four times efficient than that of the first (P1).

Benchmark tests on PCs/XTs

1. NOP. The 128K NOP benchmark test is designed to measure raw clock speed and memory access time while minimizing differences in microprocessors and the effect of memory caching. This test executes almost nothing but NOP ("No Operation") machine code instructions in a big 128K-byte loop.

2. Floating-Point Calculation. The Floating-Point Calculation benchmark test measures processor speed by looping through a series of floating-point calculations, including multiplication, division, exponentials, and logarithmatic and trigonometric functions. This test program uses the floating-point library included with the Microsoft C Compiler.

3.   Conventional RAM. The Conventional RAM benchmark test allocates 256K bytes of conventional memory and treats it as a series of 64 byte records. Then 16,384 random records are read into and written from this memory.

4.   Disk Access. The Disk Access benchmark test from Core International measures the hard disks seek time, or how fast the drive responds to the disk controllers instructions (in milliseconds). The test program performs three measurements on the speed at which the drive head moves: track to adjacent track, track to randomly selected track, and the average of a series of random track accesses. Only the results for a series of random track accesses are shown here.

5.   Lotus 1-2-3 Routine. The 1-2-3 Routine benchmark test for spreadsheet applications, designed for a 640 Kbyte environment, assesses the computational speed and RAM managemment capabilities of the machine by using a 1-2-3 macro that performs a series of both global and individual worksheet tasks. The macro copies and recalculates a 10-cell range 499 times, moves 1,000 cells, deletes 1,000 cells and then systematically clears the spreadsheet.

GUIDELINES FOR CHOOSING A MICROCOMPUTER SYSTEM

Prior to looking at the market it is necessary to specify the requirements of both the hardware and software. However, due to the high cost of tailoring packages when compared with the package cost, it is preferable if the approach to computerisation can be fairly flexible.

Having drawn up the statement of requirements, this should be used as the basis for an invitation to tender. The type of company invited to tender will be different from the more traditional computing suppliers. However, a shortlist of four or five should be invited to submit proposals.

The resulting tenders are probably going to be fairly brief and must be examined carefully. Despite the low cost associated with microcomputer systems there is still a need to approach their acquisition in a systematic manner. Although the full weighted ranking by levels technique is probably not justified in terms of the effort involved, a shortened version should still be used.

When the selection process is complete the contract should be agreed and the system installed. Advice should be sought at any stage where you are unsure.

1. Specification of Requirements

Before any computer system can be purchased it is essential that you know exactly what is to be done on it. Humans can take decisions based on experience but machines cannot. Consequently it is essential to have an accurate description of your implementation requirements.

In the case of microcomputers, where the system usually performs only one job at a time, the primary concern should always be the applications software. Businesses concerned with choosing microcomputer systems frequently have little knowledge of computers and consequently wish to acquire a package. Inevitably, this becomes a trade-off between what is required and what is available.

An alternative is to pay the supplier to tailor the software. In the case of traditional computing this has always been a reasonable substitute for tailor-written programs, giving the buyer the essential requirements at minimum cost.

However, with the high cost of programming and systems staff, the alterations are quite likely to cost considerably more than the package itself. For this reason it is advisable to be as flexible as possible. Nevertheless, the starting point should always be to document the essential requirements in as much detail as possible.

2. Invitation to Tender

Once the statement of requirements report has been drawn up, it should be used as the basis for an invitation to tender.

The type of company involved in tendering is quite likely to be different from that tendering for more conventional computing. Traditionally, in the latter case the manufacturer has supplied not only the processor, peripherals and memory but also provided software, including applications packages.

However, in looking at the microcomputer scene, one thing quickly becomes apparent there is no equivalent of the mainframe manufacturer. The processor is made by the chip maker, peripherals are made by a variety of other manufacturers, and they are eventually put together by systems builders to become the end product.

The suppliers to the end-user usually fall into three broad categories:

1.   High-street computer shops

2.   Hardware manufacturers and suppliers

3.   Software houses and consultancies

Many of the suppliers are newly formed companies and are relatively small in terms of staffing levels. In deciding on a list of suppliers, the major criteria should be:

1.   Can they offer a package to do the job?

2.   Will the available hardware be of sufficient size?

3.   Is local support available?

4.   Does it fall into an acceptable price band?

Having decided on four or five suitable candidates, these should be invited to submit tenders.

3. Seeking Expert Advice

Many companies do not feel that they are sufficiently well- informed about computers to make all these decisions on their own. In these cases they are advised to consider the opinion of some of the computer consultancy firms or professionals.

4. Evaluating the Tenders

Generally speaking the tenders received will be fairly brief, comprising only few pages. In some cases they will be little more than a price list.

Have a look at the packages running on a similar system and make sure that they can handle the intended work in a satisfactory way. Discuss support arrangements and have a word with one or two local users to get their impression of the suppliers.

Finally, sit down and carry out a detailed evaluation exercise. The areas to be considered are:

1. Hardware characteristics and constraints. What are the limits on the size of the applications, how many VDUs (Visual Display Units) can be supported without affecting the response time, how much backing store can be handled, etc.

2. Software characteristics. How flexible is it, is it portable, what language is it written in, is it reliable and easily maintainable?

3. Documentation. What documentation is available and how good is it?

4. Technical support. How much, if any, installation support is included in the price, is training available and at what cost, are updates to packages automatically distributed to users, is there an error-reporting service, how many staff work full-time on support, where are they located?

Draw up a list of evaluation points and weight them according to their importance. Finally, score each proposal being considered against these points and arrive at a total weighted score for each. Divide by the five-year costs to arrive at a performance/price ratio. The proposal with the highest score represents the best value for money.

5. Terms and Conditions

Having selected a supplier the contract should be examined in great detail before signing. Professional advice should be sought by the buyer on any points which are unclear. Many companies are prepared to negotiate contractual terms, but some are not.

Deciding which microcomputer to buy can be an uphill task. Many factors have to be taken into consideration before one decides on a particular brand and model. The following procedure can be adopted for making the right choice:

1. The first thing you need to know is why you want a microcomputer. You may need if for keeping a record of the money you spend or for playing games. Make a list of reasons. This will indicate the applications for which you require the machine.

2. Check out the software available for these applications. A wide variety of software can be obtained from the computer vendors for different applications lik: business, home, education and science.

3. Find the systems which have the software support to fulfill your requirements. There are many systems offered in the market for almost all types of applications.

4. Short-list the systems according to your budget.

5. Study the hardware configuration of these systems. While doing this, the following points must be kept in mind:

   a) It is very important to know the type of microprocessor installed in the system and its clock speed as systems with faster clock speeds have a larger memory, which is always an asset, and greater processing power

   b) A system with more expansion slots is a better bargain because it can be upgraded at a later date, if required.

   c) If you intend learning some computer languages, a disk-based system would be more suitable for you in which the systems software for the languages can be loaded form the disk into the main memory. Buying a floppy works out to be cheaper than getting a language ROM installed.

   d) The Operating System that the machine uses should be a popular one as its success is directly related to the software availability for it.

6. Make another list after taking the hardware of the machines into consideration.

7. Keeping in mind the guarantee period offered by the systems and the software packages included in its price, decide on one machine.

8. Many computer shops and retailers have recently come up which stock and sell various models of microcomputers, software packages and other computer accessories. But you must always ensure yourself good after- sale service and terms, instead of being lured by the sale price alone.

MICROCOMPUTER SYSTEM SELECTION CHECKLIST

VENDOR DATA

Local Office:
Name: _____
Address: _____
Functions performed (sales, repair, etc.): _____
Headquarters:
Name: _____
Address: _____
Number of years in business? _____

Total number of systems installed? _____
Total number of similar systems installed? _____

Location of Current System Users:

Person to Contact	Corporate Name	Address	Telephone
_____	_____	_____	_____
_____	_____	_____	_____
_____	_____	_____	_____

Questions to ask references:
    Is vendor pleasant to deal with? _____
    Does vendor have a good record of resolving problems? _____
    How quickly? _____
    Does vendor meet commitments? _____

Vendor's Control Over Product:
    Specify product related functions performed by vendor:
        Design _____
        Manufacture _____
        Inspect _____
        Test _____
        Recondition _____
        Other _____

Is product subject to functions performed by other firms,

Function	Firm	Address
_____	_____	_____
_____	_____	_____

HARDWARE

Central Processor:
    Word size (bits)
    Main memory size (K bytes)
    Cycle time (microsec)
    Add time (microsec)
    Hardware multiply/divide?
    Manufacturer
    Model

Data Input/Output:

	Manufacturer	Speed
Magnetic disk	_____	_____
Magnetic cassette	_____	_____

Line printer _____

VDU _____ _____

Secondary Storage:

Disk capacity (K bytes)

Magnetic tape capacity (K bytes)

Installation Record:

Date first hardware system installed?

Number of hardware systems installed?

SOFTWARE

Operating System:

Name _____ Company _____

Main memory required (K bytes) _____

Secondary storage required (K bytes) _____

Type (Monitor, serial batch, multiprogramming, time sharing, or real-time): _____

Description of operating system: _____

_____

Language Software:

Assembler _____

Higher level language	Compiler	Interpreter
Pascal		
BASIC		
COBOL		
FORTRAN		
RPG		
C		
Other		

Description of each language: _____

_____

Utilities:

Editor _____

Sort _____

Merge _____

Other _____

APPLICATION PACKAGES

Title: _____

Company: _____

Description: _____

Number of installations? _____

Years in use? _____

Description of documentation:

    Programming _____

    User_ _____

Ease of modification? _____

Software maintenance available?_____ __ Location? _____

Hardware requirements:

    Main memory _____

    Secondary memory _____

    Other _____

Enhancement charges _____

Location of current users:

Person to contact Corporate Name Address Telephone

_____   _____   _____   _____
_____   _____   _____   _____
_____   _____   _____   _____
_____   _____   _____   _____

SYSTEM EXPANDABILITY

Maximum main memory? _____

Maximum number of disk drives? _____

Maximum number of terminals will support? _____

Application program run on other machines? _____

Maximum number of printers? _____

Total number of peripheral devices? _____

USER SUPPORT

Describe:

    System assistance _____

    _____ cost/hour_____

    Programming assistance _____ cost/hour_____

    Training courses _____ cost/hour_____

    Documentation _____

MAINTENANCE

Preventive _____ Periodicity _____
Emergency:
    Response time _____
    Hours available _____
    Location _____
Backup facilities:
    Type _____
    Location _____
Off-site repair facility:
    Location _____
    Turn around time _____

PRICING POLICY

Installation charge _____
Enhancement charges _____
Delivery guarantees _____
Purchase options _____
Acceptance period (days) _____
System price _____

APPENDIX C

APPENDIX C

COMPUTER VIRUSES

INTRODUCTION

Man is facing the ultimate truth. That his own creations can get back to him with as much vehemence as they were created with. A pointer to this hard fact is the latest phenomenon facing the computer world -- the deadly virus, that is causing havoc across international borders. Even India -- which is more often than not insulated from such vagaries of technology -- has not been left untouched. The pernicious virus is happy destroying all the high technological citadels created by man the worldover.

As incidence of viral infection increases, from larger cities to smaller towns, the necessity to gear ups to face the onslaught becomes imperative. What started as fun many years ago in AT&T's Bell Laboratories, in the form of a bizarre after-work rollick, has now started taking its toll.

That the computer virus has created international headlines goes without saving. As it multiplies, the virus leaves behind helpless despair, gobbling up database after database and crippling hundreds of computers. Since its outbreak in the US early 1988 - when suddenly it appeared in the computers of sensitive organizations like Pentagon and NASA -- many more strains of virus have been discovered. And experts believe the worst is yet to come.

Virus in reference to computers was first used by David Gerrold in his book "When Harlie was One" in 1972. He named a computer program as 'virus' which rang telephone numbers randomly until it found another computer linked to the network. In 1975, John Brunner used the term 'worm' in his novel "The Shockwave Rider". He imagined tapeworm programs that threaded their way through the computers altering records and processes which exercised social control.

A computer works by executing sets of consecutive instructions called programs. A simple program which is physically part of machine is executed when the computer is switched on. If there are no major problems with any part of hardware, the bootstrap program is loaded into the memory. This program resides in the first sector of the hard drive if the machine can boot from hard disc. Even if the computer has a hard disc and boots from hard disc directly, it can also be booted from a floppy disc which has the necessary data and files.

The operating takes care of running other software dealing with peripherals like printers, discs etc. Each computer will have its own files, set of instructions programs, storage devices and operating systems. Many computers can be interconnected to send messages from one to another, share programs and data files etc. Various makes of computers can be connected to a network if they are compatible with each other.

The operating system should provide protection against virus. Some software vendors do provide protection from virus, but it is the user who should ultimately deal with it. The user should detect and stop the virus from spreading. If virus is found on any of the PCs, that PC should immediately be isolated. The virus can be removed by giving an antidote after studying the virus. The machine should be put into use only after the virus is eliminated.

Computer viruses, like their biological counterparts, generally trick hosts or other types of computers into reproducing copies of the invading organism. They spread from computer to computer through electronic bulletin boards, telecommunication systems, and shared floppy disks. Viruses are created by humane programmers, for fun or malice, but once they begin to spread they take on a life of their own, creating disruption, dismay, and paranoia in their wake.

The discussions here attempts to explain a little about the terminology used, some types of viruses found and some hints to avoid virus attacks.

VIRUS

Virus is defined as a program inserted into another program. It gets activated by its host program. It replicates itself and spreads to others through floppy transfer. A virus infects data or program everytime the user runs the infected program and the virus takes advantages and replicates itself.

Two types of viruses have been identified. They are 'parasitic' and 'boot' virus.

Parasitic virus attaches itself to other programs and is activated when the host program is executed. It tries to get attached to more programs so that chances of getting activated is more. It spreads to other computers when the affected programs are copied. Jerusalem and Datacrime are considered as parasitic viruses.

Boot virus is designed to enter the boot sector of a floppy disc. It works by replacing the first sector on the disc with part of itself. It hides the rest of itself elsewhere on the disc, with a copy of the first sector. The virus is loaded by the built-in program when the machine is switched on. The virus loads, installs, hides the rest of itself and then loads the original program. On a hard disc, virus can occupy DOS boot sector or master boot sector.

SOME REPORTED VIRUSES

C-Brain. Amjad and Basit, two Pakistani brothers, developed this software in January 1986 to discourage people from buying illegal software at throwaway prices. This was the most famous virus ever found and has a record of damaging few millions of personal computers. This is designed to stay in the boot sector of the disc or near zero sector. The virus enters the machine memory once the PC is booted with the infected floppy.

C-Brain is designed to get linked to the input-output controller. It gets activated after a random number of interrupts are executed and quickly copies itself into unaffected discs. It corrupts the FAT (file allocation table) making the data available in the disc unreadable. The virus makes its presence felt by displaying a C-Brain message on the screen which is seen if disc information can be read using Norton Utilities or, any other program. C-Brain operates only in the zero sector and displaces the boot record and copies it elsewhere. An antidote can be written to locate boot record and put it back in place.

First sighted during the fall of 1987 at the University of Delaware. The virus changes the volume label (the name you give it) of a floppy or hard disk to (C) Brain. The boot record contains a message: "welcome to the dungeon ... Beware of this VIRUS. Contact us for vaccination." The message includes an address and phone number of Brain Computer Services, a computer company in Lahore, Pakistan, and the names of two brothers, Basit and Amjad. The virus marks some disk sectors as bad. It modifies several command files, may be all of them eventually, without changing file sizes or dates. Even it the boot sector is rewritten, the virus remains active through the command file it modified. This is the first virus to infect an American newspaper's computer system (The Providence Journal-Bulletin). When the phone number in Pakistan was called, the person who answered expressed surprise that the virus had travelled so far -- and refused to give his last name.

Macmag. This virus attacked Apple Macintosh computers only. Not much damage is reported because of this virus. This was not noticed on any IBM or compatible PCs. It displayed a message of peace on the monitor and killed itself. More data is not available on this virus.

First sighted by Chris Borton on March 8, 1988, and first mentioned in print in the Toronto Star on March 16, 1988. The virus was launched in December, 1987 by Richard Brandow, publisher of Macmaq magazine, in Montreal, Canada. The virus was designed to pop up a message of peace on Macintosh screens on March 2, the anniversary of the introduction of the Apple Macintosh SE and Macintosh II. After March 2, the virus erased itself. Although this virus was designed to be benign, it had some nasty side effects: it played havoc with users' system folders, resulting in thousands of hours of lost work. The virus spread to Europe and the west coast and it is the first virus to infect a commercial personal computer product. It was inadvertently passed to Aldus by Marc Canter, President of MacroMind Inc. of Chicago. Mr. Canter's personal machine caught the virus, which was transferred to training software he was writing for Aldus. Aldus admits that the infected disk was copied for three days. Half of the infected disks were distributed to retailers: the other half are in Aldus's warehouse.

Scores. This virus also was found only on Apple Macintosh computers. This virus was first found in March 1987. It affected mainly two programs within Electronic Data Systems Corp. Not much data is available on this virus also.

First sighting mentioned in MacWeek, April 12, 1988. It infiltrated several government agencies, Apple Sales Officers, and the Macintosh of an unidentified senator, as well as computer magazines MacWorld and Macintosh Today. This virus has several time-delay features. It's designed to attach two custom applications called ERIC and VULT, but it will infect anything. Several days after infecting a Mac system, the virus attempts to locate and modify any files with the creator code of ERIC or VULT. The code of the virus is written to make the targeted program disfunctional. The virus lies dormant for two days after infection. After two, four, and seven days various parts wake up and begin their mischief.

Two days after the initial infection the virus begins to spread to other applications. After four days the second part of the virus wakes up. It begins to watch for the VULT and ERIC applications. Whenever VULT or ERIC is run, the system fails after 25 minutes' use. After seven days the third part of the virus kicks in. Whenever VULT is run the virus waits 15 minutes, then causes any attempt to write a disk file to fail. Deleting the infected resources isn't enough to remove the virus, since the virus recognizes the attempt and modifies its resources identification and memory location when probed by resource utilities. A command, ResEdit, "thinks" that the virus's resources have been deleted, but they have been renamed and will return when the Mac is restarted. Apparently, the virus doesn't attempt to spread itself over networks. The Scores virus causes printing problems, system crashes, application crashes on launch, and damage to Excel files.

Cascade. Cascade virus attacked IBM PCs and compatibles. The letters on the screen could be seen dropping vertically down to the bottom of screen after the virus picked them off in alphabetical order. This is a sort of parasitic virus. It attaches itself to other programs and gets activated when the host program is executed. It gets copied to other PCs when the programs are copied.

Jerusalem. Found in 1987 at Hebrew University, Jerusalem, this virus was designed to activate only on Friday, January 13 and delete all the files executed on that day. This infects COM and EXE files. This is similar to Cascade virus in that it is parasitic in nature. This virus attaches itself to COM and EXE files to damage the data.

Datacrime or Columbus or October the 13th virus. Datacrime virus is similar to Jerusalem and was programmed to attack on October 13, 1989. Track zero of computer hard disc is destroyed and the contents of discs are rendered unreadable. This virus enters COM and EXE files and damages the hard disc. An antidote called 'VChecker' was developed by the American Computer Society. Fortunately the virus was located in March 1989 itself and the damage reported after October 13 was minimal. The Royal National Institute for the Blind, UK was the worst hit and much data was reported to be lost.

Internet. Robert Morris Sr is an expert on security in the UNIX operating system and is also the chief scientist at the National Computer Security Centre, a branch of American government's National Security Agency. His son, Robert Tappan Morris Jr, a graduate student from Cornell University, New York has deposited a 'worm' into a large computer network called Internet in the USA. Internet is a super network connecting several networks round the world, including ones at NASA, American and Canadian Universities and two run by Pentagon. About 6000 computes were attacked on November 2, 1988. The Cornell University Commission investigating the internet worm infection has observed that the flaws in UNIX security discovered by Robert Morris Jr were exploited in creating the worm. It made many people aware of virus and Federal Laws are being modified to deal with the people involved in inventing and spreading virus or worm.

The worm entered the network apparently through SENDMAIL program which is designed to provide facility to interchange information. The disadvantages in SENDMAIL and DEBUG programs were cleverly exploited to deposit the worm. All arrays of characters and blocks of text were encrypted. This worm attacked mainly VAX computers and Sun 3 workstations on the network. Other computers like Pyramid, Cray, Gould and other types of Sun workstations were not attacked.

Patch COM. It attaches itself only to COM files so that the infected COM files do not function. The virus spreads to all COM files executed later.

Patch EXE. It is similar to Patch COM virus but affects only EXE files.

COM EXE. This attacks both COM and EXE files.

PC Stoned or Marijuana. This virus was found in Bangalore during October 1989. It resides in the boot sector of the infected floppy. When the PC is booted through the infected floppy, the virus enters the hard disc and some sectors of file allocation table (FAT) are damaged. Whenever the PC is booted from the hard disc as usual the virus copies itself on to the boot sector of the floppy diskette in drive A and spreads to other PCs. This virus will not enter the hard disc unless the PC is booted through the infected floppy disc.

Bomb. This is also known as 'Logic Bomb' and 'Time Bomb'. An event triggered routine in a program that causes a program to crash is defined as a 'bomb'. Generally, 'bomb' is a software inserted in a program by a person working in the company. Any frustrated programmer can create a program to delete all the company files if he gets an indication that he may be sacked or transferred elsewhere.

ARPAnet Data Virus. On October 27, 1980 multiple "status" messages began appearing on the ARPAnet. Status messages are normally broadcast from each node of the network to relay its readiness to handle new data. Each node then propagates copies of incoming status messages to other nodes in an ongoing determination of the optimal path for the electronic traffic. Status messages are supposed to be deleted immediately afterward, but in this case the message from a particular node somewhere near Los Angles became mutated. Its contaminated form caused a "garbage collector" malfunction in the receiving nodes. No messages could be thrown out, thus saturating the nodes. Yet the nodes continued to propagate waves of the debilitating message, infecting others which could not dump the message, until it spread throughout the whole network like cancer and ground it to a halt. It was 72 hours before technicians could revive it.

Bell Labs Virus. A compiler program (which translates a programmer's instructions into numbers that a computer can read) had been altered so that it embedded a hidden "trapdoor" each time it created a new version of the operating system. The trapdoor altered the systems so that, in addition to normal users passwords, it would recognize a secret password known only to one person. The instructions never showed up in the program listing -- they were undetectable through normal means. The virus never escaped Bell Labs.

Israeli Virus. First sighted by Yuval Rakavy, a student at Hebrew University, and first mentioned publicly in Maariv, one of Israel's daily newspapers, on January 8, 1988. The virus was designed to begin destroying files on May 13, and to slow computer response on the 13th of any month. What called attention to the virus was an error in the virus code itself, which caused it to mistake previously infected programs as uninfected. In error, it would add another copy of itself to the program. Some programs were infected as many as

400 times and the growth in size of the program was noticeable. This one was discovered before D-day, but it had infected home, university, and military computers before it was detected.

Lehigh Virus. First sighted on November 25, 1987 by Jeffrey Carpenter. It attached itself to a few lines of the operating system used on the IBM PCs that Lehigh University provides for student use. It is a corruption of a legitimate program, Command.COM, the basic boot-up file of MS-DOS and PC-DOS. The virus does not change the length of Command.COM, which makes it more difficult to detect. The virus destroys data on floppies and hard disks by writing zeros to the first thirty-two sectors of a disk, which erases the directory and makes the data unrecoverable. The virus waits until it has been copied four times before it wipes out the data on the disk on which it resides.

MacIn Virus. First known envounter by David Sector. This virus was written by a West German and posted to CompuServe in a HyperCard stack. It's a very simple virus, easily defeated -- just a few pages of Pascal and fifty lines of assembly code. The virus is disguised as a resource that inserts itself in a system trap handler (the place where the computer catches errors so they won't cause system crashes). The virus destroys hard disks and the applications that run on them.

Atari ST Virus. First dissected March 22, 1988 by Martin Minow. Once installed, this virus will copy itself onto every non-write- protected disk used. It tests an uninfected disk to see if it contains the virus, replicates, then it keeps count of how many times the disk is used after that. When a certain limit is reached, the virus writes random data across the central directory and file allocation tables -- which contain the map of the disk's unused sectors -- making the disk unusable. The virus then removes itself from the damaged disk. The current virus doesn't affect hard disks. This virus may survive a reset (a warm boot -- resetting the machine without turning it off).

TROJAN HORSE

'Trojan Horse' or 'Trojan' is a program that seems innocuous, but conceals another function. Generally, Trojan is contained in a part of program brought from outside the company. Trojan can be dangerous sometimes. The program appears to be a computor game, but while you enjoy the game, it may be happily formatting your hard disc. It is also used as a 'back door' or 'trap door' to sneak into the operating system's information. An example is a program that mimics the actions of the system log-in program. When an unsuspecting user logs in using this terminal, the program captures the password and other relevent information. Then it may indicate a failure of log-in and exit to the real log-in program. The user may successfully log into the system next time, but by that time Trojan has also got enough details to log into the system.

These parasites are bits of code slipped into an otherwise innocent program. Viruses replicate: Trojan horses do not. Some are written from scratch: some are adulterated copies of legitimate programs. Some Trojans erase or scramble data, and some just scramble or erase the file allocation table. Some begin destruction within minutes of infection, while others perform as legitimate software for weeks or months, then touch off a time bomb.

Some Trojans put up a screen message such as: "I'm deleting all your files." then proceed to do so. Some put up a similar screen message, but don't follow through. The more sophisticated Trojan horses delete themselves with their last line of programming. In other cases the Trojan isn't actually inserted directly into the program. Only a pointer is placed in the program, telling the system which program to run, and the horse is hidden elsewhere. Some typical programs are described below.

Notroj. This Trojan horse pretends to be a program that guards against Trojans. It's actually a time bomb that wipes out the hard disk after it's more than 70 percent full.

XmasCard Trojan. First known sighting was December 9, 1987. It was written as a prank by a West German student. This Trojan began in a European academic computer network (Bitnet) and jumped through electronic gateways to five continents and to the internal E-mail system of IBM. In the IBM internal E-mail system, a holiday message promised to draw a Christmas tree on the screen if someone would type the word "Christmas" on the computer. When they did, it drew a tree but it also sent a copy of itself to all of the other network mail addresses kept in each user's electronic rolodex. Along with a very primitive tree (made of capital X's), a message was displayed: "A very happy Christmas and my best wishes for the next year. Let this run and enjoy yourself. Browsing this file is no fun at all. Just type 'Christmas'."

Once opened, the program rarely accepted commands to stop. Operators who turned off their terminals to try to stop the Christmas message lost electronic mail or unfinished reports not saved in the computer. The Trojan infected so many machines that it brought IBM's global electronic mail network to a halt, disrupting the system for 72 hours. Plant officials were forced to turn off internal links between computer terminals and mainframe systems to purge the message. A virus was written to follow and destroy the Christmas Card Trojan and then self-destruct in mid-January. The Trojan was generally stamped out by December 14, 1987. The culprit was tracked down and barred from access to his system.

Run.me. This is a graphics program which plays the Star Spangled Banner and displays the American flag while it worms its way into the hard disk and erases the data on it.

WORMS

Worm is a self-propagating program that works its way through a system, often causing damage. It does not require a host program to activate it. Someone has to insert a worm directly into network of interconnected computers where messages can be sent from one to another and data files and programs exchanged. An example is a local area network where each computer has its own files, programs operating systems and hard discs.

The worm is generally written in a high level langauge such as 'C'. A special program in the system called compiler converts the language into a form that the machine on the network understands. Once the conversion is done, the program can be run only on a particular computer. For example, the Internet worm entered the system as a 'mail message'. The responding mail system compiled the message. Once compiled, it dialled out from the newly invaded host computer and copied itself into the new host computer, damaging 6000 computers in that network.

Essentially, worms are simple creatures: memory crunchers that rewrite themselves successively through the computer's memory. The programs on individual computers are the segments, which remain in communication with each other. Almost any program can be modified to incorporate the worm mechanism.

Xerox PARC Worm. In 1980, John Shock at the Xerox Palo Alto Research Centre (PARC) devised a worm which wriggled through large computer systems, looking for machines that were not being used and harnessing them to help solve a large problem. The worm could take over an entire system.

Existential Worm. A worm whose sole purpose is to stay alive. It runs no substantive application program. The Cookie Monster Worm at MIT was one such. It might display a screen message such as: "I'm a worm, kill me if you can!"

Alarm Clock Worm. A worm that reaches out through the network to an outgoing terminal (one equipped with a modem), and places wake-up calls to a list of users.

Gladiator Worms. Bill Buckley and James Hauser developed Core Wars, where the object is to write a worm program that can replicate itself faster than another worm program can eat it. The one alive at the end wins. Some of the winning programs have a chromosome consisting of only four lines of code. Longer genes can't execute as fast as short ones, so they tend to get weeded out.

Worm Watcher. A special program which automatically takes steps to limit the size of a worm, or shut it down if it grows beyond a certain limit. The worm watcher also maintains a running log recording changes in the state of individual segments. This information can be used to analyze what might have gone wrong with a worm.

ANTIDOTES

It is generally observed that most of the viruses attach themselves mainly to either COM or EXE files or both. Instructions are given to all users not to copy-in or copy-out COM and EXE files. All the original COM and EXE files should be kept on a write-protected floppy as back-up. Whenever these files are required to be copied, they should be copied only from this write-protected floppy.

One can develop programs to save the system area of each disc and to keep the latest image of the system area and another program to check the present system area with the old image of system area. Whenever partition information is changed, the system should be checked for presence of virus and only if it is uninfected, the system image can be saved. The program should indicate the presence of virus in case system area is corrupted. This kind of program helps to check 'boot virus' which affects the system area but other viruses are not checked.

A program called 'Antidote' is available to check the infected COM and EXE files. This program checks only parasitic viruses and cannot locate boot virus. Hence it is required to run both the programs for a complete checkup.

ABORTING THE VIRAL ATTACK

The spate of 'viruses' in major computer installations the world over has provoked serious research into the problem. As a result several vaccines, both general purpose and specific, have been developed. So called computer virus programs have effected many countries. The implications of a viral assualt on an installation are more alarming than anyone cares to acknowledge. It is imperative to understand and seriously view the threat posed by these programs.

A computer virus is a modern-day version of a Trojan horse. Initially, a virus slips covertly into a site. For example, an unsuspecting user might obtain a program for a computer game, such as golf, from a friend. As the program begins, the user watches the fantastic graphics and happily starts to play, completely unaware that the program is infected with a computer virus. While that user is teeing off on the third green, the virus has already embedded itself in many other programs.

The subtlety of some virus programs is that infected programs appear to operate normally: they do not stop and print. "Oh, I feel sick." The user's trusted copy of Lotus 1-2-3 may now actually contain an embedded copy of the virus. Every time Lotus 1-2-3 is executed, the virus may continue to spread, while the user unsuspectingly adds rows and columns.

So, the virus moves along silently, affecting program after program, user after user, and yet no one is aware that the virus exists. Unfortunately, many people use more than one computer: and, to make matters worse, some users have unrestricted privileges to certain computer systems. When a privileged user runs an infected program, the virus has unlimited access to that computer system and the system is at the mercy of the virus's author.

The last aspect of a virus is the most disturbing; now that it has successfully infiltrated a computer system, what is its real purpose? The imagination alone defines the limit on what the virus can do to the operation of a company.

Users must be on guard. They must establish a strong, healthy dose of caution when executing software obtained from a friend or a bulletin-board service. In just a few seconds a virus can corrupt data programs, take selective actions based on privileged settings, determine accessible networked systems and access them using proxy log-ins.

When first executing an unknown program, be observant. Take the time to note the program's execution, whether on a personal computer or any other computer system, to determine that it makes sense and is consistent with expectations. Cautiously test and observe the software, mentally. See that the resources used by the program are logical and reasonable. A golf program probably should not attempt to access network resources or spawn sub-processes.

If one is using a central computer, it is critical never to execute programs with privileges enabled unless one is absolutely certain of the operation of the particular program. A program can easily perform a task until it detects that it has been invoked by a privileged user, at which point it performs differently. A lapse in this area can fully compromise a system.

Operators, programmers, systems administrators and any other privileged users must recognize the potential danger of using privileges too often. Users should get into the habit of enabling privileges only when necessary and then immediately disabling them. To simplify the process, systems managers should define a command to enable specific privileges -- only the ones needed, rather than all -- and a command to disable them.

If using a personal computer, initially try to install or execute the program from a floppy disk and select the floppy as the current drive before executing the software. If the disk light flashes and the program was not expected to access other disks, be careful. The light may have identified a virus being installed unexpectedly. The light, however, may be seen too late: before proceeding, one should determine why the program accessed the other disk.

Another precaution is to read the program into a text editor and search for certain key words that virus authors apparently love to incorporate into their programs. For example, check for words like 'virus', 'infected', 'infection' and so on. A phrase like, "You've been infected". may be found.

Precaution must be taken by all users at a site, not just by a handful of users. One person's carelessness can be enough to infect an entire environment. None of these precautions guarantees safety from viruses, but increased awareness will make a site less likely to suffer.

When product-tampering problems threatened consumers at the retail level in Australia, drug manufacturers there redesigned their packaging to make it easier to detect tampered products. Manufacturers could not guarantee that no one would tamper with the product -- just that it would be easier to detect tampering.

In a similar manner, the software industry should be expected to toughen its packaging and to incorporate methods into software products that will help identify -- but not prevent -- tampering. While these techniques will not identify every possible virus assualt, they could add an extra level of protection.

For example, a checksum-oriented technique could be incorporated into each software company's application. At start-up, or periodically during a program's execution the application could compare the consistency of the disk image of the company's program with some known value to determine if the image had unexpectedly been modified. If an image was discovered to be inconsistent, an error/waring message could be printed to alert the user.

Other methods can be imagined that would make the operation of a virus more difficult. Software companies should spend some time in research and development creating these antivirus techniques.

Although the odds of being infected by a computer virus are small, the effects are enormous. Common-sense procedures and precautions, combined with some logical programming techniques, can help secure a site from this type of threat.

SOME HINTS

Here are some hints to avoid virus infection in PCs:

1.   Never allow floppy discs brought from outside your company to be used directly on PC without checking the floppy for virus presence. This includes service engineers and their floppy discs for maintenance.

2.   Keep all original EXE and COM files in a write-protected floppy.

3.   If COM and EXE files are required to be copied anywhere, copy only from write-protected original floppy.

4.   In case the system is 'hanging' (or floating), the reason could be virus. Check for virus.

5.   Avoid playing computer games on a computer where important data is stored as it is generally noticed that the virus spreads faster through game floppies.

6.   Check sector information as a routine by modifying AUTOEXEC.BAT and using virus check programs.

7.   If virus is found on a PC, isolate it, identify and remove the virus. Only then should the PC be put into use again.

WHAT THE VIRUS DOES AND HOW?

A small program of 3.5K-bytes, the C-Brain virus resides in what is known as the zero or boot sector of a disk. The innermost circle of a disk, the sector in which the virus resides, contains the boot record or boot cluster. The boot record contains information called the boot strap which directs the ROM BIOS to load a DOS. When a computer is switched on, the ROM BIOS chip undergoes a configuration and environment self test to ensure that all components are functional.

The final instruction in ROM is to search for any kind of DOS such as PC-DOS, MS-DOS etc. This causes the BIOS to search for and read the boot. The BIOS is not aware that a program has been loaded into memory, resulting in the DOS getting loaded below the virus. DOS, once loaded, goes through its own configuration check where the virus captures control and informs it that the present memory available is 7000 characters less than that available on the hardware. The virus is now completely isolated from DOS and since it resides above it in memory, it can intercept any request made by DOS, thereby ensuring that any I/O operation is intercepted and the virus is copied onto the destination disk.

When a fresh floppy enters the system, DOS comands the BIOS to do some I/O operations on the disk. The virus intercepts this command, multiplies itself on to the fresh disk and only then allows the original instruction to the BIOS. Once resident on the computer, the virus multiplies itself to every disk it comes in contact with Since DOS does not recognize the virus, this location in the memory is unknown to the user.

Though the virus is generally not known to attach disks, some people claim that it does so. On a disk the virus keeps the directory copy safely hidden for a certain count of operations (developers of vaccine claim that the number of operations required to activate the virus is 49). During this time the disk functions normally. The computer doesn't realize that the directory area on the disk contains the virus since whenever directory information is required, the virus forwards the hidden copy.

Finally, the virus deletes the directory information, thereby destroying any link between the computer and the data on the disk. At this stage, there is almost no chance of retrieving the data in its original form.

FILE INFECTORS

File infectors work by inserting themselves into executable files. Where the virus inserts itself in the targeted files is of no immediate consequence, but it must make certain the virus code will be executed, or else it is to no avail. This can be done in two ways. The first is by writing all of the virus code to the start of the targeted file, where it will be executed immediately upon the file's execution. This is called a **file-overwriting virus**, because it overwrites the original file with a copy of itself, leaving the original file destroyed. The second is by writing the main body of virus code somewhere else in the targeted file (appended to the end usually, or sometimes written somewhere inside the targeted file) and then modifying the targeted file's start-up section to transfer control to the virus's main body. The start-up section can be either the first few bytes of the infected file or in the file header. This will not destroy the original file and is preferable (both to the virus and to the owner of the infected file) to the first method. Only executable files can be infected, as these are the only files wherein the virus can get its own code executed. Trying to infect a nonexecutable file is not an infection, simply plain stupidity. Naturally this severely decreases the options of the file infector- viruses, as it rules out all infection of data files, text files, document files, and so on. However, there are more executable file types than one often immediately recognizes as such. Of course, there are the standard DOS executables—EXE, COM, and BAT files—which can be directly executed at a DOS prompt, and these are also the simplest file types for a virus to infect. But besides them there are a number of other executable file types that cannot be directly executed from a DOS prompt but are executed as part of other programs—SYS (device drivers), OVL (overlay files), just to mention a few. These can also be successfully infected by a file-infecting virus.

DISK INFECTORS

Before digging into the workings of partition and boot infectors, a few facts on the computer's start-up procedure, called the *boot* procedure, are needed, along with some information on the structure of floppy and hard disks.

Boot

First we will examine the boot procedure. For the computer to do anything at all, it needs to execute some programs. When turned on, the computer starts executing some programs contained in the *read-only-memory (ROM)*. The ROM is permanently stored in the computer's chips and cannot be written to, changed, erased, or lost in any way, not even by a malicious virus. The ROM program first executed when the computer is turned on is called the ROM-BIOS *POST* (Power On Self-Test). In short, the POST performs some tests on the computer's hardware and memory, initializes the chips and standard equipment attached to the computer, and sets up the *interrupt vector table*. If all those actions show no faults, it then proceeds to load the operating system from the disk. The first part of DOS that must be loaded is the *boot record*. If a disk is inserted in the first floppy disk drive (A), the computer tries to load the boot record from the floppy disk. If no disk was inserted in the disk drive and a hard disk was initialized in the POST, it tries to load the boot record from the hard disk. Note that the order the drives are searches for the boot record can be changed in some newer PC computers, for example, from the A drive first and the C drive second (C drive being the hard disk) to the C drive first and the A drive after that. If the boot record was not successfully read from either the floppy disk or the hard disk, the computer displays an error message prompting the user to insert a system disk. If a boot-record program was found, it will be loaded into memory and executed. A normal, uninfected boot-sector program basically does only one thing. It checks the disk for the presence of two files, first the **IBMBIO.COM** (PC-DOS), or the **IO.SYS** (MS-DOS), and then the **IBMDOS.COM** (PC-DOS), or the **MSDOS.SYS** (MS-DOS). If both of these files are not found, an error message will be displayed, asking the user to insert a system disk. If they were both found, they will be loaded into memory and executed. There is more to the boot procedure, but we will not go into that here, as it has no influence on the way partition /boot-sector viruses perform.

All that happened in the boot up until the boot record was loaded was controlled forms the ROM program and took place before any program was loaded from disk. Because the ROM is read-only memory, it is beyond the reach of software to change, and so also beyond the reach of any virus. After all, a virus is just a regular piece of software doing slightly irregular things. It is once the partition/boot record is loaded that partition/boot-sector viruses come into action.

Disk

Now let's look at the disks. The operating system is not just read from anywhere on the disks. Some specific parts of the disks are reserved for different system-dependent programs to be stored on. We need to have a closer look at floppy disks and hard disks, which are the only disks targeted by DOS viruses—but by slightly different methods. All properly formatted disks are divided into a number of blocks of equal size (512 bytes), called *sectors*, and given a sector number from 0 to a maximum number depending on the size of the disk. The maximum number of sectors is equal to the size of the disk in kilobytes (1,012 bytes) times two, for example: a 1.44 MB 3½" floppy disk contains 2,880 sectors.

FLOPPY DISKS: The first sector on a floppy disk is reserved for the DOS system file, which handles the above-mentioned boot procedure; this first sector is also called the *boot sector*, and the program stored on it is called the *boot record*. The boot record is written to the boot sector by the DOS command **sys,** or alternatively by the DOS command **format/s**. This sector is reserved whether the disk is meant to contain DOS or not, and neither reading nor writing, nor even just viewing, is possible with normal DOS commands. The boot sector is outside the area normally under the control of a user. A special disk tool program must be used to view it. The rest of the disk is available to the user to store programs on.

HARD DISKS: When they first appeared, hard disks seemed able to contain such a massive amount of data that DOS had to provide for some way to make handling the data easier and more transparent for the user. For this, the ability for create several virtual disks on the same physical hard disk was added to DOS, where each virtual disk functions as a separate disk, thereby making the size of each virtual disk smaller than the whole physical hard disk. This is handled by the DOS command **fdisk**. Splitting up the disk into a number of subunits has the additional advantage of enabling the user to operate with several different operating systems, one for each virtual disk. The hard disk is also divided into a number of sectors, but now we must operate with *physical sectors* and *logical sectors*. The physical sectors go from 0 to the maximum number of sectors on the hard disk, the logical sectors from 0 to the maximum number of sectors on each virtual hard disk. Each virtual hard disk has the first logical sector reserved for a possible boot record. The first physical sector contains the *partition table/record* (alternatively called the *master boot record*); this sector is also called the *partition sector*. The partition record contains a small program, as well as some data on the composition of the hard disk. This data describes how many virtual disks (the maximum is four) the hard disk is split up into, the size of each virtual disk, and which virtual disk the operating system is to be started on (this virtual disk is called the *active partition*). If, at boot time, no disk was inserted in drive A, the program in the partition record is loaded and executed. This program first checks the validity of the partition table. If it finds an invalid entry in the partition table, the message "Invalid partition table" is displayed and the system stops. If no error in the partition table was detected, it proceeds to read and give control to the boot record from the active disk.

Partition Infectors

A partition-sector infector is a virus that infects the partition record on hard disks. In this it can be compared to the file infectors—they both infect an executable program. However, compared to the standard file infector, a partition infector has a problem. The partition sector only has room for 512 bytes, all of which is used by the partition program and data. There is not space for the virus to write its own code without overwriting some of the code or data needed for the partition program to perform correctly. An erroneous partition will result in the system stopping. Partition infectors solve this by taking a copy of the whole partition sector before infection, after which it overwrites the partition sector with its own virus code and then stores the original partition sector somewhere else on the disk. When the computer is booted from the hard disk, the virus code will be the first program executed. Typically, this code will at first do little else than install the virus in high memory, pretending to be a part of the DOS system—this is called going *resident*. From the resident state the virus will wait in silence, patiently plotting and scheming its further propagating. Here another problem arises for the partition-sector virus, because, as we have seen in the preceding section, only hard disks have a partition sector. A virus cannot spread from hard disk to hard disk—it needs a medium to carry it between the different hard disks. This medium is the floppy disk, which contains no partition sector. To be able to infect floppy disks as well as hard disks, the virus is forced to adopt an additional infection method; most often, a partition-sector virus can infect both the partition sector and the boot sector. A virus that combines two or more different infection methods is called a *multipartite* virus. Besides being an uncanny, robust virus (partition- sector viruses will not even be affected by a DOS format command) and invisible to all but the most determined users (it's not possible to look at the partition sector without a special disk tool), partition-sector viruses have an advantage not shared by the other virus types. Because the partition sector lies outside the disk that's occupied by the operating system, not being a part of the operating system proper, and because it's loaded and executed before the operating system has even been started, a virus occupying the partition sector will be untouched by the operating system. This means a partition sector will be able to perform and infect equally in all the different operating systems able to run on a PC-compatible computer.

Boot Infectors

A boot-sector virus interferes with the boot procedure, or rather adds a bit to it. All boot-sector viruses infect disks, both floppy and hard, by changing or replacing the boot-sector program with a copy of itself. This copy will then be run every time the computer is booted, turned on, or reset. Once run, it can proceed to infect other disks or programs attached to the computer. It is important to realize that the disk where the boot record is infected does not actually have to be a bootable disk. A boot-sector virus can infect the hard disk when booted from a floppy disk, even though the floppy disk contains no system files and the boot process is unsuccessful. An infected floppy disk forgotten in the disk drive at reset is how boot-sector viruses most often spread to a hard disk. If a computer is booted from the floppy disk drive, a virus infecting the floppy disk's boot sector can immediately proceed to infect the hard disk, or any other disks attached to the computer. However, if, as is most often the case, the computer is booted from the hard disk, and no other disk with a floppy disk inserted is attached to the computer, the virus has no place to spread itself at boot time. It will have to use a method of propagating that enables it to spread when at a later time a floppy disk is inserted in a disk drive. That is done, like the partition-sector virus, by going resident. From the resident state the virus keeps an eye on disk operations at all times, and if at some later time an operation on a floppy disk is detected, it can then infect it. Observe that a boot-sector virus and partition-sector virus can be viewed as a special case of file infectors that infect only boot-sector programs. Immediately one should think that boot-sector viruses are not very common, because their main way of propagating is forgotten floppy disks left in the disk drive. However, the boot-sector virus family is very successful, and it is estimated today that boot-sector viruses are behind some 50 percent of all infections.

COMPANION VIRUSES

In DOS a file name has a fixed length of at most 11 characters, 8 name characters and 3 extension characters, separated by a "." character (example: **command.com**). A specific executable file is referred to by a name part and an optional extension part. Executable programs can have only one of three extensions: COM, EXE, or BAT. Today EXE programs are the most common, and the COM extension is retained mostly for backward compatibility; BAT files are used solely for batch program files. If only the name part and no extension part is specified when a user enters a file to be executed on the command line, DOS looks first for a file with the same name part and a COM extension. If none is found it will then look for files with the EXE extension, and last for the BAT extension. If no matching file with either extension is found, this is repeated again in all the directories listed in the PATH (try the DOS command **path**). If there is still no match, DOS will output the error message "Bad command or filename." This calling procedure is what *companion viruses* takes advantage of. A companion virus searches out executable programs with the extensions EXE or BAT and makes a copy of its own virus code to a new file with the same name as those, but with the COM extension instead. This way the virus will be executed the next time a user tries to execute the legitimate, now infected file from the command line. It can then proceed to infect other files on the disk, in the same way. When done, it turns control over to the file the user intended to run in the first place. For example, if a user typed **digdug,** she might think **digdug.exe** or **digdug.bat** was started. Unfortunately, the system had already been infected, and a companion virus **digdug.com** had been copied to the same directory as the original digdug file. This virus would be called instead of the program the user intended. The virus, **digdug.com** could then locate another executable program on the disk and clone a new companion to it, and after that, run the program the user intended, digdug.exe or diggug.bat, so the user would notice nothing amiss.

At first glance this extension companion trick could look like a clever little method to create a replicating program, much easier to program than the other three virus types. Companion viruses have some severe disadvantages that greatly limit their spreading potential. First, this tend to spread only within a system, seldom to other systems. All viruses use floppy disks as transportation from computer to computer, going from one computer to a floppy disk, from that floppy disk to a new computer. But since the extension companion trick does not work when simply copying files, and few users execute files from floppy disks these days, a companion virus can have difficulties spreading beyond its current system. Apart from that, a companion virus is quite easy to spot both manually and automatically. If a disk contains a large number of executable files with the same name, but different extensions, chances are it has been infected. These can then simply be deleted, and the virus will have been removed from the system.

Besides the drawbacks already mentioned, there are some limitations the user should be aware of before entrusting his or here disks solely to an antivirus detection-by-appearance approach. To save disk space, programs are often stored in a compressed format. A considerable mount of disk space can be saved by using different compression utilities, and with the faster computers the time delay extracting them again is often insignificant. Consequently such disk-saving methods have gained much popularity in recent years. But compression involves some problems for the antivirus software. When compressed the internal code of the programs is changed, and consequently the scan strings of any possible virus are changed also. This will prevent an antivirus program from recognizing the scan string and thus detecting the virus. There are three basic ways to store data in a compressed format: disk compression, file compression, and executable file compression.

Disk compression compresses whole disks at a time. A small program to handle all the compress/extract routines is stored in memory. When a program is loaded from the compressed disk, it's extracted on the fly and stored in an expanded decompressed form in memory. Since the program is decompressed before the antivirus software accesses it, the scan strings will not be affected by this form of compression. Any antivirus program should be able to detect viruses stored on a disk compressed with a disk-compression utility. Two common disk-compression formats are Stacker and Double Space.

File-compression utilities compress single files at a time, and they compress both executable and nonexecutables. File compression is often the most efficient compression format when the smallest size is wanted. It is a much slower process both at compressing and extracting than the other two formats. Also, there is no automatic decompress routine. Before a compressed file can make sense, to you or the computer, it must be manually decompressed. Since the antivirus programs cannot perform this decompression, they will not be able to detect virus infections in programs stored in a compressed format. To scan such compressed programs, they must first be compressed and then scanned. Some common file-compression formats include Pkzip (compressed files with the extension .ZIP), Arj (compressed files with the extension .ARJ), and Lha (compressed files with the extension .LZH).

Of course, things get downright depressing from here on. The third compression format, *executable file compression*, referred to as EFC, works only on executable files. Most executable shipped with MS-DOS have been compressed with the executable compression format called the Exepack format. A program compressed with EFC is first compressed, and then a small amount of extraction code is added. When executed, the program will automatically be expanded into memory. The program can become infected in two ways, before it's compressed and after it's compressed. If it's infected after it's compressed, the virus itself will not be compressed and should be straightforward to detect by an antivirus tool. If the program becomes infected and then compressed, a scan-string search will not be able to locate the right virus data. Since the program will first decompress itself when executed, and scanners do not execute the programs they scan, a scanner will not see the program in the decompressed format. Some antivirus tools have tried to solve this problem, by first decompressing the EFC compressed programs in memory and then scanning them. However, here, as in most places in the PC world, anarchy reigns. Many different software houses offer different EFC tools, and there is no standard EFC format by which to compress/decompress. Some can scan inside some of the different EFC foremasts, but no scanner can scan inside all the EFC formats.

Another way to deal with this is, like the above file-compression scanning, first to manually decompress the program and then to scan it through. Besides being a time-demanding routine, this might not be a possible option, because, unlike the above file compression method, EFC-compressed programs do not need a separate decompress utility to work properly. If the user did not compress the program, but received it in a compressed format, he or she might not have the EFC tool to decompress it. Or alternatively, if a person wishing to spread a virus makes some small changes to the header that handles the decompress routine, the program may be able to expand itself, but the EFC program that compressed it in the first place will no longer be able to. If you think one of your programs has been infected in an EFC compression and you find yourself unable to decompress it, you will be unable to confirm your suspicion with a detection-by-appearance program. Some common EFCs are Pklite, Lzexe, Diet, Exepack, Tiny, and compact..

There are a number of ways a virus can try to elude being identified by scan strings. First, by reducing the size of any possible scan string, the virus can hope to make itself too small to be positively identified, to become indistinguishable from normal nonvirus programs. The obvious way to do that would simply be to reduce the size of the virus, thereby reducing the size of any unique code contained therein. But, as shown later, the smallest possible virus is 31 bytes long—a short but ample size for a positive scan string. So virus programmers must try to reduce the unique code is some other way. This is often accomplished by *self-encrypting*. The virus will choose a random key to encrypt with and will copy an encrypted version of itself to the target of its infection. The point is that because the outcome of the encrypted data can take many different shapes, it cannot be used as a scan string without first being decrypted. When you encrypt data, it produces some form of semirandom change to the original data; the more like random the change, the better the encryption. A virus does not have to care about good encryption techniques; all it needs is a few hundred different possible encrypted versions of its own code. This is easily decoded by a human, but if all files on a disk should be decrypted by an antivirus program, it would slow the process of scanning the disk to an unacceptable crawl. Encrypting gives the additional advantage, from the virus point of view, of making the debug process harder for the programmer of antivirus software, thereby making the production of antivirus software a more lengthy and costly process, which will give the virus more time to spread before antivirus programs become updated to include it. The process of making viruses harder to debug is called *armor* and will be dealt with later. Fortunately, not all of the viruses can be encrypted. It must be able to decrypt itself when run, and this decrypting routine can not be copied in encrypted form. Most viruses using self-encrypting can be detected using the virus's own decrypting routine as a scan string.

The natural next step for the virus would be to make it harder for antivirus programs to use the decrypting routine as a scan string. Again, the obvious way to do that would be to reduce the size of the decrypting routine. But even the smallest decrypting routine can still be used as a scan string. This leads up to *polymorphing*, which is the process of using multiple decrypting and encrypting routines, or multiple decrypting routines and just a single encrypting routine. Because only the decrypting part is visible, or useful, to an antivirus program, every different decrypting routine shows itself as a new virus when in fact it's just one virus shown different facts of itself—hence the Latin name "polymorphing" (*poly* = many, *morph* = face; many-faced). There is no way antivirus programs can adopt a single general scan string for several decrypting routines. This forces the antivirus program to treat the virus as many different viruses and to have a scan string for each possible decrypting routine. Furthermore, detection programs using scan strings always have to "beware" that their scan strings do not match other nonvirus programs, which will produce irritating false positives. A false positive is when an antivirus program detects a virus where there is none. The more scan strings, the higher the chance of one also matching nonvirus programs. The positive aspect is that polymorphing viruses often makes big viruses, thereby making it easier to detect them by other means.

Another way to elude positive scan strings would be to make each new "daughter" infection of a "mother" virus a little bit differently from the "mother"virus itself and from other"daughter" infections. This process is called *self- mutating*. It is of course not possible to find any unique code to use as scan string inside a virus that constantly changes. Now, viruses are programmed in assembler language, a low-level, very basic programming languages. All things that are possible in other higher-level programming languages are possible, with a little more work, in assembler language, and some things not possible in other languages are possible in assembler. But if a virus was to make some random changes to itself, the new version would most likely not be functional. There are just too many ways random changes in assembler make a program non functional, compared to changes leaving the program still functional. A way must be found for the virus to create an altered version of itself, where the virus can control the changes to ensure they are all functional. That is solved quite simply, by making change that do not affect the net change of the program, that change how it performs, not what it performs. In assembler, as in most other programming languages, it is possible to create different code that does the same thing, but in different ways. The easy way to change a program without affecting the way it performs would be to add some random "noise" to the program. Interspace the original code with some new code that in fact does nothing at all. It is not possible to detect such self- mutating viruses using the standard scan string; a more sophisticated scan-string search must be made. An antivirus program could have a basic scan string on the virus, and then when reading the file it's checking for viruses, filter out the noise.

There are other, more subtile ways for a virus to mutate a daughter copy of itself. Changing the basic assembler instructions of the virus, with other instructions doing the same job, and/or changing the order the instructions are executed—changing whole parts of the virus—will render a straightforward scan-string search useless. One way to accomplish such a mutating virus could be by replacing an instruction setting a variable to zero (**mov ax, 0**) with an instruction subtracting the variable with itself (**sub ax, ax** - or **xor ax, ax;** and **ax, 0;** etc.). Both instructions set the variable to zero, but by different methods. This will change the virus's appearance and leave it still producing the same result. Any scan string containing the changed part will now not be able to detect it. To detect such a mutating virus, we need another, even more complex scan-string search. An antivirus program could have a scan string where each entry is a table containing all the different instructions the virus uses interchangeably. For a match to be made, the scan only has to match one instruction in the scan with one of a number of instruction in the table. A well-programmed self- mutating virus can mutate itself into millions and millions of changed "daughter" viruses, all different from each other. Making an antivirus program using a scan-string search approach on self-mutating viruses is difficult, but so is making a self-mutating virus.. The good part of all this is that all viruses can be detected even though not one program can be programmed to detect all viruses. The sad part is that the more complicated the scan-string search becomes, the easier it is to get faulty virus signs where there are no viruses, false positives. False positives have given many a computer user a couple of frenetic hours and can, if he or she tries to disinfect a virus that's not there at all, destroy the program that showed a false positive.

Heuristic detection is basically trying to do what cannot be done, and with surprisingly good results. It is a detection by appearance, but instead of looking for already known scan strings, *heuristic detection* looks for characteristics viruses often have. This has been known before as an AI-search (artificial intelligence search). That is not an appropriate term because heuristic detection uses no AI techniques. It does not try to "understand" the code it searches, rather it looks for typical ways viruses gets things done and for code snippets frequently used in viruses. The tricky part (yes, there is always a tricky part) is the many different ways to program the same code. It cannot expect to find the same string of instructions in many different viruses. The code it looks for cannot be in a fixed order, as in scan strings, because this would be too easy to elude. It cannot even expect to find the same instructions reused in various orders, because as we have seen, there are many instructions for doing the same job. It must use a method very much like the scan-string search for self-mutating viruses. If it were only for these difficulties, we might still have a pretty good antivirus program. But as we have already discussed, there are a number of difficulties looking for typical virus code. Basically, there need not be any typical virus code in a virus. It's only slightly harder to program a virus not containing any code that could be called typical for viruses, such as code not also used in numerous other programs. However, because there need not be any typical virus code in a virus does not mean many viruses do not look alike. Many virus programmers are simply too lazy to make their own unique virus code, so they copy it from other viruses. This can be exploited by the antivirus program. Heuristic detection should be used when you suspect you have been infected but a normal scan-string search comes up with nothing.

VIRUS DETECTION BY BEHAVIOR

For a virus to propagate, it needs to preform a number of specific actions, such as reading directory entries, opening files, writing to files, etc. Most of these actions are performed all the time by the system itself and other programs alike, although a few would not be performed under ordinary conditions. *Detection by behavior* entails monitoring the system, to watch out for such dubious action. A dubious action could be opening (reading) a COM or EXE file in write mode, as one would not expect executable files to be modified. BIOS and DOS comes with a large number of built-in functions, ranging from reading files to formatting disks. All these are needed for the system to function properly and are used by both internal and external system commands, such as **dir** and **xcopy**. However, these functions are not restricted for only the system to use; many programs, both virus and nonvirus, use them too. A BIOS/DOS function can be run using the assembler command interrupt (mnemonic: int). Interrupt looks in a table (called the interrupt vector table) containing and addresses of all the different functions to see where the function requested in located and then resumes executing at the address pointed to. It is possible to change the address contained in this table, thereby redirecting the interrupt function to another address (to one's own program). That is called *hooking* the interrupt vector and is how antivirus programs snoop on the system to see if something suspect is going on. Say you had a vile virus on your computer, which will format your hard disk every Sunday. You install and run an antivirus snooper. Come Sunday, the virus will call the DOS interrupt function **format** (ACK!), but luckily the antivirus snooper had hooked the interrupt to a part of its own code. This code would then be run instead of the DOS format function and could write out "a format function had been requested" and ask if you wanted to proceed with the format. "No" would abort the format process and save your hard disk. This is an active virus defense, because it can detect, and stop, virus infections before they occur (catch the virus in the act, so to speak), while detection by appearance and detection by change are defensive and can only detect infections after they have already taken place. In addition to being able to detect actions related to the virus's spreading, detection by behavior can also be used to tect and stop action relating to other, secondary, aspects of the virus—the payloads. As has already been discussed, a virus payload is a part of the virus designated to other purposes than the main virus purpose of propagating. These can range from harmless, but annoying announcements to total destruction of all data on a disk medium. The format example is an example of such a detection. Beside the apparent good points provided by detection by behavior, it has some severe shortcomings that make it, at best, a second virus scanner. It must be resident in normal memory, not extended/ expanded memory, memory often desperately needed for other programs. Furthermore, it will slow down program executing a bit, not much, but discernible on a slow machine. And not all programs, even should they be clean, may be able to function properly with such a program resident in memory.

Using BIOS / DOS interrupts is an easier way to do things, but by no means the only way. A virus that has its own functions and uses them instead of the BIOS / DOS functions, cannot be detected by hooking interrupt vectors, simply because it does not use them. Also, a virus that does not call BIOS / DOS functions by way of the interrupt vector table, but rather calls them directly (as **Anthrax**, by instructions **call, jmp**, or whatever), will circumvent a detection abased on interrupt hooking. With a small bit of extra work, all partition- and boot-sector viruses can easily adopt such an evasive strategy. There is no counter for a detection-by-behaviour program to these virus defenses, but at least it forces the viruses to adopt larger and more complicated ways to propagate itself, making them easier to spot in some of the other ways.

Moreover, a virus can include some code that checks the interrupt table. If it finds a hooked interrupt, it can simply unhook it, there by putting the detection by behaviour out of commission.

VIRUS DETECTION BY CHANGE

All viruses cause some change to the system in which they infect. Detection of this change is called, imagine that, *detection by change*. The change is almost always very easy to spot with normal DOS tools: increase in file length (use DOS command **dir** and a bit of arithmetic), decrease in memory (use **chkdsk** or **mem**), change of time/date stamp (use **dir**), etc. For you to detect any change, it is of course required you have the initial state, file length, respectively mem-size before infection, to compare with, which is not always possible. If you receive a disk from a friend or a commercial program, the size of the programs on the disk before any possible infection is not known. But even if you do not know if your system is virusfree (has the initial state), it is possible to detect any further virus spread, when the virus changes the size of other, until now clean, files. Sometimes it's not enough just to have the size of the file before infection. There is a group of simple viruses, file overwriting viruses, that just overwrite the targeted program with a copy of itself (therby destroying the original program). They cannot be detected by their file size increase since they do not necessarily increase it. To detect them, a little more complex method of detecting change must be performed. All computer code can be represented in numbers. By adding up all the code in a file, the result will with a very high probability be a unique number, representing just that file. That is called a *checksum*, and it can be used to compare a file before and after a possible infection. If the checksum of a file has changed, but the file size and date/time stamp are the same, the file has been changed. It is very easy for a virus to restore the date/time of a file to what they were before an infection, and only slightly harder to, at least seemingly, retain the original file size. It is, however, all but impossible to make a file produce the same checksum before and after an infection.

Keeping account of the file size, time/date, and checksums of all files on your system can be hard work. Fortunately, there are a number of antivirus programs that can help you do it. Typically, they must at a minimum be able to save the size of the program, the time/date of last update, the checksum on the file, and a copy of the partition and boot sector for partition-/boot-sector infectors, preferably in one separate file that can be backed up to another disk, this will ensure no virus tries to mess with it to hide its own presence. Today many programs come with their own checksum checker. When run these programs will performs a fast self-test to check for change, and if they find any, they will inform the user that the program has been modified. Warning! McAfee's antivirus package SCAN contains a program that performs a checksum on disks. It is implemented in a very unusual (read: lame) way, since it modifies all programs on the disk to contain such a self-checker. This will increase the file size of all the executable (EXE and COM) files, thereby messing up other antivirus programs' checksums and any possible self checksum checker. McAfee and associates should not mess with other people's files. But at least this method does not leave thousands of small checksum files lying around all over your hard disk, as many other checksum program do.

A checksum will not be able to detect a companion cirus on the disk, since the companion virus class does not modify the programs they infect. The only way to detect a companion is with a detection-by-appearance program.

One of the most common virus protection schemes is called *Stealth*, Stealth is when a crafty virus uses interrupt hooking to run some of its own code that performs according to the virus's wishes. There are numerous ways to use and implement stealth and can, when performed right, be a very cunning way for the virus to hide itself. It is, however, not a new thing. One ofd the earliest viruses, **Brain**, used some stealth techniques. Brain redirected a request to read the boot sector (now infected) to the original boot sector and thus showed no infection. This would fool an antivirus program using a scan-string search and a checksum search. Stealth is an active defense of the virus and requires that the virus have been run. As such it can easily be defeated using a know clean, uninfected, write-protected disk to boot your computer.

We have already stated the need for the uninfected initial state of the programs we want to keep check on. If a program has already been infected when a detection-by-change program first sees it, this infection will not be detected. This is taken advantage of by some viruses, such as **startship**. Startship only infects files in the process of being copied to or from a floppy disk, never files already on floppy or hard disks. The above virus-detection method will not be able to detect such infections, because the modifications of the infected programs occur before the antivirus program obtains the initial state of the infected files.

VIRUS DETECTION BY BAIT

There is one unusual virus-detection method not yet discussed: a program that offers itself as bait to any possible virus, and then at regular intervals checks itself to see if it has been modified. If it finds it has been changed, it might be infected. The self-check can be a simple checksum. The bait could consist of performing some actions that are often found very tempting to viruses. This is a very uncertain virus-detection method; most viruses would simply ignore it, or infect some other file. Sometimes it's worth its while to try, though.

Cleaning File Infectors

Cleaning out an infected file is always best done by restoring it form the original diskette or a previously taken backup. Unfortunately, this is not always possible—may be no original/backup exists, may be it is also infected—and it is always a very time-consuming and dull process restoring large amounts of data. This has given way for disinfecting programs that automatically remove viruses from infected programs/disks. Removing a virus from an infected program without knowing the infected program before infection can be very tricky and is possible only when the virus does not destroy any data belonging to the original program. First of all, it is necessary to know the exact identification of the virus. When the virus infects a program, if it is not of the overwriting kind—and thus not cleanable—it moves some of the data of the infected programs to new locations. To properly restore this moved data to the right location, the location after the virus infection must be known. Naturally, those locations differ from virus to virus, and trying to disinfect one virus with a disinfecting procedure meant for another virus will most likely not find the right data. This will result in lost data and, in the worst scenario, leave the virus still functional and the user thinking he or she has cleaned out all viruses. We have already seen that the only way to positively identify viruses is with can strings, and this is where the false identification of new/unknown virus strains and false positives become a problem. I will not go into the numerous ways viruses can try to elude cleaning, because before a disinfecting should even by considered the computer must be booted from an uninfected disk and the virus must be identified correctly. If this is not the case, the things can go wrong are numerous. On the other hand, if the virus has been identified correctly, the cleaning process can be very swift and easy, much preferable to manual restoration.

CLEANING PARTITION INFECTORS

Disinfecting a partition-sector infector is often more difficult than disinfecting a file infector. A faulty disinfect will not only cause the one program to be destroyed, but it will make the whole disk unbootable. The same rules go in partition-sector disinfecting as in file disinfecting. Boot from a clean disk, and make a positive virus identification. There are two different roads to take when disinfecting the partition sector. Restore the original partition record from wherever the virus infecting it put it. Or rebuild a new partition record and overwrite the virus-infected partition sector with it. When *restoring* the partition record, it is vital to have an exact identification of the virus, to know where it put the original partition record. When *rebuilding* the partition record, it is only necessary to know it is indeed a partition-sector virus; we do not need the original partition record, so a precise identification is not necessary. There are a number of commercial and shareware programs that can build the partition record, but if such is not available, there is also one DOS utility that can help. **Fdisk** called with the switch mbr (mbr = Master Boot Record = partition sector), **fdisk/mbr,** should do the job. This is not documented in the DOS manual, possibly because when used wrong it's likely to do more damage than good. Fdisk/mbr only rebuilds the partition record, it does not touch the boot record. If the boot record has been targeted by a virus, fdisk/mbr will not help you. (Note that fdisk/mbr was included in DOS 5.0; previous DOS versions will not be able to perform this service. A DOS version 5.0 or above will be able to clean out an infected disk formatted by a DOS version prior to DOS 5.0.)

Some people have advocated the rather drastic format disk as the correct answer to all virus infections. A format is supposed to wipe all data from the hard/floppy disk, thereby also removing the viruses. Talk of a cure that kills the patient. Besides being an unnecessary hard policy, restoring all the data on a hard disk takes time—lots, it's not even a foolproof method. Sure, it will remove all file infectors and boot infectors, but since the partition sector lies outside the area the format procedure can write to on the disk, outside the virtual disk, which is the only part the format will touch, partition-sector viruses will be completely unaffected by a format. If your hard disk has been infected by a partition-sector virus, and you do not have access either to a DOS v.5.0+, to another program that can rebuild your hard disk's partition sector, or to an antivirus program that promises disinfecting, and you cannot find the original partition sector on your hard disk, a partition-sector virus can still be removed by way of the old, pre-DOS 5.0 **fdisk** command. But since **fdisk** not only writes a new partition sector, but also wipes the whole physical disk all the smaller virtual disks you may have divided your hard disk into, clean of all data, this is reserved as a last stand.

CLEANING BOOT-SECTOR INFECTORS

Like disinfecting partition infectors, there are two ways to disinfect boot-sector viruses. Restore the original where the virus stored it, or rebuild a new one. To restore the original, a positive identification is needed; to rebuild, simply transfer a new DOS to the infected disk. The new DOS will overwrite the virus-infected boot sector and thus eradicate it. To transfer a new DOS, boot from a DOS diskette and type **sys [drive letter]:** (e.g., **sys** c:). And, as always, boot from a certified uninfected DOS diskette, and do not start any programs that might have been infected.

WHERE WILL IT ALL END?

Thus what makes the bug potentially dangerous is its ability to copy itself onto every unaffected disk, rather than what it does after this. It is only if the virus is not dected at all that any danger exists to the data on it. And this damager is increasing.

The most difficult part about the virus is bringing it under control. With the kind of rampant usage of pirated software that goes on, the C-Brain and Ashar viruses have already demonstrated how fast they can spread. And 40 years after the beginning of the computer era, when society has almost become dependent on high-speed information processing for its very sustenance, the computer world is threatened by an enemy from within — which on most occasions chooses to remain invisible.

The most important question that arises with the coming of the virus is that of information security. If we are to move into a century where information technology is to play a major role, we have got to be on our guard. One can well imagine a situation where the virus gets through the international finance and defense networks and wrecks the worst over havoc. It has already been prophesized by James Martin. Will it really happen?

ENCODING SCHEMES

ENCODING SCHEMES

RS-232-C Encoding

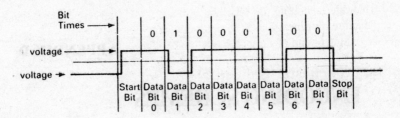

The technique most often used with low-speed data communication over an ordinary telecommunications channel is defined in a standard called *RS-232-C*, which is published by the Electronics Industry Association (EIA). With RS-232-C transmission, a negative voltage on the line for a bit time represents the value 1 and a positive voltage the value 0.

Zero-complemented Differential Encoding

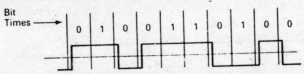

Many high-performance line control procedures, such as IBM's Synchronous Data Link Control (SDLC), often employ a more complex encoding scheme called *zero-complemented differential encoding to represent bit values. With this technique, a transition of the line from negative to positive or from positive to negative within a bit time indicates the value 0; the lack of transition during a bit time represents the value 1.*

Manchester Encoding

For electrical purposes, it is desirable in many local area network implementations that transitions from positive to negative and from negative to positive occur often with predicable regularity. *Manchester encoding* produces the desired number of transitions and is used in many local area network implementations. With a typical implementation of Manchester encoding, a negative voltage for the first half of the bit time followed by a positive voltage for the second half of the bit time represents the value 1; a positive voltage followed by a transition to a negative voltage represents the value 0. Thus with Manchester

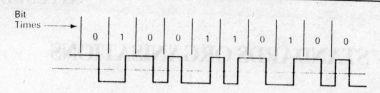

encoding, a transition from negative to positive or from positive to negative occurs *every* bit time.

With Manchester encoding, bit times in which the signal is held either positive or negative for the entire bit time are used to represent something other than a bit value, for example, the beginning or end of a transmission block.

Differential Manchester Encoding

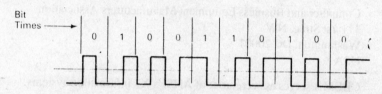

A form of Manchester encoding called *differential Manchester encoding* is used in some local area network implementations. With this technique, a transition occurs during each bit time, as with conventional Manchester encoding. However, the interpretation of the transition from positive to negative or from negative to positive depends on whether the previous bit time represented a 0 or 1. To represent the value 1, the polarity remains the same as it was at the end of the previous bit time and then changes in polarity at the midpoint of the bit time only. To represent the value 0, the polarity changes at the beginning of the bit time and also at the midpoint of the bit time. With this form of encoding, a change from positive to negative can represent either a 0 or a 1 depending on the state of the line at the end of the previous bit time. Whether a transition occurs or does not occur indicates the value. No transition at the beginning of the bit time indicates the value 1; a transition at the beginning of the bit time indicates the value 0.

As with conventional Manchester encoding, bit times in which no transition occurs at the midpoint of the bit time are often used for control purposes.

STANDARDS ORGANISATIONS

ANSI   American National Standards Institute
1430 Broadway
New York, NY 10018
USA

ANSI is the coordinating body for America's federated national standards system. The federation consists of 900 companies and some 200 trade, technical, professional, labour and consumer organisations.

CBEMA   Computer and Business Equipment Manufacturers Association
311 1st Stree, NW
Washington, DC 20001
USA

CBEMA serves as secretariat of ANSI's X3 information systems.

IEEE   Institute of Electrical and Electronics Engineers
245 East 47th Street
New York, NY 10017
USA

IEEE is a professional society for the advancement of theory and practice in associated fields. IEEE is a major force in the establishment of standards.

IEEE Computer Society
1109 Spring Stree, Suite 300
Silver Springs, MD 20910
USA

Deals with IEEE's Project 802 for development of local area network (LAN) standards.

NBS   National Bureau of Standards
Centre for Computer Systems Engineering
Systems and Network Group
Building 225, Room 226
Washington, DC 20234

NBS provides the basis for measurement standards of many kinds. The branch listed here is primarily concerned with data processing standards.

CCITT   Consultive Committee on International Tel. and Tel.
Place des Nations
1211 Geneva 20
Switzerland

A division of the International Telecommunication Union; involved with international standards.

IEC   International Electrotechinal Commission
1 Rue de Varembe
1211 Geneva 20
Switzerland

Coordinates the unification of international standards. Works with ISO.

ISO   International Organisation for Standards
1 Rue de Varembe
1211 Geneva 20
Switzerland

EIA   Electronic Industries Association
2001 Eye Street, NW
Washington, DC 20006
USA

An organisation of US manufacturers.

NUA   Network Users Association
Boeing Computer Services Company
Box 24346 M/S 7A-05
Seattle, WA 98124
USA

Active in the development and promotion of network standards.

ISO OSI STANDARDS DOCUMENTS

The following open systems interconnection standards documents are some of the most relevant to local area networks. They are available from the International Standards Oraganisation, General Secretariat, 1 Rue de Varembe, 1211 Geneva, Switzerland, or from the national standards organisations. The document number quoted is that of the service definition, with the corresponding protocol document number in parenthesis at the end of the entry. The following abbreviations are used:

ISO	Full International Standard
DIS	Draft International Standard
DP	Draft Proposal
ADD	Addendum

General

ISO 7498	Description of the Basic Reference Model for Open Systems Interconnection
DP 7498/3	Naming and Addressing
DP 9646	Conformance testing Methodology and Framework
DP 7498/4	Management Framework
DP 9595	Management Information Service (Protocol DP 9596)

Application layer

DP 9545	Application Layer Structure
DIS 8649	Common Application Service Elements (Protocol-DIS 8650)
DP 8751	File Transfer Access & Management
DP 8831	Job Transfer and Manipulation Service (Protocol-DP 8832)
DIS 9040	Virtual Terminal Basic Class Service (Protocol-DIS 9041)
DIS 8505	Functional Description and Service Specification for Message-Oriented Text Interchange Systems (MOTIS)
DIS 9065	MOTIS-Message Interchange Formats and Protocols
DIS 8883	MOTIS-Message Interchange Service and Message Transfer Protocol
ISO 7942	Graphical Kernel System (GKS)
DIS 8907	Network Database Language

Presentation layer

DIS 8822	Connection-Oriented Presentation Service (Protocol-DIS 8323)

Session layer

DIS 8326   Basic Connection-Oriented Session Service (Protocol-DIS 8327)

Transport layer

ISO 8072   Transport Service Definition
                         (ADD 1 Connectionless-Mode Transmission)
                         (Connection-Oriented Protocol-DIS 8073)
                         (Connectionless Mode Protocol-DIS 8602)

Network layer

ISO 8348   Network Service Definition
                         (ADD 1-Connectionless-Mode Transmission) (connectionless Mode
                         Protocol-DIS 8473)
                         (DAD 2-Network Layer Addressing)

DIS 8878   Use of X.25 to Provide the Connection-Mode Network Service.

DP 8880   Protocol combinations to Provide and Support the Network
                         Service

DIS 8881   Use of the X.25 Packet Level Protocol in ISO 8802 Local Area
                         Networks

Data link and MAC layers

DIS 8886   Data Link Service Definition
DIS 8802/2   Logical Link Layer
DIS 8802/3   Local Area Networks CSMA/CD
DIS 8802/4   Local Area Networks Token Passing Bus
DIS 8802/5   Local Area Networks Token Ring
DP 8802/6   Fibre Optic Slotted Ring.

ABBREVIATIONS AND ACRONYMS

A

AC	Alternating Current
ACK	Acknowledgement
ADD	ADDendum
AI	Artificial Intelligence
ALGOL	ALGOrithmic Language
ALU	Arithmetic and Logic Unit
AM	Amplitude Modulation
AMP	Active Monitor Present
ANS	American National Standard
ANSI	American National Standards Institute
API	Application Program Interface
APL	A Programming Language
APPC	Advanced Program to Program Communications
ARPANET	Advanced Research Project Agency Network
ASCII	American Standard Code for Information Interchange
ASK	Amplitude Shift Keying
ATM	Automatic Teller Machine
AT&T	American Telephone and Telegraph
AUI	Attachment Unit Interface
AWG	American Wire Guage

B

BASIC	Beginners All Purpose Symbolic Instruction Code
BBS	Bulletin Board Service
BCD	Binary Coded Decimal

BHCA	Busy Hour Call Attempts
BIOS	Basic Input Output System
BISYNC	Binary Sunchronous
BIT	Binary digit
BIU	Bus Interface Unit
BSI	British Standards Institution

C

CAD	Computer Aided Design
CAE	Computer Aided Engineering
CAI	Computer Aided Instruction
CAM	Computer Aided Manufacturing
CASE	Computer Aided Software Engineering
CATV	Community Antenna Television
CBX	Commuterised Branch Exchange
CCB	Coin Collection Box
CCITT	Consultative Committee on International Telegraphy and Telephony
CCT	Computer Compatible Tape
CCTV	Closed Circuit TV
CEN	European Committee for Standardisation
CENELEC	European Electrical Standards Co-ordinating Committee
CGA	Colour Graphics Adapter
CHILL	CCITT High Level Language
CI	Cluster Interface
CICS	Customer Information Control System
CLIP	Connectionless Internet Protocol
CLNS	Connectionless Network Service
CMOS	Complementary Metal Oxide Semiconductor
CNMA	Communications Network for Manufacturing Applications

COBOL	Common Business Oriented Language
CODEC	COder DECoder
COM	Computer Output Microfilm
CP/M	Computer Program for Microcomputer
CPS	Character Per Second
CPU	Central Processing Unit
CRC	Cyclic Redundancy Check
CRCC	Cyclic Redundancy Check Character
CRT	Cathode Ray Tube
CSMA	Carrier Sense Multiple Access
CSMA/CA	Carrier Sense Multiple Access/Collision Avoidance
CSMA/CD	Carrier Sense Multiple Access/Collision Detection

D

DAD	Draft Amendment Document
DARPA	Defense Advanced Research Projects Agency
DAT	Digital Audio Tape
DBMS	Data Base Management System
DC	Direct Current
DCE	Data Circuit-Terminating Equipment
DEC	Digital Equipment Corporation
DES	Data Encryption Standard
DIBI	Device Independent Backup Interface
DID	Direct Inward Dialling
DIS	Draft International Standard
DIU	Data Interface Unit
DIX	Digital Intel Xerox
DM	Disconnect Mode
DMA	Direct Memory Access

DNA	Digital Network Architecture
DOD US	Department of Defence
DOS	Disk Operating System
DOV	Data Over Voice
DP	Draft Proposal
DSAP	Destination Service Access Point
DSS	Digital Switching System
DTE	Data Terminal Equipment
DTMF	Dual Tone Multi Frequency

E

EBCDIC	Extended Binary Coded Decimal Interchange Code
ECMA	European Computer Manufacturers' Association
ECSA	Exchange Carriers Standards Association
EDI	Electronic Data Interchange
EDIFACT	Electronic Data Interchange For Administration, Commerce and Transport
EDP	Electronic Data Processing
EEC	European Economic Community (Common Market)
EFT	Electronic Fund Transfer
EGA	Enhanced Graphics Adapter
EISA	Extended Industry Standard Architecture
EMI	Electro-magnetic interference
ENIAC	Electronic Numerical Integrator and Calculator
EOF	End Of File
EOQ	Economic Order Quantity
EPROM	Erasable Programmable Read Only Memory

F

FAT	File Allocation Table

FAX	Facsimile System
FCS	Frame Check Sequence
FDDI	Fibre Distributed Data Interface
FDM	Frequency Division Multiplexing
FIFO	First-In First-Out
FM	Frequency Modulation
FNP	Front-End Network Processor
FORTRAN	FORmula TRANslator
FSK	Frequency Shift Keying
FTAM	File Transfer, Access, and Management
FTP	File Tranfer Protocol

G

GB	Giga Bytes
GHz	Giga Hertz
GIGO	Garbage In Garbage Out
GKS	Graphical Kernal System
GPIB	General Purpose Interface Bus
GUI	Graphical User Interface

H

HAM	Hybrid Access Method
HDLC	High-Level Data Link Control
HIPO	Hierarchy and Input/Processing/Output (diagram)
HSC	Hierarchical Storage Controllers
HSLN	High-Speed Local Network

I

| IBM | International Business Machines |

IC	Integrated Circuit
ICMP	Internet Control Message Protocol
IDE	Integrated Device Electronics
IEEE	Institute of Electrical and Electronics Engineers
IGES	Initial Graphics Exchange Specification. Standard-code for exchange of graphic data among various computer systems.
INTELSAT	International Telecommunications Satellite
I/O	Input/Output
IP	Internet Protocol
IPX	Internetwork Packet Exchange
ISA	Industry Standard Architecture
ISD	International Subscriber Dialling
ISDN	Integrated Services Digital Network
ISO	International Standards Organisation

L

LAN	Local Area Network
LBT	Listen Before Talk
LCC	Lost Calls Cleared
LCD	Lost Calls Delayed
LCD	Liquid Crystal Display
LDDI	Local Distributed Data Interface
LED	Light Emitting Diode
LIFO	Last-In Last-Out
LIM EMS	Lotus/Intel/Microsoft Expanded Memory Specification
LISP	List Processor
LLC	Logical Link Control
LRCC	Longitudinal Redundancy Check Character
LSI	Large Scale Integration
LU	Logical Unit
LWT	Listen While Talk

M

MAC	Medium Access Control
MAN	Metropolitan Area Network
MAP	Manufacturing Applications Protocol
MAU	Medium Access Unit
MAX	Main Automatic Exchange
Mb	Mega bits
MB	Mega Byte ·
Mbit/s	Mega-bits per second
MHS	Message Handling Service
MHz	Mega-Hertz
MICR	Magnetic Ink Character Recognition
MIPS	Million Instructions Per Second
MIS	Management Information System
MMFS	Manufacturing Message Format Standard
MML	Man-Machine Language
MMS	Manufacturing Message System
MODEM	Modulator-Demodulator
MOTIS	Message Oriented Text Interchange System
MS-DOS	MicroSoft Disk Operating System
MSI	Medium Scale Integration
MTBF	Mean Time Between Failures

N

NAK	Negative Acknowledgement
NBS	National Bureau of Standards
NC	Numerical Control. Program control of a machine tool.
NCB	Network Control Block
NCC	Network Control Centre

NETBIOS	NETwork Basic Input/Output System
NFS	Network File System
NI	Network Interconnect
NIC	Network Interface Card
NIU	Network Interface Unit
NMI	Non-maskable Interrupt
NOS	Network Operating System
NRZ	Non-Return to Zero

O

OA	Office Automation
OBL	Ocean Bill of Lading
OCR	Optical Character Recognition
OEM	Original Equipment Manaufacturer
OOPS	Object Oriented Programming System
OR	Operations Research
OS	Operating System
OS/2	Operating System/2
OSI	Open Systems Interconnection

P

PABX	Private Automatic Branch Exchange
PBX	Private Branch Exchange
PC	Personal Computer
PCB	Printed Circuit Board
PCM	Pulse Code Modulation
PCSA	Personal Computing System Architecture
PDN	Public Data Network
PDU	Protocol Data Unit

PERT	Programme Evaluation and Review Technique
POS	Point Of Sale
PROM	Programmable Read Only Memory
PSDN	Packet Switching Data network
PSI	Packetnet System Interface
PSK	Phase Shift Keying
PSTN	Public Switched Telephone Network
PTT	Postal, Telegraph and Telephone
PVC	PolyVinyl Chloride

Q

QBE	Query By Example

R

RAM	Random Access Memory
RAX	Rural Automatic Exchange
RDBMS	Relational Data Base Management System
REJ	Frame Reject
RFI	Radio Frequency Interference
RH	Relative Humidity
RNR	Receiver Not Ready
ROM	Read Only Memory
RPC	Remote Procedure Call
RPG	Report Programme Generator
RPM	Revolutions Per Minute
RPS	Revolutions Per Second

S

SAGE	Semi Automatic Ground Environment

SAP	Service Access Point
SCSI	Small Computer System Interface
SDF	System Data Format
SDL	Specification and Description Language
SDLC	Synchronous Data Link Control
SFT	System Fault Tolerance
SIMD	Single Instruction Multi-Data Stream
SIMULA	SIMUlation LAnguage
SMAP	Station Management Application Protocol
SNA	System Network Architecture
SNOBOL	StriNg Oriented SymBOlic Language
SNS	Secondary Network Server
SPC	Stored Program Control
SQL	Structured Query Lanaguage
SSI	Small Scale Integration
STD	Subscriber Trunk Dialling

T

TAG	Technical Advisory Group
TAX	Trunk Automatic Exchange
TCP	Transmission Control Protocol
TCP/IP	Transmission Control Protocol/Internet Protocol
TDM	Time-Division Multiplexing
TIU	Trusted Interface Unit
TMS	Time-Multiplexed Switching
TOP	Technical and Office Protocol
TP	Transport Protocol
TSI	Time-Slot Interchange
TTS	Tansaction Tracking System

U

UA	Unnumbered Acknowledge
UDF	User Defined Function
UDP	User Datagram Protocol
UI	Unnumbered Information
UPC	Universal Product Code
UPS	Uninterruptible Power Supply

V

VAN	Value-Added Network
VDU	Visual Display Unit
VGA	Video Graphic Array
VLSI	Very Large Scale Integration
VSAM	Virtual Storage Access Method
VTP	Virtual Terminal Protocol

W

WAN	Wide Area Network
WATS	Wide Area Telephone Service
WBS	Work Breakdown Structure
WDM	Wave Division Multiplexing
WP	Word Processor

X

XDR	eXternal Data Representation
XID	eXchange Identification
XNS	Xerox Network Service

—

GLOSSARY

?70. An IBM data communications protocol designed to provide communications between ₁ IBM dumb terminal and an IBM mainframe

₁bend. The abnormal termination of a computer program.

₁bstract data type. A data type whose values are defined by specifying the available ₁erations rather than by describing the representations.

₁bstraction. The consideration or representation of a general quality or characteristic above ₁d apart from any actual instance or specific object that possesses that quality or characteristic.

₁cceptance testing. The validation of the system or program to user requirements.

₁ccess Methods. The technique and/or program code for moving data between main storage ₁d Input/Output devices.

₁ccess time. The time interval between when data is called for or requested to be stored in storage device and when delivery or storage is completed.

₁dapter. An interface card that allows a PC to connect to a peripheral. In this book these ₁e usually network adapters (usually called network interface cards), but there are also ₁apters for connecting to monitors, serial devices, and the like.

₁dd-on-Memory. An auxiliary storage device connected to main memory by a communi-₁tions channel.

₁ddress. A sequence of bytes representing the logical location of a station, or process within ₁tation, on the network. It is usually prefixed onto the relevant "onion layer" of the protocol ₁t.

₁ddress Translation. The process of changing the address of an item of data or an ₁struction to the address in main storage at which it is to be loaded or relocated.

₁dministrator. The person or persons responsible for managing a local area network. ₁metimes called the network administrator or network supervisor.

₁fferent module. A module that obtains its input from its subordinate(s) and delivers it ₁ward to its superordinate(s).

₁fferent stream. A hierarchy of afferent modules on a structure chart; or on a data flow ₁agram, a string of processes whose chief function is to collect or transport data from its physical source, or to refine input data from the form provided by its source to a form suitable for the major functions of the system.

Algorithm. A deterministic procedure that, when followed, yields a solution to a problem.

Amplifier. A device which regenerates an analogue signal, thus increasing the distance which the signal can be sent.

Amplitude shift keying. The modulation (i.e., modifying) of a signal to carry data, by changing the amplitude (i.e., strength) of the signal to reflect the data value.

Analogue transmission. The sending of data by using a continuous signal over a medium.

Anticipatory retrieval. (alias input buffering) A technique for optimising the reading of data from a slow storage device by fetching more data than is immediately required and by retaining it in a faster medium until it is actually needed.

Appletalk. Apple Computer's proprietary network communications protocol, originally intended to interconnect groups of Macintosh computers. Appletalk is often used when connecting Macintoshes to PC- based LANs, and it can be used to connect PCs (using a PC Appletalk card) to the Appletalk networks. The most common use for Appletalk networks is to connect a group of Macintosh computers to a printer.

Application. A software program that performs a task such as word processing, spreadsheet or database management. Usually the main use to which a computer is put. Also, the top layer of the OSI model.

Architecture. The fundamental design of a system. Architecture includes the software, hardware, and interconnection between system components or modules from the perspective of the way the system was designed.

Archiving. Saving backups of software programs and data for future reference or use.

ARCnet. One of the major local area network protocols. ARCnet does not specifically conform to an IEEE standard. However, as one of the most widespread of the LAN protocols, it has evolved into a standard of its own. ARCnet was developed by the Datapoint Corporation for connecting that company's minicomputers, and Datapoint is very active in ensuring that ARCnet standards are manintained. ARCnet is trademark of Datapoint.

Artificial language. A language based on a set of rules established prior to its usage and without a precise relationship to the user applications for which the language will be used.

ASCII. American Standard Code for Information Interchange, the code used by most PCs to communicate. ASCII codes are used internally by the computer, and they are used in communications between computers in most cases.

Asysnchronous transmission. The sending of one data character at a time, each preceded by a start bit and terminated by one or more stop bits.

Attenuation. The loss of strength of a signal as it passes through a medium.

Audit trail. A log or journal of occurrences on a LAN. An audit trail usually contains a record of each logon, who logged on, when, and what actions the user performed. Audit trails are useful for establishing details surrounding data loss, illegal logons, and system failures. Audit trails are created automatically by some LAN operating software.

$$\boxed{B}$$

Back-End Processor. A computer, subordinate to the host processor, that handles administrative tasks associated with the retrieval and manipulation of data in database.

Background Processing. The execution under automatic control of lower priority computer programs when higher priority programs are not using the system resources.

Backup. The copying of information to provide a means of recovery from lost or corrupt data.

Balanced system. A system that is neither physically input- or physically output-driven (q.v.); a system in which the top modules deal with logical rather than physical data.

Balancing. The correct correspondence in leveled data flow diagrams between a process and its decomposition in a lower-level diagram, particularly with regard to its input and output data flows.

Bandwidth. The range of frequencies offered by a medium for the transmission of signals. Now in common usage as the data rate on a LAN.

Bar-Code Scanner. A device used to read a bar code by means of reflected light, such as the scanners that read the Universal Product Code.

Baseband. The transmission of a signal without modulation. In a LAN, this implies that the whole medium is used to carry one signal at a time.

Baseline. A specification or product that has been formally reviewed and agreed upon, which serves as a basis for further development and can be changed only through formal change procedures.

Baskin-Robbins effect. The effect of "31 flavors of code," occurring when a system has been subjected to the stylistic idiosyncrasies of many generations of maintenance programmers.

Baud. A unit of measure of the rate of signal modulation. For most data purposes it is equivalent to bits per second.

Beneficial Wishful Thinking. An informal problem-solving strategy by which one identifies the particular details of a problem that hamper its solution and then, by imagining a more perfect world, one ignores as many details or constraints as necessary in order to arrive at a broad first-cut solution.

Benutzefreundilichkeit. (literally "user-friendliness") The philosophy that a system should be constructed with the interests of the user as the chief concern.

Bit. The smallest unit of digital information. Because digital information is expressed using binary states, a bit can be either a 1 or 0.

Black box. A process with known inputs, known outputs, and a known function but with an unknown (or irrelevant) internal mechanism.

Blocking Factor. The number of logical records combined into one physical record or block.

Bottom up. Proceeding from the particular to the general or from the detailed to the broad.

Bottom-up implementation. (equivalent to bottom-up testing) A special case of incremental implementation (q.v.), in which modules at a lower level on the structure chart are implemented and tested before those at a higher level.

Bottom-up Testing. Testing a computer program by beginning with individual subroutines or modules and then testing increasingly larger units.

Bridge. A device for linking two or more LANs which may be dissimilar at the physical layer but run the same Link Layer protocols. Usually consisting of both hardware and software.

Broadband. The transmission of a signal using modulation. This permits many simultaneous signals on the same medium.

Bug. A euphemism for a defect (q.v.).

Bundling. The collection of unrelated items of data to form an artificial and meaningless composite data structure.

Bus. A topology comprising a single linear medium to which all the stations are attached. Also the internal data path of a computer.

Byte. A set of (normally) 8 binary digits (bits).

Cache. A method for reducing the access time to data that is stored in a large, slow medium by retaining the most often accessed data in a smaller, faster medium. A special type of buffer used by fixed disk systems to move data between the computer and the hard disk drive efficiently. Because the cache operates at the computer's clock speed instead of the slower hard disk speed, frequently used data can be held in cache and accessed more quickly than if it were still on the disk. The advent of high speed personal computers has also led to the development of the memory cache, which is a special type of buffer using very fast memory that can keep up with a fast CPU and then feed data into the computer's main memory as it can accept it.

Carrier. A high frequency signal which can be altered (modulated) by data to achieve high data rates, carry several data streams, and interconnect several LANs in a backbone. Broadband networks and Ethernet use carriers.

CD-ROM. Compact Disk-Read Only Memory. An optical disk subsystem that can store more than 800 MB of information but cannot be written to, only read. A CD-ROM is very similar to the CD that's used for music reproduction, and many CD-ROM players will also play audio CDs.

Central Transform. The portion(s) of a data flow diagram or structure chart that remains when the afferent and efferent streams have been removed; the major data-transforming functions of a system.

Channel. A range of frequencies used to carry a single transmission in a Broadband network.

Cheapernet. A slang term for a low cost version of Ethernet that runs over thin coaxial cable.

Checksum. An arithmatic computation on the data within a packet which is then transmitted with the packet. The receiver can then perform the same computation to determine if any data has been corrupted during transmission.

Circuit switching. The provision of a direct, dedicated, physical path between two communicating devices.

Client server. A model for a particular type of network database management system that splits processing between the workstation and a specialised server called a database server.

Coaxial. A type of cable comprising a solid inner conductor separated from an outer shield by a non-conducting material.

Codec. Stands for Coder/Decoder. A device for converting analogue signals to digital signals.

Cohesion. (alias strength) A measure of the strength of functional association of processing activities (normally within a single module).

Coincidental Cohesion. A random grouping of activities.

Collisions. An anomaly that occurs when more than one packet of data is present on a network such as Ethernet at the same time. When a collision occurs, the data is lost and must be resent by the sending workstation or server. In today's implementation of Ethernet, such collision potential is detected and usually avoided.

Commitment time. (alias binding time) The time during the life cycle of a system at which a value is assigned to an item of data.

Common coupling. The type of coupling characterised by two modules referring to the same global data (area).

Communicational cohesion. A grouping of activities such that each activity uses the same input data and/or contributes to producing the same output data (without regard to order of execution).

Communications Controller. A dedicated computer with special processing capabilities for organising and checking data, and handling information traffic to and from many remote terminals or computers, including functions such as message switching. Usually a minicomputer that is configured as a "Front end" to a larger (mainframe) computer.

Composite data. (alias data structure) Data that can be decomposed into other meaningful items of data.

Computer system. Part of a system (q.v.) that is implemented on an electronic automation.

Computer systems design. The activity of transforming a statement of what is required to be accomplished into a plan for implementing that requirement on an electronic automaton.

Concurrent Processing. The simultaneous processing of more than one program.

Conditional Transfer. An instruction that may cause a departure from the sequence of instructions being followed, depending on the result of an operation, the contents of a register, or the setting of an indicator.

Constraints estimating. The determination of resources available to carry out a project.

Content coupling. (alias pathological coupling) A type of coupling in which one module affects or depends upon the internal implementation of another.

Context diagram. The top-level diagram of a leveled set of data flow diagrams.

Control coupling. A type of coupling in which one module communicates information to another module for the explicit purpose of influencing the execution of the latter.

Conway's Law. An observation by Mel Conway that the structure of a system reflects the structure of the organisation that built it.

Coordinate module. A module concerned with coordinating the activities and information of subordinates.

Core Image Library. A collection of machine language versions that have been produced as output from link-editing. The programs in the core image library are in a format that is executable either directly or after processing by the relocating loader in the supervisor.

Corrective Maintenance. Maintenance done for the purpose of eliminating a problem. It may occur as either emergency maintenance or deferred maintenance.

Coupling. The degree of dependence of one module upon another; specifically, a measure of the chance that a defect in one module will appear as a defect in the other, or the chance that a change to one module will necessitate a change to the other.

CSMA/CD. Carrier Sense Mutilple Access with Collision Detection: a bus access technique.

Cyclic redundancy check. Same as Checksum.

D

Data access diagram. (alias data structure diagram) A graphic tool for depicting the ways by which a data store can be referred to by means of the information contained in another data store.

Data base. A collection of interrelated data stored together with controlled redundancy to serve one or more applications, so that the data stored are independent of the programs that use them and so that a common, controlled approach can be used for adding, modifying and retrieving data.

Data circuit equipment. A device which provides a network attachment point for a user device, e.g., a modem.

Data Compression. A technique that saves storage space by eliminating gaps, empty fields, redundancies, or unnecessary data to shorten the length of records or blocks.

Data coupling. A form of coupling in which one module communicates information to another in the form of parameters, each parameter being either a single field, or a table, each of whose entries holds the same type of information.

Data dictionary. A repository of definitions of all data flows and data stores in a data flow diagram, in a process specification, or in the data dictionary itself; defines composite data (q.v.) in terms of its components, and elementary data (q.v.) in terms of the meaning of each value that it can assume.

Data flow. A pipeline along which information of known composition is passed.

Data flow diagram. (alias bubble chart) A graphic tool for depicting the partitioning of a system into a network of activities and their interfaces, together with the origins, destinations, and stores of data. Graphical representation of a system, that shows the sources and processes performed on data, and the flow of data between the nodes.

Data store. A reservoir in which data can be held for an indefinite period.

Data structure. Synonym for composite data.

Data terminal equipment. A device which acts as the origin of, or destination for data, e.g., a computer, terminal or printer.

Datagram packet switching. The splitting of messages into small packets, each of which is transmitted independently across the network.

Debugging. The process of removing defects from a computer system.

Decision-split. The existence of the data for a decision's recognition part and that for its execution part in different modules.

Decision table. A normalized (i.e., non-hierarchical) tabular form of a decision tree (q.v.)

Decision tree. A graphic tool for portraying a hierarchy of independent conditions and the activities resulting from each valid combination of conditions.

Defect. (euphemistically, bug) A discrepancy between an actual system and its specification.

Deferred storage. (alias output buffering) A technique for optimizing the writing of data to a slow storage device by retaining the data in a faster medium until enough has been collected to be written out in a large group.

Device cluster. A set of modules that have exclusive right of access to a particular device (normally used to localise the physical characteristics of the device to a small part of the system).

Digital transmission. The sending of data using discrete signals in the medium.

Documentation Aids. Materials that help automate the documentation process, and include flowcharts, programs, etc.

Driver. (alias test harness, test monitor) A primitive implementation of a superordinate module, which is normally used in the bottom-up testing of subordinate modules.

Dynamic Analyzer. A program that monitors the execution of another program for purposes of evaluation.

Dynamic call. An invocation of one module by another, each being in a different load unit (q.v.) (see also static call).

Dynamic Programming. A method of sequential decision making in which the result of the decision in each stage affords the best possible position to exploit the expected range of likely (yet unpredictable) outcomes in the following decision-making stages.

Effective system. A system that demonstrably works according to its specification.

Efferent module. A module that obtains its input from its superordinate(s) and delivers it downward to its subordinate(s).

Efferent stream. A hierarchy of efferent modules on a structure chart or on a data flow diagram, a string of processes whose chief function is to transport or dispatch data to its physical sink, or to format output data from the form produced by the major functions of the system to a form suitable for its sink.

Efficient system. A system that uses few resources.

Elementary data. Data that is not decomposed into other items of data.

Encapsulation. Enclosing a packet from one protocol by a header, and somtimes a trailer, of the next protocol down the ISO model.

Encryption. The translation of one character string into another by means of a cypher, translation table, or algorithm, in order to render the information contained therein meaningless to anyone who does not possess the decoding mechanism.

Ethernet. A type of LAN which uses a simple twisted pair cable to connect the computers in the network.

Factoring. The separation of a function contained as code in one module into a new module of its own.

Fan-in. The number of immediate superordinates of a module.

Fan-out. (alias span of control) The number of immediate subordinates of a module.

Filestore. A system, usually a station on a LAN, which provides shared disc storage for the stations on the LAN.

Fisher's Fundamental Theorem. The law first stated by the biologist Ronald A. Fisher that the better adapted a system is to a particular environment, the less adaptable it is to a new environment.

Flag. A piece of information that either describes other data (a descriptive flag), or is used to explicitly influence the future execution of the system (a control flag).

Flowchart. A graphic tool for depicting the sequence of activities in a system.

Frame. A collection of bits grouped as one entity for transmission. Generally this refers to the packets at the Link Layer.

Frequency agile modem. A device used to connect stations to braodband networks which is capable of selecting one of several channels from which to transmit and receive data.

Frequency division multiplexing. The splitting up of a medium by frequency to enable several signals to be transmitted simultaneously.

Functional cohesion. A grouping of activities such that each and every activity contributes to the execution of the same single problem-related function.

Functional primitive. A process on a data flow diagram that is not further decomposed on a lower level; a bottom-level bubble.

Functional standard. A set of protocols for a given application or function, which tightly define the protocols, classes, subsets and options to be used.

Gateway. A device which links two or more networks, or a network and a computer, which use different protocols or have different characteristics which prevent normal connection via a bridge.

Graphic data dictionary. A depiction of a data dictionary (q.v.) as a diagram in a form first proposed by Jackson.

Gray box. A process whose function cannot be fully determined without studying the mechanism that accomplishes that function.

Hat. A symbol on a module signifying its compression into the module's superordinate; the unfactoring symbol.

Headend. A piece of equipment at the 'root' of a broadband network which receives all transmissions and regenerates them to the receivers, shifting the channel frequency if required.

Heuristic. A partly deterministic procedure that, when followed, is likely to yield a result that is close to a desirable solution to a problem.

Host. A computer system which provides general user services over the network.

Hrair limit. (alias conceptual counting limit) An information term for the limit to the number of problems, activities, or items of information that can easily, correctly and simultaneously be dealt with by the brain.

Hunt group. A collection of ports which share a common name. When called, the system selects the first free port.

Hybrid coupling. The use of different parts of a range of values that a data item can assume for different and unrelated purposes.

Implementation. The activity of a project during which the design of a system is tested, debugged, and made operational.

Incremental Implementation. (equivalent to incremental testing) An implementation/testing strategy whereby one part of a system is implemented and tested, and then other implemented and tested parts are added, one by one, until the system is complete.

Informational Cluster. A set of modules that have exclusive right of access to a particular item or items of data (normally used when the data has a complex structure or has sensitive security).

Injection laser diode. An expensive high speed and high powered light source for fibre optic transmission.

Intermediate file. A temporary file used to communicate data between job steps or, sometimes, jobs.

Inversion of authority. A special case of control coupling (q.v.) in which a subordinate module communicates information to a superordinate module for the explicit purpose of influencing the execution of that superordinate.

Jitter. The slight changes in phase which a signal undergoes when passed round a ring without being stored and re-timed.

Job. A sequence of one or more job steps that is activated by a human operator (or another agent outside of the executing computer); the smallest unit that can be activated in this way (see also job step).

Job step. One main program that has (optionally) a hierarchy of one or more subprograms and that is activated by an operating system; the smallest unit that can be activated in this way (see also program).

LAN. Local area network.

Light emitting diode. A relatively cheap light source for fibre optic transmission, supporting slow speeds over short distances.

Link Redundancy Level. The ratio of actual number of links to the minimum number of links required to connect all nodes of a network.

Literal. A raw constant that does not have a name.

Load unit. A hierarchy of one or more programs whose calls are linked before execution time (see also program).

Logical. Free of the characteristics or constraints of any particular implementation; opposite of physical (q.v.).

Logical cohesion. A grouping of activities based on a real or imagined similarity of implementation (without regard to data flow, order, or time of execution).

Loopback. A test mechanism whereby a signal or message is reflected back to the source.

M

Main program. A program that is called by the operating system.

Maintainable system. A system whose defects are easy to remove; a system that can be easily adapted to meet the changing requirements of its users or the changing environment in which it operates.

MAP. Manufacturing Application Protocol. A set of protocols defined by General Motors for factory applications.

Mealy's Law. An observation by George Mealy that there is an incremental person, who, when added to a project, consumes more resources than he adds.

Message switching. The technique of sending whole messages as one entity across a network.

Mini-specification. (alias process specification) A statement of the policy that governs the transformation of input data flow(s) into output data flow(s) for a given functional primitive (q.v.).

Model. An intentional arrangement of a portion of reality (the medium) to represent another portion of reality (the subject) such that in certain ways the model behaves like the subject; the part(s), the set(s) of details, and the abstraction(s) of the subject that the model represents are called the viewpoint of the model; the set of ways in which the model is intended to behave like the subject is called the purpose of the model.

Modem. Stands for 'Modulator/Demodulator'. A device which converts the digital output (signals) of a computer into an analogue signal capable of being transmitted over a conventional telephone line. It can also receive the same and convert it back into a digital form.

Module. A collection of program statements with four basic attributes; input and output function, mechanics, and internal data.

Multiplexing. A technique designed to carry many signals simultaneously over the same medium.

Multi-threading. A program construction technique which allows more than one logical path through the program to be executed simultaneously.

Nag flag. A colloquial term for a control flag (see flag).

Network Control Program. The interface program that communicates with the network on one side and with user programs in the host computer on the other side.

New logical data flow diagram. An old logical data flow diagram (q.v.) modified by the addition of any new, required functions and by the deletion of any old, unrequired functions.

New physical data flow diagram. A data flow diagram that portrays the projected future (often, largely automated) implementation of a system.

Node. Any station, terminal, terminal installation, communications computer, or communications computer installation in a computer network.

Old logical data flow diagram. A data flow diagram that portrays the essential functions underlying a policy without committing to any particular means of implementing that policy.

Old physical data flow diagram. A data flow diagram that portrays the current (often, largely manual) implementation of a system.

Optimization. The modification of a system with respect to a criterion to approach the stated criterion as closely as possible, while changing other qualities of the system as little as possible; often used with respect to system run time.

Orthogonal set. (in the context of system development) A set of tools or programming constructs that do not overlap in function or purpose and, hence, can be used independently.

Over-general module. A module that has an unnecessarily broad function or that can handle data of a greater range of values, types, or structures than is ever likely to be needed.

P

Packaging. The set of decisions and activities that sub-divide a system into implementation units; or the result of those activities.

Packet. A collection of bits, including some addressing information called start and stop bits, which are grouped as a single entity for transmission. This is usually used to describe Network Layer entities (see Frame).

Phase shift keying. The modulation of a signal to carry data by altering the phase of the signal to reflect the value of the data.

Physical. Having some characteristics of a particular implementation, by (a) being dependent on a particular medium for bearing information; (b) being dependent on a particular agent for executing an activity; (c) being partitioned or organised in a way that has been constrained by (a) or (b) or by the requirements of time, space, cost, or politics; or (d) containing activities or data only necessary to satisfy the constraints of (a), (b), or (c); opposite of logical (q.v.).

Physically input-driven system. A system that does too little processing on its afferent side, so that the top modules have to deal with raw, physical, unedited input data.

Physically output-driven system. A system that does too little processing on its efferent side so that the top modules have to deal with the particular physical formats of the output data.

Playthrough. (alias dynamic design review, runthrough) The mental execution of a product by a small group of people using a set of test cases to discover defects in the product.

Procedural cohesion. A grouping of activities based on order of execution in a particular implementation (without regard to data flow).

Process. An activity on a data flow diagram that transforms input data flow(s) into output data flow(s).

Program. The smallest set of computer instructions that can be executed as a stand-alone unit; in COBOL, the set of computer instructions that comprises four divisions (IDENTIFI-

CATION, ENVIRONMENT, DATA, and PROCEDURE) and that can be either a main program (q.v.) or a subprogram (q.v.)

Program inversion. An arrangement of the procedural components (e.g. modules) of a system that is inverted with respect to the structure of the data being processed.

Protocol. A set of rules which govern the interchange of data between two communicating computers.

Pseudocode. A language tool used chiefly for module programming, but also for module specification and for module maintenance; normally, pseudocode is at a higher level than any existing compilable language.

R

Recursion. The act of invoking (or the ability to invoke) a module as a subordinate of itself.

Reliable system. A system that is consistently available and consistent in its results.

Repeater. A device which regenerates a digital signal on a LAN, thus, extending the area which a LAN can cover.

Requirements estimating. The determination of the resources needed to carry out a project.

Restrictive module. A module whose function is needlessly specific or is confined to handling data of a smaller range of values, types, or structures than is likely to be needed.

Ring. A topology where the stations are connected in a loop, with each station responsible for passing the data on to the next.

Ripple effect. The manifestation of a defect in one part of a system as a defect in other parts of the system; the effect of a change in one part of a system causing defects in other parts of the system and/or necessitating further changes to other parts of the system.

ROM. Read only memory. Term applied to semiconductor memory devices whose content cannot be altered once they have been set.

Route-mapping. An informal term for the decomposition of a data flow diagram into simpler diagrams, each of which depicts the flow of a single transaction.

RS-232. A "standard" interface for asynchronous communications, typically found on terminals, PCs and printers.

S

Schema. A chart of the overall logical structure of a data base.

Sequential cohesion. A grouping of activities such that output data produced by one activity serves as input data to another activity.

Server. A special purpose utility on the LAN which provides services for other LAN users e.g., a file server or print server. The most common is a file server, which is a computer dedicated to the storage of information for use by all LAN users. A print server is a printer facility which can be used by all LAN users.

Sink. A receiver of data flows from a system.

Skeleton system version. A partially implemented system that performs a small but useful subset of the functions of the complete system.

Slotted ring. A technique for access to a ring whereby an empty packet, or slot, is continuously circulating round the stations. A station may fill the slot when it receives it.

Source. A provider of data flows for a system.

Spooling. The collection of information from several sources at one point, followed by the orderly delivery of that information to a device, e.g., a printer.

Stamp coupling. A type of coupling characterised by two modules referring to the same composite data structure.

Standard. An agreed protocol governing some aspect of data interchange between systems.

Star. A topology where all of the stations are connected to a central switch.

Star-coupler. A fibre optic device which can connect several LANs into a star topology.

State memory. Data internal to a module that survives unchanged from invocation to invocation of that module.

Static call. An invocation by one module of another module such that both modules are in the same load unit (see also dynamic call).

Stepwise refinement. An alias for top-down design (q.v.) that is used in Structured Programming.

Structure chart. A graphic tool for depicting the partitioning of a system into modules, the hierarchy and organisation of those modules, and the communication interfaces between the modules.

Structure clash. A term coined by Jackson to describe the situation in which N items of data A are required to produce M items of data B (N and M being relatively prime).

Structured. Bounded in content; limited for the sake of orthogonality; arranged in a top-down way in both level of detail and degree of abstraction; partitioned to achieve minimal interfaces between parts; concerned with both data and activities; as simple as possible.

Structured Analysis. The activity of deriving a structured model of the requirements for a system; specifically, the activity of deriving a structured specification (q.v.).

Structured Design. The development of a blueprint of a computer system solution to a problem, having the same components and interrelationships among the components as the original problem has.

Structured Design Specification. (alias Structured Design blueprint) A structured plan of the parts of a system that are to be implemented on a computer; specifically the target document of Structured Design comprising structure charts, a data dictionary, module specifications, systems flowcharts, and a minimal amount of additional information.

Structured English. A tool that is used for describing policy, and that is a subset of the English language (with a restricted syntax and vocabulary), imbedded in the procedural constructs of Structured Programming.

Structured information modeling. The activity of identifying and representing informational objects, references, properties, relations, and time dependencies in a way that is independent of any particular computer implementation.

Structured Programming. A programming technique for developing source code logic that is understandably and verifiably correct; specifically, a technique that employs a top-down refinement strategy to produce code built from a small set of logical constructs (chiefly, the sequence construct, the decision construct, and the loop construct).

Structured specification. A structured model of the manual and automated procedures of a system; specifically, the target document of Structured Analysis (q.v.) comprising data flow diagrams, a data dictionary, mini-specifications, data access diagrams.

Stub. (alias dummy module) A primitive implementation of a subordinate module, which is normally used in the top-down testing of superordinate modules.

Subprogram. A program that is called by another program.

Subschema. A chart of one user's or one application's view of the data stored in a data base.

Switch. A device which routes data between several attached inputs and outputs.

Synchronous transmission. The sending of data in frames, i.e., blocks of data preceded by SYNC characters.

Syntax. The correct way of writing a command, including the allowed words and the order in which they must be used. Sandwich implementation. (equivalent to sandwich testing) A special case of incremental implementation whereby selected modules at the bottom levels of the structure chart are implemented and tested bottom-up, whereas modules at higher levels of the structure chart are implemented and tested top-down (or by the umbrella method, q.v.).

System. A set of manual and automated activities that is organised in such a way as to reproducibly accomplish a set of stated purposes; (on a computer) a set of application-related jobs (q.v.).

System Integration. An implementation/testing strategy in which all the subsystems of a system are brought together at once to be tested and debugged.

Systems Flowchart. A graphic tool for depicting a computer system in terms of its inputs, outputs, jobs, job steps, intermediate files, and physical devices.

$$\boxed{T}$$

Tag. (alias transaction code) An item of information associated with a transaction (q.v.) for the purpose of identifying the type of that transaction.

Tap. The physical attachment point to a LAN cable.

TCP/IP. Transmission Control Protocol/Internet Protocol. A protocol for interconnecting networks or devices on the same network. For example, using TCP/IP is the accepted way to interconnect a DOS LAN with a UNIX system because the DOS and UNIX operating systems normally have no LAN operating software that works on both types of machines.

Temporal cohesion. A grouping of activities based on time of execution in a particular implementation (without regard to data flow or to order of execution).

Testing. The fiendish and relentless process of executing all or part of a system with the intent of causing it to exhibit a defect.

Time division multiplexing. The splitting up of a medium into time slots to permit the multiple transmission of several digital signals.

Timeout. The expiry of a given time during which some event should have occurred.

Token. A special type of packet that's used in a token passing network to pick up and deliver data around the network.

Token bus. A bus system using token ring type access methods: i.e., each station must wait for a token before transmitting.

Token ring. A LAN access technique in which a special packet containing a token travels round the ring from computer to computer and a station (i.e., a computer) attached to the ring can only transmit when it has the token.

TOP. Technical Office Protocol. A set of protocols defined by Boeing for general technical and business applications.

Top down. Proceeding from the general to the particular or from the broad to the detailed.

Top-down design. An informal design strategy in which a problem is arbitrarily decomposed into yet simpler problems; each simpler problem then is successively decomposed into yet simpler problems until the problems are simple enough to be solved by means of available program statements; top-down design is a subset of structured design.

Top-down implementation. (equivalent to top-down testing) A special case of incremental implementation (q.v.) in which modules at a higher level on the structure chart are implemented and tested before those at a lower level.

Topology. The pattern of wiring connections used in a LAN or shape of the network, e.g., star, bus, ring or tree.

Tramp data. An item of data that, although irrelevant to the function of a given module, has to pass through that module in order to reach another module.

Transaction. Any element of data, control, signal, event, or change of state that causes, triggers, or initiates some action or sequence of actions; an (usually composite) item of data that can be any one of a number of types, each type having a specific set of processing that must be performed on it.

Transaction analysis. (alias transaction-centred design) A design strategy by which the structure of a system is derived from a study of the transactions that the system must process.

Transaction centre. A portion of a system that can obtain a transaction, analyse it to determine its type, dispatch it in the way appropriate to its type, and complete the processing of the transaction.

Transceiver. A device which transmits and receives signals. Usually used in reference to CSMA/CD LANs.

Transform analysis. (alias transform-centred design) A design strategy in which the structure of a system is derived from a study of the flow of data through a system and of the transformations to that data.

Transform module. A module that obtains its input from its superordinate and returns its output to the same superordinate.

Tree. A topology consisting of linked bus networks, sometimes known as 'root and branch'.

Twisted pair. A cabling method using standard telephone wire or other similar cable medium.

ULA. Uncommitted logic array. These are semiconductor devices which can be designed by the user to provide complex functions previously only available either with a large number of devices, or by expensive mass-manufacture of specialised parts.

Umbrella implementation. (equivalent to umbrella testing) A special case of incremental implementation (q.v.) in which modules on the afferent and efferent branches of the structure chart are implemented and tested (usually in a top-down manner) before those in the central transform of the structure chart.

Unreliable service. A protocol layer which does not guarantee to deliver packets correctly or in the correct order, for the layer above.

V24. A standard for modem connection used by the computer industry.

VAN. Value added network. A network which provides some service as well as interconnection. British Telecom's Prestel is an example.

Vaporware. Software that has been announced but not delivered or put into production.

Virtual circuit packet switching. The technique of providing a logical path between two communicating systems, along which packets are transmitted.

Walkthrough. (alias static review, peer-group review) The review of a product by a group of people to discover the flaws in the product.

WAN. Wide area network. A network covering large areas, usually connected via radio or telephone links, rather than dedicated lines.

White box. A process whose function can be determined only by studying the mechanism that accomplishes that function.

Windowing. The technique of permitting a transmitter to send a number of packets in advance of receiving acknowledgements for packets already sent.

X.25. A standard for packet-switching, which is relevant to LANs where interconnection with other networks is required.

LIST OF COMPUTER JOURNALS

1. ACM : Communication of the ACM (M), USA

2. ACM : Computing Reviews (M), USA

3. ACM : Guide to Computing Literature, USA

4. ACM : Transaction on Database System (Q), USA

5. ACM : Transactions on Graphics (Q), USA

6. ACM : Transactions on Mathematical Software (Q), USA

7. ACM : Transactions on Office Information Systems (Q), USA

8. ACM : Transaction on Programming Languages and Systems (Q), USA

9. Artificial Intelligence, Netherlands

10. Business Computer (M), Bombay, India

11. Byte, USA

12. Computational Statistics and Data Analysis, Netherlands

13. Computer Abstracts (M), USA

14. Computer and Artificial Intelligence, Czechoslovakia

15. Computer and Industrial Engineering, UK

16. Computers and Communications (M), Bombay, India

17. Computers and Operational Research (Bi-M), UK

18. Computers and Security, Netherlands

19. Computer Decisions, USA

20. Computer Education, UK

21. Computer Education For You (M), Bombay, India

22. Computer Journal, UK

23. Computer Review, USA

24. Computer Science and Informatics, India

25. Computer Surveys, UK

26. Datamation, N.Y., USA

27. DataQuest (M), New Delhi, India

28. Decision Support Systems (M), North-Holland, The Netherlands

29. EDP Analysis, Bethesdo, MD

30. Electronics for You (M), New Delhi, India

31. Electronics Information and Planning (M), India

32. IBM Systems Journal (Q), USA

33. IEEE Transactions on Computers, New York, USA

34. IEEE Transactions on Software Engineering, USA

35. IEEE Transactions on Systems Man and Cybernetics, USA

36. IEEE Transactions : Industrial Engineering Research and Development, USA

37. Information and Decision Technology, Netherlands

38. Information and Management, Netherlands

39. Information and Software Technology (10/Year), UK

40. Information Executive formerly Data Management (M), USA

41. Information Processing and Management, UK

42. Information Sciences, USA

43. Information Technology, New Delhi, India

44. INFOTEL, New Delhi

45. International Journal of System Science, UK

46. Journal of Computer and System Sciences (Bi-M), USA

47. Journal of Computer Society of India, Bombay, India

48. Journal of Microcomputer Applications, UK

49. Journal of the ACM

50. Journal of Management Information System, USA

51. Management Information System (Q), USA

52. PC Quest (M), New Delhi, India

53. PC Tech Journal, USA

54. PC World

55.   Parallel Computing, Netherlands

56.   Plus, The Total Computer Magazine (M), Bombay, India

57.   SIAM Journal of Computing, USA

58.   Science of Computer Programming, Amsterdam

59.   Simulation (M), USA

60.   Software Practice and Experience (M), UK

M   Monthly

Q   Quarterly

Bi-M Bimonthly

REFERENCES

1.   Archer, Rowland, The Practical Guide to Local Area Network, Osborne McGraw Hill, USA, 1986

2.   Basandra, Suresh K., Computer Science Question Bank, Galgotia Publications Pvt. Ltd., New Delhi, 1994

3.   Basandra, Suresh K., Understanding Computers Through Common Sense, Galgotia Publications Pvt. Ltd., New Delhi, 1993

4.   Basandra, Suresh K., Computers Today, Galgotia Publications Pvt. Ltd., New Delhi, 1994

5.   Basandra, Suresh K., Software Engineering, Galgotia Publications Pvt. Limited, New Delhi, 1994

6.   Bates, William, and Fortino, Andres G, dBASE III Plus and Local Area Networks, BPB Publications, New Delhi, India, 1987

7.   Black, Uyless, Computer Networks - Protocols, Standard and Interfaces, Prentice-Hall, Inc, USA, 1987

8.   Bridges, Stephen P M, Low Cost Local Area Networks, Galgotia Publications Pvt. Ltd., New Delhi, 1990

9.   Brooner, E G, The Local Area Network Book, Howard W Sams and Co, Inc, USA, 1984

10. Chorafas, Dimitris N, Personal Computers and Data Communications, Computer Science Press, Inc, USA, 1986

11. Croucher, Phil, Novell Netware Companion, Galgotia Publications Pvt. Ltd., New Delhi, 1991

12. Durr, Michael, Networking IBM PCs - A Practical Guide, Que Corporation, USA, 1984

13. Durr, Michael, Networking IBM PCs, Que Corporation, USA, 1987, 2nd Edition

14. Durr, Michael and Walker, Dwayne, Micro to Mainframe: Creating an Integrated Environment, Addison-Wesleay, USA, 1985

15. Gould, Carol C, Information Web: Ethical and Social Implecation of Computer Networking, Westview, Boulder, USA, 1989

16. Handwork of Data Communications, NCC Publications, The National Computing Centre Limited, England, 1982

17. Hudson, Brian and Taylor, Bill, Implementing a Broadband LAN, NCC Publications, Manchester, UK, 1986

18. Hutchison, David, Local Area Network Architecture, Addison-Wesley, Int. Computer Science Series, USA, 1988

19. Kleeman, Michael, Andersen, Bart, Angermeyer, John, Fisher, Sharon and McCoy, Spank, PC LAN Primer, Macmillan Inc, USA, 1987

20. Kopeck, Ronald F., Micro to Maniframe Links, Osborne McGraw-Hill, USA., 1989

21. Langley, G., Telecommuniations Primer, Galgotia Publications Pvt. Ltd., New Delhi, 1986.

22. Lawrence, Bill, Using Novell Netware, Que Corporation, Carmel, 1990

23. Lehrman, Steven Ruth, Local Area Networking with Microcomputers - A Guide for the Business Decision Maker, Prentice Hall Press, Simon & Schuster, Inc, USA, 1986

24. Martin, James, Computer Networks and Distributed Processing - Software, Techniques and Architecture, Prentice Hall of India Pvt. Limited, New Delhi, 1991

25. Martin, James, and Chapman, Kethleen Kavanagh, Local Area Networks: Architectures and Implementation, Prentice-Hall, USA, 1989

26. McDonald, Timothy K, Illustrated Novell NetWare, BPB Publications New Delhi, India, 1989, First Indian Edition

27. Raghavan, S.V., Solutions to Local Area Netowrks - The Indian Context, Tata McGraw Hill Publishing Company Ltd., New Delhi, 1991

28. Reiss, Leszek, Introduction to Local Area Networks with Micro Computer Experiments, Prentice-Hall Inc, USA, 1987

29. Stallings, William, Local Networks, Macmillan Publishing Company, USA, 1990, third edition

30. Tangney, Brenden and O'Mahony, Donald, Local Area Networks and their Applications, Prentice-Hall International (UK) Ltd, UK, 1988

31. Tannebaum, Andrew S., Computer Networks, Prantice-Hall, Inc, USA, 1981

32. Weidlein, James R and Cross, Thomas B, Networking Personal Computers in Organisations, Dow Jones - Irwin, USA, 1986

READERS COMMENTS FORM

Your opinions count

If you have any comments, criticisms, or suggestions for us, we are quite eager to get them. Your comments help us to improve the books, and make sure that they are what you need. And if you find any errors, typographical or otherwise, in this book, please do point them out so that we can correct them in the next printing.

We thank you for your continued help.

Book Tiltle: LOCAL AREA NETWORKS

Edition: 1994

Author: Suresh K Basandra

1.   Which parts of this book did you find particularly helpful, and why?

2.   Which parts of this book did you find particularly unhelpful, and why?

3.   If you have found any errors, or have any suggestions for improvements, please mention here.

Name:

Position:

Company (if company address):

Address:

City, State, Pin Code:
Phone No.
Fax No.

YOU WILL BE INTERESTED

IN OTHER BOOKS

BY THE SAME AUTHOR

COMPUTER SCIENCE QUESTION BANK

UNDERSTANDING COMPUTERS THROUGH COMMON SENSE

COMPUTERS TODAY

SOFTWARE ENGINEERING

ALL PUBLISHED BY

GALGOTIA PUBLICATIONS PVT LTD

COMPLETE CATALOGUE COMPUTERS

No.of Copies		Price, Rs.

ACCESS

....	A Quick Course in Access 2 for Windows	Cox	60.00
....	PC World MS Access 2 Bible	Progue & Irwin	360.00
....	Computer Facts & Formulae—Access 2	S. Mehta	50.00

ALGORITHMS

....	Fundamentals of Computer Algorithms	Horowitz & Sahni	160.00

ARTIFICIAL INTELLIGENCE

....	Designing Artificial Intelligence Based Software	Bahrami	105.00
....	Artificial Intelligence & Turbo Pascal	Christopher F Chabris	105.00
....	With Diskette		75.00
....	Program Design for Knowledge Based Systems	Graham Winstanley	80.00
....	Artificial Intelligence with Common Lisp	James & Noyes	160.00

AS 400

....	RPG on the IBM PC	W J Tomlinson	185.00

ASSEMBLY LANGUAGE

....	Classic Utilities Using Assembly Language with disk	Vinoj Kr.	150.00
....	Fundamental of Assembly Language Using IBM PC	Detmer	130.00
....	Starting MS-DOS Assembler	Sinclair	75.00

AutoCAD

....	Advanced Techniques in AutoCAD 13	Tickoo	I/P
....	AutoCAD 13 with Applications	Sham Tickoo	455.00
....	AutoCAD Tips and Tricks	Head	175.00
....	AutoCAD : 3D Book - Version 12	Head	145.00
....	10-Minute Guide to AutoCAD Rel. 13 for DOS & Windows	S. Mehta	60.00
....	AutoCAD Release 13- for DOS & Windows Quick Reference Guide	S. Mehta	160.00
....	Computer Facts and Formulae- AutoCAD Release 13 for DOS & Windows	S. Mehta	50.00
....	Computer facts & Formulae- AutoCAD Release 13	S. Mehta	50.00
....	AutoCAD 11 - The trainer for beginners	Procket	55.00
....	AutoCAD Database Book	Jones & Martin	150.00
....	AutoCAD : A Concise Guide	Leigh	115.00
....	The Autocad Productivity Book	Brittain	136.00
....	Understanding AutoCAD 13	Tickoo	I/P

AutoLISP

....	Unofficial Guide To AutoLISP	Vijay Mukhi	250.00
....	AutoLISP in AutoCAD 11	Schmidt	160.00
....	AutoLISP in Plain English 2nd edition	Head	105.00

BASIC, TURBO BASIC

....	BASIC for Beginners	Conley	45.00
....	BASIC : A Short Self Instructional Course	Oatey	39.00
....	BBC BASIC for School & Collage	Bindlay	35.00
....	BASIC Programmer's Phrase Book	Clark	45.00
....	Using Turbo BASIC'	James, Ewbank	70.00
....	Computer Facts & Formulae- BASIC [GW-BASIC & Quick BASIC]	S. Mehta	50.00
....	Learning and Using Basic in a day	Jaiswal	36.00

BUSINESS MANAGEMENT

.... How to design and develop Businesss Systems	Steve Eckols	110.00

C/C++/TURBO C/TURBO C++

.... Learn C Now!	Chitgopkar	80.00
.... Jamsa's 1001 C/C++ Tips	Kris Jamsa	305.00
.... Success with C++	Kris Jamsa	240.00
.... Rescued by C++	Kris Jamsa	95.00
.... C++ Real Time Graphics	A Tyler	110.00
.... C User Interface Library	Ted Pugh	110.00
.... C Toolbox for Database Development	Henn	110.00
.... C-in Ten hours	R.G. Srinivasan	65.00
.... Workout C: Learn Through Exercises witth two disk	Himmel	330.00
.... Master C++: Let the PC teach you	Lafore	370.00
Object Oriented Programming includes 3 Disk Tutorial		
.... Practical Data Structures in C/C++	Byran Flemig	190.00
.... Same " (original)		695.00
.... C++ Primer+	Prata	250.00
.... Object-Oriented Programming in Turbo C++	Lafore	260.00
.... Turbo C Quick Start	Lence Leventhal	160.00
.... Programming in C++	Edgar Huckert	160.00
.... C Complete Manual	Herold Unger	160.00
.... Programming in C	Kris A Jamsa	80.00
.... Practical C	Harrison	55.00
.... Big Red Book of C	Sullivan	55.00
.... Professional Programmers Guide to C	McKay	65.00
.... C Programmer's Phrase Book	Clark	45.00
.... Lexicon of C	Alex Ragen	65.00
.... Programming in Zortech C++	John M. Hughes	110.00
.... Turbo C Programmer's Resource Book	Holtz	100.00
.... The C Tutorial Turbo C	Backhurst	69.00
.... Unix C Programming	Davignon	185.00
.... Object-oriented programming Microsoft C++	Lafore	240.00
.... Borland C++ Developer's Bible	Peterson	260.00
.... C User Interface Library	Pugh	110.00
.... C/C++ Programming Guide to using PC Bios	Taylor	210.00
.... Computer Facts & Formulae-C/C++	S. Mehta	50.00

C++ VISUAL

.... The Visual C++ Construction Kit	Bugg, Tackett, Jr.	190.00
.... Same " (Original)	Bugg	495.00

CAD (COMPUTER AIDED DESIGN)

.... Fundamentals of CAD	Gray R. Bertoline	110.00

CLIENT/SERVER

.... Client/Server Strategies: A survival	D. Vaskevitch	315.00
guide for corporate reengineers		

CLIPPER

.... CA Clipper 5.2: Second Edition Quick Reference Guide	Subhash Mehta	160.00
.... Clipper, Library: Quick Reference Guide	Mehta / Hazarika	100.00
.... Clipper Debugger Quick Reference Guide	Mehta / Hazarika	80.00
.... Computer Facts & Formulae-CA Clipper 5.2	Subhash Mehta	50.00

No.of Copies		Price, Rs.
.... Clipper Developers Library 2nd Edition ver. 5.01 with disk	Occhiogrosso	250.00
COMPUTER ARCHITECTURE		
.... PC Architecture & Assembly Language	Kauler	110.00
.... Modem Computer Architecture	Rafiquzzman	125.00
.... Introduction to Computer Architecture	Stone	100.00
COMPUTER HARDWARE		
.... Compiler Construction Theory and Practice 2nd Ed.	William A. Barrett	110.00
.... Computer Hardware and Organization	M.E. Sloan	110.00
COMPUTER TEXT BOOKS		
.... ABC of Computers Book A	B.Mehta/S.Mehta	29.00
.... ABC of Computers Book B	B.Mehta/S.Mehta	29.00
.... ABC of Computers Book C	B.Mehta/S.Mehta	29.00
.... ABC of Computers Book D	B.Mehta/S.Mehta	29.00
.... ABC of Computers Book E	B.Mehta/S.Mehta	29.00
.... ABC of Computers Book F	B.Mehta/S.Mehta	29.00
.... Business Software Made Simple	S.Mehta/B.Mehta	100.00
.... Computer Primer Book 1	V.K. Jain	39.00
.... Computer Primer Book 2	V.K. Jain	39.00
.... Computerised Business Applications	Ramachandran	90.00
.... Computer Science Concepts Class XII	Naveen Kr.	100.00
.... Elements of Computer Science (A.M.I.E.)	Jaiswal	75.00
.... Fundamentals of E D P (CA-Intermediate)	Jaiswal	75.00
.... GW BASIC Quick Course	S.Mehta/B.Mehta	110.00
.... I.C.S.E. Computer Studies	Bhattacharya	100.00
.... Turbo Pascal Quick Coursse	S.Mehta/B.Mehta	110.00
.... Learn C Now! [DOE "A-Level"]	Chitgopkar/Mehta	80.00
.... Principles & Techniques of Programming [DOE "O-level"]	Ramachandran	90.00
CorelDRAW!		
.... CorelDRAW! 5 Revealed	Harrel	240.00
.... CorelDRAW! 4- Visual Quick Start Guide		136.00
.... Mastering CorelDRAW! 4	Dickman	360.00
.... Mastering CorelDRAW! 3 (2 Disk)	Dickman	405.00
.... CorelDRAW! 3 Visual Quick Start Guide	Webster	160.00
DATA PROCESSING		
.... Data Processing : A first course	Harrison	55.00
DATA STRUCTURES		
.... Elementary Data Structures Using Pascal	Shiflet	105.00
.... Pascal Plus Data Structures-Algorithms & Advanced Programming 3rd Edition	Dale/Lilly	225.00
.... Applied Discrete Structures of Computer Science	Doerr	145.00
DATABASE MANAGEMENT		
.... Principles of Database Systems	Ulman	160.00
.... An Introduction to Database Systems	Desai	230.00
.... Database Processing : Fundamentals Design, Implementation 2nd Edition	Kroenke	110.00
DBASE III, DBASE III PLUS, DBASE IV		
.... Illustrated dBASE Book	Russel A. Stultz	70.00
.... dBASE III PLUS for Beginners 2nd Rev. Ed.	Rajiv Mathur	136.00

No.of Copies		Price, Rs.
.... dBASE II PLUS for Programmers	Dinerstein	160.00
.... Advanced Programming in dBASE III+	Kneght	125.00
.... Cases and Applications in dBASE III PLUS	Smith	110.00
.... Using dBASE IV	Leonard Presby	49.00
.... dBASE III+ Quick Reference Guide	S. Mehta	105.00
.... 10 Minute Guide to dBASE III PLUS	S. Mehta	80.00
.... Computer Facts & Formulae- dBASE III PLUS	S. Mehta	50.00
.... Learning & Using dBASE in a day	Jaiswal	36.00

DEBUGGER
.... Clipper Debugger	Subhash Mehta/Hazarika	80.00

DESKTOP PUBLISHING: GENERAL: PAGEMAKER: VENTURA
.... PageMaker 5 for Windows	Sanders	255.00
.... PageMaker 5 in Easy Steps	Basham	75.00
.... Desktop Publishing Companion	Jones	55.00
.... 101 Design Solution to Desktop Publishing	Parker	110.00
.... Advanced PageMaker 4.0 for Windows	Sanders	160.00
.... PageMaker 4.0 for Windows	Sanders	150.00
.... 101 PageMaker Tips		40.00
.... The Ventura Design Companion	Berst & Roll	110.00
.... Ventura Adventure— Moving up to version 2	Philip Crookes	60.00
.... Computer Facts & Formulae- Ventura for Windows	Subhash Mehta	50.00
.... Computer Facts & Formulae-DTP	Subhash Mehta	50.00
.... DTP for PC User	Houghton	110.00

DIGITAL TECHNOLOGY
.... Digital Technology Lab Manual 2nd Edition	Williams	50.00

DOEACC "O-LEVEL" EXAM
.... GW BASIC QUICK COURSE	S.Mehta/B.Mehta	110.00
.... Business Software Made Simple	S.Mehta/B.Mehta	100.00
.... Principles & Techniques of Programming	Ramachandran	90.00
.... Computerised Business Applications	Ramachandran	90.00

DOS [MS-, PC-, DR-]
.... Rescued by DOS	Jamsa	95.00
.... PC Guide to DOS-Step-by-Step Guide to using DOS	ITC Pub	75.00
.... PC World DOS 6.2 Command Reference and Problem Solver		205.00
.... PC World DOS 6.2 Handbook	Socha	305.00
.... DOS 6.2 Secrets	Socha	305.00
.... DOS 6 & 6.2-Everything you need to know	Kamin	205.00
.... Microsoft DOS 6,2-Quick Reference Guide	DDC	60.00
.... PC World You can do it with DOS	C.Van Buren	105.00
.... MS-DOS Programmers handbook	Gunter Bron	240.00
.... DOS Made Simple 2nd Ed.	Subhash Mehta	146.00
.... DOS for Dummies	Dan Gookin	95.00
.... The least you need to know about DOS v.6	Bultema	95.00
.... The only DOS book you'll ever need v.6	Bultema	126.00
.... DOS Quick Reference Guide	Mathur	75.00
.... MS DOS Revealed	Last	75.00
.... Exploiting MS-DOS	Davies	75.00
.... Starting MS-DOS Assembler	Sinclair	75.00
.... Computer Facts & Formulae- Microsoft DOS 6.2	Subhash Mehta	50.00

| .... | Learning & Using DOS in a day | Jaiswal | 36.00 |
| .... | DOS Based Software | Jaiswal | I/P |

ENTRANCE/COMPETITION/COMPETENCE EXAM. GUIDES

....	MCA Question Bank [A guide to MCA Entrance Exam]	Subhash Mehta	120.00
....	Elements of Computer Science [A.M.I.E. Examinations]	Jaiswal	75.00
....	Fundamentals of EDP [CA-Intermediate Exam.]	Jaiswal	75.00

EXCEL

....	A Quick Course in Excel 5 for Windows	Cox	60.00
....	Computer Facts & Formulae—Excel 5	S Mehta	50.00
....	Computer Facts & Formulae—Excel 7 for Windows 95	S Mehta	50.00
....	The Essential Guide to Excel 5.0 for Windows		160.00
....	The Little Excel 4 book	Tim Toyoshima	105.00
....	PC Guide for Excel for Windows		90.00
....	PC World Excel 4 for Windows HB	Walkenbach	260.00
....	Rescued by Excel for Windows	Wyatt	95.00

EXPERT SYSTEMS

....	Expert Systems for Personal Computers	Chadwick	75.00
....	Build Your Own Expert System	Naylor	75.00
....	Business Expert Systems	Clyde W. Holsapple	89.00
....	Expert Systems Development in Prolog & Turbo Prolog		75.00
....	Expert System Applications	Sunil Vadhera	89.00

FLOWCHART

| .... | Learning & Using Flowchart in a day | Jaiswal | 36.00 |

FORTRAN

| .... | Fortran 77—A Problem Solving Approach | Smith | 90.00 |

FoxBASE+ 2.1

....	FoxBASE+ 2.1—Quick Reference Guide	S. Mehta	146.00
....	10 Minute Guide to FoxBASE+ 2.1	S. Mehta	80.00
....	Computer Facts & Formulae—FoxBASE+ 2.1	S. Mehta	50.00
....	Learning and Using FoxBASE+ in a day	Jaiswal	45.00

FoxPro

....	Understanding FoxPro 2.6	Jaiswal	136.00
....	FoxPro 2.5/2.6 for Windows Programming Guide	Antonovich	250.00
....	Your FoxPro for Windows Consultant	Mathews	240.00
....	Debugging & Maintaining FoxPro Applications	Antonovich	260.00
....	FoxPro Business & MIS Applications	Chambers	210.00
....	FoxPro Developer's Library with disk	E. Powell	285.00
....	FoxPro Programming Guide	Antonowich	240.00
....	Computer Facts & Formulae—FoxPro	S. Mehta	50.00
....	FoxPro 2.6 for Windows in a day	Jaiswal	36.00
....	Visual FoxPro Bible	Jaiswal	295.00
....	Visual FoxPor Quick Reference Guide	Jaiswal	200.00
....	10 Minute Guide Visual FoxPro	Jaiswal	79.00
....	Understanding Visual FoxPro for Windows (ver 3)	Jaiswal	I/P
....	Learning and Using Visual FoxPro for Windows	Jaiswal	50.00
....		Kooros.	135.00

GENERAL

| .... | Computer Crime Prevention Technique | Schiver | 260.00 |

HANDBOOKS

.... Handbook for Computer Engineers—Software	Subhash Mehta	295.00

HARD DISK

.... Hard disk secrets with one disk		305.00
.... Hard disk Tips, Tools and Techniques	Balfe	70.00

HARVARD GRAPHICS

.... Harvard Graphics for Windows		260.00

IBM PC & COMPATIBLES, AS/400

.... RPG on the IBM AS/400	W.J.Tomlinson	185.00
.... DOS, WordPerfec . and Lotus (A 3-in-1 Guide) Essentials	Bultema	205.00
.... Microsoft Office in Concert	Weingarten	190.00
[Access 2, Excel, Word 6, PowerPoint]		
.... A Quick Course in Microsoft Office 4.3	Joyce Cox	75.00
.... PC 386 Companion	Allen Brown	95.00
.... PC secrets with two disks	Halliday	406.00
.... PC secrets with tips & tricks		60.00
.... The PC Novice's Handbook	Harshad Kotecha	75.00
.... Using PCs [Personal Computers]	S.Mehta/B.Mehta	146.00
.... PC Guide for Internet and On-Line Services		75.00
.... PC Guide for Introduction to Computers		75.00
.... PC Guide for DOS		75.00
.... PC Guide for Windows		75.00
.... PC Guide for Word 6 (Windows)		75.00
.... PC Guide for WordPerfect 6 (Windows)		75.00
.... PC Guide for Upgrading & Fixing Your Computer		95.00
.... PC Software Bible	Jaiswal	176.00
.... PC User Handbook	Subhash Mehta	320.00
.... Servicing & SupportingIBM PCs & Compatibles	Moss	136.00
.... Rescued by Upgrading & Fixing Your PC	Jamsa	195.00

INTERNET

.... Success with Internet	Wyatt	230.00
.... Internet Programming	Jamsa	250.00
.... Internet Information Server	Wyatt	250.00
.... PC Guide for Internet and On-Line Services		75.00
.... Quick Course in the Internet Using Netscape Navigator Vr 2&3		I/P
.... Interactive Internet	Shefski	195.00

INTRODUCTION

.... Understanding Computers throughcommon sense	Basandra	105.00
.... Adhunik Computer Vigyan (Hindi)	Jain	60.00
.... Introduction to Computers	Gear	65.00

JAVA

.... Java Programmer's Library	Lalani	375.00
.... Java Now	Jamsa	200.00
.... Java Script		I/P

ISDN [INTEGRATED SERVICES DIGITAL NETWORKS]

.... Communication with ISDN	Edgar Martin	160.00
.... Integrated Digital Network	Lawton	136.00

LEARNING & USING SERIES

.... Basic in a day	Jaiswal	36.00

January 1997

.... DOS in a day	Jaiswal	36.00
.... dBASE in a day	Jaiswal	36.00
.... Flowchart in a day	Jaiswal	36.00
.... FoxBASE in a day	Jaiswal	45.00
.... Lotus in a day	Jaiswal	36.00
.... Unix in a day	Jaiswal	36.00
.... FoxPro 2.6 for Windows in a day	Jaiswal	36.00
.... WordStar 7 in a day	Jaiswal	I/P

LISP

.... How to solve it in LISP	Hall	65.00

LOCAL AREA NETWORK

.... Low-cost Local Area Networks	Bridges	75.00
.... Local Area Networks, 2nd Revised Ed.	Basandra	185.00

LOTUS 1-2-3

.... A Quick Course in Lotus 1-2-3 for Windows	Cox	70.00
.... Lotus 1-2-3 Macro Programmers Phrase	Clark	45.00
.... The least you need to know Lotus 1-2-3 for DOS	Bultema	105.00
.... Practical Guide to Lotus 1-2-3	Bultema	136.00
.... The Essential Guide to Lotus 1-2-3 for Windows Release 4	Prince	160.00
.... Lotus 1-2-3 Quick Reference Guide	Mathur	89.00
.... Understanding Lotus 1-2-3	Mathur	160.00
.... Lotus 1-2-3 - A tutorial	Cicilioni	136.00
.... Inside Lotus 1-2-3 Release 3	James	105.00
.... Developing Applications Cases and Applications in Lotus 1-2-3	Holt	125.00
.... The Illustrated Lotus 1-2-3 Book	Berliner	70.00
.... Advanced Lotus 1-2-3	Bidgoli	160.00
.... Lotus 1-2-3 Workbook	Spinetto	75.00
.... Learning Lotus 1-2-3 for IBM & PC Compatibles	Blanc & Vento	85.00
.... Using Lotus 1-2-3		49.00
.... Computer Facts & Formulae-Lotus 1-2-3 for Windows Rel.4	S Mehta	50.00
.... Computer Facts & Formulae-Lotus 1-2-3 for Windows Rel.5	S Mehta	50.00
.... Computer Facts & Formulae-Lotus 1-2-3 for DOS Rel.4	S Mehta	50.00
.... Learning and Using Lotus in a day	Jaiswal	36.00

MACHINE CODE OPTIMIZATION

.... ZEN of Code Optimization	Abrash	240.00

MADE SIMPLE SERIES

.... PC Made Simple 3rd Ed.	Subhash Mehta	205.00
.... DOS Made Simple 2nd Ed.	Subhash Mehta	146.00

MICROCOMPUTERS' (PC's) APPLICATIONS

.... Using Microcomputers Revised Ed.	Brightman	110.00
.... Introduction to Microcomputer	Tempke	55.00
.... Introduction to Microcomputer and its Applications: PC DOS, WordStar, Lotus 1-2-3 and dBASE III PLUS	Chen	175.00
.... Diskette		75.00

MICROPROCESSORS/MICROCONTROLLERS

.... Programming Microcontroller in C	Sickle	150.00
.... Microprocessors/Microcontrollers	Singh	136.00
.... Microprocessor Systems Design Concepts	Alexandridis	125.00
.... Microprocessors and its Applications	Aspinall	85.00

MICROSOFT OFFICE

....	A Quick Course in Microsoft Office 4.3	Cox	70.00
....	Microsoft Office in Concert Proff. Edition	Weingarten	180.00

MULTIMEDIA

....	Visual Basic Multimedia Adventure Set		240.00
....	Multimedia, CD-ROM & Compact Disc		126.00

NEURAL NETWORKS

....	Introducing Neural Networks	Curling	110.00
....	Neural Networks:Fundamentals, Applications, Examples	Kinnebrock	85.00

NORTON'S UTILITIES

....	Norton's Utilities	Udo Schmidt	50.00

NOVELL NETWORK

....	Novell Netware Lite(simplified network solutions)	Duncan	130.00
....	Netware 3.X: A do-it-yourself Guide		160.00
....	Novell Netware Companion	Croucher	110.00

OBJECT-ORIENTED PROGRAMMING

....	An introduction to theObject-Oriented Programming	K.U. Witt	70.00

OPERATING SYSTEMS

....	Introduction to OperatingSystems Design	Habermann	100.00

ORACLE

....	Computer Facts & Formulae—Oracle7	S Mehta	50.00
....	Computer Facts & Formulae—RDBMS/PL/SQL in Oracle 7	S Mehta	50.00

PAGEMAKER

....	Computer Facts & Formulae—PageMaker Release 5 for Windows & Macintosh	Subhash Mehta	50.00
....	PageMaker 5 for Windows	Sanders	255.00
....	PageMaker 5 in Easy Steps	Basham	75.00
....	Advanced PageMaker 4.0 for Windows	Sanders	160.00
....	PageMaker 4.0 for Windows	Sanders	150.00
....	101 PageMaker Tips		45.00

PARALLEL PROCESSING

....	Parallel Processing	Carling	75.00

PASCAL/TURBO PASCAL

....	Turbo Pascal Quick Course	S.Mehta/B.Mehta	110.00
....	Pascal Plus Data Structure, Algorithms & Advanced Programming	Dale/Lilly	225.00
....	Pascal for Science and Engineering	McGregor	55.00
....	Programming in Pascal	Gear	65.00
....	Pascal-An introduction toMethodical Programming	Findlay/Watts	45.00
....	Complete Turbo Pascal	Dunteman	100.00
....	Turbo Pascal 6.0 How To..	Gary Syck	136.00
....	Programming with Turbo Pascal	Kassera	110.00
....	Using Turbo Pascal	Berliner	136.00
....	Turbo Pascal-Quick Course	Subhash Mehta	110.00
....	Computer Facts & Formulae- Turbo Pascal	Subhash Mehta	50.00

POWERBUILDER

....	Understanding Power Builder	Rajeev Mathur	250.00
....	Application Development withPowerBuilder 4.0	R. K. Sedani	195.00

POWERPC
.... Inside PowerPC revolution — Duntemann — 136.00

POWERPOINT
.... A Quick Course in Power Point 4 for Windows — Cox — 60.00

PROGRAMMING
.... Principles & Techniques of Programming — Ramachandran — 75.00
.... Fundamentals of Programming Languages — Horowitz — 160.00
.... The Programming Language Landscape:
Syntax, Semantics and Implementation — Marcotty — 90.00
.... Programmer's Reference Manual
for IBM Personal Computers — Armbrust — 250.00
.... Prog. Tech, Reference MS_DOS, IBMPC — Williams — 125.00
.... Fundamentals of Assembly
Language Using the IBM PC — Detmer — 130.00
.... PC Programming Made Simple — Subhash Mehta — 100.00

PROLOG/TURBO PROLOG
.... Prolog through Examples — Lavrac — 70.00
A practical programming approach
.... Turbo Prolog: Features for programmers — 65.00

QUESTION BANK, QUESTIONS AND ANSWERS
.... MCA Question Bank — S. Mehta — 120.00
.... Questions & Answers- DOS 2nd Ed. — S. Mehta — 146.00
.... Question Bank-Computer Science 2nd Ed. — Basandra — 130.00

QUICK LEARNING SERIES/QUICK COURSE
.... Quick Computer Course- For Stenos,
Secys., Assistants, Executives — S.Mehta/B.Mehta — 100.00
.... GW BASIC Quick Course-DOEACC
'O' Level Module IV — S.Mehta/B.Mehta — 110.00
.... Turbo Pascal Quick Course — S.Mehta/B.Mehta — 110.00
.... A Quick Course in Access for Windows (ver. 2) — Cox — 60.00
.... A Quick Course in Excel 5 for Windows — Cox — 60.00
.... A Quick Course in Lotus 1-2-3 for Windows — Cox — 70.00
.... A Quick Course in Microsoft Office 4.3 — Cox — 70.00
.... A Quick Course in PowerPoint 4 for Windows — Cox — 60.00
.... A Quick Course in WordPerfect 6 for Windows — Cox — 60.00
.... A Quick Course in Word 6 for Windows — Cox — 60.00

QUICK REFERENCE GUIDES/MANUALS
.... AutoCAD Release 12 Revised Ed. — Subhash Mehta — 160.00
.... Clipper 5.2 2nd Ed. — Subhash Mehta — 160.00
.... Clipper Debugger — Subhash Mehta/Hazarika — 80.00
.... Clipper Library — Subhash Mehta/Hazarika — 100.00
.... dBASE III PLUS — Subhash Mehta — 105.00
.... FoxBASE+ 2.1 — Subhash Mehta — 146.00
.... Lotus 1-2-3 — Rajiv Mathur — 89.00
.... Microsoft DOS — DDC — 60.00
.... Microsoft Windows 3.1 — DDC — 60.00
.... Supercharging Windows & DOS — Subhash Mehta — 185.00
.... WordStar 7.0 — Subhash Mehta — 150.00
.... Using WordStar — 49.00

January 1997

No. of Copies		Price, Rs.
.... Using Lotus 1-2-3		49.00
.... Using dBASE IV		49.00
RAPID LEARNING SERIES		
.... Computer Course Level 1	S.Mehta/B.Mehta	146.00
REAL TIME SYSTEMS		
.... Developing Real Time Systems- A practical introduction	Evesham	75.00
REFERENCE		
.... Programmer's Reference Manual for IBM Personal Computers	Armbrust	250.00
.... The Programmer's Technical Reference: MS-DOS, IBM PC & Compatibles	Williams	125.00
.... Computers Today	Basandra	285.00
.... Computer Terms	Carter	35.00
RELATIONAL DATABASE MANAGEMENT: RDBMS		
.... Relational Database-Concepts, Selection and Implementations	Page	85.00
.... SQL & Relational Database	Vang	160.00
.... Computer Facts & Fromulae—RDBMS-PL/SQL in Oracle7	S Mehta	50.00
SOFTWARE ENGINEERING		
.... Object-Oriented Software Engineering	Mehta/Basandra	230.00
.... Software Engineering	Wattman	105.00
SQL (STRUCTURED QUERY LANGUAGE)		
.... SQL and Relational Database	Vang	160.00
.... A primer on SQL	Ageioff	85.00
SPREADSHEETS		
.... Spreadsheet Style Manual	Yu, Harrison	105.00
SYSTEM ANALYSIS AND DESIGN		
.... System Analysis and Design	E.M. Awad	160.00
.... Basic System Analysis	A. Daniels	65.00
.... System Design HCI	Shorrock	75.00
.... System Analysis and Design	Wetherbe	110.00
.... System Analysis and Design Methods	Whitten	250.00
.... Practical System Design	Daniels	60.00
SYSTEMS MANAGEMENT/ADMINISTRATION		
.... System Administration under UNIX Terminal Book	Trommer	89.00
.... System Management under UNIX	Backhurst	65.00
TROUBLESHOOTING		
.... Servicing & Supporting IBM PCs & Compatibles	Moss	136.00
.... PC Troubleshooter	Sinclair	70.00
.... PC Troubleshooting	Engelsing	75.00
UNIX		
.... UNIX Shell Programming	Arthur, Burns	190.00
.... Same " (original)		495.00
.... System Administration under UNIX- Terminal Book	Trommer	89.00
.... System Management under UNIX	Backhurst	65.00
.... Rescued by UNIX	Hansen	95.00
.... Unix on the IBM PC	Twitty	60.00
.... Unix the book	Banahan	60.00
.... Professional Programmer's Guide to Unix	Bird	60.00
.... Unix User's Handbook	Parker	260.00

January 1997

.... Unix C Programming	Davignon	185.00
.... Unix System V	Braun	60.00
.... Unix-The Complete Book	Manger	186.00
.... Computer Facts & Formulae-Unix	Subhash Mehta	50.00
.... Learning and Using Unix in a day	Jaiswal	36.00

USER INTERFACES(PROGRAMMING FOR USING MENUS)

.... Designing User Interfaces	Powell	160.00

VIRTUAL REALITY

.... The Virtual Reality Construction Kit [with disk]	Joe Gradecki	195.00
.... The Virtual Reality Construction Kit (Original)	Joe Gradecki	550.00
.... The Visual C++ Construction Kit	Bugg, Tackett, Jr.	190.00

VISUAL BASIC

.... Visual Basic for Applications	Kamserthy	210.00
.... Visual Basic Multimedia Adventure Set	Jarol	240.00
.... Microsoft Visual Basic-The Programmer's Companion	Penfold	110.00

WINDOWS 95

.... PC Guide for Windows 95		100.00
.... Migrating to Windows 95	David Kipping	250.00
.... The Windows 95 Book	Stuple	250.00
.... Windows 95 A to Z	The Eddy Group	250.00
.... Windows 95 Quick Course	Joyce Cox	70.00

WINDOWS

.... PC Guide for Windows-Step-by-step Guide to using Windows	ITC Pub	75.00
.... PC Guide for Excel for Windows		90.00
.... PC Guide for Word for Windows		90.00
.... Supercharging Windows & DOS	Subhash Mehta	185.00
.... Rescued by Windows	Jamsa	95.00
.... Windows Gizmos with 4 disks	Livingston	595.00
.... Windows 3.1 Secrets with 3-high density 5¼" disks	Livingston	506.00
.... Windows API Bible	Conger	406.00
.... PC World-You can do it with Windows	Buren	110.00
.... Windows 3.1-Visual Quick Start		105.00
.... 101 Windows Tips & Tricks		105.00
.... 1001 Windows 95 Tips	Greg Perry	250.00
.... Windows Magazine: Power of Windows & DOS		136.00
.... Windows Programming Primer Plus		260.00
.... Working with Windows 3.1	Sinclair	110.00
.... Windows Magazine-Encylcopedia for Windows	Eddy Group	370.00
.... Windows 3.1 Bible	Fred Davis	406.00
.... Windows 3.1-The trainer for beginners	Katharina	85.00
.... Object Windows-How to	Syck	205.00
.... Windows Programming Made Easy	Lafore	305.00
.... The least you need to know about Windows 3.1	Eckols	146.00
.... Jamsa's 1001 Windows Tips	Jamsa	305.00
.... Windows 3.1 Connectivity Secrets (with 4 Disks)	Connally	496.00
.... Windows 3.1-A Complete Tutorial	Subhash Mehta	160.00
.... Windows Programming Power with Customs Control		240.00
.... Windows 3.1 Configuration Secrets	Blakey	305.00

January 1997

No.of Copies		Price, Rs.
.... Windows in Easy Steps	Harshad Kotecha	75.00
.... Microsoft Windows, 3.1 IBM PC Quick Reference Guide	DDC	60.00
.... Microsoft Windows 3.1-A Quick Study	Brown	85.00
.... Computer Facts & Formulae-Windows 3.1	S. Mehta	50.00
.... Success with Windows 95	Jamsa	250.00

WINDOWS NT

Windows NT Quick Reference Guide	Karl, Joanne	80.00
.... Computer Facts & Formulae-Windows NT	S. Mehta	50.00

WordStar/WORD/WORD PROCESSING/WordPerfect

PC Guide for Word 6 (Windows)		75.00
.... PC Guide for WordPerfect 6 (Windows)		75.00
.... PC Guide for Word for Windows		90.00
.... A Quick Course Word 6 for Windows		60.00
.... A Quick Course in WordPerfect 6 for Windows	Cox	60.00
.... The Essential Guide: WordPerfect 6 for Windows		160.00
.... PC World WordPerfect 6 Handbook with disk		496.00
.... Computer Facts & Formulae-WordPerfect SIX0	Subhash Mehta	50.00
.... Word 6 for Windows Handbook	Heslop	360.00
.... Word 6 for Windows-Visual Quick Start Guide		136.00
.... Word for Windows 2- Desktop Publishing by Example	Webster & Associates	260.00
.... The Essential Guide Word 6.0 for Windows	Eckols	160.00
.... Rescued by Word for Windows	Jamsa	95.00
.... WordStar 7.0-Quick Reference Guide	S. Mehta	156.00
.... WordStar 7.0-A Handbook	Subhash Mehta	100.00
.... Computer Facts & Formulae-WordStar through version 7.0	S Mehta	50.00
.... Word Processing	Hollerback	20.00
.... Moving up to WordStar 5 & 5.5 with DTP Applications	Hollins	85.00
.... WordStar 5 & 5.5	Auten	40.00
.... Using WordStar		49.00
.... Learning & Using WordStar 7 in a day	Jaiswal	i/P

COMPETITION

.... REA's GRE Engineering		160.00
.... REA's Computer Science		75.00
.... REA's General Test		150.00
.... REA's TOEFL (including 2 cassettes)		160.00
.... Barron's Guide to GMAT		150.00
.... Barron's Guide to GRE		150.00
.... Barron's Guide to TOEFL		150.00
.... Barron's Guide to SAT		150.00
.... Bank Probationary Officer's Guide	Ravi Chopra	176.00
.... State Bank Probationary Officer's Guide	Ravi Chopra	176.00
.... Assistant's Grade Examination Guide	Ravi Chopra	100.00
.... Income Tax, Sales Tax & Customs Inspectors' Guide	Ravi Chopra	100.00
.... Reasoning N' Reasoning	Ravi Chopra	85.00
.... Peterson's SAT Success		95.00
.... Peterson's Success with Words		75.00
.... NDA Guide	Ravi Chopra	150.00
.... MBA Guide	Ravi Chopra	160.00

No. of Copies		Price, Rs.
.... Sub-Inspector Police Guide	Ravi Chopra	120.00
.... SSC Clerk Grade Examination Guide	Ravi Chopra	80.00
.... General Knowledge	Ravi Chopra	50.00
.... Railway Recruitment Board Exam	Ravi Chopra	69.00
.... CAT	Ravi Chopra	150.00
.... Model Solutions to IIT-JEE(1991-95)		175.00
.... Problem Solver IIT Mathematics		125.00
.... Medical Entrance Question Bank		240.00
.... Hotel Management	Ravi Chopra	126.00
.... Objective Arithmetic	Ohri	50.00
.... Indian History & Culture	Ahluwalia	200.00
.... Bank Clerical Exam. Guide	Ravi Chopra	65.00
.... CDS	Ravi Chopra	150.00
.... G.K. for Schools	Ravi Chopra	15.00
.... Object English Digest	Ravi Chopra	75.00

SCHOOL

.... Model Test Papers Mathematics — Class XII		55.00
.... Model Test Papers Physics — Class XII		55.00
.... Question Bank Physics (Class XII)		110.00
.... Question Bank Maths (Class XII)		110.00
.... Question Bank Chemistry (Class XII)		100.00
.... Computer Science Concepts (Class XII)	Naveen Kr	100.00
.... Question Bank Maths (Class X)		100.00
.... Question Bank Science (Class X)		75.00
.... Question Bank Economics (Class XII)		110.00
.... Question Bank Physics (Class XI)		110.00
.... Physics Facts and Formulae		40.00
.... Question Bank Chemistry		20.00
.... G K for Schools		15.00
.... Quiz Book Science		20.00
.... ICSE Computer Studies	Bhattacharyya	100.00
.... Comprehensive Solutions to IE IRODOV's Problems in General Physics	Partha Goswami	169.00

MENTAL MATHS

.... Addition and Subtraction	29.00
.... Multiplication and Division	29.00

MEDICAL

.... CATARACT in Developing Countries for students- and practitioners in Ophthalmology	Dr. R.P. Dhanda/Kalver	80.00
.... A textbook of Clinical Ophthalmology	R.P. Dhanda	160.00
.... Learning Objectives in Gross Anatomy	Dr. Bijlani	50.00
.... Obstetrics Gynecology 8th Edition	Wilson	135.00
.... MOSBY's Medical Dictionary II Edition		360.00
.... Conver Pocket Guide to Electrocardiography		35.00
.... MCQ's in Psychiatry	Dr. H.M. Chawla	50.00
.... MCQ's in Medical Sciences Vol III	Dr. J.K. Grover	95.00
.... MCQ's in Medical Sciences Vol IV	Dr. J.K. Grover	65.00
.... MCQ's in Pharmacology	Dr. J.K. Grover	95.00
.... GOTH's Medical Pharmacology 12th Edition		115.00

January 1997

No. of Copies		Price, Rs.
.... Glossary of Ophthalmology		49.00
.... Clinical Research Handbook		295.00
.... Radiation Safety in Medical Practice	Rehani	50.00
.... Scientific Basis of Sex Education	Grover	55.00
.... Understanding Human Brain & Spinal Cord	Hasan/Abdi	55.00
.... Medical Entrance Question Bank		240.00
.... Textbook of Obstetrics & Gynecology Vol. 1	Dr. V.L. Bhargava	140.00
.... Textbook of Obstetrics & Gynecology Vol. 2	Dr. V.L. Bhargava	164.00
.... The Garden Doctor	Chandra	85.00

HEALTH SERIES

.... Homeopathic Remedies	Dr. Phyllis Speight	29.00
.... The Traveller's Guide to Homeopathy	Dr. Phyllis Speight	29.00
.... Sports Injuries: Their Treatment by Homeopathy and Acapressure	Dr. Lesliej Speight	29.00

HARRAP/GALGOTIA SERIES

.... Your Active Body	Colin Fergusson	36.00
.... Your Child	Suzy Powling	36.00
.... Your Diet	Brain Wood	36.00
.... Your Heart and Lungs	Dr. Peter Toon	36.00
.... Your Mind	Dr. Peter Toon	36.00
.... Your Pregnancy and Children	Celia Mcinnes	36.00
.... Your Sex Life	Dr. Peter Bromwich	36.00
.... Your Skin	Dr. Graham Colver	36.00

MANAGEMENT/ECONOMICS

.... Management of Industrial Disputes (some important aspects)	J.P. Saxena	160.00
.... The Fifty-Minute Supervisor Rev. Edition	Chapman	45.00
.... Team Building: An Exercise in Leadership	Maddux	45.00
.... Successful Negotiation Revised Edition	Maddux	45.00
.... Project Management From Idea to Implementation	Haynes	45.00
.... Managing Performance	Haynes	250.00
.... Management Information Systems	Obrien	175.00
.... Manufacturing Planning and Control System	Berry	125.00
.... Macro economics Analysis 5th Edition	Shapiro	150.00
.... Marketing		49.00
.... Marketing Terms		39.00
.... Book Keeping and Accounting Terms		39.00

CRISP SERIES

.... Increasing Employee Productivity		45.00
.... Plan Your Work/Work Your Plan		45.00
.... Twelve Steps to Shelf Improvement		45.00
.... Developing Positive Assertiveness		45.00
.... The Personal Planning Guide	David H. Bangs	65.00
.... The Market Planning Guide	David H. Bangs	65.00
.... The Cash Flow Control Guide	David H. Bangs	50.00
.... Problem Employees: How to improve their performance	Whilie, Growthe	75.00
.... Office Management		45.00
.... Management for Commitment		45.00
.... Effective Performance Appraisals		45.00